Quantum Theory
of
Atoms, Molecules,
and the Solid State

A Tribute to John C. Slater

John C. Slater

Quantum Theory
of
Atoms, Molecules,
and the Solid State

A Tribute to John C. Slater

Edited by

PER-OLOV LÖWDIN

*Quantum Theory Project, University of
Florida, Gainesville, Florida and Quan-
tum Chemistry Group, University of
Uppsala, Uppsala, Sweden*

ACADEMIC PRESS   New York • London • 1966

ACADEMIC PRESS INC.
111 Fifth Avenue, New York, New York 10003

United Kingdom Edition published by
ACADEMIC PRESS INC. (LONDON) LTD.
Berkeley Square House, London W.1

LIBRARY OF CONGRESS CATALOG CARD NUMBER: 66-29044

PRINTED IN THE UNITED STATES OF AMERICA

List of Contributors

Numbers in parentheses indicate the pages on which the authors' contributions begin.

LELAND C. ALLEN, Department of Chemistry, Princeton University, Princeton, New Jersey (39)

S. ASANO, The Institute for Solid State Physics, The University of Tokyo, Tokyo, Japan (497)

JOHN BARDEEN, Department of Physics and Materials Research, University of Illinois, Urbana, Illinois (511)

S. F. BOYS, Theoretical Chemistry Department, University of Cambridge, Cambridge, England (253)

W. BYERS BROWN, Theoretical Chemistry Institute, University of Wisconsin, Madison, Wisconsin (123)

EARL CALLEN, U.S. Naval Ordnance Laboratory, White Oak, Silver Spring, Maryland (439)[1]

HUNG CHENG, Bell Telephone Laboratories Incorporated, Murray Hill, New Jersey (587)

E. U. CONDON, Joint Institute for Laboratory Astrophysics, Boulder, Colorado (185)

JOHN A. COPELAND, Bell Telephone Laboratories Incorporated, Murray Hill, New Jersey (537)

C. A. COULSON, Oxford University Mathematical Institute, Oxford, England (97)

S. J. CZYZAK, General Physics Laboratory, Aerospace Research Laboratories, Wright-Patterson Air Force Base, Dayton, Ohio (167)

R. DAUDEL, Sorbonne and Centre de Mécanique Ondulatoire Apliquée, Paris, France (295)

---

[1] Present Address: Department of Physics, Faculty of Engineering Sciences, Osaka University, Toyonaka, Japan.

J. O. DIMMOCK, Lincoln Laboratory, Massachusetts Institute of Technology, Lexington, Massachusetts (361)

C. EDMISTON, Department of Chemistry, The Johns Hopkins University, Baltimore, Maryland, and Institute for Atomic Research, Department of Chemistry and Department of Physics, Iowa State University, Ames, Iowa (263)[2]

A. J. FREEMAN, National Magnet Laboratory, Massachusetts Institute of Technology, Cambridge, Massachusetts (361)

J. FRIEDEL, Physique des Solides, Faculté des Sciences, Orsay, France (445)

H. FRÖHLICH, Department of Theoretical Physics, University of Liverpool, Liverpool, England (465)

ARTHUR A. FROST, Department of Chemistry, Northwestern University, Evanston, Illinois (147)

F. GAUTIER, Institut de Physique, Faculté des Sciences, Strasbourg, France (445)

A. A. GOMÈS, Physique de Solides, Faculté des Sciences, Orsay, France (445)

G. G. HALL, Mathematics Department, University of Nottingham, Nottingham, England (565)

M. C. HARRISON, The Courant Institute of Mathematical Sciences, New York University, New York, New York (227)

F. HERMAN, Lockheed Palo Alto Research Laboratory, Palo Alto, California (381)

R. B. HERMANN, Illinois Institute of Technology, Chicago, Illinois (335)[3]

J. O. HIRSCHFELDER, Theoretical Chemistry Institute, The University of Wisconsin, Madison, Wisconsin (217)

A. C. HURLEY, Division of Chemical Physics, C.S.I.R.O., Chemical Research Laboratories, Melbourne, Australia (571)

R. P. JAMES, Stanford University, Stanford, California (537)

H. JONES, Department of Mathematics, Imperial College, London, England (469)

CHR. KLIXBÜLL JØRGENSEN, Cyanimid Research Institute, Cologny (Geneva), Switzerland (307)

R. L. KORTUM, Lockheed Palo Alto Research Laboratory, Palo Alto, California (381)

[2] Present Address: Department of Chemistry, University of Wyoming, Laramie, Wyoming.

[3] Present Address: Eli Lilly and Company, Indianapolis, Indiana.

T. K. KRUEGER, General Physics Laboratory, Aerospace Research Laboratories, Wright-Patterson Air Force Base, Dayton, Ohio (167)

C. D. KUGLIN, Lockheed Palo Alto Research Laboratory, Palo Alto, California (381)

J. LAWSON, Physics Department, University College, London, England (203)

MELVIN LAX, Bell Telephone Laboratories Incorporated, Murray Hill, New Jersey (587)

P. LENGLART, Physique des Solides, Institut d'Electronique du Nord, Lille, France (445)

PER-OLOV LÖWDIN, Quantum Theory Project, Nuclear Sciences Building, University of Florida, Gainesville, Florida and Quantum Chemistry Group, University of Uppsala, Uppsala, Sweden (5, 601)[4]

H. C. LONGUET-HIGGINS, Department of Theoretical Chemistry, University Chemical Laboratory, University of Cambridge, Cambridge, England (105)

P. G. LYKOS, Illinois Institute of Technology, Chicago, Illinois (335)

H. MARGENAU, Yale University, New Haven, Connecticut (81)

H. S. W. MASSEY, Physics Department, University College, London, England (203)

F. A. MATSEN, Molecular Physics Group, The University of Texas, Austin, Texas (133)

R. MOCCIA, Illinois Institute of Technology, Chicago, Illinois (335)

PHILIP M. MORSE, Department of Physics, Massachusetts Institute of Technology, Cambridge, Massachusetts (1)

J. W. MOSKOWITZ, Chemistry Department, New York University, Washington Square College, New York, New York (227)

ROBERT S. MULLIKEN, Laboratory of Molecular Structure and Spectra, Department of Physics, University of Chicago, Chicago, Illinois (5, 231)[5]

R. K. NESBET, IBM Research Laboratory, San Jose, California (157)

D. NEUMANN, Chemistry Department, New York University, Washington Square College, New York, New York (227)

H. ODABASI, Joint Institute for Laboratory Astrophysics, Boulder, Colorado (185)

---

[4] April 1-December 1: Quantum Chemistry Group, University of Uppsala, Uppsala, Sweden.

[5] Winter Address: (December 15-April 15) Institute of Molecular Biophysics, Florida State University, Tallahassee, Florida.

JASHBHAI C. PATEL, Department of Chemistry, Northwestern University, Evanston, Illinois (147)

LINUS PAULING, Center for the Study of Democratic Institutions, Santa Barbara, California (303)

GEORGE W. PRATT, JR., Materials Theory Group, Department of Electrical Engineering, Massachusetts Institute of Technology, Cambridge, Massachusetts (429)

H. PREUSS, Max-Planck-Institut für Physik und Astrophysik, Munich, Germany (281)

H. PRIMAS, Laboratory of Physical Chemistry, Swiss Federal Institute of Technology, Zurich, Switzerland (319)

ALBERTE PULLMAN, Université de Paris, Institut de Biologie Physico-Chimique, Paris, France (345)

BERNARD PULLMAN, Université de Paris, Institut de Biologie Physico-Chimique, Paris, France (345)

J. RIESS, Laboratory of Physical Chemistry, Swiss Federal Institute of Technology, Zurich Switzerland (319)

K. RUEDENBERG, Department of Chemistry, The Johns Hopkins University, Baltimore, Maryland and Institute for Atomic Research, Department of Chemistry and Department of Physics, Iowa State University, Ames, Iowa (263)

D. R. SCOTT, Molecular Physics Group, The University of Texas, Austin, Texas (133)[6]

J. D. SHARP-RITTER, Department of Chemistry, Illinois Institute of Technology, Chicago, Illinois (335)[7]

R. A. SHORT, Lockheed Palo Alto Research Laboratory, Palo Alto, California (381)

W. SHOCKLEY, Stanford University, Stanford, California and Bell Telephone Laboratories Incorporated, Murray Hill, New Jersey (537)

JOHN CLARKE SLATER, Jefferson Physical Laboratory, Harvard University, Cambridge, Massachusetts (17)

L. H. THOMAS, IBM Watson Laboratory, Columbia University, New York, New York (93)

D. G. THOMPSON, Physics Department, University College, London, England (203)

---

[6] Present Address: Department of Chemistry, Texas Technical College, Lubbock, Texas.

[7] Present Address: Department of Chemistry, Roosevelt University, Chicago, Illinois.

J. H. VAN VLECK, Department of Physics, Harvard University, Cambridge Massachusetts (475)

A. C. WAHL, Theoretical Chemistry Institute, The University of Wisconsin, Madison, Wisconsin and Argonne National Laboratory, Argonne, Illinois (217, 243)

S. WAKOH, The Institute for Solid State Physics, University of Tokyo, Tokyo, Japan (497)

R. E. WATSON, Brookhaven National Laboratory, Upton, New York (361)

E. P. WOHLFARTH, Department of Mathematics, Imperial College, London, England (485)

J. YAMASHITA, The Institute for Solid State Physics, The University of Tokyo, Tokyo, Japan (497)

Preface

One of the outstanding pioneers in the development of quantum theory and particularly its applications to atoms, molecules, and the solid state is Professor John Clarke Slater. He has published more than one hundred original papers in the field, and his achievements are so fundamental and numerous that there is hardly any area of the quantum theory of matter which is not basically influenced by his work. In addition, he has been an excellent and stimulating teacher, and his series of textbooks has proven to be of essential value in universities all over the world.

His many students, colleagues, and friends felt the need to honor him at this stage of his scientific career with a special birthday volume dedicated to the field of atomic, molecular, and solid-state theory in recognition of his fundamental discoveries and achievements. Since, for practical reasons, the book has to be limited in size, only a selected number of papers could be included, but the volume is still a tribute from all of us who have benefited from his work and friendship. The volume is striking evidence of the stimulating influence on the current research in the field of Professor Slater's work, and also of the impact it will have in the future.

Even though more than forty years have now passed since Professor Slater published his first scientific paper, there are no signs that he is approaching an age at which many would prefer to retire, and he is as active in teaching and research as ever before. With this birthday volume, his many students, friends, and colleagues enclose warmest wishes for many happy years to come.

PER-OLOV LÖWDIN

September, 1966

Contents

Quantum Theory
of
Atoms, Molecules,
and the Solid State

John Clarke Slater, a Biographical Note of Appreciation

PHILIP M. MORSE

MASSACHUSETTS INSTITUTE OF TECHNOLOGY, CAMBRIDGE, MASSACHUSETTS

I first met John Slater on the morning of the day of Karl Compton's inauguration as President of M.I.T., in June of 1930. He looked more like a young graduate student than the newly appointed head of the Institute's Department of Physics. As he drove us, in an elderly, open car, around Cambridge, he talked enthusiastically about Compton's plans to emphasize basic science at the Institute and his own plans to reorganize the department. By the time we returned from Europe, a year later, many of these plans were being implemented and the Department was in the process of becoming one of the outstanding departments of physics in the country.

Slater was fitted, in many ways, to lead this rapid progress. He grew up in an academic family, his father being head of the English Department at the University of Rochester. After receiving his bachelor's degree from Rochester in 1920 he came to Harvard as a graduate student, in time to receive solid training in classical physics under Bridgeman, and later, to be on hand to help lead the explosive development of the new physics, following the break-throughs of Schrödinger, Heisenberg, and others. In 1922 he went to England and to Copenhagen, where he worked with Bohr, returning in 1924 to Harvard as instructor and assistant professor. Already his interest had turned to problems of atomic and molecular structure; his papers on the ground state of helium, on screening constants for light atoms, and on the calculation of equations of state appeared between 1926 and 1930. By then he had begun the task of computing the physical and physico-chemical properties of atoms, molecules, and solids from the basic equations of quantum mechanics, which has held much of his interest since.

After another year at Zürich and Leipzig, in 1929–1930, he returned to become head of the department at M.I.T. By the time I returned, in 1931, he had reorganized the undergraduate and graduate courses in physics, which were to educate a growing number of future leaders in the field. Although, even then, the department was among the larger ones in the country in regard to size and teaching load, it was still small enough to maintain close personal contacts. John knew, in detail, what all of us were doing and gave encouragement when needed. Daily teas in the Moore Room served to bring the graduate students and faculty together, and the Slaters' small house, overlooking the Charles River beyond Lars Anderson bridge, served as a social center for department members. To us newcomers, John and his gracious wife, with their many contacts at Harvard, eased our introduction to the peculiar attractions of Cambridge life.

Although he spent much time planning and teaching undergraduate (including freshman) courses, Slater found time to continue his own research and to supervise the research of students. He supervised the bachelor's thesis of Richard Feynman and the doctoral thesis of William Shockley, among others. A visit to Slater's office would, often as not, find him typing out his next paper or integrating out a Hartree equation—by hand, of course, since electronic computers were only a gleam in the eye of Vannevar Bush in those days. Mention of a few titles of his papers in the Physical Review, "Molecular Energy Levels and Valence Bonds" (1931), "Electronic Energy Levels in Metals" (1934), "The Ferromagnetism of Nickel" (1936), "The Nature of the Superconducting State" (1937), indicate the nature of his ground-breaking during the thirties. As was aptly said by one who should know, "the invention of the transistor was the outgrowth of the pioneering theoretical work of John C. Slater and a few other academicians in solid state physics." And, between papers, he and Frank wrote, and tested out in class, their perennially useful texts on theoretical physics. This was one of the first undergraduate courses in theoretical physics specifically preparatory to quantum mechanics. The fact that, even now, undergraduate physics at the Institute is taught by professors, not teaching assistants, is due to Slater's insistence that teaching improves research and vice versa.

In the years 1939 and 1940, when we turned to defense research, Slater was active in organizing the Radiation Laboratory, which carried on the development of radar, initiated in Britain. Slater took the theory of the magnetron as his assignment, thus applying his experience in the theory of electron waves in metal lattices to the theory of plasma oscillations in periodic structures. When Bell Telephone Laboratories organized to design and produce magnetrons, Slater transferred his activities to New York, where his principles of circuit design enabled magnetron power to be increased nearly a hundredfold, earning him a Presidential Certificate of Merit at the end of the war.

In 1946 he returned to M.I.T. eager to organize the department's extension in the rapidly growing field of nuclear physics, persuading Weisskopf and Zacharias and many others to move from Los Alamos to Cambridge. But his own research returned to solid-state physics, as evidenced by the series of papers and books, familiar to us all, which appeared during the fifties. He organized and directed the research program of the Solid-State and Molecular Theory Group, which has attracted many graduate students as well as post-doctoral fellows and visiting professors.

In 1951 he turned over his administrative responsibilities as department head to N. H. Frank, was appointed H. B. Higgins Institute Professor of the Solid State, and concentrated on his research and on fostering the research of others. By the years 1960 and 1961, this work culminated in the organization of the interdepartmental Center for Materials Science and Engineering, now occupying a new building, completed in 1965. Though active in its conception and materialization, Slater preferred to relinquish its direction to others. By the time of its completion he had entered into an arrangement whereby he spends winters at the University of Florida and summers at the Institute. In both places his continued interest in solid-state research continues to inspire students and colleagues.

John Clarke Slater
His Work and a Bibliography

ROBERT S. MULLIKEN*

Slater began his scientific career [see bibliography (*2,12*)] with his Ph.D. research with Bridgman, working on the experimental investigation of the compressibilities (using single crystals) " of twice as many of the alkali halides as had been previously measured and (seeing) how much information these data are capable of yielding about the forces in the crystal." Besides getting better data than before, he was able to determine the crystal potential energy as a function of volume at $0°K$ and to break this down sharply into a sum of Madelung interionic cohesive energy plus energies of repulsive forces for which he obtained series expansions. This early work keynotes Slater's lifelong interest in the empirical structure of matter and its theoretical explanation. He finished his Ph.D. work just two or three years before quantum mechanics burst over the horizon, and for the next few years he participated first in the efforts [see many of Papers *1–16*] which led up to quantum mechanics (efforts to understand dispersion theory, spectroscopic transition probabilities, interpretation of spectra, radiation theory, etc.), and thereafter in the application of the then new quantum mechanics to the chemical, spectroscopic, magnetic, and other properties of atoms, molecules, and solids. Slater constantly emphasizes and analyzes the interrelations between experiment and theory, and between physical and chemical ideas and mathematical formulations.

Slater's papers in the period from 1928 to 1933 penetrated, in many directions, into the major problems of atomic, molecular, and metallic structures, and of interatomic and intermolecular interactions. Thus, his paper "On the Normal State of He" (*20*) includes a theoretical derivation of an approximate formula for the interaction energy of two He atoms (van der Waals attraction and closed-shell repulsions). Later, with Kirkwood (*27*) (who came to work with Slater as a postdoctoral fellow), the work was extended to calculations of the van der Waals cohesive forces for a number of gases. A further development appeared in "The Quantum Theory of the Equation of State" (*29*) for imperfect gases.

A "Note on Hartree's Method" (*24*), following an analysis (*19*) of Hartree's

* With the co-operation of Per-Olov Löwdin and James Conklin.

self-consistent-field method, gives briefly a justification of the method in
terms of a variational approach to the solution of Schrödinger's equation, and
also states briefly the idea of what is now called the Hartree-Fock method
(Fock's paper appeared almost simultaneously). Few ideas have turned out
to be more fruitful for atomic theory. In his paper "Theory of Complex
Spectra" (22) Slater introduced an extremely practical approach, in a critique of
Hund's rule, to the calculation of the energy separations among the different
L and S states of an atomic electron configuration; he wrote antisymmetrized
functions using the now well-known "Slater determinant" forms, and broke
up the Coulomb and exchange integrals into linear combinations of his now
well-known F and G integrals. The "Slater determinants" are now one of the
most useful tools in the quantum theory of matter. In his paper on "Atomic
Shielding Constants" (25) he introduced the specifications for the extremely
useful approximations to atomic orbitals which are now known as "Slater
orbitals," and in his paper "Analytic Atomic Wave Functions" (32) he
discussed clearly how SCF (self-consistent-field) orbitals differ from H atom
orbitals, and showed how Hartree's numerically tabulated SCF orbitals can
be fitted by analytical expressions which are linear combinations of what are
called "Slater-type orbitals" (STO's), namely, Slater orbitals scaled up or
down in size. This idea has been used later by Roothaan in his LCSTO
molecular-orbital SCF wave functions for molecules, in the Hartree-Fock-
Roothaan method. Slater's paper (23) "Cohesion in Monovalent Metals"
begins by comparing the Heitler-London and LCAO molecular-orbital
methods for H_2, discussing the need for adding ionic to the Heitler-London
atomic functions. A more detailed discussion of this important paper is given
elsewhere in this volume.

In a paper (26) on "Directed Valence in Polyatomic Molecules" Slater,
independently of Pauling [J. Am. Chem. Soc. 53, 1367 (1931)] discussed
directional effects of Heitler-London bonding in atoms of the types F, O,
N, and C, and pointed out that where the valences come from p electrons, they
should tend to be directed at right angles, while the four valences of C have
tetrahedral symmetry through formation of tetrahedral sp hybrid valence
electron orbitals. Slater in this paper introduced and used the criterion of
maximum overlapping. He also discussed polar character in molecules like
HCl, and introduced the concept of the stabilization of benzene by the mixing
of the two Kekule wave function structures (later extensively discussed by
Pauling as quantum-mechanical "resonance"). This paper, which contains
many photographs of molecular models, makes use of methods previously
employed by Slater in the paper on "Complex Spectra" (22) and also applied
in the paper on "Cohesion in Monovalent Metals" (23) which initiated his
work in valence theory. In a paper (28) on the structure of the groups XO_3,
he shows how the pyramidal structure of such ions as ClO_3^- on the one hand

and the planar structure of those like NO_3^- can be understood in terms of the directional properties of valence. The paper on "Molecular Energy Levels and Valence Bonds" (*30*) developed more fully and extends the ideas presented in paper (*26*). Slater's paper "The Virial and Molecular Structure" (*35*) called attention for the first time to the importance of applications of the quantum-mechanical virial theorem for the understanding of molecules. In some of his papers, Slater has discussed the sizes of atoms, including tables of atomic radii, simple formulas for estimating the size of atomic radii from Slater orbitals, and instructive comparisons between sums of these atomic radii and observed interatomic distances in molecules and crystals.

In his later work, Slater has continued to explore in many directions methods for the theoretical understanding of the properties of atoms, molecules, and solids, the emphasis in his later work as in his earliest work being on crystalline solids, and, in this area, his contributions are as numerous and important as those which have already been mentioned.

With his remarkable ability to correlate physical truth with the models used to understand it, he was among the first to clearly demonstrate the failures of the free-electron theory of metals in explaining their electronic properties, at the same time pointing out the areas in which the theory did correctly depict the properties of the conduction electrons. In Paper *36* he showed that the electrons in a metal have atomic, rather than free-electron, properties near the nuclei, but that, away from the nuclei, their wave functions might have a strong resemblance to free-electron functions. He further pointed out that, for sodium, the energy as a function of **k** is very similar to a perturbed free-electron energy curve, thus explaining the success of the free-electron model for that metal. More recently he has carried these ideas even further, showing specific conditions which must be fulfilled by the electronic wave functions in order for the energy bands to be free-electronlike. He has illustrated [see, for example, bibliography (*113*)], the manner in which these conditions are, in fact, fulfilled for the alkali metals—notably free-electronlike—and how they are not fulfilled in some of the metals for which the electrons are not describable at all by the free-electron model.

With Slater's understanding of the inaccuracies of the free-electron model of metals, it is not surprising that he has had an active part in the development of better methods for the calculation of electronic properties of solids. His publications include calculations by many methods, including the Thomas-Fermi statistical model and the Wigner-Seitz method, but it was Slater himself who proposed the method which is today one of the most widely used approaches to the calculation of electron energy bands in solids—the augmented plane wave (APW) method. Originally proposed in 1937 (*44*), and described in more detail and from other points of view in later publications, the method is based on Slater's realization that the wave function of an electron in a solid is very atomlike near the nuclei, but more like the plane waves of free electrons away from the nuclei. Therefore, why not use an expansion which also had this characteristic, to obtain rapid convergence? Thus, in the APW method, the wave function is constructed from functions which are plane waves in the regions outside of imaginary spheres surrounding the nuclei, and atomiclike solutions of a spherically symmetric potential within these spheres. This approach eliminates the slow convergence of pure plane-wave expansions and the many-center integrals which cause so much difficulty with LCAO approaches. It is still a difficult problem for hand calculation, but quite feasible on modern high-speed digital computers, and it is currently being used in theoretical solid-state groups in many countries of the world as a technique for the advancement of our knowledge and understanding of the properties of solids.

The band theory of solids is, of course, interesting only insofar as it is useful in explaining properties which can be measured experimentally, and Slater has taken a leading role in the efforts to understand many of these effects. In addition to developing new ideas, he has used the older more approximate theories to teach all they are able about the physics he seeks to understand, often finding bits of truth upon which can be built more accurate models. In this way he used the older theories of conduction to pave the reader's way to an understanding of the more difficult but far better quantum-mechanical description of conduction in his paper (37). Slater has not hesitated to extend or discard approaches which he felt were not truly descriptive of the important physical aspects of the problems he sought to understand, as is well illustrated in his series of papers on ferromagnetism in metals. As he felt that the Heisenberg model was not suitable for describing ferromagnetism in metals, he showed that the very limited band theory of ferromagnetism which Bloch had developed could be extended to account for the important experimentally observed magnetic phenomena and still be consistent with the other ideas of electronic properties of solids which had been so well explained by the band model. His treatment of spin waves in magnetic materials also led him to an idea concerning possible semilocalized states which would explain the huge diamagnetic effects encountered in superconducting solids, and so his name is also counted among those whose work had a part in the understanding of superconductivity (43).

In other areas of solid-state physics he anticipated concepts which were not to become prominent or familiar to specialists in the field until several decades later. For example, in paper (45), we find a discussion of "Damped Electron Waves in Crystals." By introducing an empirical damping constant in the form of a pure imaginary term added to the real crystal potential, he was able to describe the inelastic damping of electrons observed in electron-diffraction experiments. The complex or "optical" model for a potential has, of course, been a popular one in both optics and nuclear physics. It has been only very recently that solid-state theorists have looked seriously into the problem of defining electron states in disordered crystals and liquid metals. They have quite independently arrived at the description of the damping of Bloch states due to the effects of disorder in terms of a complex or "optical" model for the crystal potential. They have thus rediscovered in a fashion a concept initiated under somewhat different circumstances by John C. Slater back in 1937.

Besides being the author of numerous research papers, Slater is the author of a number of valuable books both on general physics and on chemical physics (*33,52,56,62,63,70,77,102,109,111,113*). The most recent series of volumes (*109*, two volumes, and (*111*), two or more volumes) are intended by Slater to summarize and digest the content of his research papers and other work on the structure of matter from the point of view of a chemical physicist.

There were and are many other areas of interest in which the name of Slater is synonymous with progress in physical understanding. Not only this, but also there are now many of Slater's students and an increasing number of his students' students in whom there has been imbued some of the same spirit of seeking the physics behind the model, and seeking a model that describes the physics. This may well prove to be as great a contribution to the physical sciences as his own personal findings. One begins to appreciate the real magnitude of his contribution to physics and chemistry when one discovers how many of those doing creative work in these fields today must count some form of association with John Clarke Slater as having had a significant effect on their own creativity.

Bibliography

Publications of John C. Slater

1. Radiation and atoms. *Nature* **113**, 307 (1924).
2. Compressibility of the alkali halides. *Phys. Rev.* **23**, 488 (1924).
3. The quantum theory of radiation (with N. Bohr and H. A. Kramers). *Phil. Mag.* **47**, 785 (1924).
4. Uber die Quantentheorie der Strahlung (with N. Bohr and H. A. Kramers). *Z. Physik* **24**, 69 (1924).
5. A quantum theory of optical phenomena. *Phys. Rev.* **25**, 395 (1925).
6. Line breadths and absorption probabilities from line absorption (with G. R. Harrison). *Phys. Rev.* **25**, 783 (1925).
7. Physically degenerate systems and quantum dynamics. *Phys. Rev.* **26**, 419 (1925).
8. The nature of radiation. *Nature* **116**, 278 (1925).
9. Interpretation of the hydrogen and helium spectra. *Proc. Natl. Acad. Sci. U.S.* **11**, 732 (1925).
10. Alternating intensities in band lines. *Nature* **117**, 555 (1926).
11. Spinning electrons and the structure of spectra. *Nature* **117**, 587 (1926).
12. Measurement of the compressibility of the alkali halides. *Proc. Am. Acad. Arts Sci.* **61**, 135 (1926).
13. A dynamical model for complex atoms. *Phys. Rev.* **28**, 291 (1926).
14. Radiation and absorption on Schrödinger's theory. *Proc. Natl. Acad. Sci. U.S.* **13**, 7 (1927).
15. Action of radiation and perturbations on atoms. *Proc. Natl. Acad. Sci. U.S.* **13**, 104 (1927).
16. The structure of the helium atom, I. *Proc. Natl. Acad. Sci. U.S.* **13**, 423 (1927).
17. Central fields and Rydberg formulas in wave mechanics. *Phys. Rev.* **31**, 333 (1928).
18. Light quanta and wave mechanics. *Phys. Rev.* **31**, 895 (1928).
19. The self-consistent field and the structure of atoms. *Phys. Rev.* **32**, 339 (1928).
20. The normal state of helium. *Phys. Rev.* **32**, 349 (1928).
21. Physical meaning of wave mechanics. *J. Franklin Inst.* **207**, 449 (1929).
22. Theory of complex spectra. *Phys. Rev.* **34**, 1293 (1929).
23. Cohesion in monovalent metals. *Phys. Rev.* **35**, 509 (1930).
24. Note on Hartree's method. *Phys. Rev.* **35**, 210 (1930).
25. Atomic shielding constants. *Phys. Rev.* **36**, 57 (1930).
26. Directed valence in polyatomic molecules. *Phys. Rev.* **37**, 481 (1931).
27. Van der Waals forces in gases (with J. G. Kirkwood). *Phys. Rev.* **37**, 682 (1931).
28. Note on the structure of the groups XO_3. *Phys. Rev.* **38**, 325 (1931).
29. Quantum theory of the equation of state. *Phys. Rev.* **38**, 237 (1931).
30. Molecular energy levels and valence bonds. *Phys. Rev.* **38**, 1109 (1931).
31. Note on molecular structure. *Phys. Rev.* **41**, 255 (1932).
32. Analytic atomic wave functions. *Phys. Rev.* **42**, 33 (1932).
33. **" Introduction to Theoretical Physics "** (with N. H. Frank). McGraw-Hill, New York, 1933.
34. The electron theory of metallic conduction. *Science* **77**, 595 (1933).
35. The virial and molecular structure. *J. Chem. Phys.* **1**, 687 (1933).
36. Electronic energy bands in metals. *Phys. Rev.* **45**, 794 (1934).
37. The electronic structure of metals. *Rev. Mod. Phys.* **6**, 209 (1934).
38. The Thomas-Fermi method for metals (with H. M. Krutter). *Phys. Rev.* **47**, 559 (1935).

39. The ferromagnetism of nickel. *Phys. Rev.* **49**, 931 (1936).
40. The ferromagnetism of nickel. II. Temperature effects. *Phys. Rev.* **49**, 931 (1936).
41. Theory of inelastic scattering of electrons from solids (with E. Rudberg). *Phys. Rev.* **50**, 150 (1936).
42. Optical absorption by the alkali halides (with W. Shockley). *Phys. Rev.* **50**, 705 (1936).
43. The nature of the superconducting state. *Phys. Rev.* **51**, 195 (1937).
44. Wave functions in a periodic potential. *Phys. Rev.* **51**, 846 (1937).
45. Damped electron waves in crystals. *Phys. Rev.* **51**, 840 (1937).
46. Electronic structure of alloys. *J. Appl. Phys.* **8**, 385 (1937).
47. The theory of ferromagnetism: lowest energy levels. *Phys. Rev.* **52**, 198 (1937).
48. The nature of the superconducting state II. *Phys. Rev.* **52**, 214 (1937).
49. Charles Elwood Mendenhall (1872–1935). *Proc. Am. Acad. Arts. Sci.* **71**, 529 (1937).
50. Electrodynamics of ponderable bodies. *J. Franklin Inst.* **225**, 277 (1938).
51. Excited energy levels of insulating crystals. *Trans. Faraday Soc.* **34**, 827 (1938).
52. **"Introduction to Chemical Physics."** McGraw-Hill, New York, 1939.
53. Note on Grüneisen's constant for the incompressible metals. *Phys. Rev.* **57**, 744 (1940).
54. Note on the effect of pressure on the Curie point of iron–nickel alloys. *Phys. Rev.* **58**, 54 (1940).
55. Theory of the transition in KH_2PO_4. *J. Chem. Phys.* **9**, 16 (1941).
56. **"Microwave Transmission."** McGraw-Hill, New York, 1942; Dover, New York, 1959.

Various classified reports and memoranda for M.I.T. Radiation Laboratory, Bell Telephone Laboratories, during the years 1942–1946.

57. Physics and the wave equation. *Bull. Am. Math. Soc.* **52**, 392 (1946).
58. Superconductivity of lead at 3-cm wavelength (with F. Bitter, J. B. Garrison, J. Halpern, E. Maxwell, and C. F. Squire). *Phys. Rev.* **70**, 97 (1946).
59. Microwave electronics. *Rev. Mod. Phys.* **18**, 441 (1946).
60. The phasing of magnetrons. *RLE Tech. Rept. No. 35* April, 1947.
61. The theory of symmetrical waveguide T's. *RLE Tech. Rept. No. 37* April, 1947.
62. **"Mechanics"** (with N. H. Frank). McGraw-Hill, New York, 1947.
63. **"Electromagnetism"** (with N. H. Frank). McGraw-Hill, New York, 1947.
64. The design of linear accelerators. *RLE. Tech. Rept. No. 47* September, 1947; *Rev. Mod. Phys.* **20**, 473 (1948).
65. Electromagnetic waves in iris-loaded waveguides. *RLE Tech. Rept. No. 48* September, 1948.
66. The physics of metals. *Phys. Today* **2**, 6 (1949).
67. Electrons in perturbed periodic lattices. *RLE Tech. Rept. No. 113* May, 1949; *Phys. Rev.* **76**, 1592 (1949).
68. The M.I.T. International Conference on the Physics of Very Low Temperatures, September 6–10, 1949. *Science* **110**, 465 (1949).
69. Surface impedance of normal and superconductors at 24,000 megacycles per second (with E. Maxwell and P. M. Marcus). *Phys. Rev.* **76**, 1332 (1949); *RLE Tech. Rept. No. 109* May, 1949.
70. **"Microwave Electronics."** Van Nostrand, Princeton, New Jersey, 1950.
71. The Lorentz correction in barium titanate. *Phys. Rev.* **78**, 748 (1950).
72. Structure and polarization of atoms and molecules. *Elec. Eng.* **69**, 855 (1950).
73. A simplification of the Hartree-Fock method. *Phys. Rev.* **81**, 385 (1951).
74. Note on orthogonal atomic orbitals. *J. Chem. Phys.* **19**, 220 (1951).
75. The effects of radiation on materials. *J. Appl. Phys.* **22**, 237 (1951).
76. Magnetic effects and the Hartree-Fock equation. *Phys. Rev.* **82**, 538 (1951).

77. "**Quantum Theory of Matter.**" McGraw-Hill, New York, 1951.
78. The electron theory of solids. *Am. J. Phys.* **19**, 368 (1951).
79. Note on superlattices and Brillouin zones. *Phys. Rev.* **84**, 179 (1951).
80. The effect of chemical combination on the internal conversion in Tc. *Phys. Rev.* **84**, 1261 (1951).
81. Electromagnetic resonant behavior of a confocal spheroidal cavity system in the microwave region (with J. C. Simons). *J. Appl. Phys.* **23**, 29 (1952).
82. The M.I.T. linear electron accelerator (with P. T. Demos and A. F. Kip). *J. Appl. Phys.* **23**, 53 (1952); *RLE Tech. Rept. No.* 203 May, 1951.
83. Particle dynamics in the linear accelerator (with J. R. Terrall). *J. Appl. Phys.* **23**, 66 (1952).
84. Field strength measurements in resonant cavities (with L. C. Maier, Jr.). *J. Appl. Phys.* **23**, 68 (1952).
85. Determination of field strength in a linear accelerator cavity (with L. C. Maier, Jr.). *J. Appl. Phys.* **23**, 78 (1952).
86. High energy accelerators. *Ann. Rev. of Nucl. Sci.* **1**, 199 (1952).
87. A soluble problem in energy bands. *Phys. Rev.* **87**, 807 (1952).
88. Ferromagnetism and the band theory. *Rev. Mod. Phys.* **25**, 199 (1953).
89. A generalized self-consistent field method. *Phys. Rev.* **91**, 528 (1953).
90. A two-electron example of ferromagnetism (with H. Statz and G. F. Koster). *Phys. Rev.* **91**, 1323 (1953).
91. An augmented plane wave method for the periodic potential problem. *Phys. Rev.* **92**, 603 (1953).
92. An augmented plane-wave method for the periodic potential problem, II (with M. M. Saffren). *Phys. Rev.* **92**, 1126 (1953).
93. Simplified LCAO method for the periodic potential problem (with G. F. Koster). *Phys. Rev.* **94**, 1498 (1954).
94. Electronic structure of atoms and molecules. *SSMTG Tech. Rept. No. 3* M.I.T., February, 1953.
    Electronic structure of solids. I. The energy band method. *SSMTG Tech. Rep. No. 4* M.I.T., July, 1953.
95. Electronic structure of solids. II. The perturbed periodic lattice. *SSMTG Tech Rept. No. 5* M.I.T., December, 1953.
96. Work on molecular theory in the solid-state and molecular theory group, M.I.T., Symposium on Molecular Physics, Nikko, 1953.
97. Problem of ferromagnetism. *Proc. Intern. Conf. Theoret. Phys., Kyoto and Tokyo, 1953* p. 679.
98. Wave functions for impurity levels (with G. F. Koster). *Phys. Rev.* **94**, 1392 (1954).
99. Electronic structure of solids. III. Configuration interaction in solids. *SSMTG Tech. Rept. No. 6* M.I.T., April, 1954.
100. Simplified impurity calculation (with G. F. Koster). *Phys. Rev.* **96**, 1208 (1954).
101. One-electron energies of atoms, molecules, and solids. *Phys. Rev.* **98**, 1039 (1955).
102. "**Modern Physics.**" McGraw-Hill, New York, 1955.
103. Band theory of bonding in metals. *In* "Theory of Alloy Phases," p. 1. *Am. Soc. Metals*, 1956.
104. The electronic structure of solids. *In* "Encyclopedia of Physics," Vol. 19, p. 1. Springer-Verlag, Berlin, 1954.
105. Barrier theory of the photoconductivity of lead sulfide. *Phys. Rev.* **103**, 1631 (1956).
106. Interaction of waves in crystals. *Rev. Mod. Phys.* **30**, 197 (1958); *SSMTG Tech. Rept. No. 10* M.I.T., September, 1957.

107. Band theory. *J. Phys. Chem. Solids* **8**, 21 (1959).

108. Note on the interatomic spacings in the ions $I_3^- \cdot FHF^-$. *Acta Cryst.* **12**, 197 (1959).

109. "**Quantum Theory of Atomic Structure,**" Vols. I and II. McGraw-Hill, New York, 1960.

110. Symmetry and free electron properties of the gallium energy bands. *Phys. Rev.* **126**, 1307 (1962).

111. "**Quantum Theory of Molecules and Solids,**" Vol. 1. McGraw-Hill, New York, 1963.

112. The electronic structure of atoms—the Hartree-Fock method and correlation. *Rev. Mod. Phys.* **35**, 484 (1963).

113. "**Quantum Theory of Molecules and Solids,**" Vol. 2. McGraw-Hill, New York, 1965.

114. Robert Mulliken of Newburyport, *in* "Molecular Orbitals in Chemistry, Physics, and Biology," p. 17. Academic Press, New York, 1964.

115. Energy band calculations by the augmented plane wave method. *Advan. Quant. Chem.* **1**, 35 (1964).

116. Atomic radii in crystals. *J. Chem. Phys.* **41**, 3199 (1964).

117. Space groups and wave-function symmetry in crystals. *Rev. Mod. Phys.* **37**, 68 (1965).

In addition to these contributions, there have been a great many items in the Quarterly Progress Reports of the Solid-State and Molecular Theory Group, M.I.T., from 1951 to 1966.

Comments on Professor J. C. Slater's Paper
"Cohesion in Monovalent Metals"

PER-OLOV LÖWDIN

Among the scientists contributing to the Slater volume, it was felt that, in order to give a more complete picture of Professor Slater and his scientific personality, it would be desirable and appropriate to enclose a reproduction of one of his own classical papers. There is an early paper written in 1930 about "Cohesion in Monovalent Metals," a subject which has played a fundamental role in the development of molecular and solid-state theory. This paper has turned out to be a gold mine of fruitful ideas which, many decades later, is not yet completely exhausted. It is reproduced here as a typical representation of Professor Slater's writing.

The paper deals with the situation of the electrons in an alkali metal. In order to give a simple model of the metal, Professor Slater first discusses the hydrogen molecule in great detail. He studies, for the first time, the interrelation between the valence bond method and the molecular-orbital method, and he shows that the former, including ionized states, gives the same result as the latter including superposition of configurations. His discussion of the behavior of the energy curves for separated atoms is basic for later studies of the correlation problem. He uses the results obtained to investigate the electronic structure of a metal and its cohesive, electric, and magnetic properties.

The paper contains a discussion of the spin-degeneracy problem which is a landmark in the development of this field. After a discussion of "spin waves," Professor Slater discusses such spin arrangements with "different spins on different sublattices" which have proved to be fundamental for the alternant molecular-orbital method and for the modern treatment of the correlation problems using "different orbitals for different spins."

In discussing the atomic model of a solid, he emphasizes the importance of the overlap integrals between atomic orbitals associated with neighboring centers and the resulting "nonorthogonality catastrophe." He also indicates a solution of this problem through the equivalence between the valence bond method and the molecular-orbital method, which later was realized in the construction of the Wannier functions.

The focus of the paper is on the physical problem and the associated model but, even if the formal mathematics and the number of equations is kept strictly to a minimum, the mathematical structure underlying the general discussion is strict and clear and brought to life through the simplified models and examples used.

The paper is a beautiful and typical example of Professor Slater's clear and pedagogical style in treating even some of the most difficult phenomena in the quantum theory of matter. The importance of its influence on the development of the theory through more than three decades can hardly be overestimated.

COHESION IN MONOVALENT METALS

By J. C. Slater

Jefferson Physical Laboratory, Harvard University

(Received January 27, 1930)

Abstract

The theory of metallic structure, of Sommerfeld, Heisenberg, and Bloch, is carried far enough to explain cohesive forces, and calculations are made for atoms with one valence electron, particularly metallic sodium. The numerical results, though rough, are in qualitative agreement with experiment. It is found that the forces in general are of the same nature as those met in ordinary homopolar binding, discussed by Heitler and London; except that the purely electrostatic force from penetration of one atom by another is relatively more important, the valence effect from the exchange of electrons relatively less important, than in diatomic molecules.

As a preliminary to the calculation, the relations of the methods of Heisenberg and of Bloch are discussed, and it is shown that they are essentially equivalent in their results when properly handled. Remarks are made both about conductivity and ferromagnetism. In connection with conduction, it is shown that a definite meaning can be given to free electrons, that they are necessary to conduction, and that a method can be set up for computing their number, which is rather small compared with the number of atoms. Ferromagnetism is discussed in connection with a recent paper of Bloch. It is shown that a metal like an alkali cannot be ferromagnetic, for atoms at such a distance that the interatomic forces keep the metal in equilibrium, are too close to be magnetic. For ferromagnetism, rather, it seems necessary to have one group of electrons responsible for cohesion, and another group, of smaller orbit and therefore relatively farther apart, producing the magnetism; a situation actually found only in the iron group and the similar groups.

I. Introduction

A CRYSTAL of a metal is an enormous molecule, with electronic energy levels depending on the positions of all the nuclei, just as the electronic energy of a diatomic molecule depends on the internuclear distance. In this paper, in which we are interested in cohesive forces, we must find this energy of the lowest state in terms of the size of the crystal. We limit ourselves to geometrically similar arrangements of the nuclei, with changing scale. From the minimum of the curve, we find the heat of dissociation, grating space, and compressibility of the metal. But also we can investigate the wave function of this lowest state, and obtain information about the electric and magnetic properties of the metal. In this way we are naturally led to a discussion of the calculations of Heisenberg[1] and of Bloch on these subjects; in order to be sure that we really understand the arrangement of energy levels, we discuss the relationships of their methods, and arrive at a consistent picture combining them.

---

[1] W. Heisenberg, Zeits. f. Physik **49**, 619 (1928);
F. Bloch, *ibid.* **52**, 555 (1929).

As for the results, one naturally asks first, what are the forces holding a metal together? Are they ordinary attractions on account of penetration of atoms, or valence forces, or electrostatic forces of ionic attraction, or van der Waals forces, or some special sort not found in other cases? This question cannot be answered categorically; no doubt all the forces are simultaneously present, and the problem is to find the relative magnitudes. The tentative result at which we arrive is that the simple penetration of one atom by another is the most important part of the effect. But valence effects are also present, although weakened by having the valences shared by many neighbors, and are responsible for a considerable fraction of the attraction. Although these actual magnitudes may not be verified by more accurate calculation, still we have discussed the problem in enough detail so that the general relations can be understood in any case.

The other question one will ask is, what is the situation of the electrons in the metal? Can one give a meaning to the question, how many free electrons are there? The answer, from whichever side we look at the question, seems to be the same. Most of the valence electrons are at any time attached to their atoms. These electrons cannot take part in conduction; they could do it only by having a whole file of such electrons simultaneously jump to the next atom in line, a most unlikely occurrence. But a few electrons at any time—calculation suggests a few percent—will be detached from their atoms, leaving an equal number of positive ions behind them; and they are what, by all rights, one should call free electrons. These electrons, and the positive ions left behind, can take part in conduction. First, the free electrons can move easily from one atom to the next. Second, a bound or associated electron on one of the atoms next a positive ion can jump to that ion, leaving its own atom ionized. We are thus led precisely to the dual theory of conduction, by free and by associated electrons, which Professor Hall[2] has suggested and elaborated. When we look at the metal by the method of Heisenberg, these results become clear. In that method, a wave function consists of the assignment of electrons to atoms. We find that we must go beyond Heisenberg, in assigning sometimes two electrons to one atom, sometimes none, instead of always one; for we need such states to solve the problem of the stationary states of the metal. That is, we introduce free electrons. And when we consider transitions from one state to another, it is easy to see that these transitions can result in conduction only when such free electrons are present. On Bloch's scheme, where we describe directly the velocity, rather than the position, of the electrons, it is less easy to see the relation; but here too one can show that, if there are no free electrons, the velocities of all electrons must compensate, so that there is no net current. Since this paper is not primarily about conduction, we do not go into these points with any detail.

The only metals specifically treated are those with one valence electron per atom, and that in an s state; that is, the alkalies. And it is assumed that they can be replaced by single valence electrons moving in non-coulomb

[2] E. H. Hall, Proc. Nat. Acad., 1920–1921.

fields. This can be easily justified. It is to be noted that the other metals are more complicated, not merely by having more electrons, but by having them in p or d orbits, thus introducing new degeneracies. The actual calculations of cohesion have been carried through for sodium, with satisfactory results. They are only done roughly, however; the primary purpose of this paper is to make clear the general relations, rather than to attempt accurate calculations. The work is being carried further by Dr. Bartlett, and I wish to thank him for help on some of the calculations used in this paper. The work described here has been done while the writer was on leave, working in Leipzig. He wishes to thank Professor Heisenberg for his courtesy in extending the privileges of his laboratory, and for a number of illuminating conversations on the subject of the paper; and also to thank Harvard University for granting leave, and the Guggenheim Foundation for the assistance of a fellowship.

2. COMPARISON OF HEISENBERG'S AND BLOCH'S METHODS

The problem of a metal must be attacked by perturbation theory, and the unperturbed functions which we use can be set up in two quite different ways, one used by Heisenberg, the other by Bloch, either giving us a finite set of unperturbed functions. We regard the perturbation problem in the following way: we seek those linear combinations of these functions which, in the sense of the variation method, form the best approximations to solutions of Schrödinger's equation. This problem is solved by computing the matrix of the energy operator with respect to these functions, and solving the equations

$$\sum_k (H(i/k) - \delta(i/k)W)S(k) = 0$$

for the coefficients $S(k)$ to be used in making the linear combinations, and the energy values W of the resulting terms. (The term $\delta(i/k)$ must be given a slightly different form if the unperturbed functions are not orthogonal). This differs from the more conventional method: there one starts with an infinite, complete set of unperturbed functions, instead of our finite set, but solves only as a power series in the non-diagonal terms of the energy matrix, breaking off after the second power in all ordinary applications. It resembles more closely the quite different method ordinarily used with degenerate systems, where one takes only very few unperturbed states, but correctly solves the problem of combining them. For a nearly degenerate problem like the present one, with a great many states near together, the conventional method of developing in series will not work well, for the series do not converge well, and we are forced to use something like the present method. The justification comes simply from the assumption that the lowest states can be well approximated by such a linear combination of Heisenberg's or Bloch's functions (which correspond to having the atoms in their normal states). Surely this is not exact; for better results we should have to consider also the excited states of the atoms. But also certainly it is a fair approximation for the lowest states of the metal.

Heisenberg's functions, amplified in a simple way, form good approximations when the crystal is extended, for they are derived from the separated atoms. Bloch's functions on the other hand come by analogy with the free electron theory of Sommerfeld, and are good approximations when the crystal is compressed. The actual solutions of the perturbation problem are of course linear combinations of either Heisenberg's or Bloch's functions, not individual ones, and one gets the same final result whichever set one starts with (for the two sets of functions can be written as linear combinations of each other). But the fact that in the limiting cases the functions of one of the two sets become rather good approximations can be used, along with interpolation, to derive the general nature of the real stationary states. This comparison is made in the present section, and is illustrated by the interesting case of H_2, where the calculations can be made exactly. At the outset, we must recognize two facts: first, that we must amplify Heisenberg's method by including polar states, to make it general enough to agree with Bloch's and to permit conductivity; second, that although Bloch has the proper set of functions, he has nowhere attempted to solve the perturbation problem, but has merely taken his unperturbed functions as being correct, which amounts to getting the energy to the accuracy of the conventional "first order perturbations."

The first step in either Heisenberg's or Bloch's method, as we apply them, is to write an approximate solution as a product of functions of the individual electrons. Heisenberg takes, for these separate functions, the wave functions of electrons attached to individual nuclei; the number of such functions is the product of the number of nuclei, multiplied by the number of different sets of quantum numbers we consider for an individual nucleus. If we restrict ourselves to s states, there are then only two states per nucleus, corresponding to the two orientations of the spin. For nucleus a, we denote these two[3] by $u_\alpha(a/x)$, $u_\beta(a/x)$, and we have such a function for each nucleus $a \ b \ . \ . \ . \ n$. Bloch takes, on the other hand, combinations of these functions:

$$u_\alpha(klm/xyz) = \sum_{g_1 g_2 g_3} e^{2\pi i(kg_1/G_1 + lg_2/G_2 + mg_3/G_3)} u_\alpha(g_1 g_2 g_3/xyz),$$

where $g_1 g_2 g_3$ are the coordinates of a particular nucleus, $G_1 G_2 G_3$ the dimensions of the rectangular crystal, and $u_\alpha(g_1 g_2 g_3/xyz)$ the wave function (as used by Heisenberg) for an electron moving around the nucleus situated at $g_1 g_2 g_3$. The function with k, l, m represents an electron, in general moving in the direction k, l, m, but pausing at the various atoms on the way. There are as many sets k, l, m allowed as there are atoms in the crystal; for larger k, l, m the function proves to be merely a repetition of one already counted.

---

[3] We use here for convenience in writing Pauli's notation u_α, u_β for the spin, rather than the more explicit but more cumbersome notation $u(n/x_i)$ $\delta(m_s/m_{si})$ used in a previous paper. See J. C. Slater, Phys. Rev. **34**, 1293 (1929). The method used in the present paper is described, as applied to atoms, in the paper referred to; it should be understood that, although we speak here of using Heisenberg's and Bloch's methods, our actual procedure is quite different from that of these authors.

Now we actually set up the product of functions mentioned in the previous paragraph: we pick one out and let it be a function of the coordinates x_1 of the first electron, a second for the coordinates x_2 of the second, and so on to the nth, and multiply them all together. By the exclusion principle, no function can be chosen more than once. Then we form an antisymmetric combination, by permuting the indices of the electron coordinates, and adding the permuted functions with appropriate signs, obtaining essentially a determinant. These antisymmetric functions are the ones with which we start our perturbation calculation. Many such functions can be set up: there are $2n$ functions of a single electron, of which only n are to be chosen for each antisymmetric function, so that there are $(2n)!/(n!)^2$ different functions. Our perturbation problem is that of finding which linear combinations of these functions most nearly satisfy the wave equation. We may note the restriction of Heisenberg's method as he uses it; he does not include polar states. That is, he does not allow for example the two functions $u_\alpha(a/x)$, $u_\beta(a/x)$ to appear together in any product. This greatly limits the number of functions; but although the terms obtained by it certainly represent the lowest energy levels, since it requires energy to form a positive and a negative ion from two neutral atoms, we do not make this limitation.

Having set up the unperturbed functions, we next make linear combinations of them, by the method described in a previous paragraph. This process can be simplified by using a property of the spin. Every unperturbed function has a certain definite component M_S of spin along the axis, equal to $(n_\alpha - n_\beta)/2$, where n_α is the number of electrons with positive component of spin, n_β the number with negative. If now we neglect the magnetic interaction between the spins and the orbital motion, the problems with each value of M_S can be handled separately: the components $II(i/j)$ from a function with one value to a function with another are zero. The states with a given M_S include, as one readily sees, all those states whose total spin S is equal to or greater than M_S (for just these S's can be so oriented, on the vector model, as to give a component M_S along a fixed axis). Thus by solving each such problem, and comparing, we can identify the spin of each term.[4]

The two methods can be illustrated by the case of H_2. Here there are $4!/(2!)^2 = 6$ different wave functions. On Heisenberg's method, the four functions for an individual electron can be symbolized by (αa), (βa), (αb), (βb); two of these are to be picked out for each antisymmetric wave function. Thus the six are $(\alpha a)(\alpha b)$; $(\alpha a)(\beta a)$, $(\alpha b)(\beta b)$; $(\alpha a)(\beta b)$, $(\beta a)(\alpha b)$; $(\beta a)(\beta b)$. They are arranged, first, by M_S: the first has the value 1, the next four the value 0, and the last -1. Thus the terms consist of one triplet and three singlets. Among the four terms with $M_S = 0$, the first two are polar (and not considered by Heitler and London, or Heisenberg), the last two are non-polar. Immediately one finds that the sum of these non-polar functions is the component of the triplet. We are then left with three functions: the

[4] This is essentially the method used in the paper already quoted It has already been applied by Bloch to problems in the theory of metals. See F. Bloch, Zeits. f. Physik., **57**, 545 (1929).

two polar ones, and the difference of the non-polar ones, from which to find our three singlets. The difference of the polar ones is antisymmetric in the nuclei, giving one state; their sum, and the difference of the non-polar functions, give two functions symmetrical in the nuclei, between which we finally solve the simple perturbation, resulting now in a quadratic secular equation, and obtain the two remaining singlet states. The energy levels as a function of the distance of separation are plotted in Fig. 1. The energy level of the lowest, $^1\Sigma S^N$, is almost exactly as given by Heitler and London, but its wave function contains quite an appreciable contribution from the polar state. The triplet is just the repulsive state of Heitler and London. The other two levels are essentially polar. They go at infinite separation to the energy of $H^+ + H^-$, greater than the other limit by the ionization potential less the electron affinity of H (this rough approximation gives $-\frac{1}{4}Rh$ for the electron

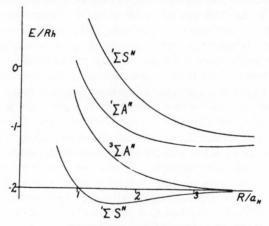

Fig. 1. Energy levels of H_2.

affinity, so that the terms go to $5/4Rh$). The lower of these has a minimum; it is presumably the polar part which, by combination with other functions, leads to the experimentally known B state of the molecule. We notice that at large separations the functions behave just like Heisenberg's (extended) unperturbed functions: a triplet and a singlet are non-polar, and go to the lower energy; while two singlets are polar, and go to the higher level.

Next we consider Bloch's method for the same problem. His functions for one electron, for this case, are

$$u_\alpha(0/x) = u_\alpha(a/x) + u_\alpha(b/x)$$
$$u_\alpha(1/x) = u_\alpha(a/x) - u_\alpha(b/x),$$

with similar functions for β. (These do not follow quite directly from the general formulas given above; Bloch's functions must be slightly modified for finite systems, for they apply rather to infinite but periodic ones.) The discussion of multiplicity given above goes through without change, if we only substitute 0, 1 for a, b. We can easily show by direct calculation that the resulting unperturbed antisymmetric functions are linear combinations of those found by Heisenberg's method. For example, for $M_s = 1$, there is only one function by either method, so these must be identical, except for a numerical factor. By Heisenberg's method the function is

$$u_\alpha(a/x_1)u_\alpha(b/x_2) - u_\alpha(b/x_1)u_\alpha(a/x_2).$$

By Bloch's it is

$$u_\alpha(0/x_1)u_\alpha(1/x_2) - u_\alpha(1/x_1)u_\alpha(0/x_2)$$
$$= [u_\alpha(a/x_1) + u_\alpha(b/x_1)][u_\alpha(a/x_2) - u_\alpha(b/x_2)]$$
$$- [u_\alpha(a/x_1) - u_\alpha(b/x_1)][u_\alpha(a/x_2) + u_\alpha(b/x_2)]$$
$$= -2[u_\alpha(a/x_1)u_\alpha(b/x_2) - u_\alpha(b/x_1)u_\alpha(a/x_2)].$$

We can set up the whole perturbation problem in these functions; and the solution can be carried out as easily as before, leading of course to just the same answers. The interesting question now is, how closely do Bloch's individual functions approximate the correct ones, for small values of R? The functions are respectively as follows: a singlet with both electrons in the state 0; a singlet and triplet with one in the state 0, the other in the state 1; and a singlet with both in the state 1. The state 0 corresponds to the lowest vibrational state on Sommerfeld's theory, the state 1 to the next higher one, so that the first state has on the simple interpretation only the zero-point vibrational energy, the next two have each one quantum, and the last two. Examination of the actual wave functions shows that they agree quite closely with the functions of Bloch: the lowest one is made, it is true, by combination of the (00) and (11) states, both being S^N, but the coefficient of the first is about eight times as large as that of the second, when R is such that the energy is at its minimum. The next two are made up of the (01) states. The highest is about eight parts of (11) to one of (00). The energies also show, for high compression, the behavior expected: the two states which should have one quantum of vibrational energy draw together, and the one with two quanta is just about twice as far above the lowest state as those with one. Even the spacing of these levels is just about what would be calculated on Sommerfeld's theory for an electron vibrating in a region the size of the molecule. Thus we see that Bloch's unperturbed functions form fairly good approximations to the real functions for the compressed state, as Heisenberg's do for the extended state.

We can now return to the general case, and make use of the fact that Heisenberg's functions approximate the real wave functions well for large separations, Bloch's for small. First, for the extended system, the energy is the ionization energy, on account of having many ions as well as neutral atoms. For a metal, it requires about 6 volts to form a positive and negative ion from two neutral atoms. Thus if all the atoms were ionized, we should have $n/2$ such pairs, or an energy per atom, or per electron, of about 3 volts. This measures the extension of the group of terms, for large R. It is a simple problem in permutations to find the number of terms of each multiplicity with each energy value in the limit. The one term of highest multiplicity will approach the lowest limit, for large R; it must be entirely nonpolar, for all spins point in the same direction, so that no two electrons can be in the same atom. For the next lower multiplicity, only one electron has a reversed spin; it is the only one which can be in an atom with another electron, so that there can be just one pair of atoms ionized. Following out, we easily see that terms of lower and lower multiplicity, in the limit of large R, lie higher and higher, and at the same time are more and more spread out. They spread in such a way that there are terms of each multiplicity way down to the bottom limit, although not to the top. As we shall see later, for R large but not infinite, in the normal case, the really lowest terms have small spins; but near them are many terms with large spin.

For the compressed system, the arrangement is as given by Bloch's theory. The total extension of the group of terms increases with $1/R^2$; for ordinary values of R, it is of the order of the mean zero-point energy, times n, which is decidedly larger than 3 volts$\times n$. Thus not only do the curves tend upward for decreasing R, giving repulsive energy levels, but they are definitely doing this at the actual size of the metal. The general physical interpretation of this repulsion is obvious: the valence electrons act here approximately as a perfect gas, and the energy levels are those of such a gas as it is compressed adiabatically against gas pressure, the energy varying therefore as $V^{-2/3}$ or as $1/R^2$. Here the terms of high multiplicity lie in the center of the pattern; those of lower spin also average in the center, but are more and more spread out. Since the terms of high spin are so low for large R, but not for small R, they must be even more repulsive than the others. The possibility seems very remote that any terms except those with very low multiplicity could be so low as to have minima, and come into the question for the normal state. We see that for cohesion we are interested only in the very lowest fraction of the whole set of terms. These terms almost all will go to the lowest energy level at infinite separation; they become in this limit non-polar. And the accuracy with which one can compute the lowest states of H_2 from Heitler and London's non-polar functions suggests that here too this may be possible. Accordingly for our actual calculation of these lowest states, we shall use Heisenberg's method with only non-polar functions. We shall find here, as we expect from our qualitative discussion, that the terms of low multiplicity really do lie below, some of them being attractive; while those of high multiplicity are repulsive, the highest spins lying highest. Finally we shall consider the effect of polar terms, and conclude that it is really small on the low energy levels, although not on the wave functions; for it is the polar character of the wave functions which makes conductivity possible.

3. ELECTRIC AND MAGNETIC PROPERTIES

Conductivity. In the introduction we have mentioned the interpretation of electric conduction on Heisenberg's and on Bloch's scheme. One notices that a single one of Bloch's functions implies conduction—the diagonal term of the momentum matrix is different from zero—whereas with Heisenberg's functions we must have a continual change from one stationary state to another. But it is particularly important to notice that, without polar states, or free electrons, no conduction is possible; we cannot set up combinations of non-polar states with a resultant momentum. For example, with two electrons, we can set up an arbitrary non-polar function $c_1u(a/x_1)u(b/x_2)$ $+c_2u(b/x_1)u(a/x_2)$. If now we compute the momentum, whose operator is $h/2\pi i(\partial/\partial x_1+\partial/\partial x_2)$, the only possibly significant terms are the cross terms, like

$$c_1c_2\frac{h}{2\pi i}\int u(a/x_1)u(b/x_2)\left(\frac{\partial}{\partial x_1}+\frac{\partial}{\partial x_2}\right)u(b/x_1)u(a/x_2)dv_1dv_2$$

$$=c_1c_2\frac{h}{2\pi i}\left\{\int u(b/x_2)u(a/x_2)dv_2\int u(a/x_1)\frac{\partial}{\partial x_1}u(b/x_1)dv_1\right.$$

$$\left.+\int u(a/x_1)u(b/x_1)dv_1\int u(b/x_2)\frac{\partial}{\partial x_2}u(a/x_2)dv_2\right\}.$$

On account of the penetration of one atom by the other, the integrals $\int u(b/x_2)u(a/x_2)dv_2$ are not zero. The integral $\int u(a/x_1)(\partial/\partial x_1)u(b/x_1)dv_1$ is also different from zero. But it is exactly cancelled by $\int u(b/x_2)(\partial/\partial x_2)u(a/x_2)dv_2$, as one can show by Green's theorem, so that the whole is zero. On the other hand, if we set up a polar combination like $c_1u(a/x_1)u(a/x_2)+c_2u(b/x_1)u(b/x_2)$, we again get two terms, but now they add, and give a current. As another example, we can take the term of maximum multiplicity in any system. In this term, we have seen by Heisenberg's scheme that each atom has just one electron, so that we expect no conduction. But in Bloch's scheme, each value k, l, m has just one electron. Since each such value is balanced by one with $-k, -l, -m$, having opposite momentum, the total momentum is zero, and there is again no current.

We can now see the importance of considering exactly the wave functions, as well as the energy levels, of the lowest state. In the ordinary low states there will, of course, be no current. But near the lowest state, if there is to be conductivity, there must be combinations of polar states, having a current, which are assumed in the presence of a field, and whose added energy comes simply from the kinetic energy of the electrons and the self-induction. Such states are possible only on account of the presence of positive and negative ions, with the resulting free and associated electron conductivity.

Magnetism. The lowest state of H_2 is the non-magnetic $^1\Sigma$, and we have found such a situation in general. In the region where the lowest states have their minimum, the metal must surely be in a compressed state, Bloch's arrangement of energy levels must be a good approximation, and the states of large spin must lie very high. We are thus led to the quite general conclusion that the outer electrons, which are largely if not entirely responsible for both cohesion and conduction, cannot produce ferromagnetic effects. If a metal is to be ferromagnetic, there must then be other electrons than these outer ones which are responsible for it, and these others must have smaller orbits, so that at the equilibrium distance of the outermost ones, the inner ones will be relatively further apart, and can be treated as an extended rather than as a compressed system. It is a very attractive hypothesis to suppose that in the iron group the existence of the $3d$ and $4s$ electrons provides in this way the two electron groups apparently necessary for ferromagnetism; for it is only in the transition groups that we have two such sets of electrons, and this criterion would go far toward limiting ferromagnetism to the metals actually showing it.

We next ask just how such inner electrons could be ferromagnetic. Certainly the general trend of the terms of high spin to the low energy values at large R is an essential part of the question: there will be terms of large spin near the lowest level. Bloch[5] has discussed the problem, concluding that for large R's the terms of high spin actually lie lower than those of smaller spin (he does not specifically discuss the dependence on R, but his energy formulas all contain it parametrically). This conclusion, however, is not correct; Bloch has merely computed diagonal values of the energy, with respect to his functions, and for large R these by no means form approximations to the actual energy values. From the correct treatment of the problem as we have given it, it is plain that at all R's there are terms of low multiplicity as low as those of high spin, or lower. It may be, however, that the mere presence of so many low terms of high multiplicity may be enough, on account of their high *a priori* probability and large number, to insure that the terms of large spin should be well represented at ordinary temperatures, even though there are low terms of zero spin, and so produce ferromagnetism. If, however, this should prove on calculation not to give the right effect, we should be led to consider Heisenberg's assumption that the normal order of terms is inverted in ferromagnetic atoms, the terms of high multiplicity lying lowest. He has shown by a general argument that electrons of large total quantum number (which the $4s$ electrons of iron have) have an exchange integral of the opposite sign to that found in hydrogen, so that the order of the non-polar terms would be reversed. This we should fit into our scheme in the following way: although this exchange integral is anomalous at large R, it presumably changes sign and becomes normal at smaller R; for first, Heisenberg's general argument only applies at large R; and second, our condition that the energy levels should approach those of Bloch at small R, with the terms of large spin lying high, seems quite general. Thus we should assume that the terms at small R lie as in Fig .1 but that at a considerable value of R, there is a crossing over (in this case the $^3\Sigma A^N$ crossing and lying under the $^1\Sigma S^N$), described by a change in the sign of the exchange integral K used in the next section from negative to positive. By assuming the existence of an inner group of electrons with these properties, we seem to secure a consistent picture of ferromagnetism. On the other hand, of course it is always possible that ferromagnetism is connected with the fact that the valence electrons of iron have an orbital angular momentum different from zero.

---

[5] F. Bloch, Zeits. f. Physik, **57**, 545 (1929).

4. COHESION

We are now prepared to begin the actual calculation of the lowest stationary states. We make several simplifications, which we later remove. First, we consider only non-polar states, in Heisenberg's scheme, and disregard exchange integrals except between adjacent atoms; this is the approximation also made by Heisenberg. Finally, for the present, we consider a linear lattice, n atoms uniformly spaced along a line, rather than a space lattice. Our problem, of course, is to compute the matrix of the energy with respect to the wave functions we have chosen, and then solve the problem of making proper linear combinations. The computation of the matrix is simple. By a fundamental formula of the previous paper mentioned above, the diagonal components are a sum, first, of the energies of the separate atoms, which we need not consider; next, a sum over all adjacent pairs, as the pair of atoms a and b, of integrals $J(a/b)$, which is essentially the diagonal energy E_1 of Heitler and London; finally, a sum over all adjacent pairs which have the same spin, of terms—$K(a/b)$, where K is the exchange integral E_2 of Heitler and London. Further, it is easy to show that all non-diagonal terms are zero, except those for which the distributions in the two states differ only by the exchange of an adjacent α and β; in such cases, the term is $-K$. In the normal case, to which we shall refer specifically, J and K as functions of R are both negative, K numerically greater than J. But in Heisenberg's case, K must be taken to be positive for large R, although presumably negative for small R.

To illustrate by H_2, we have one state with both spins parallel; then the energy is $J-K$. Next we have the problems with one parallel, the other anti-parallel; there are two such states (the two polar ones being omitted). Each has the diagonal energy J, and the non-diagonal energy between them is $-K$. Thus the equations for the linear combinations are

$$(J-W)S(1)-KS(2)=0$$
$$-KS(1)+(J-W)S(2)=0,$$

giving energy values $W=J\pm K$, the first evidently being the singlet, the second the component of the triplet.

In the general case, the computation of the matrix is no more difficult; the real problem is the solution of the linear equations for the S's. We cannot do this exactly; but we adopt two methods of approximation, one holding for larger spins, the other for smaller spins. We first discuss the former.

Method for large spins. First we take the problem where all spins are parallel, $n_\alpha=n$, $n_\beta=0$. Here there is but one state. Since with our linear lattice there are $(n-1)$ adjacent pairs, and all spins are parallel, the energy is simply $(n-1)J-(n-1)K$. Since J and K are normally both negative, but K numerically greater than J, this is a positive energy for all values of R, and results in a repulsive term. For Heisenberg's case, on the other hand, K is positive, and this term is attractive. Next we take the problem $n_\alpha=n-1$, $n_\beta=1$. There are now n unperturbed wave functions: the one electron β can be attached to any of the n atoms. We number the functions by the number of the atom where the electron is, only decreased by $\frac{1}{2}$: we have $u_{1/2} \cdots u_{n-1/2}$. Each of these functions will have the diagonal energy $(n-1)J - (n-3)K$, since two of the adjacent pairs now have opposite spins, except for the two functions $u_{1/2}$ and $u_{n-1/2}$ where our β electron is at an end of the lattice, and the energy is $(n-1)J - (n-2)K$. Also, all non-diagonal terms will be zero except those between terms of adjacent number, as for example between those symbolized by

$$\cdots \alpha \, \alpha \, \alpha \, \beta \, \alpha \, \alpha \, \alpha \cdots$$

and

$$\cdots \alpha \, \alpha \, \alpha \, \alpha \, \beta \, \alpha \, \alpha \cdots,$$

and which differ by just one interchange of an α and β. As a result, the perturbation equations will be

$$[(n-1)J - (n-2)K - W]S\left(\frac{1}{2}\right) - KS\left(\frac{3}{2}\right) = 0$$

$$-KS\left(\frac{1}{2}\right) + [(n-1)J - (n-3)K - W]S\left(\frac{3}{2}\right) - KS\left(\frac{5}{2}\right) = 0$$

$$-KS\left(\frac{3}{2}\right) + [(n-1)J - (n-3)K - W]S\left(\frac{5}{2}\right) - KS\left(\frac{7}{2}\right) = 0$$

$$\cdots \cdots \cdots \cdots \cdots \cdots \cdots \cdots \cdots \cdots$$

$$-KS\left(n-\frac{3}{2}\right) + [(n-1)J - (n-2)K - W]S\left(n-\frac{1}{2}\right) = 0$$

These equations are easily solved; they occur, for example, in the problem of a string weighted at equal intervals,[6] the S's being the displacements of the weights. To solve, we merely assume $S(k) = {}^{\cos}_{\sin}(\alpha k)$. The first and last equations give boundary conditions. They become like the others if we introduce an $S(-\frac{1}{2})$ and $S(n+\frac{1}{2})$, the first equation becoming

$$-KS(-\tfrac{1}{2}) + [(n-1)J - (n-3)K - W]S(\tfrac{1}{2}) - KS(\tfrac{3}{2}) = 0,$$

and if we further set $S(-\frac{1}{2}) = S(\frac{1}{2})$ and $S(n+\frac{1}{2}) = S(n-\frac{1}{2})$. These are then the boundary conditions; and to satisfy them we must take

$$S(k/p) = \cos p\pi k/n, \quad \text{where} \quad p = 0, 1, \cdots, n-1.$$

Now we substitute this form in our difference equations; and we get for W

$$-K\left(\cos\frac{p\pi}{n}(k-1) + \cos\frac{p\pi}{n}(k+1)\right) + [(n-1)J - (n-3)K - W(p)]\cos\frac{p\pi k}{n} = 0,$$

from which in each case

$$W(p) = (n-1)J - (n-3)K - 2K\cos\frac{p\pi}{n}.$$

[6] See, for example, Rayleigh's "Theory of Sound."

We now have the transformation coefficients $S(k/p)$ and the energy values $W(p)$ for the rotation of axes to the pth stationary state; the W's are the exact energy levels. They are evidently distributed between the values $W(0) = (n-1)J - (n-1)K$, and $W(n-1) = (n-1)J - (n-3-2\cos \pi(n-1)/n)$ $K = (n-1)J - (n-5)K$, almost, for large n. Obviously $W(0)$ is the energy of the level of highest multiplicity, which we have found before. Thus the levels $1 \cdots (n-1)$ are those of next to highest multiplicity.

Next we take the problem with two electrons of spin β. There are $n(n-1)/2$ such terms: each of the two indistinguishable β's can be on any one of the n atoms, so long as they are not on the same atom. Now it is convenient to denote states by the two atoms, say i and j (each going from $\frac{1}{2}$ to $n-\frac{1}{2}$) on which electrons β are. Our problem becomes analogous to that of a square membrane loaded at equally spaced points. The diagonal terms of the energy are all $(n-1)J - (n-5)K$, unless one of the β's is at an end of the lattice, or unless the two β's are adjacent. There are four non-diagonal terms for transitions from each wave function: for $i \to i \pm 1$, or for $j \to j \pm 1$. A typical equation can be written

$$-KS(i,j-1)$$
$$-KS(i-1,j) + [(n-1)J - (n-5)K - W]S(ij) - KS(i+1,j)$$
$$-KS(i,j+1) = 0.$$

This we satisfy by a product of cosine functions, $S(ij/pq) = \cos(p\pi i/n)\cos(q\pi j/n)$. We easily find that these exactly satisfy the boundary conditions when i or $j = \frac{1}{2}$ or $n - \frac{1}{2}$. There remains the condition when i is nearly equal to j. If $i = j \pm 1$, the diagonal energy is $(n-1)J - (n-3)K$, since the two β's are together; on the other hand, since the β's cannot be on the same atom, the coefficients $S(jj)$ and $S(j+1, j+1)$ vanish, so that only two transitions, rather than four, are possible. If now we define an $S(jj)$ and $S(j+1, j+1)$, we can make the equations of the same form as the general one, if only $S(jj) + S(j+1, j+1) = 2S(j+1, j)$. This furnishes our second boundary condition, which is evidently along the diagonal of our square "membrane." Unfortunately we cannot satisfy this condition exactly with our cosine functions; closer investigation shows that one must have much more complicated functions, with hyperbolic cosines, to satisfy it exactly, and one cannot carry the method through for the general case. Approximately, however, we can easily take care of our condition. If the p and q are not too great, so that the "wave-length" of the waves in our membrane is large, we can replace our condition by a differential one: it states that the amplitude at a point next the diagonal is the mean of the two adjacent values on the diagonal, and this very nearly means that the normal derivative of the function, at right angles to the diagonal, is zero. This we can satisfy by making our function symmetrical about the diagonal, or using $\cos(p\pi i/n)\cos(q\pi j/n) + \cos(q\pi i/n)\cos(p\pi j/n)$. We may expect this to hold best for small p and q, not so well for large values. It is clearly not right; for example, it yields $n^2/2$ functions, instead of the correct number $n(n-1)/2$.

Our function is an exact solution of the difference equations, if not of the boundary condition; and we find for the energy

$$W(p,q) = (n-1)J - (n-5)K - 2K\left(\cos\frac{p\pi}{n} + \cos\frac{q\pi}{n}\right),$$

where p, q go from 0 to $n-1$, but each pair is counted only once. The term of highest multiplicity comes from $p=q=0$; the $(n-1)$ terms of next highest value are those with either p or $q=0$, but the other not; the remaining terms are of multiplicity smaller by two.

This result can now be generalized without trouble: if we have many β's, the energy levels are given by

$$W = (n-1)J - (n-1-2n_\beta)K - 2K\sum_{i=1}^{n_\beta} \cos\frac{p_i\pi}{n}, \quad p_i = 0 \cdots n-1.$$

The terms where one or more p_i's equal zero are those whose total spin is greater than $(n_\alpha - n_\beta)/2$; those with all p's different from zero are those whose total spin equals $(n_\alpha - n_\beta)/2$. The latter value is evidently enormously greater than the other: every spin has enormously more terms than any higher spin. Thus the terms of a given component of spin along the axis, and those of the same total spin, are approximately the same. We can at once find the distribution in energy of the terms of a given spin. They evidently cluster about the value $(n-1)J - (n-1-2n_\beta)K$; they are distributed about this value like the displacements of a point simultaneously acted on by a sum of n_β periodic vibrations of equal amplitudes but arbitrary phases. This gives, of course, approximately a Gauss distribution. The width of the distribution curve can be derived very easily: we compute the mean square deviation of the energy from its mean, $\overline{(W-\overline{W})^2} = 4K^2[\Sigma \cos(p_i\pi/n)]^2$, the average being taken when each p varies independently from 0 to n. We can take this variation to be continuous rather than discrete. Then the product terms in the square of the sum of cosines all average to zero, the square terms average to $\frac{1}{2}$, and the result is $2K^2 n_\beta$. These results may be compared with those obtained by Heisenberg on the group theory, and which as Bloch has shown can also be found from the present method. In the notation of the present paper, putting the number of neighbors of each atom equal to 2, and leaving out the terms in J, Heisenberg finds

$$\overline{W} = -(n - 2n_\beta + 2n_\beta^2/n)K$$
$$(\overline{W-\overline{W}})^2 = 2K^2 n_\beta(1 - n_\beta/n)(1 + 2n_\beta/n - 2(n_\beta/n)^2).$$

Our formulas agree with these exact ones to terms in n_β but no further, as we expect from the fact that our approximations hold only for small n_β. For small p's, as we have seen, our results should be good even for large n_β; for the case of ferromagnetism, when on Heisenberg's hypothesis the terms are reversed, these are the lowest terms, so that this result should be very useful here. In the normal case, however, the lowest terms are those of large p, and these are the ones we need for cohesion. About these lowest terms, we can be fairly sure that they lie higher than the lowest ones we have found, or $(n-1)J-(n-1-4n_\beta)K$, since the mean lies higher than the mean we found. For zero spin, for example, we can be fairly sure that the term lies above $(n-1)J+nK$. But this value need not be a very good approximation; we actually find, by the method of the next section, that the lowest term for zero spin is about $(n-1)J+0.290nK$. Fortunately even this has a positive coefficient for K, and is so an attractive rather than a repulsive term.

Method for zero spin. For zero spin, $n_\alpha=n_\beta=n/2$, and there are $n!/(n/2!)^2$ terms. We adopt quite a different method of classifying them. Before, most of the terms of a given n_β had nearly the same diagonal energy; but now the range of energy is large, from $(n-1)J$ for the state with alternating α's and β's so that there are no parallel spins, to $(n-1)J-(n-2)K$ for the state where all the α's come at one end of the lattice, all the β's at the other. With this large range, we find it convenient to classify terms by their diagonal energies; and we find as we should expect, that for the lowest states of the perturbed system we must consider most the low unperturbed states. We do not need to take into account all states: we find that approximately (though by no means exactly) the terms can be divided into a number of non-combining sets, and we set up one such set in the following way. We commence with the lowest state, of energy $(n-1)J$, where α's and β's alternate. Next we consider the $n-1$ states which combine with it, coming from interchanging one pair, and each having the energy $(n-1)J-2K$, except those from the two end pairs, with energy $(n-1)J-K$. We leave these two out, retaining for our set the $n-3$ states which have the energy $(n-1)J-2K$. Each of these has $n-3$ states with which it combines, coming from interchange of one of the $n-3$ adjacent pairs with opposite spins. Of these $n-3$, the two in which the new interchanged pair is next the one already interchanged have the energy $(n-1)J-2K$; the one in which the pair already interchanged is changed back has the energy $(n-1)J$; the two where the end pair is interchanged have the energy $(n-1)J-3K$; and the remaining $n-8$ have the energy $(n-1)J-4K$. We retain for our set only these $n-8$ terms of energy $(n-1)J-4K$. So we proceed, asking which terms combine with those already set up, and retaining just those whose energy is $-2K$ greater than for those with fewer interchanges. We find that a term of our set, with the energy $(n-1)J-2pK$, has non-diagonal terms to p terms of the set of energy $(n-1)J-2(p-1)K$ and to $(n-3-5p)$ terms of the set of energy $(n-1)J-2(p+1)K$. Evidently so long as p is small, the terms we leave out of the set and yet which combine with terms of the set are comparatively few. It is only for the large p's that we make serious error by leaving out these terms, and for large p the diagonal energy is high enough so that for the lowest states of the perturbed system these unperturbed states are unimportant. Thus we may reasonably believe that the low energy levels found by solving this restricted problem will be approximately some of the low levels of the actual problem. We can at least be sure of the following: by the variation principle, they can be no lower than the actual stationary states.

The other sets of non-combining terms which we can set up are easily described, and are of considerable physical interest. Instead of starting from the state with spins alternating, we start from a state where the spins alternate up to a given point; there the sequence is interrupted, and alternation commences again, so to speak, in the opposite phase, as

$$\cdots \alpha \beta \alpha \beta \beta \alpha \beta \alpha \beta \alpha \cdots .$$

With a few such interruptions in the course of the crystal, the energy is very little above the really lowest state; yet a great many individual interchanges would be required to pass to the lowest state. With such a state to start with, we proceed just as we did before, and construct a whole system of states; and the non-diagonal terms between this and the first system come only from high values of p, involving many interchanges, and can be neglected. Physically, at the interruption of phase, one essentially has a slight interruption of crystal structure. Our catalogue of all possible states of the metal includes not only that where it is one perfect crystal, but also where it is composed of many smaller crystals not perfectly joined together. Obviously each problem can be treated separately; physically it would take a very long time to change from one to the other. And obviously each problem will give us essentially the same set of energy levels.

We now take our set of wave functions, and try to solve the perturbation problem between them. For each value of p, we have many wave functions; and we look for those particular solutions for which all these functions have the same coefficient $S(p)$. Afterwards we shall show that we really find the lowest solutions this way. Then, remembering the number of transitions with non-diagonal term K from a given state, computed above, we have for a typical equation

$$-KpS(p-1)+[(n-1)J-2pK-W]S(p)-K(n-3-5p)S(p+1)=0.$$

This set of difference equations for the S's is somewhat similar to what we had before; it also corresponds to a weighted string. But now the properties, and hence the wave-length, change from point to point, and we seek the various overtones. The equation is a close analogue to Schrödinger's equation, in many ways; the fact that it is a difference equation rather than a differential one is quite immaterial. To solve, we assume $S(p)=e^{\int \alpha \, dp}$, where α is to vary slowly with p. Then $S(p)=e^\alpha S(p-1)$, etc., so that we have

$$-Kp+e^\alpha[(n-1)J-2pK-W]-e^{2\alpha}K[n-3-5p]=0,$$

$$e^\alpha = \frac{-[(n-1)J-2pK-W] \pm ([(n-1)J-2pK-W]^2-4K^2p[n-3-5p])^{1/2}}{-2K[n-3-5p]}.$$

The equation expresses e^α as a function of p, for any particular W. Now we must remember that there are essentially boundary conditions; the S's must remain finite for $p=0$ and $p=$ an extreme value. To tell how to apply this condition, we must investigate the solution we have found.

The ratio e^α of successive coefficients is real or complex, according as $[(n-1)J - 2pK - W]^2$ is greater than or less than $4K^2p[n-3-5p]$. Regarded as a function of p, the limiting cases, where the two are equal, come from $(n-1)J - W = 2pK \pm 2K[p(n-3-5p)]^{1/2}$. The right hand side, plotted as a function of p, forms an ellipse; the straight line represented by the left side intersects the ellipse in two points, or in none, depending on the value of W. The region of W where it intersects can be found by computing the maximum and minimum ordinates of the ellipse; that is, the values of $(n-1)J - W$ for which $(d/dp)(2pK \pm 2K[p(n-3-5p))]^{1/2}) = 0$. This gives $p = (n-3)/10$ $[1 \pm (1/6)^{1/2}] = (n-3) \times (0.0592, 0.1408)$. At these two limits, substituting, $W = (n-1)J + (n-3)K \times (0.290, -0.690)$. For values of W between these limits, there is a range of p for which e^α is complex, and the solution is oscillatory; outside this region, which is closed, the solution is in any case exponential. To satisfy our boundary conditions, now, we have a problem much like that with Schrödinger's equation in one dimension; and boundary conditions can be satisfied only if there is an oscillatory region. As a result, the actual energy levels of the problem must lie between the limits given. Closer examination shows that a "quantum condition" can be applied, and that between these limits there are just the number of energy levels there should be. We now have the lowest level: it lies arbitrarily close to our lower limit, or is

$$W = (n-1)J + 0.290(n-3)K,$$

as we stated in the last section. In this lowest state, we can show without trouble that the unperturbed wave functions with p near $0.0592(n-3)$ are represented most strongly. Thus the value of p is really quite small; relatively few pairs are interchanged, and we are safely in the region where we can treat the different systems separately.

We have solved our problem for the lowest state in which all terms of the same p have the same coefficient. We can now investigate the effect of removing this assumption, varying the coefficient of one function of a given p in one direction, varying the rest to keep the same total representation for functions of this p, and calculating the change in the energy. When we do this, we find the energy to be a minimum with respect to such variation; in fact, the changes of energy compensate each other to a higher order, showing that the problem is nearly degenerate with respect to these coefficients. Thus we may be rather confident that we have a good approximation to the lowest non-polar states. It is of course obvious that this method becomes worse as we go to higher states.

It is instructive to ask what ordinary perturbation theory would give us for the lowest state. The lowest unperturbed state has the diagonal energy $(n-1)J$; this represents the ordinary first order perturbation calculation. Now we pass to the second order calculation. The lowest state is not degenerate, so that we can use the power series development method. The next term in the expansion is $\Sigma_j(H_{ij}H_{ji})/E_1 - E_j)$, summed over all excited states j. Now there are non-diagonal terms H_{1j} only to the $n-1$ states with $p=1$.

Thus the H_{1j}'s are all equal to $-K$, and the energy differences are all given by $E_j = E_1 - 2K$. Thus we have as second approximation

$$W = (n-1)J + (n-1)\frac{K^2}{2K} = (n-1)J + \frac{1}{2}(n-1)K.$$

This differs from our result in having the factor $\frac{1}{2}$ rather than 0.290; we have only the first term of a series development, but it is reassuring that agreement is as good as it is. For finding the order of magnitude, we could use this term alone; we shall find this simple method useful with the space lattice.

Effect of polar states. One can make an estimate, by a method like that used here, of the effect of the polar states in depressing the non-polar ones, which alone we have considered so far. We can build up a series of states by starting with a given non-polar state; then removing one of the electrons to an adjacent atom, producing a positive and a negative ion; then removing a second; and so on. The series of states so found behave formally like those used above. If we solve the problem by the previous method, or by the second order perturbation method, we get a further depression of the lowest state, which again can be written as

$$(n-1) \times \sum \frac{\text{square of non-diagonal term}}{\text{energy difference}}.$$

The non-diagonal term which comes in here is presumably of the same order of magnitude as before, although it is a somewhat different integral. But the diagonal energy difference is now essentially an ionization energy, which is of the order of several volts, rather than the fraction of a volt that K is. Thus the effect on the energy is a number of times smaller than what we found before, and we can neglect it. It is not worth while calculating more accurately, in this approximation; for with H_2, it appears that on account of the lack of orthogonality of the wave functions, the actual depression of the energy is very much less than this rough method would indicate, although the effect on the wave function is about what we should expect. One can reasonably believe for this reason that the polar states in the crystal depress the energy only very little. But we recall that their effect on the wave function is to introduce free electrons. By our rough method described above, we infer that the fraction of free electrons is of the order of 1 percent, for reasonable choice of the constants. This could easily be in error by a factor of 10 either way; but at least we see that a definite meaning can be attached to the number of free electrons, and that there is a definite procedure for calculating this number.

Normalization and orthogonality. We have not considered the lack of orthogonality of the wave functions, resulting in factors like the $1/1 \pm S$ of Heitler and London. When one tries to do this, one immediately strikes a difficulty which appears insurmountable: the factor in the denominator, instead of being like $1+S$, is like $1+nS+\cdots$, where n is the number of atoms, so that the term nS is enormous compared with unity. On examination of simple cases, it appears that the remaining terms, coming from other permutations than the simple interchange, are also important, in many cases the terms almost cancelling each other. Further, in every expression for energy, like the simple $(J \pm K)/(1 \pm S)$, there are more terms in the numerator, also of great importance. But the simple cases give no suggestion of how to treat the general case. The key to this difficulty comes from Bloch's method. For example, the term of maximum multiplicity has one function, which can be expressed either by Heisenberg's or Bloch's functions. But the difference is that Bloch's functions are really orthogonal, unlike Heisenberg's, so that we meet no such difficulty. Of course, the same terms occur, but now in the normalization of the individual functions. And the numerators, and denominators like $1 + nS + \cdots$, appear as products of n factors, each of approximately a simple Heitler and London form; further, all but one or two of these factors of the denominator cancel against equal factors in the numerator, giving very simple results. Essentially the same method can be used with the other states; for this method is one for treating a determinant of Heisenberg's wave functions, and converting it into a determinant of Bloch's functions; and all of our wave functions are products of two such determinants. When we calculate in our case, it appears that the terms S will have small effect; we are roughly half way between the cases $1 + S$ and $1 - S$, and the effects of S nearly average out. This method at the same time gives the proper way of considering more distant pairs, as well as adjacent ones; these contribute the further terms in the numerators, as $J \pm K + \cdots$. We see from the next paragraph that these more distant pairs are really quite important.

Method for space lattice. So far, we have spoken about a linear lattice of atoms, rather than a space distribution. We now extend this theory to a crystal; but we shall not carry it through in the same detail. We consider only the problem of zero spin, and use our second order perturbation approximation. Let us take the body-centered cubic lattice, which the alkalies have. The lowest unperturbed state of this lattice can be set up much as with the linear one: we let the electrons at the corners of the cubes have the spin α, those at the centers the spin β. Then each electron is surrounded by eight others of opposite spin, so that if we consider only adjacent pairs, the diagonal energy of this state is $4nJ$, where there are n electrons, $4n$ pairs. This lowest state now has non-diagonal terms, each equal to $-K$, to the $4n$ states obtained by interchanging an adjacent pair. Each of these states has two misplaced spins, each surrounded by 7 spins of the same sign, so that the energy has a term $-14K$. Thus for our perturbation problem, we have a non-diagonal energy $-K$, an energy difference $14K$, and $4n$ non-diagonal terms, so that the perturbed energy is $4nJ + (4nK^2/14K) = 4nJ + (2/7)nK$.

This formula is rather significant. We compare the energy with that of the lowest state of the diatomic molecule, $n = 2$, which is $(n/2)J + \frac{1}{2}nK$. We observe that for the crystal the coulomb interaction, the term J, has a coefficient eight times as great: each atom has eight neighbors instead of one, each penetrating. On the other hand, the valence term K has a coefficient only $2/7$, instead of $1/2$. The valence, so to speak, is spread out among all the neighbors, and weakened in the process. It is partly on this account that we can say that the coulomb interaction is the more important part of the cohesive force, in metals.

We have considered only those pairs with smallest separation, and they give a definite attraction. But in this lattice, there are not only the eight nearest atoms at distance R; there are also six, in directions parallel to the edges of the cube, at distance of $1.155R$, and these have parallel spins, producing therefore a repulsion. In the diagonal energy, each pair will then contribute an energy $J-K$, a positive amount, so that the diagonal energy of the lowest state if $4nJ+3n(J(1.155\ R)-K(1.155\ R))$. The next higher diagonal energy also will differ from this not merely by $-14\ K(R)$, but also by an amount $12\ K(1.155\ R)$, because by interchange of two spins some of these repulsive terms are removed. Thus the lowest energy level, counting also these pairs, is

$$4NJ(R)+3n(J(1.155R)-K(1.155R))+\frac{4nK^2(R)}{14K(R)-12K(1.155R)}.$$

This results, on computation, in a much weakened attraction. If we were to consider in succession the effects of pairs at greater and greater distance, we should come in succession to attracting atoms with antiparallel spin, and repulsive ones with parallel, so that the successive approximations to the energy would oscillate, falling first above, then below, the true value.

Application to sodium. For the sodium crystal, approximate calculations have been carried out, to test these formulas. These were made by taking a simple analytical expression for the wave function of the valence electron of sodium, and computing the integrals J and K. The details of the calculation will not be given here. The first thing that one notices is that, for Na, J is several times larger in proportion to K than in hydrogen. It is this fact, taken together with the increased coefficient of the J term, that results in the importance of the coulomb term. It is also significant in connection with the question, why do the alkalies, and metals in general, form metallic lattices, while hydrogen does not? We can see the essential answer from our energy formulas of the previous page. For substances where J is the important term, the coefficient of J will be greater, and the energy lower, for the crystal than for the same number of atoms in diatomic molecules, and the crystal will be the stable form. For hydrogen, on the other hand, the valence term K is the important one. Here the coefficient in the molecular form is greater; and even if the metallic form of such a substance were stable in the sense of having a minimum of energy for some definite size, as seems quite possible, still the energy in the molecular state would be lower. The atoms in the crystal would tend to form pairs, resulting in a molecular lattice; the molecules would repel each other, and would be held together only by van der Waals forces, which have been neglected in this paper. This seems to be exactly what hydrogen does.

The numerical values for Na are approximately as follows. If we take only the adjacent pairs, the minimum comes at $R = 4.9a_H$ approximately, rather seriously less than the correct value 7; this can partly be explained by the observation that the best atomic wave function for use in the crystal would be more extended than that determined from the free atoms, which are here used. The energy at this point comes out about -40 kg cal/gm mol, the coulomb term supplying about four fifths of this; the observed heat of vaporization is 26.4 kg cal, so that this gives, as we should expect, too large a value. If now we consider the repulsive pairs at distance of 1.155 R, the situation is quite changed. In the first place, the energy is reduced from -40 to about -9 kg cal. When we remember that these two values are the first two terms of a series, whose value oscillates on both sides of the answer, it seems very reasonable that the final result should be not far below the experimental value. The problem of properly computing this energy must be done by the method, using Bloch's functions, described in the preceding section. In the next place, the minimum of the curve is greatly broadened: for quite a range of values, from $R = 4.9$ (the previous minimum) to $R = 7$, the energy stays about constant, the change of the attractive term being just about balanced by the relatively more rapid change of the smaller repulsive effect. (For smaller R's, a situation can be found when the denominator $14 K(R) - 12 K(1.155 R) = 0$, so that the function becomes infinite; but this is without physical significance.) No doubt a persistence of this effect in the final answer helps to correct the improperly low grating space we have already found. It also is interesting in connection with the compressibility. The alkalies are remarkably compressible, and if we compute the compressibility for the case where only adjacent pairs are considered, the result is too small by a factor of 2 or 3. On the other hand, considering the next set of atoms, our very broad maximum would give much too great a compressibility. Here again it seems that our result may oscillate, perhaps approaching eventually something near the right value.

A New Approach to Many-Electron Theory at Intermediate Densities*

LELAND C. ALLEN

DEPARTMENT OF CHEMISTRY,
PRINCETON UNIVERSITY, PRINCETON, NEW JERSEY,

I. A Tribute to John Clarke Slater

Professor Slater has been, and continues to be at age 65, one of the twentieth century's great men of science. Even a partial documentation of his direct contributions to physical science is most impressive and quite awe-inspiring to anyone who envisions himself a participant in physical research. Indeed, as C. P. Snow has said of Lord Rutherford, "He seemed ten percent larger than life." Rather than a tabulation and analysis of accomplishments this appreciation offers some observations and a viewpoint on the style, environment, and type of emphasis Slater has brought to electronic structure theory—particularly in the period since World War II.

A student confronting J. C. Slater in the late 1940's or 1950's found a

* Research supported in part by the Chemistry Section of the National Science Foundation, Grant Number NSF-GP-5052, the Directorate of Chemical Sciences of the Air Force Office of Scientific Research, Contract Number AF 49(638)-1625, and Chemical Programs Section of the Atomic Energy Commission Research Division, Contract Number AT(30-1)-3532.

legendary and distinguished figure, full of honors and authority as head and essential creator of the Physics Department of the Massachusetts Institute of Technology. When first encountered he appeared to all, and remained for most, a rather terrifying person—one felt reluctant to ask questions or attempt scientific interchange. In his papers, and especially in his course lectures and research talks, one quickly found a very different man. Not only were the presentations perfectly organized and timed, but the words were clear, well phrased, and in basically simple language. All in all the transfer of ideas occurred as a highly communicative process. At all levels the courses and the method of description were completely unique and, although ranging over the whole structure of matter (save the nucleus), the material itself was almost entirely original. Perhaps half mathematics, the theory was not couched in the popular formalism of field theory or diagramatic schemes and one easily obtained a very direct physical picture of phenomena. The lectures had sweep and style—on the one hand a fundamental, unified, and general approach was always maintained, on the other hand one distinctly felt the methods capable of practical implementation. It was forever the many-electron wave function, its properties and description, that mattered rather than specific applications to current topics in chemistry or solid-state physics. Although there were many personal occasions to remind oneself of Slater's thorough knowledge of experimental physics, the courses and most of the research were oriented more toward methods for generating many-electron wave functions than to the analysis of specific experimental data. Development of theorems and approximation schemes having direct parentage in Schrödinger's equation, reliance on physically well-defined theory, and instinctive mistrust of simple model theories have been cornerstones to Slater's approach. In view of this orientation it is not at all surprising that many of Slater's penetrating insights have only manifest their efficacy with the advent of large-scale digital computers and only after elaborate calculations have been performed. It is revealing in this regard to find that Slater's texts alone, among all of those devoted to molecular quantum mechanics and quantum chemistry, emphasize and fully develop Hartree-Fock theory. Yet it is now clear that the molecular Hartree-Fock solution is the most fundamental and practically important starting point for all of chemical structure theory.

Looking back a generation to the small collection of distinguished men who since the middle 1920's have contributed so much to modern physical theory one is struck by the fact that Slater alone among this vanguard of great mathematical physicists continued to pursue electronic structure theory. Already in 1933 he had produced a comprehensive text ("Introduction to Theoretical Physics") containing chapters that brought one to the forefront of electronic structure theory. His characteristic style and much of the outline for the next 33 years of an enormously productive career are clearly apparent.

Now again during these last two years, 1965 and 1966, we find two more completely unique and original texts ("Quantum Theory of Molecules and Solids," Vols. I and II), again representing the most up-to-date and definitive works on *ab initio* electronic structure theory! It is well known that fads in physics change rapidly and Slater's path of "sticking with the problem" has not been universally fashionable, either in the worlds of physics or chemistry. It would be untrue to represent it otherwise. In physics, of course, the main line of fundamental investigation since the 1930's has been toward elementary particles while those in solid state have most often been satisfied with much more empirical and restricted theory, closely tied to specific experiments. Chemistry is overwhelmingly a problem of complexity, largely organized by qualitative, macroscopic rules—only now is the desire arising to understand phenomena on a more quantitative microscopic basis and only just now are we approaching adequate technical tools for handling the simplest molecules of genuine chemical interest. Thus we conclude with perhaps the most significant aspect of Slater's career: on the eve of institutional retirement, when the impact of even great men wanes, we find that physical science is beginning to realize a need for full and fundamental understanding of complex electronic structure theory and is now "catching up" with Slater in his approach to this problem. There is no question that Slater's influence on the course of science will be even greater during the next thirty-five years than it has been in the past thirty-five.

II. Nature of the Problem

The principal reason why intermediate density many-electron theory deserves to be classed as one of the most important problems in contemporary science is because the overwhelming majority of natural phenomena find their origin in the detailed pattern of electron motion. Diversity, complexity, and vast variety are the characteristic features of this problem, in sharp contrast to mathematical abstraction and ultimate simplicity, the predominant elements in problems handled successfully by the methods of theoretical physics. A key concept in organizing ideas is the relative information content of a set of data obtained from experiment by instrumental measurements or generated theoretically. In a general way the information-content concept best illuminates the various aspects of current electronic structure research.

A. Chemistry from small polyatmomic molecules

Quantitatively meaningful *ab initio* polyatomic solutions have been obtained during the last two years for molecules with one, two, or three atoms of those from He to Ne and up to eight attached hydrogens. (The next section of this paper reviews a good part of this work.) Relative to the 103 different atoms of the periodic table and to the size of most chemically important molecules these polyatomic species at first appear to be insignificantly closer to chemical reality than the diatomics for which well-established sets of wave functions now exist. However, chemistry really starts at three-atom systems and the amount of fundamental chemical information brought forth from wave functions for even simple polyatomic molecules is truly surprising —particularly if the solutions are carried out for numerous nonequilibrium geometries (1). Examples from the Princeton Laboratory are: the origin of rotational barriers; the nature of the hydrogen bond; the properties and characteristics of electron-deficient species (e.g., BH_3 vs B_2H_6 and B_2H_6 vs C_2H_6); the origin and generality of Walsh's rules (inorganic stereochemistry); characterization and comparison of boron–nitrogen bonding with carbon–carbon bonding; the basis for bond formation with noble gas atoms and predictions for possible new compounds; proton affinities of ammonia, water, and methane, and criteria for certain structural changes in water and ice; stability and shape of important organic radicals and reaction intermediates (e.g., CH_5^+, methylene, the methyl carbanion, and cyclopropenyl cation, $C_3H_3^+$). These latter four species are among a small number of relatively simple radicals and ions which are central to a large fraction of organic reactions but are generally inaccessible to direct instrumental measurement. Another area in which theory has a unique role occurs where a repulsive potential surface is likely or where synthetic pathways are very indirect (e.g., HeF_2, NeF_2, HeO, NH_4, H_3O, BH_3).

B. LIMITATION ON *Ab Initio* SOLUTIONS

In spite of two hundred years of instrumental measurements, the chemical structure symbols and reaction equations which have been derived from this experience do not yield near enough information to tell us all that we desire to know about properties and detailed mechanisms. On the other hand, it is equally clear that numerical experiments based on *ab initio* solutions to Schrödinger equation contain far too much information.

The size of molecule for which an *ab initio* wave function may be obtained is limited simply by the time required to generate and manipulate three and four center two-electron integrals. In some of the calculations reported in the next section there are 50,000 of these and each is computed to nine significant figures—certainly representing many times more bits of information than required to delineate all chemical aspects of the problem no matter how indirectly the desired chemical numbers are related to the many-center integrals. Our approach to this information problem is twofold: First, we are plotting integral distribution functions for the various types of integrals involved under various geometries and at various levels of approximation. Second, we are developing mathematical inequalities relating changes in sums of one-electron molecular orbital energies to changes in total energies. Already this investigation has revealed that there is an inherently low information content in the specification of bond angles. One of the most important future efforts will be attempts to relate additional chemical properties to well-defined subunits of *ab initio* wave functions.

C. CONNECTION BETWEEN *Ab Initio* SOLUTIONS AND SIMPLE MODEL THEORIES

Unquestionably the major issue facing electronic structure theory is that of making continuous connection between *ab initio* solutions and the often successful, largely *ad hoc*, model theories of chemistry and solid-state physics. As more quantitative results for low-symmetry electronic systems are demanded it is becoming apparent that implicit to this task is the fact that current model theories are inadequate—at least in the sense that we do not know what circumstances are required for the models to yield reliable predictions. Extended Hückel theory and other models, like chemical structural formulas, do not generate enough information to convincingly differentiate many chemical phenomena. On the other hand, it is also true that to make electronic structure theory an everyday tool of chemical research quite simplified theories are going to be required.

It appears likely that the most promising resource for developing simplified theories will be *ab initio* numerical experiments on polyatomic molecules rather than the traditional recourse to data from instrumental experiments. Similarly, the appropriate mathematical methods will be more akin to techniques in statistical communication theory than they will to the transformation theory and diagramatic techniques derived from the field of mathematical analysis. It is perhaps not surprising that a longer period has elapsed between the enunciation of Schrödinger's equation and the present day than between the discovery of the electron and the advent of wave mechanics.

III. Recent Advances in Polyatomic Electronic Structure Theory

A. BASIS SETS AND MANY-CENTER MOLECULAR INTEGRALS

The two principal impediments to widespread realization of *ab initio* polyatomic molecular wave functions have been: First, the intricate, numerically complex and time-consuming effort required to generate the very large number (500–50,000) of two-electron, three- and four-center, six-dimensional electrostatic interaction integrals. Second, the choice of analytical form for the basis set and the multidimensional nonlinear parameter search identified with an adequate representation of the charge distribution. These two problems are interdependent. Among the several attractive schemes for evaluating the many-center molecular integrals the currently most successful methods are all based on the special properties of Gaussian functions. Among the Gaussian based methods the simplest and fastest is direct use of lobe functions, largely because of the elimination of spherical harmonics and because only the simplest Gaussian forms are employed (2). With respect to the orbital basis, the key decision is choice of Hartree-Fock atomic orbitals, because these lead to molecular wave functions close to a molecular Hartree-Fock solution thereby largely eliminating the parameter search problem, and because they lead to direct chemical interpretability of the wave functions (3,4). It is not obvious at first that Gaussian lobe functions can efficiently span an atomic Hartree-Fock solution, particularly since one must be concerned with simultaneous matching of both the radial and angular dependence of the Hartree-Fock orbitals. Nevertheless, after considerable experimentation, it has turned out that sufficient accuracy can be realized with relatively few Gaussian lobe functions (15 or 16 for atoms such as C, N, O, and F) (5). The accuracy of this representation has been tested not only in terms of total energy but also by computing expectation values such as the quadrupole moment and quadrupole coupling constant for individual orbitals. Essentially double-zeta function quality is found for all tests.

B. MANY-ELECTRON FORMULATION

During the last few years there has been a resurgence of interest, by both physicists and chemists, in formal many-particle theory, particularily the question of how electron correlation may best be represented in the wave function. One promising approach, currently in active development, is the natural spin-orbital expansion. Another scheme, the MO-IS method, is described in the next part of the paper. Many sophisticated techniques have been reported, numerous excellent reviews of this subject now exist, and any further detailed analysis is inappropriate to our purposes. All of the work reported here has been carried out by the well-known SCF MO, and VB methods. Wave functions at this level of approximation (particularly the Hartree-Fock MO) are generally treated as a zeroth order starting solution in contemporary many-particle theory. One of the most important new results that is coming out of our laboratory at Princeton and from several other centers is the full realization that this zeroth order starting point is very good in itself, encompassing by far the largest share of all chemistry and solid-state physics. One possible corollary is that we may obtain sufficient chemical, physical, and numerical information from these well-established schemes that it will become unnecessary to push approximations appreciably further.

The digital computer program for our Roothaan MO-SCF scheme is similar to those which have been written at MIT, Chicago, and elsewhere. At the time of writing, this program is limited to closed-shell cases but will be able to handle odd-electron ground-state molecules very soon and excited states somewhat later. A general capability for carrying out valence bond calculations has not existed heretofore. The method we have employed is formulated in terms of a nonorthogonal basis via Löwdin's overlap determinant prescription. Because reasonably accurate VB wave functions require at least several configurations, our digital computer program for this method is more limited as to size of system than the MO, but it is capable of treating odd-electron species.

1. Molecular Orbital Results. The principal objective of the work reported here is to give examples of *ab initio Polyatomic* molecules—but to be reliable and quantitative in the representation of chemical properties, the wave functions must be close to true molecular Hartree-Fock solutions. This is clearly indicated by results using a single Gaussian per orbital (*6,7*). We have found similar results employing a single Gaussian per lobe. It is quite easy to produce an *ab initio* solution with single gaussians for a sensationally large molecule but, for the most part, these wave functions are even qualitatively worthless. When compared with molecular Hartree-Fock solutions it is also apparent that less drastic, but nevertheless chemically significant, errors are introduced through use of a single exponential function per orbital (*8*). Fortunately, we have available a fundamental set of *reference* wave functions from which we can make controlled and continuous excursions to slightly less accurate solutions always keeping track of our source of errors in chemically important expectation values. It is essential to explore how far one can go from the reference solutions and still produce quantitatively significant results because small simplifications can make a large difference in the size of system one is able to treat. These reference wave functions are the true molecular Hartree-Fock solutions obtained for diatomic molecules at the University of Chicago under the direction of C. C. J. Roothaan (*9*). Table 1 gives total energy comparisons for six representative diatomic molecules. Our solutions employ only s and p basis orbitals while the University of Chicago solutions have small d and f contributions in C_2, N_2, and F_2. In all six molecules the effect of a coordinate scale factor was explored, and it is only for hydrogen that an appreciable effect is observed although B in the BH wave function also contracts somewhat. The last three wave functions allow the linear expansion coefficient for the outer group of Gaussian lobe functions to be energy determined. This permits the tails of the 2s and 2p to move in or out relative to a fixed Hartree-Fock AO. Freedom of this sort has been introduced into about half the calculations reported here and, aside from the special contraction of hydrogen, appears to be the primary modification of the strict LCAO worth considering. For example, this modification can frequently change prediction of internuclear separations from 10% too large to ±2% error, but does not change most conclusions in comparing one molecule with another. It has been

TABLE 1

COMPARISON WITH MOLECULAR HARTREE-FOCK WAVE FUNCTIONS[a]

Species	Atoms		Molecule		Difference in total molecular energies, eV
	Princeton[b]	Chicago	Princeton[b]	Chicago	
LiH	Li, 7.43119	7.43273			
			7.972852	7.98687	0.38 (0.17%)
	H, 0.5000	0.5000			
BH	24.52409	24.52905	25.10007	25.13136	0.85 (0.12%)
Li_2	7.43119	7.43273	14.86501	14.87152	0.18 (0.044%)
C_2	37.68052	37.68861	75.35003	75.40620	1.52 (0.74%)
N_2	54.38815	54.4004	108.91896	108.9922	2.00 (0.067%)
F_2	99.38232	99.40928	198.69293	198.76825	2.04 (0.38%)

[a] Atomic and molecular total energies are given in Hartree units. All energies are negative and all calculations are for the observed internuclear separation.

[b] R. J. Buenker, J. L. Whitten, and L. C. Allen (submitted to *J. Chem. Phys.*).

observed by other workers that the hydrogen atom, almost unique among atoms, contracts appreciably when it enters into chemical combination. We now have widespread confirmation of this effect. Relative to the exact free atom orbital, e^{-r}, an in situ contraction from $e^{-1.2r}$ to $e^{-1.5r}$ is to be expected: the specific value can be related to the electronegativity of the atom attached to the hydrogen. It is to be noted that these two modifications in the rigid LC (Hartree-Fock) AO basis set are very much in the spirit of our approach because they are simple well-defined perturbations which do not require an elaborate nonlinear parameter search, and retain the simple chemical interpretability of the results.

2. Valence Bond Results. The most noticeable feature of the valence bond results is that a moderate number of configurations yields energies a bit lower than molecular Hartree-Fock solutions and, of course, greatly improves the shape of potential curves at larger internuclear separations. Figure 1 shows F_2 using a rigid LC(Hartree-Fock)AO basis and eight configurations. Four configurations correspond to FF and four to F^+F^-, representing all possible occupancy combinations for the 2s and 2p orbitals keeping the 1s orbitals always doubly occupied. The total energy at the predicted equilibrium separation ($12\frac{1}{2}$% too large) is -198.7780 Hartree units and the predicted binding

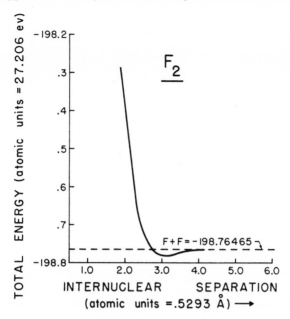

FIG. 1. Potential curve for F_2 constructed from a valence bond wave function using an LC (Hartree-Fock) AO basis.

energy is .35 eV (experimental = 1.37 eV). The valence bond solution was obtained for F_2 because it alone among the simple diatomics yields a negative binding energy (-1.37 eV) for the molecular Hartree-Fock wave function. Das and Wahl (*10*) have recently carried out an optimized orbital MO-configuration interaction treatment and obtained results comparable to ours: $E_T = -198.8378$ Hartree units at an R_{equil} 9% too large. BE = 0.54 eV (experimental = 1.37).

In Table 2 we give a series of comparative results for the well-known reference molecule hydrogen fluoride. We are just beginning to compute properties for our wave functions and some of those for the valence bond HF solution are compared with the molecular Hartree-Fock wave function in Table 3. The fluorine function has not been completely optimized in its molecular environment, and our experience indicates that for valence bond solutions this accounts for the relatively poor dipole moment result. For the other properties there is no strong reason to believe that values obtained from one function are better than those from the other. For LC (Hartree-Fock) AO solutions several of the polyatomic molecules (e.g., H_2O) give dipole moments 30% too large. Although allowing tails to vary and hydrogens to contract improves results the addition of d functions is almost certain to be required in some cases.

LELAND C. ALLEN

TABLE 2
Wave Functions for Hydrogen Fluoride

Method	Basis set	Total Energy (Hartree units)	Dipole moment (Debyes)	Energy comparison with molecular Hartree-Fock eV
SCF MO	Single experimental AO[a]	− 99.53614	1.44	14.5 (0.53%)
SCF MO	Hartree-Fock AO[b]	− 99.96339	1.99	2.9 (0.11%)
SCF MO	One centre[c]	− 100.00529	2.10	1.8 (0.07%)
SCF MO	Gaussian, nuclear center[d]	− 100.01785	2.35	1.4 (0.05%)
SCF MO	Gaussian, lobe[e]	− 100.02238	1.98	1.3 (0.04%)
SCF MO	Molecular Hartree-Fock[f]	− 100.07030	1.945	
SCF MO CI	Hartree-Fock AO[b]	− 99.98352	1.835	2.36 (0.09)%
Valence bond	Gaussian, lobe[g]	− 100.10434	2.00	0.925 lower
Experimental		− 100.4393	1.82	

[a] B. J. Ransil, *Rev. Mod. Phys.* **32**, 245 (1960).
[b] A. M. Karo and L. C. Allen, *J. Chem. Phys.* **31**, 968 (1959).
[c] R. Moccia, *J. Chem. Phys.* **40**, 2164 (1964).
[d] M. C. Harrison, SSMTG, *Quart. Prog. Rep. No.* 49. July 15, 1963, MIT.
[e] J. L. Whitten and L. C. Allen (to be submitted to *J. Chem. Phys.*).
[f] P. E. Cade and W. Huo (to be submitted to *J. Chem. Phys.*).
[g] R. M. Erdahl, J. F. Harrison, and L. C. Allen (to be submitted to *J. Chem. Phys.*).

TABLE 3
Predicted Expectation Values for Hydrogen Fluoride[a]

Function	Total energy	Dipole[b] moment	Quadrupole Moment relative to F	$\langle 1/r_F \rangle$	$\langle 1/r_H \rangle$	Field Gradient at F	Field gradient at H
Valence bond (Princeton)	− 100.10434	0.790	1.777	2.7743	0.6241	3.3001	0.4922
Molecular Hartree-Fock (Chicago)	− 100.07030	0.765	1.884	2.7169	0.6112	2.8687	0.5398

[a] All values in atomic units. Valence bond results from the Ph.D. thesis of J. F. Harrison (to be submitted to *J. Chem. Phys.*).
[b] Experimental value = 0.716 atomic units = 1.827 Debye.

C. Correlation Energy Correction

Because molecular Hartree-Fock solutions are in general quite successful in predicting expectation values for one-electron operators at the equilibrium configuration, it is worthwhile to seek an empirical correlation correction for binding energies—the principal shortcoming of the Hartree-Fock solution. This correction will be a single number rather than a complex functional dependence in a wave function. If possible, it would also be most useful if this molecular number could be obtained in terms of the atomic (or ionic) constituents. The basic idea for such a correlation comes from the long-standing realization that the standard Hartree-Fock approximation is a pair-preserving theory, thus separating into ionic states at large internuclear distances. It has also been known from the early days of molecular quantum mechanics that the major part of the correlation energy occurs for electrons of opposite spin occupying the same orbital. It should then be true to first order that one could obtain an R_{equil} binding energy correction by taking the difference in the correlation energy between Hartree-Fock solutions for neutral free atoms and the ions into which the molecule separates and add this to the binding energy computed from a molecular Hartree-Fock solution. Nesbet (*11*) appears to be the first to have specifically stated this prescription and applied it to a molecule. Clementi (*12*) and others have also made use of it.

We (13) have systematically employed this scheme for all of the University of Chicago diatomic Hartree-Fock reference wave functions. The results are

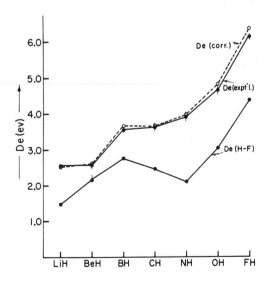

Fig. 2. Correlation corrected dissociation energies compared to experimental values for the hydrides Li to F.

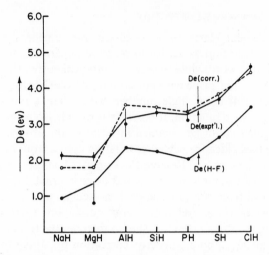

FIG. 3. Correlation corrected dissociation energies compared to experimental values for the hydrides Na to Cl.

very encouraging: Dissociation energies are predicted to within $\pm\frac{1}{4}$ eV—essentially as accurate as the experimental values themselves. Figures 2 and 3 illustrate the results for second and third row hydrides. Similar graphs have been obtained for homonuclear species, 12-electron, and 14-electron heteronuclear diatomics. We have also gone beyond this simple method in two ways. First, we have used the diatomic derived results as a per-bond basis and simply added the correlation energy corrections for each bond for a number of our polyatomic wave functions. In most polyatomic molecules, however, we do not possess a precise Hartree-Fock solution, and thus we must first correct to the Hartree-Fock level and then apply the correlation energy correction on top of this. For example, for 10-electron polyhydrides we have calculated a wave function close to the molecular Hartree-Fock solution and at the same accuracy level for each molecule. Assuming a constant isoelectronic discrepancy the difference was calibrated to HF and added to the correlation correction. Figure 4 shows typical results—again, an order of error not different from experimental values. Second, we have devised a set of rules for the correlation energy in isolated ions and these yield smoother curves with slightly greater average accuracy over a range of molecules and they also provide a basis for extrapolation beyond existing computations.

There is one corollary to this correlation correction scheme which is worth noting because of the accuracy we have achieved: The atomic (ionic) based nature of the corrections implies that the correlation energy is independent of bond angle. Our present results are too crude to use this fact in seeking the

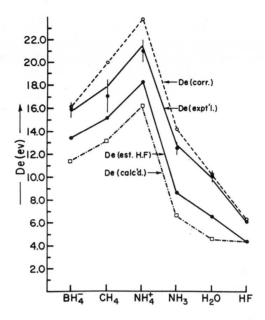

Fig. 4. Adjustment to the molecular Hartree-Fock level plus correlation correction for some ten-electron polyhydrides.

origin of rotational barriers, but it does indicate that molecular-shape prediction is within the capability of approximate molecular Hartree-Fock solutions.

D. Examples from Chemistry and Physics

1. The Chemical Bond at Large Internuclear Separation—The Hydrogen Bond (14). The perturbed-atom nature of the valence bond formulation and its correct free-atom separation at large internuclear distances make this the proper choice of representation for interactions such as the hydrogen bond. The particular system that we have investigated is the strongest known hydrogen bond, the bifluoride ion, $[FHF]^-$. In this and all of the other examples to chemistry and physics there is an enormous wealth of details and data available—a great deal more in fact than one is used to from experience with diatomic solutions. This large quantity of important data can only be adequately dealt with in the full-length journal articles currently being prepared. Here we can only give a broad survey, primarily relying on selected graphs, which is bound to appear superficial to the deeply interested reader. Underlying all of our work is a constant search for answers to a number of fundamental technical questions such as the following: Have we explored variation in the quality of the basis set sufficiently so that we are not missing fundamental chemical effects? Have we carried out enough check calculations and repeated enough existing work to know that there are no errors in our elaborate digital computer routines? For example in the valence bond program we have reproduced the often checked HF calculations of Kastler and the LiH wave function of Karo. For [FHF]⁻ an elaborate set of calculations were carried out to obtain a fluorine solution that would simultaneously optimize the HF, F, and F⁻ systems. The H atom was carefully scaled in situ.

Our wave function for the bifluoride ion embodies a complete valence bond configuration interaction, including all neutral and ionic states except F 1s excitations. Figure 5 shows symmetric stretch of the F–F distance and

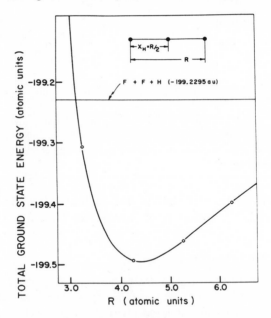

FIG. 5.   Energy variation with linear, symmetric F–F displacement in the bifluoride ion.

demonstrates that our calculation predicts nearly the correct experimental distance of 4.25 au. Figure 6, asymmetric linear stretch at the equilibrium F–F distance, shows two stages in the development of an improved wave function. The reasonable approximation to the experimental force constant obtained from our wave function can be inferred from the figure. Figure 7 displays the asymmetric stretch for several internuclear F–F distances, and for the same two levels of approximate solutions illustrated in Fig. 6. A fundamental objective of our study was to demonstrate the single minimum nature of the potential curve around the F–F equilibrium separation which has long been postulated for this ion. Also of considerable interest for understanding

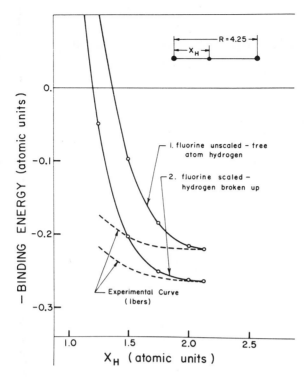

FIG. 6. Potential energy surface for motion of hydrogen in [FHF]⁻ at equilibrium F–F positions.

hydrogen bonding in general is the point at which a double minimum potential first appears. We see that this occurs at an F–F separation of approximately 5 au—a result not available from instrumental measurement. Figure 8 gives further details of the complex nature of the potential surface for this system.

Another detailed study of this sort, whose existence we mention here, is the interaction between two HF molecules. These calculations were undertaken to understand dimerization and hydrogen bonding as a function of H–F distances and as a function of angle and distance between the two molecules. A novel feature of this investigation is separate treatment of the problem with and without ionic state mixing between the two molecules, thus giving an estimate of the magnitude of van der Waals forces compared to the chemical bond forces.

2. The Chemical Bond at Large Internuclear Separation—Noble Gas Compounds (15). Here again a valence bond wave function is appropriate for two reasons: First, we are particularly interested to know whether certain species

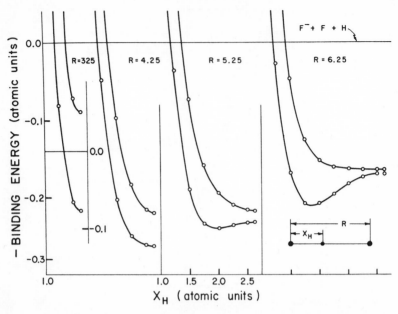

FIG. 7.   Potential energy surface for motion of hydrogen in [FHF]⁻ along F–F axis.

are bound or unbound and a Hartree-Fock solution can definitely lead to ambiguities because of its correlation and ionic separation errors. Second, noble gas atoms have all orbitals doubly occupied to a first approximation and highlying first excited states, thus leading to repulsive curves for the zero order VB solution or separating into ions for the MO solution rather than the zero activation energy neutral atom state observed experimentally. In order to make a continuous connection between the free noble gas atoms and the possibility of molecule formation the best representation is a VB configuration interaction treatment. VB wave functions have been constructed for a number of possible noble gas compounds. Intensive efforts have been made and are continuing for the experimental synthesis of fluorides of the lower rare gas atoms. Also numerous qualitative and semi-quantitative predictions for the existence of He and Ne containing molecules have been made (*16–18*). Thus it has been especially important to obtain rigorous *ab initio* wave functions for a number of these species. For HeF_2 chemical structures included were: F He F, F^- He^+ F + F He^+ F^-, F^- He F^+ + F^+ He F^-, and F^- He^{2+} F^-. In general, each of these structures corresponds to many states differing in orbital occupancy, and the states in turn are composed of sums of twenty-row determinantal functions with symmetry-determined coefficients. Symmetric arrangements of atoms on a line lead to 11 states and 33 determinants,

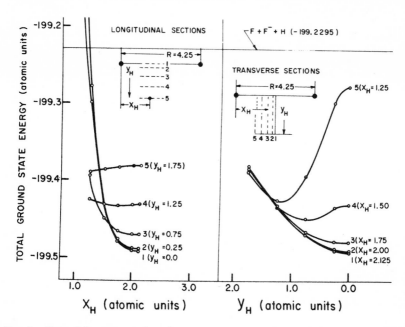

FIG. 8. Potential energy surface for motion of hydrogen in [FHF]⁻ perpendicular and parallel to the F–F axis.

asymmetric linear arrays to 18 states and 33 determinants, and offline equal bond length arrangements to 18 states with 53 determinants. These states represent a complete configuration interaction calculation with a ground-state atomic orbital basis (except for excitations of the fluorine 1s electrons).

Molecular potential energy curves were obtained for three geometrical types: linear symmetric, linear asymmetric, and bent configurations with the He atom midway between the fluorine atoms. Representative curves are shown in Figs. 9–11. The chemically most-significant states, with their approximate weights, for the linear symmetric wave function at a separation near that expected if the molecule were stable (F–F distance = 4.25 au = 2.25 Å) are given below along with isoelectronic [FHF]⁻ at its equilibrium separation (also 4.25 au):

FHeF

$$\Psi \cong + 0.621 \{\overset{2p\text{——}2p}{\text{F He F}}\} + 0.432\{\text{FHe}^+\text{F}^-\}$$

$$+ 0.070 \{\overset{2s\text{——}2p}{\text{F He F}}\} + 0.150 \{\text{F}^+ \text{ He F}^-\}$$

$[FHF]^-$

$$\Psi \cong +0.118 \{\overset{2p\text{------}2p}{F\ H^-\ F}\} + 0.464\{F^-H^+F^-\}$$
$$+ 0.471\{\overset{2p\text{-}1s}{F\ H\ F^-}\} - 0.142\{\overset{2s\text{-}1s}{F\ H\ F^-}\}.$$

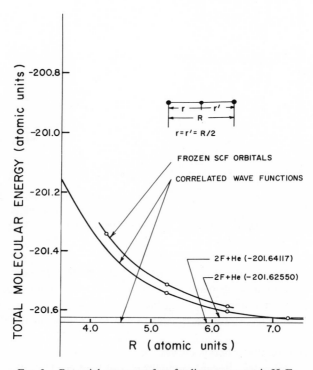

FIG. 9.   Potential energy surface for linear symmetric HeF_2.

One of the strongest reasons for belief in the HeF_2 repulsive potential energy surface is our complete potential surface for $[FHF]^-$ which agrees closely with experiment. The most important terms in the equilibrium position $[FHF]^-$ wave function are displayed directly below the HeF_2 valence bond expansion to aid qualitative understanding of the difference between these two systems. It is basically the ability to form an ordinary electron-pair bond between singly occupied orbitals on adjacent atoms that is required for binding.

In addition to the ionic states discussed above we have also carried out calculations including further configuration interaction for HeF_2:

(a) In-out or split orbital, $(1s)(1s')$, flexibility was introduced into the He

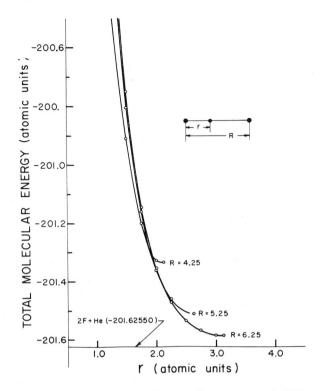

FIG. 10.   Potential energy surfaces for linear asymmetric HeF_2.

orbital. Results for a nonoptimized version of this are shown by the lower curve in Fig. 9. The total atomic energy was lowered 0.43 eV and the total molecular energy 0.72 eV by this process.

(b) A He $2p\sigma$ function was introduced. For linear HeF_2 at $R = 4.25$, $r = R/2$, this lowers the total molecular energy by a very small value, 0.125 eV. The effect on the energy of adding these two types of terms to our basic valence bond wave function was shown to be insignificant, and they certainly produce no new qualitative insight into the repulsive forces. However, the great variety of speculations as to possible binding mechanisms made it imperative that these effects be quantitatively evaluated.

A complete configuration interaction over the occupied atomic orbitals was also carried out for HeO, HeF, NeO, NeF, and NeF_2. Thus the NeO wave function includes the chemical structures NeO, Ne^+O^-, $Ne^{2+}O^{2-}$, and is composed of 16 states made up from twenty-four 18 × 18 determinants. As shown in Fig. 12, the potential energy curves for all species are repulsive (for NeF_2 and HeF_2 the linear symmetric molecule is plotted). The curves are all singlets with the oxygen atoms going to a ^1D configuration at infinite

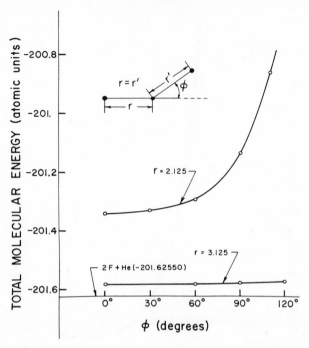

FIG. 11.   Potential energy versus angle for HeF_2 (constant, equal bond lengths).

separation. Triplet states for the oxides also were calculated. For these the free oxygen atom is in its ground state ^3P configuration (calculated to be 0.0805 atomic units lower than the ^1D), but the molecular potential energy curves lie even higher than the corresponding fluorides. Table 4 displays the chemically

TABLE 4

WAVE FUNCTIONS AT 2.0 ATOMIC UNITS (1.06 Å)[a]

HeO $\Psi \cong + 0.714\text{HeO}(2s)^2(2p_\pi)^4 - 0.072\text{HeO}(2s)(2p_\pi)^4(2p_\sigma) - 0.071\text{HeO}(2p)^6$
$\quad - 0.051\text{HeO}(2s)^2(2p_\sigma)^2(2p_\pi)^2 + 0.377\text{He}^+\text{O}^-(2s)^2(2p_\sigma)(2p_\pi)^4$

NeO $\Psi \cong + 0.600\text{NeO}(2s)^2(2p_\pi)^4 - 0.157\text{NeO}(2s)(2p_\sigma)(2p_\pi)^4 - 0.037\text{NeO}(2p)^6$
$\quad - 0.031\text{NeO}(2s)^2(2p_\sigma)^2(2p_\pi)^2 - 0.364\text{Ne}^+(2s)^2(2p_\sigma)(2p_\pi)^4\text{O}^-(2s)^2(2p_\sigma)(2p_\pi)^4$
$\quad - 0.107\text{Ne}^+(2s)(2p)^6\text{O}^-(2s)^2(2p_\sigma)(2p_\pi)^4 + 0.043\text{Ne}^+(2s)^2(2p_\sigma)(2p_\pi)^4\text{O}^-(2s)(2p)^6$

HeF $\Psi \cong + 0.848\text{HeF}(2s)^2(2p_\sigma)(2p_\pi)^4$
$\quad + 0.282\text{He}^+\text{F}^-$

NeF $\Psi \cong + 0.770\text{NeF}(2s)^2(2p_\sigma)(2p_\pi)^4$
$\quad - 0.360\text{Ne}^+(2s)^2(2p_\sigma)(2p_\pi)^4\text{F}^- + 0.104\text{Ne}^+(2s)(2p)^6\text{F}^-$

[a] Contained in the Ph.D. thesis of A. M. Lesk.

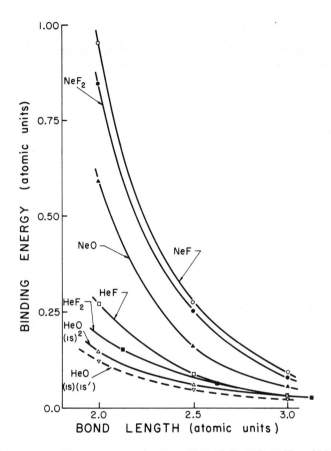

FIG. 12. Potential energy curves for HeO, HeF, HeF$_2$ NeO, NeF, and NeF$_2$.

significant terms in the wave functions for the various species. The fact that the neon-associated species lie above those with helium can be attributed simply to the relative size of these atoms, although it is difficult to assign an effective radius to helium or bond length for HeO or HeF (the leading term in the wave functions effectively represents two neutral atoms repelling one another, and its coefficient measures the extent to which they have achieved a free atom-like behavior). As would be expected, the triatomic bifluorides lie below the diatomic fluorides because of their extra symmetry element. The particularly interesting result showing the oxides to lie lower in energy than the fluorides arises from three factors which together override the greater electronegativity of fluorine. In the *neutral* states 2s-2p hybridization, favored in oxygen over fluorine because of the smaller orbital energy separation, together with the existence of half-filled π orbitals in the oxygen containing species permits an energy lowering charge redistribution. Hybridization in these states allows charge to move away from the between atom repulsive region. Among the singly ionized states there are three in NeO and one in HeO which significantly lower the energy through formation of electron-pair bonds between open shells on each atom. Hybridization in the ionic states has the opposite sense to that in the neutral states, favoring the pair bonds by building up the charge between atoms. Purely ionic contributions are almost identical for both the fluorides and oxides and the doubly ionized states, possible for the oxides but not the fluorides, make such an insignificant contribution that they have been omitted from the approximate wave function tabulation in Table 4. In general binding is discouraged because in the dominant states one of the atoms always has a closed-shell configuration. Since HeO exhibited the least repulsion an even more elaborate configuration interaction including different orbitals for different spins on helium was carried out with the result shown by the dotted curve in Fig. 12.

3. The Ten-Electron Polyhydrides (19). We have employed MO SCF wave functions to predict the equilibrium geometry and properties of the sequence: NH_2^-, NH_3, NH_4^+, HF, H_2F^+, OH^-, H_2O, H_3O^+, NeH^+, CH_3^-, CH_4, CH_5^+, and BH_4^-. For all of these which have known structures we obtain agreement with experiment on bond angles and bond distances to $\pm 2\%$. There are obviously a great many other interesting properties such as dipole, quadrupole moments, proton affinities, etc., but we have selected two points to illustrate the type of chemical information obtained by virtue of carrying out calculations for *sequences* of molecules for a large number of geometrical configurations. It is of interest to organic chemists concerned with conformational analysis to know the following trend in the HAH angle:

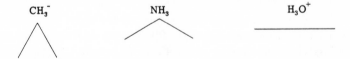

The fact that H_3O^+ would be planar in the gas phase (with a very shallow potential curve) is not apparent from crystallographic studies where it always appears bent. The trend in angles is matched by decreasing s character of the s-p hybride on the central atom as one goes to the right, thereby justifying the qualitative chemical rule relating bond angle to s character on the central atom. In Fig. 13 we show two potential curves for angle bending in the gaseous water molecule. What is interesting here is the coupling between bond length and angle showing that one gets a quite wrong estimate of the energy required to change the angle in water from 104.5° to the tetrahedral configuration if one considers the angular variation of potential energy with fixed equilibrium

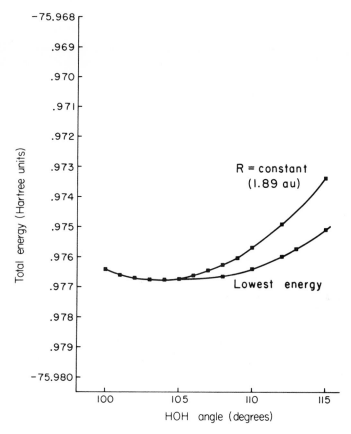

Fig. 13.   Potential energy versus angle in the water molecule.

bond length. We estimate that the energy required for bending from 104° to 109° is in the order of 1 kcal or less, and this can be important for theories of the structure of water and ice.

4. The Geometry of Molecules (20). A number of years ago Walsh (*21*) proposed a set of orbital energy versus angle graphs for AH_2, AH_3, AB_2, AB_3, ABC, H_2AB, HAAB, etc., systems. These curves, based on spectroscopic evidence and qualitative reasoning, have proved to systemize and predict the shape of a very large number of molecules. In fact, Walsh's diagrams have become one of the most celebrated hypotheses of inorganic stereochemistry.

Because the sum of one-electron orbital energies does not equal the total energy in Hartree-Fock theory it has been felt (*22*) that the dependent variable on these graphs could not be the one-electron eigenvalue of the Hartree-Fock equations. However, we now have accurate data for a large number of 6, 8, 10, 12, 14, and 16 electron molecules of types AH_2, AB_2, AH_3, AB_3, ABC, and we find that in fact the one-electron energy is the appropriate mathematical and chemical dependent variable. For all of the various types of systems our one-electron energy curves show the same general form as those of Walsh while this is not true for that one-electron energy quantity, e_i, in Hartree-Fock theory which adds up to the total energy

$$E_T = \tfrac{1}{2}\left(\sum_i \left(\varepsilon_i + (i|f|i) \right) \right) = \sum_i e_i.$$

Figure 14 shows the original Walsh diagram for an AH_2 molecule superimposed on our calculated curve for BH_2^+. (The apparent discrepancies are primarily caused by Walsh's incorrect omission of 2s orbital contributions on the central atom at 90°. This error was pointed out some time ago by Mulliken and when compensated for doesn't change the arguments). The basic reason why the sum of one-electron energies may be used to simulate the predictions of the total energy is because there is inherently a low information content in the determination of bond angles. This can be shown by analyzing the energy expressions in terms of the mathematical inequalities:

$$\frac{\dfrac{\partial}{\partial \Theta}\left(\sum\limits_{i}^{n} \varepsilon_i \right)}{\dfrac{\partial}{\partial \Theta}\left[V_N - \tfrac{1}{2}\sum\limits_{i,j} \{(ii|jj) - (ij|ji)\} \right]} > 0, \tag{1}$$

$$\left| \frac{\partial}{\partial \Theta}\left(\sum_i^n \varepsilon_i \right) \right| > \left| \frac{\partial}{\partial \Theta}\left[V_N - \tfrac{1}{2}\sum_{i,j} \{(ii|jj) - (ij|ji)\} \right] \right|. \tag{2}$$

If either of these hold then the sum of the one-electron energies will give the same prediction as the total energy. These inequalities are in fact satisfied for almost all molecular wave functions. Curves of the two quantities are shown for a typical AH_2 case in Fig. 15. In Fig. 16, we show a curve for a typical AH_3 system (BH_3). The solid lines are calculations that allow adjustment in the tails of the atomic orbitals while the dotted lines are the frozen LC (Hartree-Fock) AO result. We see that they both give a satisfactory representation.

5. Electron Deficient Species (23). Molecules in which there are a larger number of available orbitals than available electrons are, in some sense, midway between the typical saturated covalent electron-pair bond compound and a metal. They often play an important role as organic intermediates. One such species is CH_5^+. We have found, in contrast to previous speculations and calculations, that the trigonal bipyramid D_{3h} is *not* the lowest energy configuration but rather C_{4v} is lower. There may be another lower symmetry form with even lower energy and we are continuing our search for this possibility. The interesting feature here is that both the D_{3h} and C_{4v} forms have perfectly well-defined minima in their potential energy surfaces and one can

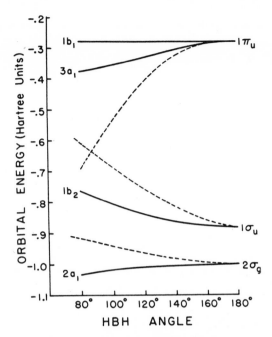

FIG. 14. Walsh's diagram for AH_2 species (dotted lines) and one-electron energies versus angle for BH_2^+ (solid lines).

specify well-defined bond lengths. (For D_{3h}: long bond = 1.16 Å, short bond in plane = 1.13 Å. For C_{4v}: the carbon atom is 0.4 Å out of the plane with four bonds each of length = 1.15 Å, the bond perpendicular to plane is 1.11 Å). The total energies of the two forms are very close, and this suggests that either form could exist in a given circumstance—the particular one being determined by the surrounding environment. The simplest carbonium ion, $C_3H_3^+$, is also an important organic reaction intermediate and there is no instrumental means for ascertaining its stability and geometry. Our current values show a C–C distance of ≈ 1.50 Å and a remarkably high-binding energy of 29.2 eV (relative to the infinitely separated atoms). This is also the simplest species in which we can investigate the famous problem of "bent bonds." Although incompletely optimized as yet, our present calculations show a charge density maxima outside the triangle, away from the line of carbon centers.

Another electron-deficient species for which we have carried out an extensive geometry search and analysis is diborane, B_2H_6. We have simultaneously determined the energy and geometry for BH_3, being careful to always maintain a perfectly balanced basis set between the two so as not to prejudice a comparison of the energies between them. Our results show

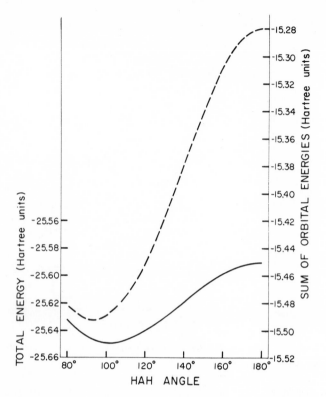

FIG. 15. Total energy versus angle compared with the sum of one-electron energies versus angle for a typical AH_2 species (BH_2^-).

diborane to be a little over 1 eV lower in total energy than 2 BH_3 molecules, thus supporting some recent mass spectrometric and kinetic studies of this hard-to-measure system. Another aspect of the diborane work has been calculation of B_2H_6 in the C_2H_6 geometry and vice versa. The results can again be analyzed in terms of Walsh's rules.

6. *Excited States of Simple Molecules* (24). A long-standing challenge to quantum chemistry has been a priori prediction of the ground and excited states of CH_2. A very accurate wave function calculated by Foster and Boys (25) has existed for some time, but this does not give the experimentally observed results of Herzberg (26). His results indicate a ground-state triplet approaching linearity rather than the $125°$ $^3B_1$ ground state predicted by Boys' work. It turns out that this is a rather subtle problem, and we are just now confident that we almost have the answer in hand. Figure 17 shows our present result with a minimum between $135-140°$ as the result of a complete VB configuration interaction with the frozen Hartree-Fock AO's. Basis

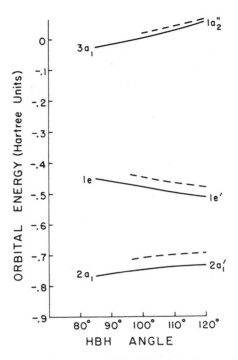

FIG. 16.   One-electron energies versus angle for BH_3: dashed curves, LC (Hartree-Fock) AO; solid curves, AO's allowed to adjust to molecular environment.

function modification explorations already carried out for this and other studies clearly indicate that adjustments in the tails of the carbon 2s and 2p orbitals will yield a somewhat larger angle (perhaps to 160°) and this will be within the range of experimental uncertainty. The excited $^1A_1$ state is correctly predicted (as it was by Boys) to be 103°. A number, not available from experiment but of interest to organic chemists, is prediction of the energy separation between the singlet and triplet (≈ 1.1 eV).

The valence bond scheme provides a very good method for obtaining the valence state excitations of a system and Figs. 18–20 show typical curves for some diatomic species that have been measured spectroscopically at the National Research Council Laboratories in Ottawa. All experimentally accessible levels appear to agree well with our calculations.

7. Rotational Barriers (*27*). We have been carrying out an extensive set of calculations on the molecules CH_3CH_3, CH_3OH, and O_2H_2 (we also are working on singly and doubly fluorinated ethanes) to see if the origin of rotational barriers may be found within the Hartree-Fock approximation. *Sine qua non* to this investigation is a great deal of exploration as to the adequacy of

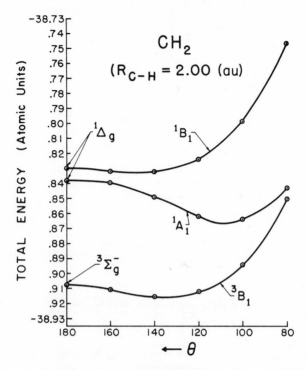

FIG. 17. Potential energy versus angle for first three states of CH_2.

the basis set and relation of the solution to a true molecular Hartree-Fock result. Perhaps most of all, a convincing explanation must correctly order and describe the barriers for a *sequence* of molecules—calculations on any one molecule by itself are inadequate. The necessity for obtaining theoretical numerical results on a sequence of systems is completely analogous to the tradition in experimental chemistry where it is well-established practice that meaningful conceptual understanding of phenomenon may be derived only by examining a given class, series, or sequence of compounds: this is particularly true for ethane because the high symmetry of the barrier tends to obscure the detailed mechanism of its origin. Computed results versus angle are shown in Figs. 21a, b, c for the three molecules noted above. In general, we get the correct ordering and reasonable magnitudes for the barriers, and analysis of our H_2O_2 solution gives confidence that further improvements in our wave function will correct our present values around 180°. Thus we have accomplished our first objective of proving that the origin of rotational barriers may be found within the framework of a molecular Hartree-Fock solution. In addition we have further decomposed the energy into nuclear-electron plus kinetic energy and electron-electron repulsion components. These two

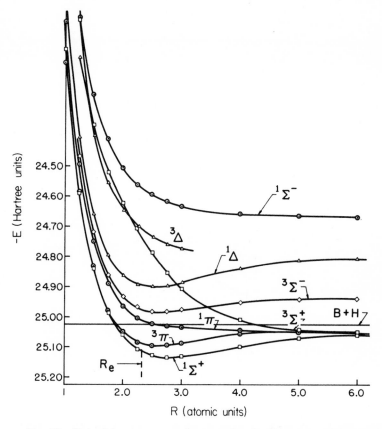

Fɪɢ. 18.   Potential energy curves for ground and excited states of BH.

components are found to be always out of phase with one another, and it is the detailed balance between these two which is basically the origin of the barriers. At present we are constructing a simplified model in terms of localized orbital contributions which will serve to organize and unify our results. Because of the vast amount of previous work on this problem it is worth noting from our results that the nuclear-electron and electron-electron components are always of greater magnitude than the nuclear-nuclear repulsion terms and that the phase relationship between the nuclear-electron and nuclear-nuclear repulsion terms changes from molecule to molecule. Lone pair electrons also play an important role in the H_2O_2 case. It is thus apparent that a screened nuclear-nuclear repulsion model or a hydrogen-hydrogen only interaction model cannot elucidate the origin of rotational barriers.

8. Many-Electron Energy Bands for Small Crystals (28). There are certain problems in solid-state physics that may be approached by the many-electron

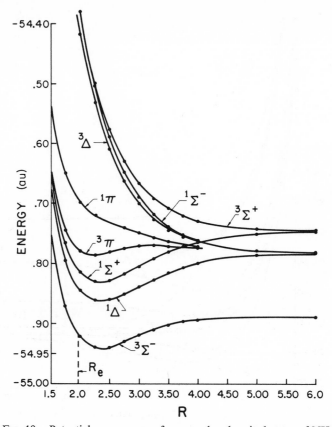

FIG. 19.   Potential energy curves for ground and excited states of NH.

techniques built up for molecules. In the future this may well provide an entirely new viewpoint for the electronic structure of solids. We have constructed an LC (Hartree-Fock) AO SCF MO wave function for a 32-atom hydrogen solid for sc, fcc, and bcc lattices. At this stage the surface-to-volume ratio is not particularly favorable, and it proves technically impossible to construct Bloch sums and put in periodic boundary conditions, but we are able to watch the buildup of bands and we are going to be able to go to larger systems.

9. Inorganic Compounds Composed of First and Second Row Atoms (29). In addition to the molecules we have discussed, there is a great deal of inorganic chemistry to be obtained from combinations of the atoms from H to Ne. As one can imagine, there are many exciting opportunities for understanding the subtleties of electronic structure in the following species (for which we have carried out high-precision wave functions as a function of geometry): Li_2O, $LiOH$, HOF, F_2O, HCN, N_2H_2, N_2H_4, N_2F_2, N_4, N_3^-, NO_2^+, NO_2^-, CO, C_3,

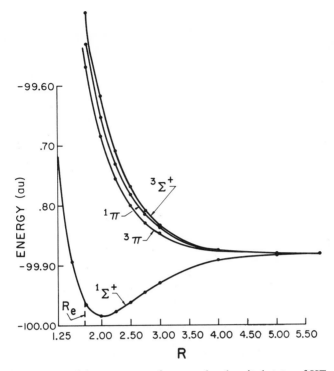

Fig. 20. Potential energy curves for ground and excited states of HF.

O_3, CO_2, and O_2F_2. Incidentally, the first two molecules violate Walsh's rules since these rules would predict a bent species. Experimental molecular beam results and our calculations show a linear Li_2O molecule. Our calculations yield a linear LiOH molecule also and this stands as a before-the-experiment prediction.

E. Decomposition Analysis for Many-Electron Wave Functions

It is obvious from our experience that chemically and physically interesting systems made from aggregates of atoms three, four, or five times larger than our examples will be inaccessible to direct a priori calculations because of the enormous number of three- and four-center integrals. Our first approach to this problem has been to look for an approximate *physical* or *chemical* relation that would avoid direct computation of these integrals. This approach, of course, is implicit to all existing model theories. But none of the present model theories really have an a priori predictive capability, and detailed examination of them shows that again it is just on the question of three- and four-center electrostatic interaction integrals where no satisfactory answer is

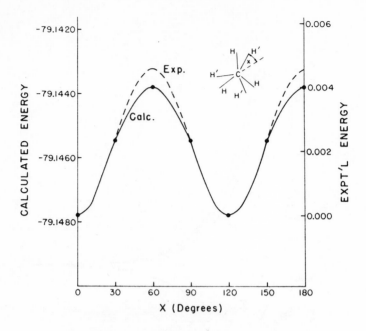

FIG. 21a. Barrier to internal rotation in ethane.

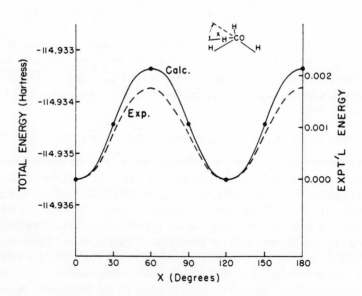

FIG. 21b. Barrier to internal rotation in methyl alcohol.

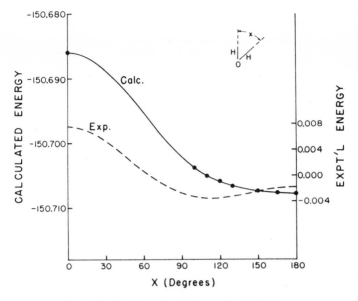

FIG. 21c. Barrier to internal rotation in H_2O_2.

available. We have also made rather extensive tests of the well-known Mulliken approximation,

$$\chi_i(1)\chi_j(1) \cong S_{ij} \frac{\chi_i^2(1) + \chi_j^2(1)}{2},$$

for three-dimensional molecules where there is no simple separation of π and σ electrons (30). In summary our conclusions are that, if employed for a single pair of orbitals, the results are roughly equivalent to those obtained with the use of single exponential basis orbitals—just a little too erratic to be used with confidence a priori. Using Mulliken's approximation for both pairs of orbitals is generally worthless from an a priori standpoint. However, even if this approximation were completely adequate it would not help because the central question is simply the number of integrals occurring— in fact our method of generating three- and four-center integrals is even a bit faster than use of the Mulliken approximation. The value of the Mulliken rule is that it approximately relates the magnitude of three- and four-center integrals to two-center integrals, but this relation is only approximate and we have not yet developed a practical method to use this knowledge in reducing the number of three- and four-center integrals.

Another kind of data which is potentially useful is the distribution functions for the magnitude of molecular integrals in typical cases. Here again we meet the relatively crude state of the art in treating problems primarily characterized

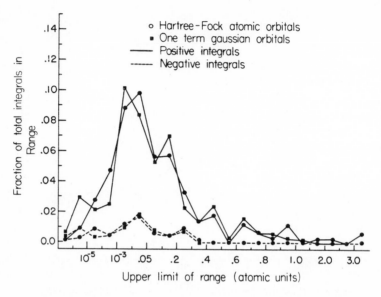

FIG. 22. Distribution of molecular integrals as a function of energy range for NH_2^-.

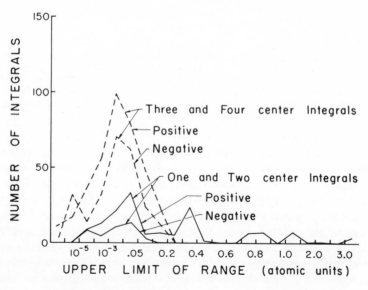

FIG. 23. Distribution of molecular integrals with energy range: Dashed lines, three- and four-center integrals; solid lines, one- and two-center integrals.

by their complexity: Until now there simply has not been the capability for generating enough of the basic data required for developing effective parametric and model theories. Figure 22 shows the effect of different orbital basis sets on the distribution function for the sum of all integrals in a molecular calculation of NH_2^- at its equilibrium separation (*31*). We have computed such distributions for almost all of the ten-electron polyhydrides and for such diverse other species as NeO_2, $C_3H_3^+$, H_4, and N_4. All have much the same appearance with maxima at nearly the same magnitude. Crude basis sets give the same general shape but contain many erratic excursions—it is as if improvement in the quality of the basis set corresponded to putting the distribution function through a low-pass filter. Fig. 23 for H_3O^+ (at equilibrium geometry) separates the three- and four-center integral distribution functions from the one and two (*31*). Again the curves appear to have a universal shape. Unfortunately, the three- and four-center integrals have too broad a peak with a maximum that occurs almost over the maximum of the one- and two-center curves (on the average it is even slightly shifted to the right of the example in Fig. 23). Simple addition theorems (e.g., the sum of the negative one-, two-, three-, and four-center integrals does not very closely equal the positive three- and four-center integrals) do not appear likely. When bond distances are expanded or contracted the distribution function moves to the left or right as might be expected. Only at quite short distances does distortion in the shape show up, giving rise to bimodal distributions. While interesting, these distribution functions have not as yet provided a scheme for reducing the number of three- and four-center integrals in any general way. The principal application of these distribution functions that can be anticipated at present is their use as criteria for deciding the number of significant figures required in the generation of various classes of two-, three-, and four-center integrals. Although not presently employed in any digital computer program in any laboratory, it should be possible to compute different integrals to different accuracies and still end up with the total energies computed to the present high accuracy standard of eight significant figures. Crude estimates indicate that a well-written digital computer program based on this principle might enjoy an additional order of magnitude in speed over existing programs. In order to increase the number of potential internal relationships among the integrals one needs to assume a particular model for constructing the wave function. The only simple model that has enough a priori generality to be useful is the MO SCF method (the number of important configurations varies too much from molecule to molecule in a VB wave function). Thus we are constructing term ratios and distribution functions for our SCF wave functions. For example, it may be that significant and general numerical relationships will show up in the final molecular Hartree-Fock solution that were not present in the input ingredients, and thus we are separating three- and four-center contributions from one- and two-center contributions in the matrix elements of the SCF Hamiltonian.

IV. The Method of Molecular Orbitals-Ionic States

From the standpoint of formal many-electron theory the results discussed in the previous section prove two very important numerical theorems. First, molecular Hartree-Fock solutions give a remarkably good description of the system in terms of predicted properties and geometries: quite a bit better than one dared hope even with a knowledge of Brillouin's theorem and the extended Brillouin theorem. Second, the LC (Hartree-Fock) AO approximation is a definitely good and almost always adequate representation of the molecular Hartree-Fock solution. Thus, to a very large degree, molecules really are made out of atoms.

In addition to the lowest single configuration energy, the other well-known advantages of the Hartree-Fock solution are: (a) definition of one-electron orbitals and energies and identification of the energies with ionization potentials; (b) quantitative determination of hybridization effects in the most efficient manner; (c) maximum use of molecular symmetry and fewest number of assumptions required to determine molecular charge distributions.

These overwhelming chemical advantages coupled with the relative computational simplicity of the single determinant SCF procedure virtually guarantee that practically all *ab initio* wave functions for large systems will employ an approximate Hartree-Fock solution as leading term.

In view of the great practical success of the molecular Hartree-Fock solution we must carefully examine what specific chemical and physical effects require us to go beyond this level of approximation. Three effects are listed below, but it is apparent that they have a common mathematical origin.

(a) Hartree-Fock solutions are inadequate for constructing potential surfaces. Although equilibrium bond angles and bond lengths are predicted to $\pm 2\%$ the region of satisfactory representation is $\approx R_e \pm 15\%$. For internuclear separations larger than about 15%, rise of the Hartree-Fock potential surface to ionic states at infinite separation noticeably manifests itself. This behavior plus even small errors in electron correlation energy estimates can make it impossible to distinguish between a repulsive and an attractive potential energy curve.

(b) It is well known that the extra molecular correlation energy produces 20–80% errors in dissociation energy predictions (even to the extent of sometimes yielding a negative binding energy as in F_2 and some polyatomics). Empirical correlation energy rules like those noted in the previous section and calibration of results through experience considerably lessen the severity of this problem but slight erratic fluctuations remain (as in F_2), and this reduces the ability to sharply distinguish one type of atom from another.

(c) From the textbook example of H_2, and many more complicated cases, we know that even at equilibrium separations there is too large an ionic state contribution, that is, the occupancy of the atomic shell structure is improperly represented. In effect the Hartree-Fock approximation does not give an accurate enough representation of the oxidation state of an atom in a molecule. This can lead to the incorrect sign of the charge distribution as appears to be the case in CO.

It is ironic that just as the LC (Hartree-Fock) AO MO SCF method is especially appropriate and useful as a starting point it is singularly poor as a basis for generating correction terms. Disadvantages of the MO superposition of configurations technique are: (i) There are many configurations which have the same energy and there is no adequate criterion for selecting in advance those groups of configurations which are most important. (ii) The logical orbitals for constructing the configuration interaction are the unoccupied excited states of the finite expansion Hartree-Fock Hamiltonian but the shape and energy of these states often changes radically with occupancy. (iii) The one- and two-electron many-center integrals over atomic orbitals which serve as input data for generating the initial solution must be transformed to the final SCF basis for carrying out the configuration interaction. Although the four index transformation required is mathematically simple it is frequently a very time consuming process. (iv) The MO configuration interaction scheme does not utilize the fact that the initial solution was LCAO. Closely related is the lack of chemical and physical interpretability.

The Molecular Orbital Minus Ionic States Method (MO-IS) has been conceived to avoid these difficulties in the MO-configuration interaction technique. The central fact that we can take from chemical experience and numerical experiments is the high degree to which the LC (Hartree-Fock) AO approximation is obeyed (*32*). But everyone is familiar with the LCAO expansion of the hydrogen molecule MO solution which shows the characteristic overweighting of ionic terms. In polyatomic systems the principal problem occurs for terms in the LCAO expansion corresponding to pairs of ionic valence electron states on adjacent atoms. This difficulty can be overcome by subtracting off valence bond-like ionic states from the wave function. The MO-IS method is designed to accomplish this in the following manner: We start by calculating the standard single determinant LCAO MO SCF solution. If a true molecular Hartree-Fock solution is available for a starting point, so much the better. Next we set up determinants corresponding to ionic states or in some cases neutral atom states. The ionic states to be included correspond to the singly or doubly charged bonds between adjacent atoms into which the molecular orbital solution will separate. An important feature is that for any given molecular problem there will be relatively few of these states, and so the number of configuration interaction terms in the total wave function will be kept small. Finally, the total wave function is now made up from a linear combination of the MO and the ionic states, each with a linear coefficient determined by energy minimization. The MO-IS wave function is simply an MO configuration interaction treatment which uses ionic and atomic-like states to mix with the parent MO SCF state. The principal new mathematical feature is adoption of a *non orthogonal* basis. In previous times this would have been considered an overriding disadvantage, but now that the technical facilities are available to handle this numerically, we can turn this feature to great advantage: it enables us to retain the identity of the atoms in the molecule. It is also to be noted that the particular aspects which characterize the MO-IS wave function are of a strictly *molecular* nature. At the atomic limit of infinite internuclear separations it reduces to a standard Valence Bond configuration interaction expansion. From a chemical standpoint most of the vast store of qualitative knowledge about the electronic structure of molecules is contained in *atomic* rules, and the MO-IS scheme offers a way to couple this chemical information into a well-defined mathematical formalism. At this point it is appropriate to inquire why one doesn't use the VB method itself in a straightforward way. Extensive experience at Princeton and elsewhere demonstrates the following:

(a) For even simple polyatomic molecules there are generally many determinants representing neutral molecules, all with rather similar energy determined weighting coefficients, but none with anywhere near the weight of the Hartree-Fock solution in an equivalent MO CI expansion. It takes many more determinants and greatly increased manipulative complexity to represent the hybridization effects so efficiently accomplished by the parent MO state. Comparison of solutions for particular molecules by VB and MO methods shows that a rather large number of VB states are generally required to yield the same energy as the Hartree-Fock state.

(b) So many states are required (neutral and ionic) to assure a symmetric and unbiased description of the molecular-charge distribution that the size of system which may be treated is much more limited than for the MO method. The resulting wave function always has a somewhat lower energy than the Hartree-Fock state but analysis shows that the chemical effects represented by most of the VB states are satisfactorily treated by the single Hartree-Fock determinant.

The MO and VB methods have opposing virtues and difficulties and the MO-IS method attempts to exploit the virtues of both (*33*). Most of structural chemistry is described and interpreted in a qualitative valence bond framework and it is important to see if the MO-IS method can be described in this type of language. Basic to this attempt is recognition of a dichotomy of thirty years' standing between the descriptive language of textbook chemistry and the fractional charge distribution picture suggested by molecular orbital theory. On the one hand chemistry has been successfully organized in terms of a periodic table of atoms with a specified integral number of valence electrons surrounding a given atom. For a particular atom this number may vary under different bonding conditions but always remains integral. On the other hand, molecular orbital theory distributes charge in fractional amounts on all atoms and bond regions throughout the nuclear framework. Indeed, as Linnett (*34*) has pointed out, "It is interesting that exponents of the molecular orbital method, which provides the clearest way for constructing molecular wave functions, have never felt the need to provide *chemical* formulas which illustrate and symbolize the wave functions. ... It is very probable that one of the reasons why molecular orbital treatments were accepted only slowly by experimental chemists was that theoreticians were unwilling to devise chemical formulas to represent their ideas". In this paper we do not pretend to directly solve this traditional and continuing problem but rather make some observations which appear to the present author to considerably reduce the difficulty. First, if one concentrates on the properties of the bonds rather than questions as to the oxidation number of the participating atoms, then to the zeroth approximation both viewpoints are identical and yield an answer expressed as an integral number of electrons. This result, of course, is just the simplest use of the *bond order* concept. Second, Linnett (*34*) has recently introduced an improved qualitative language and notation, based on the valence bond approach, which retains integral numbers of electrons but distinguishes between α-spin and β-spin electrons. His scheme, termed the "Double Quartet" or "Non-Pairing" method includes the conventional "electron dot" picture as a subclass but is able to describe a far larger number of bonding situations—including, in fact, almost all known classes of chemical compounds. Although the electrons are loosely identified with atoms, this new description actually permits a far more flexible distribution of electrons around the nuclear framework than the traditional picture in terms of a rigid number of electrons identified with a specific atom. Linnett has devised a prescription for constructing a many-electron wave function from atomic orbitals corresponding to his symbolic notation. We have expanded an MO LCAO wave function for several of the systems treated by Linnett and his co-workers, and if we arbitrarily cross out terms in this expansion corresponding to pairs of doubly occupied atomic orbitals on adjacent atoms we find that the remaining wave function contains the same type of terms represented in Linnett's wave functions. Qualitatively this is the same argument on which the MO-IS method is based, thus demonstrating the close similarity between his modified valence bond scheme and our modified molecular orbital scheme. This further suggests that MO-IS wave functions will lead to useful pictures for descriptive chemistry.

The numerical procedure for computing MO-IS wave functions is fortunately straightforward and makes use of well-established digital computer routines (35). First, an LCAO MO SCF solution is obtained (36). Second, ionic valence bond states, and perhaps others selected on chemical criteria, are set up as determinants made from atomic orbitals. Third, matrix elements of the Hamiltonian between determinants are calculated in the usual way using the same one- and two-electron integrals computed over atomic orbitals required as input data for the SCF solution. The only new kind of matrix element is that between the MO state and a valence bond determinant, but this simply involves linear combinations of integrals with already determined coefficients. Of course, the orbitals in the ionic state terms are not orthogonal to those in the MO state, and this means that it is necessary to use the overlap determinant formalism for the matrix elements (37), but this occurs already in the valence bond method itself and, as discussed in the previous section, this technique, like the MO SCF procedure, has been thoroughly reduced to practice.

At the time of writing MO-IS results are just being completed for NeH_2, LiH, Li_2, C_2, N_2, and F_2. Although not yet completely analyzed, the results are very encouraging for all cases—an especially gratifying situation because MO-IS is basically a per bond, left-right correlation scheme and thus an almost complete test of the method can be achieved by calculations on diatomic species alone. It is also important to note that spin symmetrization problems in MO-IS enjoy the same simplicity as in the standard MO method.

ACKNOWLEDGMENT

The services and computer time for the studies reported here were made available by the Princeton University Computer Center, and they are gratefully acknowledged. This center is supported in part by National Science Foundation Grant NSF-GP-579.

REFERENCES

1. The surprising information content advance is matched by the large technological discontinuity required to go from diatomics to even the simplest polyatomics.
2. J. L. Whitten and L. C. Allen, *J. Chem. Phys.* **43**, S170 (1965).
3. L. C. Allen and A. M. Karo, *Rev. Mod. Phys.* **32**, 275 (1960).
4. In addition to some of our results on total *energies* given in Table 1, we have carried out a great deal of graphical analysis on the orbital composition of all of the University of Chicago diatomic molecular Hartree-Fock solutions. Aside from very small d and f contributions (which must be considered in greater detail in regard to certain expectation values) the functions are quite closely approximated by Hartree-Fock AO's.
5. J. L. Whitten, *J. Chem. Phys.* **44**, 359 (1966).
6. I. G. Csizmadia, M. C. Harrison, and B. T. Sutcliffe, LCAO-SCF calculations on formyl fluoride with a minimal Gaussian basis set, *SSMTG Quart. Prog. Rept. No. 59* (Jan. 15, 1966). Massachusetts Institute of Technology.
7. J. M. Shulman and J. W. Moskowitz, *J. Chem. Phys.* **43**, 3287 (1965).

8. B. J. Ransil, *Rev. Mod. Phys.* **32**, 245 (1960).
9. Some of these solutions have appeared in print: A. C. Wahl, *J. Chem. Phys.* **41**, 2600 (1964) (F_2); W. Huo, *J. Chem. Phys.* **43**, 624 (1965) (Co and BF); S. Peyerimhoff, *J. Chem. Phys.* **43**, 998 (1965) (HeH$^+$ and NeH$^+$); A. C. Wahl, *Science* **151**, 961 (1966) (A survey of homonuclear solutions H_2 and Ne_2 and charge density plots). Other results are in press (*J. Chem. Phys.*) by P. E. Cade, G. L. Mali, K. D. Sales, J. B. Greenshields, T. L. Gilbert, and A. C. Wahl.
10. G. Das and A. C. Wahl, *J. Chem. Phys.* **44**, 87 (1966).
11. R. K. Nesbet, *J. Chem. Phys.* **36**, 1518 (1962).
12. E. Clementi, *J. Chem. Phys.* **38**, 2780 (1963); **39**, 487 (1963).
13. D. S. Bartow and L. C. Allen (submitted to *J. Chem. Phys.*).
14. Much of this work is part of the Princeton Ph.D thesis of R. M. Erdahl. To be submitted to *J. Chem. Phys.*
15. The wave function for HeF_2 is contained in the Ph.D. thesis of R. M. Erdahl and those for HeF, NeF, NeF_2, HeO, and NeO are contained in the Ph.D. thesis of A. M. Lesk. Detailed treatments are being prepared for submission to the *J. Chem. Phys.* The data given here are also included for the most part in: L. C. Allen, R. M. Erdahl, and J. L. Whitten, *J. Am. Chem. Soc.* **87**, 3769 (1965), and L. C. Allen, A. M. Lesk, and R. M. Erdahl, *J. Am. Chem. Soc.* **88**, 615 (1966).
16. G. C. Pimentel and R. D. Spratley, *J. Am. Chem. Soc.* **85**, 826 (1963); G. C. Pimentel, R. D. Spratley, and A. R. Miller, *Science* **143**, 674 (1964).
17. C. K. Jørgensen, "*Inorganic Complexes,*" p. 33. Academic Press, New York, 1963.
18. R. M. Noyes, *J. Am. Chem. Soc.* **85**, 2202 (1963).
19. Work on the ten-electron systems is part of the Ph.D. thesis of W. Fink.
20. The section on Walsh's rules was carried out by S. D. Peyerimhoff and R. J. Buenker and is part of the latter's Ph.D. thesis. One paper, "The Geometry of Molecules. I. Wavefunctions for some Six and Eight Electron Polyhydrides," S. D. Peyerimhoff, R. J. Buenker, and L. C. Allen, has been submitted to the *J. Chem. Phys.* A second, "The Geometry of Molecules. II. Diborane and Ethane," R. J. Buenker, S. D. Peyerimhoff, L. C. Allen, and J. L. Whitten will be submitted to the *J. Chem. Phys.* soon. Several others are also planned.
21. A. D. Walsh, *J. Chem. Soc.* 2260 (1953).
22. C. A. Coulson and A. H. Neilson, *Discussions Faraday Soc.* **35**, 71 (1963).
23. The work on CH_5^+ is part of the Ph.D. thesis of W. Fink, the $C_3H_3^+$ work, part of the undergraduate thesis of H. Reischer, BH_3 vs B_2H_6 part of the Ph.D. thesis of R. J. Buenker.
24. The valence bond calculations in this section are part of the Ph.D. thesis of J. F. Harrison.
25. J. M. Foster and S. F. Boys, *Rev. Mod. Phys.* **32**, 305 (1960).
26. G. Herzberg, *Proc. Roy. Soc. (London)* **A262**, 291 (1961).
27. The work on rotational barriers is part of the Ph.D thesis of W. Fink.
28. Work on the H solid has been carried out by A. Wasserman and S. D. Peyerimhoff.
29. Work on the various species noted here is being carried out by D. Pan, S. D. Peyerimhoff, G. V. Pfeiffer, J. F. Harrison, and R. Kapral.
30. Tests of the Mulliken approximation have been carried out by W. Fink and R. J. Buenker.
31. Work on the distribution functions is being pursued by T.-K. Ha and W. Fink.
32. Probably the harshest criticism that may be brought against the formal many-particle perturbation and diagrammatic techniques is failure to build in this result as a cornerstone to the mathematical development.

33. It is, of course, a cliché to note that when carried far enough, the VB and MO + CI schemes yield the same wave function, but it is never practical or useful to do so for any chemically interesting system.

34. J. W. Linnett, "The Electronic Structure of Molecules, A New Approach." Methuen, London, 1964.

35. The fact that it is possible to easily and efficiently couple the MO SCF routine to the VB routine was pointed out by J. F. Harrison. This is of great and fundamental importance for the success of the method.

36. It is not necessary that this be a strictly LCAO solution, but this will frequently be the case and it is easier to describe the procedure in these terms.

37. P. O. Löwdin, *Phys. Rev.* **97**, 1474, 1490 (1955).

Exclusion Principle and Measurement Theory[*]

H. MARGENAU

YALE UNIVERSITY, NEW HAVEN, CONNECTICUT

I. The Exclusion Principle and Intermolecular Forces

It is almost an axiom of science that the interaction energy between two atoms, and hence the forces between them, shall vanish when the distance between them becomes very great. For if this were not true the universe would contain no isolated systems and the idealizations implicit in every physical science become meaningless. In classical physics this belief is clearly warranted, for it is known that all forces between the elementary constituents of nature fall off with distance R between interacting partners at least as rapidly as R^{-2}, those between nuclear particles much more rapidly, and the problem of isolation presents no difficulty. But in quantum mechanics, which requires the use of Pauli's exclusion principle, curious features appear which, unless fully understood, cast doubt on the existence of isolated systems containing similar particles (e.g., electrons). Perhaps because they give rise to some perplexity these features remain undiscussed. In this article the author wishes to expose them and show that they disappear under an analysis which involves basic aspects of the theory of measurement; this analysis, in turn, places the exclusion principle in a new light and raises questions of some interest.

The situation at issue arises in the theory of intermolecular forces and will here be sketched in broad outline. For details Hirschfelder's (*1*) impressive book, the review articles by Pitzer (*2*) or this author (*3*) may be consulted.

Let two interacting atoms be labeled a and b. Atom a contains m electrons; atom b, n electrons. Their energies are, respectively,

* Work done under Contract AFOSR 249-64.

$$H_a = T_a - z_a e^2 \sum_{\lambda=1}^{m} r_{a\lambda}^{-1} + e^2 \sum_{\lambda > \mu = 1}^{m} r_{\lambda\mu}^{-1}, \tag{1}$$

$$H_b = T_b - z_b e^2 \sum_{\lambda=m+1}^{n} r_{b\lambda}^{-1} + e^2 \sum_{\lambda > \mu = m+1}^{m+n} r_{\lambda\mu}^{-1}, \tag{2}$$

while their energy of interaction is given by

$$V = -z_a e^2 \sum_{\lambda=m+1}^{m+n} r_{a\lambda}^{-1} - z_b e^2 \sum_{\lambda=1}^{m} r_{b\lambda}^{-1} + e^2 \sum_{\lambda=1}^{m} \sum_{\mu=m+1}^{m+n} r_{\lambda\mu}^{-1} + z_a z_b e^2 R^{-1} \tag{3}$$

As to notation, T_a and T_b are the kinetic energies of all electrons in atoms a and b; in terms of the momentum p_i of the ith electron and its mass m, $T_a = \sum_{\lambda=1}^{m} p^2{}_\lambda/2m$; r_{ai} is the distance of electron i from nucleus a, r_{ij} the distance between electrons i and j. Finally, R is the separation of the nuclei of the two atoms.

We note first that V vanishes when R becomes very large, provided the electrons remain attached to their parent atoms, for in that case every inter-atomic r_{ij}—and only these occur in V—becomes infinite. This is the reason for the classical result that the interaction between distant atoms tends to naught.

The story is not much different in quantum mechanics, provided each atom is treated as an identity and the full requirement of the Pauli principle is not imposed. The latter must be applied, of course, to the electrons of each atom separately in order that the result shall have even a semblance of validity. The customary method is this. One writes a product of orbitals for atom a, one for each electron, viz.,

$$\varphi_a = a_1(1)a_2(2)a_3(3) \cdots a_m(m) \tag{4}$$

and likewise for atom b:

$$\varphi_b = b_1(m + 1)b_2(m + 2) \cdots b_n(m + n). \tag{5}$$

Each of these is then "antisymmetrized" by applying operators

$$\mathscr{A}^a = \sum_{\lambda} (-1)^\lambda P_\lambda^\alpha \tag{6}$$

and

$$\mathscr{A}^b = \sum_{\mu} (-1)^\mu P_\mu^b \tag{7}$$

to the product functions. In these formulas, P^a and P^b stand for all permutations among the electrons of atoms a and b, the subscripts label a given permutation, and are taken to be even for even, odd for odd permutations, i.e., for permutations composed of an even or odd number of elementary transpositions. The individual atomic functions then become

$$\psi_a = \mathscr{A}^a \varphi_a, \qquad \psi_b = \mathscr{A}^b \varphi_b \qquad (8)$$

and the energy of atoms a and b, in the approximation provided by this choice of orbitals, is

$$\bar{h}_a = \frac{\int \psi_a^* H_a \psi_a \, d\tau}{\int \psi_a^* \psi_a \, d\tau}, \qquad \bar{h}_b = \frac{\int \psi_a^* H_b \psi_b \, d\tau}{\int \psi_a^* \psi_b \, d\tau}. \qquad (9)$$

Here $d\tau_a$ and $d\tau_b$ are volume elements in the spaces of the electrons of atom a and of b; their product will be written $d\tau$.

The interaction energy is

$$\bar{v} = \frac{\int \psi_a^* \psi_b^* V \psi_a \psi_b \, d\tau}{\int \psi_a^* \psi_a \, d\tau_a \int \psi_b^* \psi_b \, d\tau_b}, \qquad (10)$$

and its properties are in accord with classical expectations, in particular, $\lim_{R \to \infty} \bar{v} = 0$. Equation (10) is indeed used in the calculation of long-range interatomic forces and gives correct answers. But for small values of R it is woefully wrong, for it neglects exchange forces.

To render a proper account of them it is necessary to antisymmetrize the state function of the entire system, which is composed of a and b. This involves the conjunction of a further antisymmetrizer, $\mathscr{A}^{ab}$, with $\mathscr{A}^a$ and $\mathscr{A}^b$:

$$\mathscr{A}^{ab} = \sum_v (-1)^v P_v^{ab},$$

where P^{ab} is the complex of intermolecular electron permutations, $(m + n)!/m!n!$ in number, which exchange electrons between a and b. The complete state function, in this approximation, then, is

$$\Psi = \mathscr{A}^{ab} \psi_a \psi_b. \qquad (11)$$

With it one can calculate the expectation values

$$\bar{H}_a = \int \Psi^* H_a \Psi \, d\tau \bigg/ \int \Psi^* \Psi \, d\tau, \qquad (12)$$

$$\bar{H}_b = \int \Psi^* H_b \Psi \, d\tau \bigg/ \int \Psi^* \Psi \, d\tau, \qquad (13)$$

$$\bar{V} = \int \Psi^* V \Psi \, d\tau \bigg/ \int \Psi^* \Psi \, d\tau, \qquad (14)$$

and these, in the literal interpretation of the elementary axioms of quantum mechanics, should be the energy values observed on the average when measurements are made. But it turns out on computation that none of the quantities $\bar{H}_a$, $\bar{H}_b$, or $\bar{V}$ shows the correct behavior when the atoms are at an infinite distance from each other; $\bar{H}_a$ does not approach $\bar{h}_a$, $\bar{H}_b$ does not approach

$\bar{h}_b$, and $\bar{V}$ does not go to zero. What does happen, and what saves the calculation from absurdity, is that the sum of these quantities

$$\bar{H} = \bar{H}_a + \bar{H}_b + \bar{V} \tag{15}$$

reduces to $\bar{h}_a + \bar{h}_b$ as $R \to \infty$, so that the remainder,

$$\bar{H} - \bar{h}_a - \bar{h}_b \equiv \Delta E$$

can be regarded as an interaction energy. Even this quantity, in spite of its correct asymptotic behavior, cannot be guaranteed to be the actual potential energy between the atoms, nor can it be placed between rigorous mathematical limits.

Evidently, $\bar{H}_a$, $\bar{H}_b$, and $\bar{V}$ are physically meaningless although they seem to satisfy the rules of computation. The mathematical reason for this collapse of meaning is easily discovered. The operator H_a is invariant with respect to all P^a, H_b with respect to all P^b, V with respect to $P^a P^b$, but none of them is invariant with respect to P^{ab}. Thus each of them commutes with $\mathscr{A}^a \mathscr{A}^b$, but not with $\mathscr{A}^{ab}$. When expectation values are computed with a state function which has the symmetry imposed by $\mathscr{A}^{ab}$, a symmetry which the operators do not share, awkward additional terms appear. The sum of (1), (2), and (3), the total energy $\bar{H}$, however, is invariant with respect to the symmetric group on all $m + n$ electrons, i.e., with respect to P^{ab} as well as P^a and P^b, so that in its computation the awkward terms of $\bar{H}_a$, $\bar{H}_b$, and $\bar{V}$ cancel out. Nevertheless there remains a basic physical paradox attached to the unwelcome features of these individual quantities, and the remainder of this paper seeks to interpret them. In the next section we illustrate what is involved by reference to a simple example.

II. Interaction of Two Hydrogen-Like Atoms

Let the nucleus of the first atom be situated at the point $\mathbf{a}$, that of the second at $\mathbf{b}$. We shall further designate the orbital function localized about the point $\mathbf{a}$ by the letter a, so that $a(1)$ is the state function of electron 1 about the proton at $\mathbf{a}$. The nuclei carry charges z_a and z_b. The functions $a(1)$ and $b(2)$ satisfy the equations

$$H_a a(1) = E_a a(1) \quad \text{and} \quad H_b b(2) = E_b b(2); \tag{16}$$

their form is well known, and

$$H_a(1) = -\frac{1}{2}\nabla_1^2 - \frac{z_a}{r_{a1}}, \quad H_b(2) = -\frac{1}{2}\nabla_2^2 - \frac{z_b}{r_{b2}} \tag{17}$$

when written in atomic units.

In this case $\psi_a = a$, $\psi_b = b$, since in the presence of a single electron $\mathscr{A}^a$

and $\mathscr{A}^b$ are 1. But $\mathscr{A}^{ab} = 1 - T_{12}$, where T_{12} effects a transposition of electrons 1 and 2. We then have

$$\bar{h}_a = E_a, \qquad \bar{h}_b = E_b, \tag{18}$$

and these values are in the present instance correct without approximation because a and b satisfy Eqs. (16) exactly. Furthermore,

$$\bar{H}_a = \int [\,] H_a[\,]\, d\tau \Big/ \int [\,]^2\, d\tau,$$

where each bracket contains the quantity $[a(1)b(2) - b(1)a(2)]$, which is real. Upon expansion, and with the use of a well-known notation we obtain

$$\bar{H}_a = \{\langle a|H_a|a\rangle - 2\langle b|H_a|a\rangle\delta + \langle b|H_a|b\rangle\}/2(1 - \delta^2)$$
$$= \{E_a(1 - 2\delta^2) + \langle b|H_a|b\rangle\}/2(1 - \delta^2), \tag{19}$$

where δ is the overlap integral $\int a(1) b(1)\, d\tau_1$. This would be the expected E_a if the term $\langle b|H_a|b\rangle$ were replaced by $\langle a|H_a|a\rangle$. Let us therefore examine that term. Since, by (17),

$$H_a(1) = H_b(1) + \frac{z_b}{r_{b1}} - \frac{z_a}{r_{a1}}$$

we have

$$\langle b|H_a|b\rangle = \langle b|H(b) + \frac{z_b}{r_b} - \frac{z_a}{r_a}|b\rangle$$
$$= E_b + \langle b|z_b/r_b|b\rangle - \langle b|z_a/r_a|b\rangle. \tag{20}$$

Below we shall need the analogous form

$$\langle a|H_b|a\rangle = E_a + \langle a|z_a/r_a|a\rangle - \langle a|z_b/r_b|a\rangle. \tag{21}$$

For the special case of hydrogen-like atoms, $\langle b|z_b/r_b|b\rangle = -2E_b$; in any case this quantity is independent of R, while $\langle b|z_a/r_a|b\rangle$ vanishes when R becomes infinite.

In the same way one finds

$$2(1 - \delta^2)\bar{H}_b = E_b(1 - 2\delta^2) + \langle a|H_b a\rangle$$
$$2(1 - \delta^2)\bar{V} = 2\langle ab|r_{12}^{-1}|ab\rangle - 2\langle ab|r_{12}^{-1}|ba\rangle + 2(1 - \delta^2)R^{-1}$$
$$- \langle a|z_a/r_a|a\rangle - \langle b|z_b/r_b|b\rangle - \langle b|z_a/r_a|b\rangle - \langle a|z_b/r_b|a\rangle$$
$$\times 2\langle b|z_a/r_a|a\rangle\delta + 2\langle a|z_b/r_b|b\rangle\delta.$$

This last expression arises from the classical potential energy

$$V = \frac{1}{R} + \frac{1}{r_{12}} - \frac{z_a}{r_{a2}} - \frac{z_b}{r_{b1}}. \tag{22}$$

As $R \to \infty$, δ as well as $\langle b|z_a/r_a|b \rangle$ and $\langle a|z_b/r_b|a \rangle$ vanish and $\bar{V}$ reduces to the two terms $-\langle a|z_a/r_a|a \rangle - \langle b|z_b/r_b|b \rangle$, which are large. They arise from the action of T_{12} on ab. They are precisely the terms which survive in $\bar{H}_a + \bar{H}_b$, but with opposite sign, so that all large components of $\bar{H}$ cancel. Indeed

$$\bar{H}_{R \to \infty} = E_a + E_b$$

We now return to consider the separate expectation value $\bar{H}_a$ which, according to Eq. (19), has the limiting form

$$\lim_{R \to \infty} \bar{H}_a = \tfrac{1}{2}[E_a + \langle b|H_a|b \rangle]. \tag{23}$$

From experiment we know that, if atom b is infinitely far away, the measured energy is E_a in every observation, yet (23) says that we find with equal probability the values E_a and $\langle b|H_a|b \rangle$, of which the latter would be the average energy of atom a if its electron were situated about b. Does the Pauli principle, which is responsible for this result, cause an obscure effect to be exerted on atom a by b even when it is infinitely far away? And if there were many other atoms, c, d, e, etc., all at infinity, would they cause the energy of a to be an average value of E_a and $\langle b|H_a|b \rangle$, $\langle c|H_a|c \rangle$, $\langle d|H_a|d \rangle$, etc.? The answer would be affirmative if the Pauli principle were a universal fact of nature, inviolable in its stringency upon all constituents of the universe. Light is thrown upon this state of affairs if the meaning of an expectation value like $\bar{H}_a$ is examined from the point of view of von Neumann's theory of measurement.

III. Theory of Measurements

A brief review of the relevant parts of measurement theory will now be given. We preface it by recalling some elementary points concerning the probabilities of quantum mechanics (4,5). When a physical system, like our atom a, whose coordinates we shall continue to designate by (1), is in a pure quantum state such as is represented by $\psi_a(1)$, the expectation value of any observable $G(1)$ which can be measured upon it is $\langle \psi_a|G|\psi_a \rangle / \langle \psi_a|\psi_a \rangle \equiv \bar{G}$. Henceforth we assume $\langle \psi_a|\psi_a \rangle$ to be 1. Another way of writing $\bar{G}$ involves the statistical matrix ρ; it is

$$\bar{G} = \mathrm{Tr}(\rho G),$$

$$\mathrm{Tr} \equiv \text{trace} \equiv \text{diagonal sum.} \tag{24}$$

In this expression G is the matrix of the operator G in some orthonormal set of basis functions $u_\lambda(1)$, $G_{ij} = \int u_i^* G u_j \, d\tau$. On the other hand, ρ is constructed from the probability amplitudes c_λ, defined through

$$\psi = \sum_\lambda c_\lambda u_\lambda$$

by the rule $\rho_{ij} = c_i c_j^*$. This matrix satisfies the relation

$$\rho^2 = \rho, \tag{25}$$

and Tr $\rho = 1$. The state $\psi_a(1)$ is called pure in the quantum sense because it conveys maximal knowledge, knowledge not mixed with ignorance, about system a. To be sure, one knows the occurrence of the values of an observable like G only with probabilities, but these probabilities are *irreducible* by physical operations in a sense discussed in Ref. 5; the uncertainty principle sets the ultimate limit of all possible reductions, and that principle is embodied in the representation of the state as ψ_a. Whenever the probabilities residing in a quantum mechanical state are thus irreducible, its statistical matrix satisfies Eq. (25), even if its origin, its construction by the rule just given, is not evident; ρ is then said to be an elementary matrix or a projection operator.

Now it often happens, for instance in statistical mechanics, that we do not know whether system a is in fact in the quantum state ψ_a. Our ignorance may commit us to saying that it is in a state $\psi_a^{(1)}$ with a probability ω_1, in $\psi_a^{(2)}$ with probability ω_2 and so on. These probabilities, which are not necessarily the squares of quantum amplitudes but have a simple classical origin, bespeak a removable kind of ignorance, they are *reducible* at will by observations or physical manipulation. Yet, whether they are present or not, one can form the expectation value of G in the manner of Eq. (24),

$$\bar{G} = \text{Tr}(\rho\tilde{G}) \tag{26}$$

provided one defines

$$\rho = \omega_1 \rho^{(1)} + \omega_2 \rho^{(2)} + \cdots \tag{27}$$

and constructs $\rho^{(1)}$ from $\psi_a^{(1)}$, $\rho^{(2)}$ from $\psi_a^{(2)}$, etc. This ρ, however, will not satisfy Eq. (25); and it is said to represent a mixture (unless all but one of the ω_i are 0). When a mixture is present, there always exist means—selection of systems from an ensemble or other forms of state preparation—whereby all ω's can be eliminated in favor of one, which then becomes 1. We thus obtain a pure case with irreducible probabilities. Whether a pure case is present can be ascertained theoretically by subjecting ρ to the test of Eq. (25).

A measurement performs the opposite of such reduction: it converts a pure case into a mixture (in the Hilbert space of the system whose properties are being measured) (6). For let the system, our atom a, be in a state $\psi_a(1)$ before measurement. The measuring apparatus might be atom b, whose state before measurement is $\psi_b(2)$. Both of them, prior to the measurement interaction when they are effectively an infinite distance apart, are in a product state $\psi_a(1) \cdot \psi_b(2)$.

When the interaction takes place that state is changed to one which must be written

$$\psi(1, 2) = \sum_{\lambda\mu} c_{\lambda\mu} u_\lambda(1) v_\mu(2) \tag{28}$$

where the u_λ, as before, label a complete orthonormal set in the space of a, while the v_μ span the space of b in similar fashion. The occurrence of the measurement interaction manifests itself in the nature of the coefficients $c_{\lambda\mu}$, which can no longer be written as products $c'_\lambda \cdot c''_\mu$ as was the case before the measurement took place.

If now we calculate $\overline{G(1)}$ with (28), we get

$$\overline{G} = \int \psi^*(1, 2) G(1) \psi(1, 2) \, d\tau = \sum_{\lambda\mu\nu} c^*_{\lambda\mu} c_{\nu\mu} G_{\lambda\mu},$$

$$G_{\lambda\nu} = \int u^*_\lambda(1) G(1) u_\nu(1) \, d\tau_1, \tag{29}$$

and this takes the form

$$\overline{G} = \mathrm{Tr}(\rho G) \tag{29a}$$

if we define

$$\rho_{ij} = \sum_\mu c_{i\mu} c^*_{j\mu}. \tag{30}$$

This statistical matrix no longer satisfies Eq. (25), as inspection will show. When describing system a alone, in its own proper Hilbert space, one must therefore conclude that the measurement has converted its originally pure state into a mixture. It may be shown that the now reducible probabilities ω_i, which appear in this mixture, are the squares of the probability amplitudes of ψ_a in the orthonormal set which forms the eigenstates of G. After the measurement, and because the mixture contains reducible probabilities, one can by physical operations select from an ensemble of systems those which are in any one of the states $\psi_a^{(1)}$, $\psi_a^{(2)}$, etc.

We shall now show that the Pauli principle "fuses" the states of atom a and atom b in the same way in which a measurement fuses the states of system and apparatus.

IV. Pauli Principle and Measurement

Combining the considerations of Sections II and III, we treat atom a as the system whose energy is to be measured, atom b as the interacting probe. To the operator $G(1)$ there corresponds $H_a(1)$, and the exclusion principle requires that we write $\psi(1, 2) = [a(1)b(2) - b(1)a(2)]/[2(1 - \delta^2)]^{1/2}$. In the limit, as $R \to \infty$, δ vanishes while a and b become orthogonal. Hence, in the notation of Eq. (28), we are dealing with two orthogonal functions,

$$u_1 = a, \qquad u_2 = b$$

and the set v is identical with set u, $v_1 = a$, $v_2 = b$. The matrix of coefficients is

$$(c) = \begin{pmatrix} 0 & \sqrt{\tfrac{1}{2}} \\ -\sqrt{\tfrac{1}{2}} & 0 \end{pmatrix}. \tag{30a}$$

Calculation of $\bar{H}_a$ leads to the result analogous to (29), and ρ_{ij} is given by (30):

$$(\rho) = \begin{pmatrix} \tfrac{1}{2} & 0 \\ 0 & \tfrac{1}{2} \end{pmatrix}. \tag{31}$$

The square of ρ is not ρ but $\rho/2$; hence we are dealing with a mixture involving reducible probabilities. The expectation value $\bar{H}_a$ does not display maximum knowledge. It says: *if* you do not know (although you could!) whether an electron is attached to nucleus a or b, the mean value of its energy is given by Eq. (23). This result is not astounding; it brings together some stray bits of knowledge but it also stimulates reflections of a rather basic sort and leads to such conclusions as the following.

First, we note once more that $\bar{H}_a$ is not an ordinary quantum expectation value, for it involves *removable* ignorance. If sufficient knowledge is available our calculation of $\bar{H}_a$ is incorrect, for it must then be computed in defiance of the exclusion principle, with the function $a(1)b(2)$ alone, for which ρ is an elementary matrix. One way of obtaining this knowledge is to subject atom a to a set of measurements (e.g., of its position relative to b, or of its energy) which give assurance of its isolation.

This, in turn, suggests the heretic thought that Pauli's principle does not have the universal validity with which it is usually endowed, for it can be breached by the selective procedures just cited. It imparts a measure of ignorance which can in principle be eliminated so far as a single system is concerned.

For infinitely separated, i.e., noninteracting, systems this claim is true. But suppose the systems interact dynamically. It is then no longer possible to measure position or energy of a alone. And if, by way of a hypothetical initial condition contradicting this fact, we were informed that at a time t_0 electron 1 was certainly attached to a, the presence of a finite V in the time-dependent Schrödinger equation would cause the fluctuations known to chemists as resonance; the initial function $a(1)b(2)$ would soon transform itself into a fused function of the form (28) with coefficients periodic in time and forever unable to satisfy the Pauli principle, representing forever a nonstationary state. This, however, is not an indictment of the principle; it merely bespeaks an internal contradiction: to claim that the initial state is $a(1)b(2)$ implies a sharp energy, $E_a + E_b$, of the total system, yet the calculation winds up with a nonstationary state, in which the energy is not sharp. Resonance can therefore not be interpreted as a periodic fluctuation between states which violate the exclusion principle. The only states of the combined system which are observed in nature are those which satisfy it.

Every observable defined for the *total* system, atoms a and b, yields expectation values with *maximal* information. A proper observable of this kind is necessarily symmetric with respect to an interatomic exchange of electrons. With respect to such an operator, say $G(1, 2) = G(2, 1)$, the basis functions are $U_1 = a(1)b(2)$ and $U_2 = b(1)a(2)$; they are orthogonal in the space $(1, 2)$. Hence, as $R \to \infty$, $\psi(1, 2) = \sqrt{\frac{1}{2}}(U_1 - U_2)$,

$$G(1, 2) = \mathrm{Tr}(\rho \tilde{G}), \quad \text{with} \quad \rho = \begin{pmatrix} \frac{1}{2} & -\frac{1}{2} \\ -\frac{1}{2} & \frac{1}{2} \end{pmatrix},$$

and this matrix satisfies $\rho^2 = \rho$.

The potential energy V considered in Section 2 is not a proper operator of this kind. It has a symmetric part, $V_s = R^{-1} + r_{12}^{-1}$, and $\bar{V}_s$ vanishes for infinite R. The remainder, according to Eq. (22), is of the form $V_a(1) + V_b(2)$. Its expectation value is

$$\bar{V} = \mathrm{Tr}[\rho(V_a + V_b)],$$

and ρ is again given by Eq. (31). Hence $\bar{V}$ is not a pure-case expectation value; what was said about $\bar{H}_a$ (and is true for $\bar{H}_b$) holds here as well.

If the distinction made in this article is ignored, the presence of nonvanishing terms in $\bar{V}$, $\bar{H}_a$, and $\bar{H}_b$ in the limit of infinite separation must be interpreted as a physical influence between distant systems, which precludes the possibility of isolation. We have shown that these finite interactions are not physical at all but reflect subjective matters, removable ignorance.

There remain, however, some fundamental questions regarding the exclusion principle. Evidently, physical operations can break its hold upon the states of infinitely separated systems. The union it provides between them is like that produced by a measurement, which imparts "knowledge" of system a to system b. In still cruder language, the operator $\mathscr{A}^{ab}$ when applied to a set of isolated orbitals seems to be an affidavit certifying that the occupants of these orbitals have "met" at some time in the past. And if all identical constituents in the universe require their states to be antisymmetrized, the implication of their having been in dynamic contact in the past is strong indeed.

In this article we have dealt only with fermions. It is clear that symmetrization has similar effects upon the statistical matrices as the action of $\mathscr{A}^{ab}$. Hence bosons are included in our analysis.

REFERENCES

1. J. E. Hirschfelder, C. F. Curtis, and R. B. Bird, "Molecular Theory of Gases and Liquids." Wiley, New York, 1954.

2. K. S. Pitzer, *Advan. Chem. Phys.* **2**, 59 (1959).

3. H. Margenau, *Rev. Mod. Phys.* **11**, 1 (1939).
4. J. von Neumann, "Mathematical Foundations of the Quantum Theory" (Transl. by E. Beyer). Princeton Univ. Press, Princeton, New Jersey, 1955.
5. H. Margenau, *Phil. Sci.* **30**, 1, 138 (1963).
6. F. London and E. Bauer, "La Théorie de l'Observation en Mecanique Quantique." Hermann, Paris, 1939. See also Ref. 5.

The Equations of the Free Motion of an
Isotropic Spinning Particle

L. H. THOMAS

IBM WATSON LABORATORY
COLUMBIA UNIVERSITY, NEW YORK

I. The Newtonian Dynamics in Hamiltonian Form

The motion of a free isotropic rigid body can be expressed in terms of the three coordinates q_x, q_y, q_z, of its center of mass, canonically conjugate components of momentum p_x, p_y, p_z, and components of angular momentum about its center of mass ω_x, ω_y, ω_z. These dynamical variables have Poisson brackets $(q_x, p_x) = 1$, $(q_y, p_y) = 1$, $(q_z, p_z) = 1$, $(\omega_y, \omega_z) = \omega_x$, $(\omega_z, \omega_x) = \omega_y$, $(\omega_x, \omega_y) = \omega_z$, the remaining Poisson brackets vanishing.

We may take as Hamiltonian functions to give displacements in position, orientation, velocity, and time, the usual components of linear momentum, angular momentum, mass times the coordinates of the center of mass, and energy, m being the mass:

$$X = p_x, \qquad L = q_y p_z - q_z p_y + \omega_x, \qquad U = mq_x$$

$$Y = p_y, \qquad M = q_z p_x - q_x p_z + \omega_y, \qquad V = mq_y, \qquad \mathscr{H} = \frac{1}{2m}(p_x^2 + p_y^2 + p_z^2).$$

$$Z = p_z, \qquad N = q_x p_y - q_y p_x + \omega_z, \qquad W = mq_z$$

That the Poisson brackets of these functions are linear combinations of the functions themselves, in general inhomogeneous, with constant coefficients, are the conditions that the corresponding equations of motion admit a group with these coefficients as structure constants. In this case we have the structure of the Newtonian group.

93

II. The Hamiltonians for Special Relativity

In order to admit the inhomogeneous Lorentz group rather than the Newtonian group, some Poisson brackets that vanished for the Newtonian group must no longer do so; we must have

$$(U, X) = \frac{1}{c^2} \mathcal{H}, \qquad (V, W) = -\frac{1}{c^2} L,$$

$$(V, Y) = \frac{1}{c^2} \mathcal{H}, \qquad (W, U) = -\frac{1}{c^2} M,$$

$$(W, Z) = \frac{1}{c^2} \mathcal{H}, \qquad (U, V) = -\frac{1}{c^2} N.$$

where c is the speed of light.

These can all be satisfied if we generalize U, V, W, and $\mathcal{H}$, and, with the other Poisson brackets, give partial differential equations to determine these. We find that we can take the usual form for $\mathcal{H}$ as for a point particle

$$\mathcal{H} = (m^2 c^4 + (p_x^2 + p_y^2 + p_z^2)c^2)^{1/2}$$

and then U, V, and W, which must form a vector, are found to be

$$U = \frac{1}{c^2} q_x \mathcal{H} - \frac{\omega_y p_z - \omega_z p_y}{mc^2 + \mathcal{H}}$$

$$V = \frac{1}{c^2} q_y \mathcal{H} - \frac{\omega_z p_x - \omega_x p_z}{mc^2 + \mathcal{H}}$$

$$W = \frac{1}{c^2} q_z \mathcal{H} - \frac{\omega_x p_y - \omega_y p_x}{mc^2 + \mathcal{H}}$$

III. The Hamiltonians for the Dirac Electron

The usual Hamiltonian for the Dirac electron may be written

$$\mathcal{H} = -mc^2 \rho_3 - c\rho_1(\sigma_x p_x + \sigma_y p_y + \sigma_z p_z)$$

where ρ_1, ρ_2, ρ_3 and σ_x, σ_y, σ_z are two independent sets of Pauli matrixes satisfying $\rho_1 \rho_2 = -\rho_2 \rho_1 = \imath \rho_3$, $\rho_2 \rho_3 = -\rho_3 \rho_2 = \imath \rho_1$, $\rho_3 \rho_1 = -\rho_1 \rho_3 = \imath \rho_2$, $\rho_1^2 = 1$, $\rho_2^2 = 1$, $\rho_3^2 = 1$, and the like, and p_x, p_y, p_z and q_x, q_y, q_z are operators such that $p_x q_x - q_x p_x = -\imath \hbar$, $p_y q_y - q_y p_y = -\imath \hbar$, $p_z q_z - q_z p_z = -\imath \hbar$, the remaining commutators vanishing.

If we now take

$$X = p_x, \qquad L = q_y p_z - q_z p_y + \tfrac{1}{2}\hbar\sigma_x, \qquad U = (q_x \mathcal{H} + \mathcal{H} q_x)/2c^2,$$
$$Y = p_y, \qquad M = q_z p_x - q_x p_z + \tfrac{1}{2}\hbar\sigma_y, \qquad V = (q_y \mathcal{H} + \mathcal{H} q_y)/2c^2,$$
$$Z = p_z, \qquad N = q_x p_y - q_y p_x + \tfrac{1}{2}\hbar\sigma_z, \qquad W = (q_z \mathcal{H} + \mathcal{H} q_z)/2c^2,$$

the commutators of these functions of operators give us back the structure of the inhomogeneous Lorentz group and show that the Dirac electron admits this group.

IV. The Foldy-Wouthuysen Transformation

We can make a unitary transformation of the dynamical variables which does not change p_x, p_y, and p_z, but reduces $\mathcal{H}$ to depending only on these and the new ρ_3', namely,

$$f' = \left\{ \frac{mc^2 + E - \iota c \rho_2 (\sigma_x p_x + \sigma_y p_y + \sigma_z p_z)}{\{2E(mc^2 + E)\}^{1/2}} \right\}$$
$$f \left\{ \frac{mc^2 + E + \iota c \rho_2 (\sigma_x p_x + \sigma_y p_y + \sigma_z p_z)}{\{2E(mc^2 + E)\}^{1/2}} \right\},$$

where $E = +\{m^2 c^4 + (p_x^2 + p_y^2 + p_z^2)c^2\}^{1/2}$.

This gives

$$p_x' = p_x \text{ etc.},$$
$$\rho_1' = \rho_1 \frac{mc^2}{E} - c\rho_3 \frac{(\sigma_x p_x + \sigma_y p_y + \sigma_z p_z)}{E},$$
$$\rho_2' = \rho_2,$$
$$\rho_3' = \rho_3 \frac{mc^2}{E} + c\rho_1 \frac{(\sigma_x p_x + \sigma_y p_y + \sigma_z p_z)}{E},$$
$$\sigma_x' = \sigma_x \frac{mc^2}{E} + \frac{c^2 p_x (\sigma_x p_x + \sigma_y p_y + \sigma_z p_z)}{E(mc^2 + E)} - \frac{c\rho_2 (p_y \sigma_z - p_z \sigma_y)}{E} \text{ etc.},$$
$$q_x' = q_x + \hbar \frac{c^2 (p_y \sigma_z - p_z \sigma_y)}{2E(mc^2 + E)} - \hbar c\rho_2 \frac{\sigma_x}{2E} + \hbar \frac{c^2}{E} \rho_2 \frac{p_x (\sigma_x p_x + \sigma_y p_y + \sigma_z p_z)}{2E(mc^2 + E)} \text{ etc.}$$

Thus

$$\mathcal{H} = -E' \rho_3'$$

while

$$X = p_x' \text{ etc.},$$
$$L = q_y' p_z' - q_z' p_y' + \tfrac{1}{2}\hbar\sigma_x' \text{ etc.},$$

and

$$V = -\rho_3' \left\{ \frac{1}{2c^2} (q_x' E' + E' q_x') - \frac{1}{2}\hbar \frac{(\sigma_y' p_z' - \sigma_z' p_y')}{(E + mc^2)} \right\} \text{ etc.},$$

where $E' = E$, and the commutators of the new variables must have the same values as those of the old.

V. Comparison of the Classical and Quantum-Mechanical Equations

If we use Dirac's rule for the correspondence of a classical Poisson bracket to a quantum-mechanical commutator

$$(A,\ B) = \{AB - BA\}/\imath\hbar$$

and write

$$\omega_x = \tfrac{1}{2}\hbar\sigma_x'$$
$$\omega_y = \tfrac{1}{2}\hbar\sigma_y'$$
$$\omega_z = \tfrac{1}{2}\hbar\sigma_z'$$

we find that the transformed quantum dynamical variables have the same Poisson brackets as the classical, while the Hamiltonian functions have the same form, except for the factor $-\rho_3'$ in $\mathscr{H}$, U, V, and W.

Since ρ_1' and ρ_2' do not occur explicitly, we have two unconnected sets of equations for the two characteristic values -1 and $+1$ of ρ_3', the first going in the classical limit to the classical equations, the second to the classical equations with the sign of m changed.

Conversely if we take two sets of classical equations for the opposite signs of m and quantise each by Dirac's rule, the Foldy-Wouthuysen transformation will transform the result into the equations for the free Dirac electron.

REFERENCES

Bakamjian, B., and Thomas, L. H. (1953). *Phys. Rev.* **92**, 1300.
Foldy, L. L., and Wouthuysen, S. A. (1950). *Phys. Rev.* **78**, 29.
Schild, A., and Schlosser, F. A. (1965). *J. Math. Phys.* **6**, 1299; contains a considerable bibliography.

Note on the Saddle-Point Character of Hartree and Hartree-Fock Wave Functions

C. A. COULSON

MATHEMATICAL INSTITUTE, OXFORD, ENGLAND

The Hartree and Hartree-Fock (HF) wave functions for an atom or a molecule are usually derived by a variational procedure. This shows that the associated energy is stationary with respect to the permitted variation of the individual orbitals. But it does not show whether, or to what extent, this energy is an absolute minimum. A rather general discussion of this topic, under the heading "Stability of Hartree-Fock States" has been written by Adams (1962). It may be interesting, however, to discuss one particular case in a little more detail, since this can bring out points not so easily noticed in the more general discussion. The purpose of this note is to provide such an account for the ground-state ^1S of atomic helium.

In general, as Hylleraas pointed out many years ago the best orbital description of this state is the open-shell function

$$\psi = u(1)v(2) + v(1)u(2) \tag{1}$$

in which u and v are the $1s$ and $1s'$ atomic orbitals, and we have omitted the spin factor as irrelevant to our discussion. However, the traditional Hartree function is the closed-shell expression

$$\psi = \phi(1)\phi(2) \tag{2}$$

Since (2) is a particular case of (1), in which $u = v = \phi$, it follows that the HF open-shell energy of (1) must be lower than the Hartree energy of (2). But this, by itself, does not decide whether in (2) we are dealing with a local minimum of the energy, or with a saddle-point. It is true that simple calculations using approximate expressions for u, v, and ϕ lead us to expect a saddle-point. The Hylleraas-Eckart wave functions (1930, 1932) put, in atomic units,

$$u = e^{-\alpha r}, \qquad v = e^{-\beta r}, \tag{3}$$

and the Kellner (1927) wave function puts

$$\phi = e^{-\gamma r} \tag{4}$$

In (3) we obtain the energy E as a function $E(\alpha, \beta)$ of the variable parameters α, β; and in (4) we obtain E in the form $E(\gamma)$. Since if $\alpha = \beta = \gamma$ (3) and (1) reduce to (4) and (2), it follows that

$$E(\gamma) = E(\gamma, \gamma).$$

It has been shown by several authors (see, e.g., Silverman *et al.*, 1960; Hurst *et al.*, 1958; Shull and Löwdin, 1956; Scherr and Silverman, 1960) that the absolute minimum of $E(\alpha, \beta)$ in the $\alpha\beta$-plane occurs at $\alpha = 1.1875$, $\beta = 2.1832$, and at the equivalent point with α and β interchanged. Contours of constant $E(\alpha, \beta)$ are symmetrical with respect to the line $\alpha = \beta$, and along this line the minimum occurs at the Hartree-type function $\alpha = \beta \, (= \gamma) = 1.6875$. The general shape of the $E(\alpha, \beta)$-contours in Fig. 1 shows that the Hartree-like energy is indeed a saddle-point. A considerable variety of changes may be made in α and β, leading to a lowering of the energy, if we relax the condition $u = v$.

This situation refers to the approximate wave functions of types (3) and (4). But it can be shown that much the same situation holds for the full

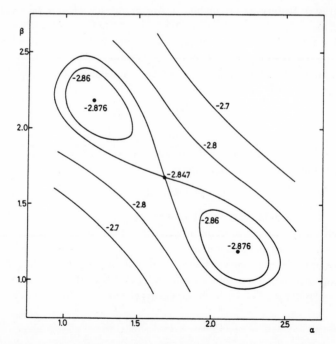

FIG. 1.   Energy contours for the $(1s)(1s')^1 S$ wave function of helium, using Slater-orbitals with exponents α and β. (The author would like to thank Dr. M. D. Poole for his help in making the calculations embodied in this diagram.)

solutions of the Hartree and HF open-shell equations. Let us write for the total Hamiltonian

$$\mathbf{H} = H(1) + H(2) + 1/r_{12} \tag{5}$$

where

$$H(1) = -\frac{1}{2}\nabla_1^2 - \frac{2}{r_1}, \tag{6}$$

and let us suppose that in the wave function $\psi = u(1)v(2) + v(1)u(2)$ the atomic orbitals u and v are normalized (and real). Then if E_ψ is the energy associated with ψ,

$$E_\psi = \langle\psi|\mathbf{H}|\psi\rangle/\langle\psi|\psi\rangle \tag{7}$$

where

$$\langle\psi|\psi\rangle = 2 + 2\langle u|v\rangle^2 \tag{8}$$

$$\langle\psi|\mathbf{H}|\psi\rangle = 2\langle u|H|u\rangle + 2\langle v|H|v\rangle + 4\langle u|v\rangle\langle u|H|v\rangle$$

$$+ 2\left\langle uv\left|\frac{1}{r_{12}}\right|uv\right\rangle + 2\left\langle uv\left|\frac{1}{r_{12}}\right|vu\right\rangle. \tag{9}$$

E_ψ may now be regarded as a functional of the atomic orbitals u and v in Hilbert space. Let us start from some assumed u, v and make changes

$$u \to u + \Delta u, \qquad v \to v + \Delta v \tag{10}$$

where, to preserve normalization, $\langle u|\Delta u\rangle = 0 = \langle v|\Delta v\rangle$ to first-order in Δu, Δv. Then

$$\Delta E_\psi = \frac{\langle\psi + \Delta\psi|\mathbf{H}|\psi + \Delta\psi\rangle}{\langle\psi + \Delta\psi|\psi + \Delta\psi\rangle} - \frac{\langle\psi|\mathbf{H}|\psi\rangle}{\langle\psi|\psi\rangle}.$$

It follows that ΔE_ψ has the same sign as

$$\langle\psi|\psi\rangle\{2\langle\Delta\psi|\mathbf{H}|\psi\rangle + \langle\Delta\psi|\mathbf{H}|\Delta\psi\rangle\} - \langle\psi|\mathbf{H}|\psi\rangle\{2\langle\Delta\psi|\psi\rangle + \langle\Delta\psi|\Delta\psi\rangle\}. \tag{11}$$

As we shall see, we may not discard terms of the second degree in $\Delta\psi$. Using (11) and (7) it follows that ΔE_ψ has the same sign as

$$2\langle\Delta\psi|\mathbf{H} - E_\psi|\psi\rangle + \langle\Delta\psi|\mathbf{H} - E_\psi|\Delta\psi\rangle. \tag{12}$$

If we start from the equilibrium $(1s)(1s')$ situation, the first term in (12) will be zero; and the second term is then necessarily positive. But we do not wish to start there. Rather let us start from the equilibrium Hartree solution

$u = v = \phi$, and consider in a little more detail the two separate terms in (12). We are now putting (to first order)

$$\psi = 2u(1)u(2)$$

$$\Delta\psi = u(1)\Delta v(2) + v(1)\Delta u(2) + \Delta v(1)u(2) + \Delta u(1)v(2) \qquad (13)$$

$$u = v = \phi.$$

It soon follows that in (12) the terms of the first degree in Δu, Δv give

$$8\langle\phi(1)\Delta v(2)|\mathbf{H} - E_\psi|\phi(1)\phi(2)\rangle + 8\langle\phi(1)\Delta u(2)|\mathbf{H} - E_\psi|\phi(1)\phi(2)\rangle. \qquad (14)$$

Now ϕ is a function which minimizes the expression

$$\frac{\langle\phi\phi|\mathbf{H}|\phi\phi\rangle}{\langle\phi\phi\,|\,\phi\phi\rangle}$$

with respect to all changes $\Delta\phi$ that preserve the normalization condition

$$\langle\phi\,|\,\Delta\phi\rangle = 0.$$

This implies that

$$\langle\phi\Delta\phi|\mathbf{H}|\phi\phi\rangle = 0. \qquad (15)$$

In our case, as (10) and (13) show, we may use Δu or Δv as particular cases of $\Delta\phi$, since we are assuming throughout that u and v are separately normalized. Thus all terms of the first degree in Δu, Δv in (12) vanish for all admissible Δu, Δv.

This leads us to terms of the second degree in (12). Straightforward substitution shows that these may be written in the form

$$2\langle\phi, (\Delta u + \Delta v)|\mathbf{H} - E_\psi|\phi, (\Delta u + \Delta v)\rangle$$

$$+ 2\langle\phi, (\Delta u + \Delta v)|\mathbf{H} - E_\psi|(\Delta u + \Delta v), \phi\rangle$$

$$+ 8\langle\Delta u\Delta v|\mathbf{H} - E_\psi|\phi\phi\rangle \qquad (16)$$

This expression does not vanish in general. Furthermore, it may be shown to have opposite signs for at least two distinct choices of Δu, Δv. In the first place, if we restrict ourselves to $\Delta u = \Delta v$, then we are dealing with the Hartree closed-shell, and not the HF open-shell problem; and we know that, for this, ΔE_ψ must be positive. In the second place, if we consider choices such that $\Delta u = -\Delta v$, the first two terms of (16) vanish identically and (see below) the third term is negative. This implies that, if we start from the Hartree solution, there are certain changes in the atomic orbitals u and v which increase the energy, and others that decrease it. The Hartree energy must therefore be a saddle-point.

We could put this pictorially in terms of Hilbert space as follows. The atomic orbitals u and v could each be represented by some point in Hilbert space. On account of the normalization condition these points lie on the surface of a sphere of unit radius. In the Hartree solution both orbitals u and v are represented (Fig. 2) by the same point P. Allowed small variations that preserve the normalization of u and v correspond to small displacements of the representative point in some arbitrary directions lying in the tangent plane to this sphere. Our conclusion is that if both representative points move together from P, the energy will increase, whatever this direction may be, provided of course that it lies in the tangent plane. But if the two representative points move in diametrically opposite directions, the energy will decrease, whatever these directions may be.

The two changes in u and v just described may be regarded as the extreme possibilities. Around each of them there must be a range of directions in the tangent plane of Fig. 2 for which the change in energy is of the same sign as for the extreme directions. There is a very close correspondence between this very general situation and the more restricted one represented in Fig. 1. For now points P in Hilbert space become points $(\alpha\beta)$ in the plane of Fig. 1. But if we start from the Hartree point $\alpha = \beta \, (= \gamma)$, then any changes for which $\Delta\alpha = \Delta\beta$ lead to an increase in energy; and any changes for which $\Delta\alpha = -\Delta\beta$ lead to a decrease; and both extremes are surrounded by a range of other $(\Delta\alpha, \Delta\beta)$ with positive, or with negative, ΔE.

To complete the proof we have still to show that if $\Delta u = -\Delta v$, the last term in Eq. (16) is negative. We have to prove that

$$\langle \Delta u \, \Delta u | \mathbf{H} - E_\psi | \phi\phi \rangle$$

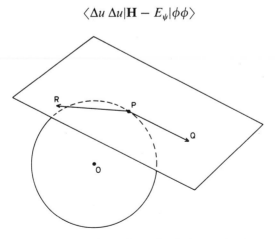

FIG. 2. Hilbert-space representation of permitted changes in the atomic orbitals u and v. P denotes the Hartree orbital γ, and PQ denotes Δu, PR denotes Δv. Δu and Δv lie in the tangent plane at P to the unit sphere.

is positive. On account of the orthogonality of Δu and ϕ, this means, from Eqs. (5) and (6), that

$$\left\langle \Delta u\, \Delta u \left| \frac{1}{r_{12}} \right| \phi\phi \right\rangle \equiv \int \Delta u(1)\phi(1) \frac{1}{r_{12}} \Delta u(2)\phi(2)\, d\tau_1\, d\tau_2 \qquad (17)$$

is to be positive. Put $\rho(1) = \Delta u(1)\phi(1)$, and put V for the solution (tending to zero at infinity) of the Poisson equation $\nabla^2 V = -4\pi\rho$, so that

$$V(1) = \int \frac{\rho(2)\, d\tau_2}{r_{12}}. \qquad (18)$$

The integral may now be written in the form

$$\int \rho(1) \frac{1}{r_{12}} \rho(2)\, d\tau_1\, d\tau_2 = \int \rho(1) V(1)\, d\tau_1$$

$$= -\frac{1}{4\pi} \int V \nabla^2 V\, d\tau. \qquad (19)$$

There are no singularities in V, so that by Green's theorem this becomes

$$-\frac{1}{4\pi} \int V\, \text{grad}\, V \cdot d\mathbf{S} + \frac{1}{4\pi} \int (\text{grad}\, V)^2\, d\tau \qquad (20)$$

where the surface integral, which is taken over the sphere at infinity, must vanish from a consideration of orders of magnitude. The new volume integral is necessarily positive, and our theorem is proved.

A few brief comments may be added:

(1) If we start from the Hartree solution $u = v = \phi$, and then consider the small changes $\Delta u = -\Delta v\ (=\Delta\phi$ say), it soon follows that

$$\psi(1, 2) = \{\phi(1)\phi(2) - \Delta\phi(1)\Delta\phi(2)\} \times \text{normalizing factor}.$$

Thus, this particular first-order variation in u and v leads to a second-order change in ψ. We could, in fact, have built up our argument from this situation, in a similar fashion to that used by Adams (1962).

(2) In the same way the one-particle density matrix becomes

$$\rho(1; 1') = \{\phi(1)\phi(1') + \Delta\phi(1)\Delta\phi(1')S\}/\{1 + S^2\} \qquad (21)$$

where

$$S = \int \{\Delta\phi(1)\}^2\, d\tau_1.$$

(3) Similarly the two-particle density matrix has a diagonal term

$$\rho(1, 2; 1, 2) = \frac{\phi^2(1)\phi^2(2) - 2\phi(1)\Delta\phi(1)\phi(2)\Delta\phi(2) + \{\Delta\phi(1)\}^2\{\Delta\phi(2)\}^2}{1 + S^2}.$$

$$(22)$$

Thus both the density matrices are changed from their Hartree values by terms of the second order in $\Delta\phi$. But we no longer have the relation, typical of a single-determinant wave function:

$$\rho(1, 2; 1, 2) = \rho(1; 1)\rho(2; 2) - \rho(1; 2)^2. \tag{23}$$

(4) The argument given in this note is easily extended to other situations where a closed subshell is split open, as in passing from wave functions of type (2) to those of type (1).

Note added in proof: A more careful consideration of orders of magnitude shows that, although the conclusion of this paper is correct, the proof needs a little tightening up, insofar as the second-order terms are concerned. Thus, if we want the new orbital $u + \Delta u$ in (10) to be normalized, we may only put $\langle u|\Delta u \rangle = 0$ to first-order. This is clear from Fig. 2 in which the points Q and R lie on the unit sphere in Hilbert space, and therefore are only on the tangent plane at P to first-order. The result of this change is to replace Δu in the fundamental formula (17) by $\Delta u - k\phi$, where k is the overlap integral $\int \Delta u \cdot \phi \, d\tau$. This new formula is correct to second-order, and leads to the stated result.

REFERENCES

Adams, W. H. (1962). *Phys. Rev.* **127**, 1650.
Eckart, C. (1930). *Phys. Rev.* **36**, 878.
Hurst, R. P., Gray, J. D., Brigman, G. H., and Matsen, F. A. (1958). *Mol. Phys.* **1**, 189.
Hylleraas, E. A. (1932). *Skrifter Norske Videnskaps-Akad. Oslo I. Mat.-Naturv. Kl.* 5–141.
Kellner, G. W. (1927). *Z. Physik* **44**, 91, 110.
Scherr, C. W., and Silverman, J. N. (1960). *J. Chem. Phys.* **32**, 1407.
Shull, H., and Löwdin, P.-O. (1956). *J. Chem. Phys.* **25**, 1035.
Silverman, J. N., Platas, O., and Matsen, F. A. (1960)· *J. Chem. Phys.* **32**, 1402.

Second Quantization in the Electronic Theory of Molecules

H. C. LONGUET-HIGGINS

DEPARTMENT OF THEORETICAL CHEMISTRY, UNIVERSITY CHEMICAL LABORATORY
CAMBRIDGE, ENGLAND

I. Introduction

One of the most useful ideas in the quantum theory of atoms and molecules is that of the Slater determinant, which represents a many-electron wave function as a determinant of electronic spinorbitals. The exclusion principle is met by the antisymmetry of a determinant under an interchange of two rows; for a closed shell the singlet character is ensured by the rotational invariance of the form $(\alpha_1\beta_2 - \beta_1\alpha_2)$, where (α_1, β_1) and (α_2, β_2) are a pair of spinors.

It is the purpose of this article to advertise to molecular theorists the use of a closely related idea, that of second quantization. The methods of second quantization are universally applied nowadays to many-body problems, such as arise in the theory of metals or of nuclear matter; but so far they have found relatively little favor among theoretical chemists. There have been good reasons in the past for adopting elementary, rather than highbrow, methods for solving chemical problems; it is silly to use a steam hammer for cracking a nut. But theoretical chemistry is becoming more and more concerned with systems, such as large conjugated molecules or crystalline molecular complexes, in which the number of particles is infinite or indeterminate; and for such systems explicit wave functions are awkward to specify, and elementary methods become clumsy in the extreme. It is then that the methods of second quantization are especially useful; but the technique can also be applied with advantage to finite systems, as I shall try to show in the following paragraphs.

This article is shamelessly unoriginal; the main ideas in it were put forward and developed by Heisenberg, Jordan, and Dirac, in the early days of the quantum theory. But good ideas, like good wine, improve with age; and it is hoped that in his capacity as a distinguished teacher Professor John C. Slater will view with indulgence this attempt to guide the less erudite reader through the difficult initial stages of understanding creation and annihilation operators, and how to use them.

II. Creation and Annihilation Operators

Suppose that we are given a complete orthonormal set of spinorbitals for an electron, denoted by

$$\varphi_1, \varphi_2, \ldots \varphi_\nu, \ldots$$

Then if N electrons are present in the system, any pure state of the electrons can be expressed as a linear combination of Slater determinants, each having the form

$$(N!)^{-1/2} \begin{vmatrix} \varphi_1(1) & \varphi_2(1) & \cdots & \varphi_N(1) \\ \varphi_1(2) & \varphi_2(2) & \cdots & \varphi_N(2) \\ \vdots & & & \\ \varphi_1(N) & \varphi_2(N) & \cdots & \varphi_N(N) \end{vmatrix} = |\varphi_1\varphi_2 \cdots \varphi_N\rangle.$$

For each spinorbital φ_ν we proceed to define the *creation operator* φ_ν^+ by the equation

$$\varphi_\nu^+|\varphi_1\varphi_2 \cdots\rangle = |\varphi_\nu\varphi_1\varphi_2 \cdots\rangle.$$

In words, the creation operator φ_ν^+, applied to the $N \times N$ Slater determinant $|\varphi_1 \cdots \varphi_N\rangle$, converts it into the (normalized) Slater determinant $|\varphi_\nu\varphi_1 \cdots \varphi_N\rangle$, which has $N + 1$ rows and columns; except that if φ_ν occurs in the original determinant, the result is zero. Thus, for example,

$$\varphi_1^+|\varphi_2\rangle = |\varphi_1\varphi_2\rangle,$$
$$\varphi_1^+|\varphi_1\rangle = 0,$$
$$\varphi_2^+|\varphi_1\rangle = |\varphi_2\varphi_1\rangle = -|\varphi_1\varphi_2\rangle.$$

It is convenient to introduce the concept of a "vacuum state", denoted by the symbol $|\ \rangle$. Then any Slater determinant may be generated by applying a succession of creation operators to the vacuum state, as follows:

$$\varphi_1^+\varphi_2^+\varphi_3^+|\rangle = \varphi_1^+\varphi_2^+|\varphi_3\rangle = \varphi_1^+|\varphi_2\varphi_3\rangle = |\varphi_1\varphi_2\varphi_3\rangle.$$

The anticommutator of φ_μ^+ and φ_ν^+, defined as

$$\{\varphi_\mu^+, \varphi_\nu^+\} = \varphi_\mu^+\varphi_\nu^+ + \varphi_\nu^+\varphi_\mu^+,$$

is readily seen to be zero. For if it is applied to a Slater determinant in which either φ_μ or φ_ν appears, each term of the anticommutator produces zero; and if the Slater determinant includes neither φ_μ nor φ_ν, we obtain

$$\{\varphi_\mu^+, \varphi_\nu^+\}|\varphi_1\varphi_2\cdots\rangle = |\varphi_\mu\varphi_\nu\varphi_1\varphi_2\cdots\rangle + |\varphi_\nu\varphi_\mu\varphi_1\varphi_2\cdots\rangle$$

$$= 0.$$

The *annihilation operator* φ_ν^- is defined by the equation

$$\varphi_\nu^-|\varphi_\nu\varphi_1\varphi_2\cdots\rangle = |\varphi_1\varphi_2\cdots\rangle$$

with the supplementary statement that if φ_ν does not occur in the Slater determinant, then the application of φ_ν^- to the determinant gives zero. Thus, for example,

$$\varphi_1^-|\varphi_1\varphi_2\rangle = |\varphi_2\rangle$$

$$\varphi_2^-|\varphi_1\varphi_2\rangle = -\varphi_2^-|\varphi_2\varphi_1\rangle = -|\varphi_1\rangle$$

$$\varphi_1^-|\varphi_2\rangle = 0$$

$$\varphi_1^-|\varphi_1\rangle = |\ \rangle.$$

The anticommutator of φ_μ^- and φ_ν^+ also vanishes identically:

$$\{\varphi_\mu^-, \varphi_\nu^-\} = \varphi_\mu^-\varphi_\nu^- + \varphi_\nu^-\varphi_\mu^- = 0.$$

It may be verified without difficulty that if φ_ν^+ is a creation operator, and φ_ν^- is an annihilation operator referring to a different spinorbital, then the anticommutator of φ_μ^+ and φ_ν^- vanishes. For instance,

$$\{\varphi_1^+, \varphi_2^-\}|\varphi_1\varphi_2\rangle = -\varphi_1^+|\varphi_1\rangle + \varphi_2^- \cdot 0 = 0.$$

But if a creation and an annihilation operator refer to the same spinorbital, then their anticommutator equals unity. For example

$$\{\varphi_1^+, \varphi_1^-\}|\varphi_1\varphi_2\rangle = \varphi_1^+|\varphi_2\rangle + \varphi_1^- \cdot 0 = |\varphi_1\varphi_2\rangle.$$

In general, then,

$$\{\varphi_\mu^+, \varphi_\nu^-\} = \varphi_\mu^+\varphi_\nu^- + \varphi_\nu^-\varphi_\mu^+ = \delta_{\mu\nu}.$$

A Slater determinant in which φ_ν appears is an eigenfunction of $\varphi_\nu^+\varphi_\nu^-$ with eigenvalue 1. For example

$$\varphi_1^+\varphi_1^-|\varphi_1\varphi_2\rangle = \varphi_1^+|\varphi_2\rangle = |\varphi_1\varphi_2\rangle.$$

Similarly, a Slater determinant in which φ_ν does not appear is an eigenfunction of $\varphi_v^+ \varphi_v^-$ with eigenvalue 0. Accordingly we designate $\varphi_v^+ \varphi_v^-$ as the *population* of φ_v, represented by the symbol $\hat{n}_v$.

A matrix element of φ_v^+, or of φ_v^-, between two Slater determinants, may be interpreted in either of two ways. Thus $\langle \varphi_1 \varphi_2 | \varphi_1^+ | \varphi_2 \rangle$ may be thought of as the scalar product of $\langle \varphi_1 \varphi_2 |$ and $\varphi_1^+ | \varphi_2 \rangle$, or of $\langle \varphi_1 \varphi_2 | \varphi_1^+$ with $| \varphi_2 \rangle$. We obtain a consistent scheme if we define $\langle \varphi_1 \varphi_2 \ \cdots | \varphi_v^+$ as the complex conjugate of $\varphi_v^- | \varphi_1 \varphi_2 \cdots \rangle$, and define $\langle \varphi_1 \varphi_2 \cdots | \varphi_v^-$ as the complex conjugate of $\varphi_v^+ | \varphi_1 \varphi_2 \cdots \rangle$. Thus when φ_v^+ acts to the left, it removes φ_v from $\langle \varphi_v \varphi_1 \varphi_2 \cdots |$ (or gives zero if φ_v is absent to begin with); and when φ_v^- acts to the left it adds φ_v to the complex conjugate determinant $\langle \varphi_1 \varphi_2 \cdots |$ (or produces zero if φ_v is there already).

It is usual, in the literature, to write a pair of creation and annihilation operators as φ_v^+ and φ_v, to emphasize their complex conjugacy. In this article we shall adhere to the notation φ_v^+ and φ_v^-, in order to avoid confusion between the operators and the spinorbital φ_v to which they are related.

The effect of φ_v^+ and φ_v^- on any Slater determinant of the φ_v is thus uniquely defined. But these Slater determinants form a complete orthonormal set of wave functions for all possible numbers of electrons. We draw the important conclusion that the φ_v^+ and φ_v^- give a uniquely defined result when applied to any wave function whatever, and that products of these operators have *uniquely defined matrix elements* between all possible pairs of electronic wave functions.

III. One-Electron Operators

The particular usefulness of creation and annihilation operators is that any physical operator can be expressed in terms of them. Every physical operator is symmetric in the variables of all the electrons, and two types of operator are especially important in practical problems, namely one-electron and two-electron operators.

A one-electron operator is an operator of the form

$$\hat{F} = \sum_i \hat{f}_i,$$

where the sum is over all the electrons. Such an operator has the property that its matrix element between any two many-electron wave functions is the same as the matrix element of $\sum_{\mu v} \varphi_\mu^+ f_{\mu v} \varphi_v^-$ between the same two wave functions, where

$$f_{\mu v} = \int \varphi_\mu^*(i) \hat{f}_i \varphi_v(i) \, d\tau_i,$$

and we may therefore write the operator identity

$$\hat{F} = \sum_{\mu v} \varphi_\mu^+ f_{\mu v} \varphi_v^-.$$

We shall not give the proof of this identity—the reader may care to construct a proof for himself—but will present some applications of it.

A simple special case is that in which $\hat{f}_i = 1$, so that $\hat{F}$ is the operator representing the total number of electrons. Calling this operator $\hat{N}$ we obtain

$$\hat{N} = \sum_{\mu\nu} \varphi_\mu^+ \delta_{\mu\nu} \varphi_\nu^- = \sum_\nu \varphi_\nu^+ \varphi_\nu^- = \sum_\nu \hat{n}_\nu.$$

Thus any wave function for an N-electron system must be an eigenfunction of this operator with eigenvalue N.

The dipole moment of a neutral molecule is represented by the operator

$$\hat{M} = \sum_i e\hat{r}_i.$$

An alternative expression for $\hat{M}$ is therefore

$$\hat{M} = \sum_{\mu\nu} \varphi_\mu^+ er_{\mu\nu} \varphi_\nu^-, \qquad r_{\mu\nu} = \int \varphi_\mu^*(r)\hat{r}\varphi_\nu(r)\, dr,$$

where $r_{\mu\nu}$ is the transition moment associated with the spinorbitals φ_μ and φ_ν.

The potential energy of the electrons in the coulomb field of an atomic nucleus, and their kinetic energy, may likewise be expressed in terms of the φ_μ^+ and φ_ν^-:

$$\hat{V} = \sum_{\mu\nu} \varphi_\mu^+ v_{\mu\nu} \varphi_\nu^-, \qquad v_{\mu\nu} = -Ze^2 \int \varphi_\mu^*(r)(1/r)\varphi_\nu(r)\, dr,$$

$$\hat{T} = \sum_{\mu\nu} \varphi_\mu^+ t_{\mu\nu} \varphi_\nu^-, \qquad t_{\mu\nu} = -(\hbar^2/2m)\int \varphi_\mu^*(r)\nabla^2\varphi_\nu(r)\, dr.$$

Very often one will be interested in the expectation values of one-electron operators for a particular state of the system, such as its ground state. Using the symbol $\langle X \rangle$ to denote the expectation value of $\hat{X}$ in a particular state, we deduce that $\langle F \rangle$ must be the following linear combination of the expectation values of the operators $\varphi_\mu^+ \varphi_\nu^-$:

$$\langle F \rangle = \sum_{\mu\nu} f_{\mu\nu}\langle \varphi_\mu^+ \varphi_\nu^- \rangle = \sum_{\mu\nu} f_{\mu\nu}\gamma_{\nu\mu}.$$

Here the matrix

$$\gamma_{\nu\mu} = \langle \varphi_\mu^+ \varphi_\nu^- \rangle$$

is called the *one-particle density matrix*, or the *one-electron density matrix* in the representation defined by the φ_ν. The point of defining the expectation value of $\varphi_\mu^+ \varphi_\nu^-$ as $\gamma_{\nu\mu}$ rather than as $\gamma_{\mu\nu}$ is that one can then express the expectation value of any one-electron operator $\hat{F}$ in the form

$$\langle F \rangle = \operatorname{trace}(\hat{f}\gamma),$$

and this expression is conveniently invariant under an orthonormal transformation of the spinorbitals φ_ν.

To sum up this section, we have seen that it is possible to calculate the matrix elements of any one-electron operator if we can find the matrix elements of the products $\varphi_\mu^+ \varphi_\nu^-$. Further, the expectation value of any one-electron operator for any state (pure or mixed) is determined by the expectation values of the $\varphi_\mu^+ \varphi_\nu^-$, that is, by the elements of the one-particle density matrix, defined as

$$\gamma_{\mu\nu} = \langle \varphi_\nu^+ \varphi_\mu^- \rangle.$$

IV. Two-Electron Operators

A two-electron operator is an operator of the form

$$\hat{G} = \sum_{i<j} \hat{g}_{ij},$$

where the sum is over all pairs of electrons. A particularly important two-electron operator is the coulomb repulsion between the electrons in a molecule; another such operator is the interaction between their magnetic moments. In terms of creation and annihilation operators, $\hat{G}$ may be written

$$\hat{G} = \tfrac{1}{2} \sum_{\mu\nu\sigma\tau} \varphi_\mu^+ \varphi_\nu^+ g_{\mu\nu,\tau\sigma} \varphi_\sigma^- \varphi_\tau^-,$$

where

$$g_{\mu\nu,\tau\sigma} = \iint \varphi_\mu^*(i)\varphi_\nu^*(j)\hat{g}_{ij}\varphi_\tau(i)\varphi_\sigma(j)\, d\tau_i\, d\tau_j.$$

The expectation value of $\hat{G}$ for a particular state is thus

$$\langle G \rangle = \tfrac{1}{2} \sum_{\mu\nu\sigma\tau} g_{\mu\nu,\tau\sigma} \Gamma_{\tau\sigma,\mu\nu},$$

where

$$\Gamma_{\tau\sigma,\mu\nu} = \langle \varphi_\mu^+ \varphi_\nu^+ \varphi_\sigma^- \varphi_\tau^- \rangle$$

is called the two-particle density matrix for the state in question. The reader should note carefully the order of the subscripts in these expressions. In $\Gamma_{\tau\sigma,\mu\nu}$ the first two subscripts indicate which row, and the last two which column, the element refers to. An invariant expression for $\langle G \rangle$ is therefore

$$\langle G \rangle = \text{trace}\,(\hat{g}\Gamma).$$

Hence if we could determine the two-electron density matrix we could calculate the electron repulsion energy of a many-electron system in a given state. In practice, of course, this is usually impossible; but there is one kind of wave function for which $\Gamma_{\tau\sigma,\mu\nu}$ can be expressed in terms of $\gamma_{\mu\nu}$, which is a much easier thing to handle. This is any wave function which takes the form of a single determinant of spinorbitals, which need not be the φ_ν themselves but may be any orthonormal combinations of them. For such a wave function, and only for such a wave function, the following relations hold:

(a)
$$\Gamma_{\tau\sigma,\,\mu\nu} = \begin{vmatrix} \gamma_{\tau\mu} & \gamma_{\tau\nu} \\ \gamma_{\sigma\mu} & \gamma_{\sigma\nu} \end{vmatrix};$$

(b) the one-particle density matrix is idempotent, in the sense that

$$\sum_\kappa \gamma_{\mu\kappa}\gamma_{\kappa\nu} = \gamma_{\mu\nu}.$$

In the particular case that the spinorbitals of the single determinant are a selection from the set φ_ν, the one- and two-particle density matrices take the specially simple forms

$$\gamma_{\mu\nu} = \delta_{\mu\nu}n_\nu$$

and

$$\Gamma_{\tau\sigma,\,\mu\nu} = (\delta_{\tau\mu}\delta_{\sigma\nu} - \delta_{\tau\nu}\delta_{\sigma\mu})n_\mu n_\nu$$

where n_ν is unity if φ_ν appears in the determinant, and 0 if it does not. Accordingly, the energy of a many-electron system with a single determinant wave function is

$$\mathscr{E} = \sum_\nu n_\nu h_{\nu\nu} + \tfrac{1}{2} \sum_{\mu\nu} n_\mu n_\nu (g_{\mu\nu,\,\mu\nu} - g_{\mu\nu,\,\nu\mu}),$$

where $g_{\mu\nu,\,\mu\nu}$ is the coulomb integral and $g_{\mu\nu,\,\nu\mu}$ the exchange integral between φ_μ and φ_ν. The latter vanishes, of course, if φ_μ and φ_ν have opposite spins.

V. Molecular and Atomic Spinorbital Operators

The results quoted in the preceding paragraphs are valid whatever the nature of the complete orthonormal set of spinorbitals, φ_ν. But when discussing molecules one may find it convenient to work with creation and annihilation operators defined in terms of molecular orbitals. For example, if we are interested in the electronic spectrum of a molecule in a closed-shell ground state, a natural choice of spinorbitals will be the solutions of the Hartree-Fock equation for the ground state. Alternatively, one could adopt Löwdin's "natural spinorbitals" ψ_ν, which diagonalize the one-particle density matrix, in the sense that

$$\langle \psi_\mu^+ \psi_\nu^- \rangle = 0, \qquad \mu \neq \nu.$$

At any rate, molecular spinorbital operators are very handy when it comes to specifying an excited state or calculating matrix elements between the ground state and the low-lying excited states of a molecule. For example, if ψ_1, ψ_{-1} and ψ_2, ψ_{-2} are the highest occupied and lowest unoccupied molecular orbitals of benzene (taken in conjugate complex pairs with the natural phase convention) then the singlet B_{1u} state is, in molecular orbital theory,

$$\tfrac{1}{2}(\psi^+_{2\alpha}\psi^-_{-1\alpha} + \psi^+_{\beta2}\psi^-_{-1\beta} + \psi^+_{-2\alpha}\psi^-_{1\alpha} + \psi^+_{-2\beta}\psi^-_{1\beta})|N\rangle,$$

where $|N\rangle$ represents the singlet A_{1g} ground state. It would be difficult to find a more compact, but equally explicit, expression. Doubly excited states may likewise be expressed in the form

$$\psi^+_{\lambda}\psi^+_{\mu}\psi^-_{\nu}\psi^-_{\sigma}|N\rangle,$$

or as linear combinations of such expressions.

In actual applications of molecular orbital theory one expresses each molecular orbital as a linear combination of certain atomic orbitals:

$$\psi_\mu = \sum_\sigma a_{\mu\sigma}\chi_\sigma.$$

Conversely, the basis atomic orbitals may be expressed in terms of a sufficient set of molecular orbitals (which we assume to be orthonormal):

$$\chi_\sigma = \sum_\nu b_{\sigma\nu}\psi_\nu.$$

The overlap integral between χ_σ and χ_τ is thus

$$S_{\sigma\tau} = \sum_\sigma b^*_{\sigma\nu}b_{\tau\nu}.$$

Introducing the atomic spinorbital creation and annihilation operators χ^+_σ and χ^-_σ, defined by

$$\chi^-_\sigma = \sum_\nu b_{\sigma\nu}\psi^-_\sigma, \qquad \chi^+_\sigma = \sum_\nu b^*_{\sigma\nu}\psi^+_\nu,$$

we find that the anticommutator of χ^+ and χ^- is

$$\{\chi^+_\sigma, \chi^-_\tau\} = \sum_{\mu\nu} b^*_{\sigma\mu}b_{\tau\nu}\{\psi^+_\mu, \psi^-_\nu\} = S_{\sigma\tau}.$$

Atomic orbital overlap thus modifies the commutation relations between the associated creation and annihilation operators, and one must be careful to take this into account when working with a nonorthonormal basis set of spinorbitals.

There is, however, one kind of orbital theory in which one is not troubled by overlap, for the simple reason that one neglects it. A most successful theory of this sort is the PPP (Pariser-Parr-Pople) theory of planar conjugated hydrocarbons. Let us consider this theory for a moment and rehearse the argument which McLachlan used for establishing the pairing properties of alternant hydrocarbons.

The theory concentrates on the π electrons, which are supposed to move over a basis set of orthonormal spinorbitals φ_ν, two on each atom (one with spin up, the other with spin down). The effective Hamiltonian for the π electrons is, accordingly,

$$\mathscr{H} = \sum_{\mu\nu} \varphi_\mu^+ h_{\mu\nu} \varphi_\nu^- = \tfrac{1}{2} \sum_{\mu\nu\sigma\tau} \varphi_\mu^+ \varphi_\nu^+ g_{\mu\nu,\,\tau\sigma} \varphi_\sigma^- \psi_\tau^-$$

and this simplifies to

$$\mathscr{H} = \sum_{\mu\nu} \varphi_\mu^+ h_{\mu\nu} \varphi_\nu^- = \tfrac{1}{2} \sum_{\mu\nu} \varphi_\mu^+ \varphi_\nu^+ \gamma_{\mu\nu} \varphi_\nu^- \varphi_\mu^-$$

if one neglects all two-electron integrals except the coulomb integrals $g_{\mu\nu,\,\mu\nu} = \gamma_{\mu\nu}$. Given the one-electron integrals $h_{\mu\nu}$ and the two-electron integrals it is then a routine matter to find the eigenvalues and eingenstates of this Hamiltonian.

Now suppose that the system is alternant. Then one can divide the atoms into two sets, starred and unstarred, in such a way that the only nonvanishing one-electron elements $h_{\mu\nu}$ are (a) the diagonal elements and (b) off-diagonal elements connecting a spinorbital on a starred atom with one on an unstarred atom. Starting with the π-electron Hamiltonian in the form

$$\mathscr{H} = \sum_{\mu} \varphi_\mu^+ h_{\mu\mu} \varphi_\mu^- + \sum_{\mu \neq \nu} \varphi_\mu^+ h_{\mu\nu} \varphi_\nu^- + \tfrac{1}{2} \sum_{\mu\nu} \varphi_\mu^+ \varphi_\nu^+ \gamma_{\mu\nu} \varphi_\nu^- \varphi_\mu^-,$$

we then proceed to transform it by stages. First we reverse the sign of all the spinorbitals on the starred atoms, and write the new spinorbitals as χ_ν rather than φ_ν. This gives

$$\mathscr{H} = \sum_{\mu} \chi_\mu^+ h_{\mu\mu} \chi_\mu^- - \sum_{\mu \neq \nu} \chi_\mu^+ h_{\mu\nu} \chi_\nu^- + \tfrac{1}{2} \sum_{\mu\nu} \chi_\mu^+ \chi_\nu^+ \gamma_{\mu\nu} \chi_\nu^- \chi_\mu^-.$$

Next, we use the commutation relation $\{\chi_\mu^+, \chi_\nu^-\} = \delta_{\mu\nu}$ and rearrange the factors in each term, so that the creation operators appear on the right and the annihilation operators appear on the left. The result is

$$\mathscr{H} = \sum_{\mu} h_{\mu\mu}(1 - \chi_\mu^- \chi_\mu^+) + \sum_{\mu \neq \nu} \chi_\nu^- h_{\mu\nu} \chi_\mu^+$$
$$+ \tfrac{1}{2} \sum_{\mu\nu} \gamma_{\mu\nu}(1 - \chi_\mu^- \chi_\mu^+ - \chi_\nu^- \chi_\nu^+ + \chi_\nu^- \chi_\mu^- \chi_\mu^+ \chi_\nu^+).$$

Finally we relabel χ_ν^- as ω_ν^+ and χ_ν^+ as ω_ν^-, so that the new operators may be thought of as creating or annihilating holes in the spinorbitals χ_ν. Finally, then,

$$\mathscr{H} = \sum_{\mu} \omega_\mu^+ h_{\mu\mu} \omega_\mu^- + \sum_{\mu \neq \nu} \omega_\mu^+ h_{\nu\mu} \omega_\nu^- + \tfrac{1}{2} \sum_{\mu\nu} \omega_\mu^+ \omega_\nu^+ \gamma_{\mu\nu} \omega_\nu^- \omega_\mu^-$$
$$+ \sum_{\mu} (h_{\mu\mu} + \tfrac{1}{2} \sum_{\nu} \gamma_{\mu\nu})(1 - 2\omega_\mu^+ \omega_\mu^-).$$

In this expression for the Hamiltonian the first three terms on the right hand side have exactly the same form as the original Hamiltonian; the only difference is in the last term. In this term the factor $(h_{\mu\mu} + \tfrac{1}{2} \sum_\nu \gamma_{\mu\nu})$ is assumed in the PPP theory to have the constant value U for a carbon $2p\pi$ orbital, because $h_{\mu\mu}$ includes attractive contributions from the cores of neighbouring atoms, and these will be compensated by placing half an electron in each spinorbital on every neighbor. If N is the total number of π electrons and M the total (even) number of spinorbitals in the conjugated system, the last term in $\mathscr{H}$ may be written

$$U \sum_\mu [1 - 2(1 - n_\mu)] = U(2N - M) = 2UQ,$$

where $Q = N - \tfrac{1}{2}M$ is the electronic charge on the system. We conclude that apart from a harmless constant the Hamiltonian for an alternant hydrocarbon ion takes the same form whether it is expressed (a) in terms of the operators φ_ν^+, φ_ν^- or (b) in terms of the hole operators ω_ν^+, ω_ν^-, which insert or remove holes in $\pm \varphi_\nu$ (the sign depending on whether the atom is starred or not). It follows that corresponding positive and negative ions have their states in a 1:1 correspondence, differing in energy by $2UQ$.

This is only a bare outline of McLachlan's elegant proof of the pairing theorems; but as the results are so important, and as they show off second quantization at its best, the reader is strongly recommended to fill in the details for himself. The great virtue of the approach is that it shows the underlying connection between the Hamiltonian of a positive ion and that of the negative ion. Thus the pairing is maintained even if there is extensive configurational interaction; nowhere in the proof is it assumed that the ground state, or any other state, can be represented as a single determinant of molecular spinorbitals. Indeed, neither molecular orbitals nor density matrices are mentioned or implicitly invoked at any point in the argument.

Atomic spinorbital operators can be used for defining the population of an atomic orbital, and the bond order between two orbitals, even when the molecular wave function is not represented as a single determinant. For simplicity we shall neglect atomic orbital overlap. Let us associate the atomic spinorbital operators φ_ν^+ in pairs, to obtain two-component operators,

$$\varphi_r^+ = (\alpha_r^+, \beta_r^+), \qquad \varphi_r^- = \begin{pmatrix} \alpha_r^- \\ \beta_r^- \end{pmatrix},$$

where the first component puts an electron into the orbital φ_r with spin up, and the second puts an electron into the same orbital with spin down. The population of φ_r is then represented by the operator

$$n_r = \varphi_r^+ \varphi_r^- = \alpha_r^+ \alpha_r^- + \beta_r^+ \beta_r^- = n_r^\alpha + n_r^\beta$$

and its expectation value is

$$q_r = \langle \varphi_r^+ \cdot \varphi_r^- \rangle = \gamma_{rr}$$

where γ_{sr} is the "spinless" one-particle density matrix in the representation based on the orbitals φ_r.

The off-diagonal elements of γ_{sr} are also of interest, as may be seen by evaluating γ_{sr} for a single determinant of molecular spinorbitals. Writing a typical molecular orbital in the form

$$\psi_j = \sum c_{jr}\varphi_r$$

we find that

$$\gamma_{sr} = \langle \varphi_r^+ \cdot \varphi_s^- \rangle = \sum_{jk} c_{jr}^* c_{ks} \langle \psi_j^+ \cdot \psi_k^- \rangle = \sum_j n_j c_{jr}^* c_{js} = p_{rs},$$

which is the Coulson bond order between the atomic orbitals φ_r and φ_s. If γ_{sr} is complex, p_{rs} is its real part. So even when the state of a molecule is not represented by a single determinant, it seems natural to define the bond order between the orbitals φ_r and φ_s as the expectation value, for that state, of the operator $\varphi_r^+ \varphi_s^-$. It is, of course, difficult to make the concept of bond order fully objective, because the concept of an optimal basis set of atomic orbitals is fraught with difficulties; but at least the bond order between two orbitals can be defined for any state whatever, once the orbitals have been exactly specified.

VI. Spin Populations

In the preceding section we introduced for each atomic orbital a two-component creation operator (and a two-component annihilation operator) of the type

$$\varphi_r^+ = (\alpha_r^+, \beta_r^+), \qquad \varphi_r^- = \begin{pmatrix} \alpha_r^- \\ \beta_r^- \end{pmatrix}.$$

These operators may be used for defining in a simple manner the spin population in the atomic orbital φ_r. Since spin is a vector (more exactly, a pseudo-vector) with three components, the spin population of φ_r is also a vector. Its three components are as follows:

$$(\hat{\rho}_x)_r = \varphi_r^+ \cdot \sigma_x \cdot \varphi_r^-, \qquad (\hat{\rho}_y)_r = \varphi_r^+ \cdot \sigma_y \cdot \varphi_r^-, \qquad (\hat{\rho}_z)_r = \varphi_r^+ \cdot \sigma_z \cdot \varphi_r^-,$$

where σ_x, σ_y, and σ_z are the three spin matrices of Pauli. Thus the z component of the spin population of φ_r is

$$(\hat{\rho}_z)_r = (\alpha_r^+, \beta_r^+)\begin{pmatrix} 1 & 0 \\ 0 & -1 \end{pmatrix}\begin{pmatrix} \alpha_r^- \\ \beta_r^- \end{pmatrix} = \hat{n}_r^\alpha - \hat{n}_r^\beta$$

in line with the usual elementary definition.

VII. Local Creation and Annihilation Operators

We now turn to creation and annihilation operators which refer to points rather than orbitals of finite extent.

The local operators $\psi^+(r')$ and $\psi^-(r')$, where r' indicates a possible position *and spin orientation* for an electron, may be formally defined in terms of any complete set of spinorbitals φ_ν and their associated operators, as follows:

$$\psi^+(r') = \sum_\nu \varphi_\nu^*(r')\varphi_\nu^+,$$

$$\psi^-(r') = \sum_\nu \varphi_\nu(r')\varphi_\nu^-.$$

In these definitions $\varphi_\nu^*(r')$ is the complex conjugate of $\varphi_\nu(r')$, which is simply the value of φ_ν at r'.

The commutation relations between the ψ^+ and the ψ^- may be obtained directly from our earlier results:

$$\{\psi^+(r'), \psi^-(r'')\} = \sum_{\mu\nu} \varphi_\mu^*(r')\varphi_\nu(r''))\{\varphi_\mu^+, \varphi_\nu^-\}$$

$$= \sum_\nu \varphi_\nu^*(r')\varphi_\nu(r'') = \delta(r' - r''),$$

where $\delta(r' - r'')$ is the three-dimensional Dirac delta function, and

$$\{\psi^+(r'), \psi^+(r'')\} = 0 = \{\psi^-(r'), \psi^-(r'')\}.$$

(The reader should note that the result of applying $\psi^+(r')$ to the vacuum state $|\rangle$ is a non-normalizable entity; but this causes no trouble if the formalism is correctly handled.)

Having gained some experience with the spinorbital operators φ_ν^+ and φ_ν^- we can review more quickly the important relations between the operators $\psi^\pm(r')$ and other, physical, operators. First we establish the effects of $\psi^-(r')$ on a Slater determinant and of $\psi^+(r')$ on its complex conjugate.

$$\psi^-(r')|\varphi_1\rangle = \sum_\nu \varphi_\nu(r')\varphi_\nu^-|\varphi_1\rangle$$

$$= \varphi_1(r')|\rangle;$$

$$\psi^-(r')|\varphi_1\varphi_2\rangle = \sum_\nu \varphi_\nu(r')\varphi_\nu^-|\varphi_1\varphi_2\rangle$$

$$= \varphi_1(r')|\varphi_2\rangle - \varphi_2(r')|\varphi_1\rangle, \quad \text{etc.},$$

and likewise

$$\langle\varphi_1|\psi^+(r') = \langle|\varphi_1^*(r'),$$

$$\langle\varphi_1\varphi_2|\psi^+(r') = \langle\varphi_2|\varphi_1^*(r') - \langle\varphi_1|\varphi_2^*(r'), \quad \text{etc.},$$

so that, for example,

$$\langle \varphi_1 | \psi^+(r')\psi^-(r'') | \varphi_1 \rangle = \varphi_1^*(r')\varphi_1(r''),$$

$$\langle \varphi_1\varphi_2 | \psi^+(r')\psi^-(r'') | \varphi_1\varphi_2 \rangle = \varphi_1^*(r')\varphi_1(r'') + \varphi_2^*(r')\varphi_2(r''),$$

with corresponding results for larger determinants. The expectation value of $\psi^+(r')\psi^-(r'')$ will be recognized as the one-particle density matrix

$$\gamma(r''|r') = \langle \psi^+(r')\psi^-(r'') \rangle,$$

and the expectation value of $\psi^+(r_1')\psi^+(r_2')\psi^-(r_2'')\psi^-(r_1'')$ is found to be the two-particle density matrix

$$\Gamma(r_1''r_2''|r_1'r_2') = \langle \psi^+(r_1')\psi^+(r_2')\psi^-(r_2'')\psi^-(r_1'') \rangle.$$

As in the previous sections, we can express any one- or two-electron operator in terms of local creation and annihilation operators. Let us first consider some one-electron operators. The easiest way to discover their operator equivalents is to work with a single-electron system, namely an electron in the spinorbital $\varphi(r')$. The electron density at r' is then

$$\varphi^*(r')\varphi(r') = \langle | \psi^*(r')\psi(r') | \rangle$$
$$= \langle \varphi | \psi^+(r')\psi^-(r') | \varphi \rangle.$$

Thus the operator representing the electron density at r' is $\psi^+(r')\psi^-(r')$, and its expectation value is $\gamma(r'|r')$, the corresponding diagonal element of the one-particle density matrix.

Similarly, for the spinorbital φ the electronic dipole moment has the expectation value

$$\int dr' \varphi^*(r')er'\varphi(r') = \langle \varphi | \int \psi^+(r')er'\psi^-(r')dr' | \varphi \rangle;$$

we infer that the operator equivalent of the dipole moment of a many-electron system must be

$$\hat{M} = \int \psi^+(r')er'\psi^-(r')\,dr'.$$

Operators involving the momentum also come out in a very simple form. First, the kinetic energy. It expectation value for an electron in φ is

$$-\frac{\hbar^2}{2m}\int \varphi^*(r')\nabla^2\varphi(r')\,dr' = -\frac{\hbar^2}{2m}\left\langle \left| \left| \int \varphi^*(r')\nabla^2\varphi(r')\,dr' \right| \right| \right\rangle$$
$$= -\frac{\hbar^2}{2m}\left\langle \varphi \left| \int \psi^+(r')\nabla^2\psi^-(r')\,dr' \right| \varphi \right\rangle;$$

accordingly the electronic kinetic energy operator for an arbitrary number of electrons is

$$\hat{T} = -\frac{\hbar^2}{2m} \int \psi^+(r')\nabla^2\psi^-(r')\,dr' = \frac{1}{2m} \int \psi^+(r')p^2\psi^-(r')\,dr',$$

where $\hat{p}$ denotes the momentum operator. The momentum itself is

$$\hat{P} = \int \psi^+(r')\hat{p}\psi^-(r')\,dr'.$$

The current density at a point in the molecule can be expressed in a specially neat manner using creation and annihilation operators:

$$\hat{J}(r) = \frac{e}{m} [\psi^+(r^\alpha)\hat{p}\psi^-(r^\alpha) + \psi^+(r^\beta)\hat{p}\psi^-(r^\beta)].$$

The expectation values of one-electron operators can all be expressed in terms of the one-electron density matrix $\gamma(r''|r')$; this is well-known, but for completeness we give the expressions for $\langle M \rangle$ and $\langle T \rangle$:

$$\langle M \rangle = \int er'\gamma(r'|r')\,dr',$$

$$\langle T \rangle = -\frac{\hbar^2}{2m} \int \int [\nabla_{r'}^2\gamma(r'|r'')]\delta(r' - r'')\,dr'\,dr''.$$

The expression for $\langle T \rangle$ is rather ungainly, and the corresponding expression for $\langle J(r) \rangle$ is still more cumbersome. The density matrix symbolism thus begins to lose its attractiveness when one works in a coordinate-spin representation, as we are now doing.

Local creation and annihilation operators also lend themselves readily to the definition of spin-dependent quantities. Thus if r denotes a point (with no spin assigned to it), one may define two-component operators

$$\psi^+(r) = [\psi^+(r^\alpha), \psi^+(r^\beta)], \qquad \psi^-(r) = \begin{bmatrix} \psi^-(r^\alpha) \\ \psi^-(r^\beta) \end{bmatrix},$$

whose invariant scalar product

$$\psi^+(r)\cdot\psi^-(r) = \hat{n}(r^\alpha) + \hat{n}(r^\beta) = \hat{n}(r)$$

is an operator representing the total electron density at r. The spin density at the point r, which is a vector operator, has the three components

$$\tfrac{1}{2}\hbar[\psi^+(r)\sigma_x\psi^-(r), \psi^+(r)\sigma_y\psi^-(r), \psi^+(r)\sigma_z\psi^-(r)] = \tfrac{1}{2}\hbar\psi^+(r)\sigma\psi^-(r),.$$

where σ_x, σ_y and σ_z are the Pauli spin matrices. To show the economical advantages of this notation, let us write down the Fermi contact Hamiltonian for the interaction between a magnetic nucleus and the surrounding electrons.

It is simply

$$\frac{16\pi}{3} g\beta g_N\beta_N \sum_i \delta(r_i - r_N)\hat{\mathbf{S}}_i \cdot \hat{\mathbf{I}} = \frac{8\pi}{3} g\beta g_N\beta_N \, \psi^+(r_N)\sigma\psi^-(r_N).\mathbf{I},$$

where g's and β's have their usual meanings and r_N is the position of the nucleus of spin $\hat{\mathbf{I}}$. A sum over all the electrons has thus been replaced by a simple expression involving only one-particle creation and annihilation operators. In each expression, of course, the final dot indicates a scalar product of two three-dimensional vectors. Later we shall show how this symbolism may be used to establish the isotropy of the nuclear spin-spin coupling constants which are determined by high-resolution nuclear magnetic resonance.

Two-electron operators can also be expressed compactly in terms of the local operators $\psi^+(r')$ and $\psi^-(r')$. For example, the coulomb repulsion energy of all the electrons is represented by the operator

$$\hat{G} = \tfrac{1}{2} \int\int \psi^+(r_1')\psi^+(r_2') \frac{e^2}{|r_1' - r_2'|} \psi^-(r_2')\psi^-(r_1') \, dr_1' \, dr_2',$$

where each integration is over all space and both spin orientations. As always, the order of the factors is essential. Likewise, the dipolar interaction Hamiltonian between the magnetic moments of a group of electrons takes the form

$$\tfrac{1}{2}(g\beta)^2 \int\int dr_1 \, dr_2 \, \psi^+(r_1^\kappa)\psi^+(r_2^\lambda)\psi^-(r_2^\mu)\psi^-(r_1^\nu)$$

$$\times \frac{1}{4}\left[\frac{\sigma^{\kappa\nu}\cdot\sigma^{\lambda\mu}}{r_{12}^3} - \frac{3(\sigma^{\kappa\nu}\cdot r_{12})(\sigma^{\lambda\mu}\cdot r_{12})}{r_{12}^5} \right],$$

in which the Greek superscripts indicate alternative spin orientations, and we sum over them all.

Expectation values of two-electron operators may be expressed in terms of the two-particle density matrix $\Gamma(r_1''r_2''|r_1'r_2')$ defined above. The complete two-particle density matrix is, however, seldom of interest, since the most important two-particle expectation values depend only upon its diagonal elements.

VIII. An Application

To illustrate the use of local creation and annihilation operators in molecular problems, let us use them to demonstrate a result which has been established by more elementary methods, but less briefly. The result concerns the electron-mediated coupling between two nuclear spins in a closed-shell molecule; we shall demonstrate that the coupling tensor is isotropic.

The perturbation responsible for the coupling is $\mathcal{H}_1 + \mathcal{H}_2$, where $\mathcal{H}_1$ is the Fermi contact interaction at nucleus 1, namely

$$\mathcal{H}_1 = \tfrac{8}{3}\pi g \beta g_1 \beta_N \psi^+(r_1)\sigma\psi^-(r_1)\cdot I^{(1)}$$

and $\mathcal{H}_2$ is similarly defined. The coupling energy between the two nuclei is a second-order perturbation energy, having the value

$$I_l^{(1)} J_{lm} I_m^{(2)} = 2 \operatorname{Re}\left[\sum_{n>0} \langle 0|\mathcal{H}_1|n\rangle (E_0 - E_n)^{-1}\langle n|\mathcal{H}_2|0\rangle\right],$$

where the sum is over all the excited states, and the subscripts l and m indicate vector components in three-dimensional space. Using Greek superscripts to indicate the orientation of an electron spin, we may thus write the coupling constant as

$$J_{lm} = g_1 g_2 [(8\pi/3)\, g\beta\beta_N]^2$$
$$\times 2 \operatorname{Re} \sum_{n>0} \langle 0|\psi^+(r_1^\kappa)\sigma_l^{\kappa\lambda}\psi^-(r_1^\lambda)|n\rangle (E_0 - E_n)^{-1}\langle n|\psi^+(r_2^\mu)\sigma_m^{\mu\nu}\psi^-(r_2^\nu)|0\rangle,$$

where the summation convention has been adopted for repeated superscripts. We now observe that if any term in this sum is not to vanish there must be a relation between the four Greek superscripts. The first two operators alter the M_S value of the ground state from 0 to $\lambda - \kappa$ (we may think of these letters as having values $\pm\frac{1}{2}$), and the last two alter it to $\mu - \nu$. To connect the ground state with the same excited state (which we may take to be an eigenstate of S_z) the pairs of operators must either satisfy $\kappa = \nu$, $\lambda = \mu$ or $\kappa = \lambda$, $\mu = \nu$. Therefore

$$\operatorname{Re} \sum_{n>0} \langle 0|\psi^+(r_1^\kappa)\psi^-(r_1^\lambda)|n\rangle (E_0 - E_n)^{-1}\langle n|\psi^+(r_2^\mu)\psi^-(r_2^\nu)|0\rangle$$
$$= A\delta^{\kappa\nu}\delta^{\lambda\mu} + B\delta^{\kappa\lambda}\delta^{\mu\nu}.$$

The coupling constant therefore takes the form

$$J_{lm} = C\sigma_l^{\kappa\lambda}\sigma_m^{\mu\nu}(A\delta^{\kappa\nu}\delta^{\lambda\mu} + B\delta^{\kappa\lambda}\delta^{\mu\nu})$$
$$= C(A\sigma_l^{\kappa\lambda}\sigma_m^{\lambda\kappa} + B\sigma_l^{\kappa\kappa}\sigma_m^{\mu\mu}),$$

which may be written in the alternative form

$$J_{lm} = C(A \text{ trace } \sigma_l\sigma_m + B \text{ trace } \sigma_l \text{ trace } \sigma_m).$$

But the Pauli matrices have the property that

$$\text{trace } \sigma_l\sigma_m = \delta_{lm} \quad \text{and} \quad \text{trace } \sigma_l = 0.$$

It follows that the coupling tensor J_{lm} is a multiple of the unit tensor δ_{lm}, and hence that the electron-mediated interaction between the two nuclei is an isotropic interaction, which may be written in the simpler form

$$J I^{(1)}\cdot I^{(2)} \quad \text{with} \quad J = CA.$$

This is what we set out to prove.

IX. Concluding Remarks

The possible applications of second quantization methods in theoretical chemistry are multitudinous. As we have seen there is a close relation between creation and annihilation operators, on the one hand, and the density matrices which one would so like to be able to calculate; the latter are simply expectation values of combinations of the former. Thus the theory of second quantization includes the theory of density matrices as a special case; problems which can be solved by density matrix methods can also be solved by second quantization. The converse is not true, however, because second quantization deals with physical operators themselves, rather than their expectation values.

Already second quantization methods are being effectively applied to the motion of excitons and charge carriers in molecular crystals, and the forces between large "metallic" molecules. Creation and annihilation operators in molecular quantum mechanics are here to stay.

BIBLIOGRAPHY

1. W. Heisenberg, *Ann. Phys.* **10**, 888 (1931).

In this paper Heisenberg uses atomic spinorbital creation operators to prove the correspondence between the states of atoms with complementary numbers of electrons in an outer subshell, e.g., p^2 and p^4, or d^3 and d^7.

2. A. D. McLachlan, *Mol. Phys.* **4**, 49 (1961).

This is the paper in which the hole-particle duality was established for the ions R^{+q} and R^{-q}, where R is an alternant hydrocarbon, by the use of creation and annihilation operators for the carbon 2p orbitals, on the assumption of zero differential overlap.

3. R. McWeeny, *Rev. Mod. Phys.* **32**, 335 (1960).

A very useful review article summarizing the main ideas and results of density matrix theory, in the field of molecular quantum mechanics.

4. J. C. Slater, *Phys. Rev.* **34**, 1293 (1929).

The birth certificate of the Slater Determinant.

On the Factorization of Secular Equations by Group Theory[*]

W. BYERS BROWN

THEORETICAL CHEMISTRY INSTITUTE, UNIVERSITY OF WISCONSIN

MADISON, WISCONSIN

I. Introduction

One of the most fundamental and practical problems in the quantum mechanics of atoms, molecules, and crystals is to solve secular equations of the form

$$(H - ES)c = 0 \tag{1}$$

where H and S are the matrix representatives of the Hamiltonian $\mathcal{H}$ and unity in some basis set ϕ, and c is a column vector of coefficients. It is well known that if the system of interest possesses symmetry, a knowledge of the irreducible representations of the symmetry group can be used to factorize Eq. (1) into a set of secular equations of lower order.

Professor Slater has been closely associated with this problem, particularly in the field of atoms. One of his major contributions was the theory of the central-field approximation for atoms (Slater, 1929), which leads to secular equations of type (1). The striking feature of his method was that he showed how to factorize and solve the secular equations *without* the use of group theory. Slater's method works well in those cases in which the irreducible representations occur not more than once in the basis and the degeneracies

* This research was supported by the following grant: National Aeronautics and Space Administration Grant NsG-275-62.

are low.   When this is no longer true, he acknowledges the value of group theory techniques (Slater, 1960).

However, the group theory methods described in the literature have an unnecessary weakness. In the general case in which degenerate irreducible representations occur more than once, they require actual matrix realizations of the representations. Yet the factorized secular equations are independent of any particular matrixes, and depend only on the invariant characteristics, all of which are contained in the character table of the group.

The object of this paper is to derive the explicitly invariant forms of the factor equations. It gives me great pleasure to dedicate it to Professor Slater, who has contributed so much to the problem of factorizing secular equations.

II. Description of Problem

Let the basis consist of n linearly independent functions $\phi_1, \phi_2, ..., \phi_n$. The matrixes H and S occurring in Eq. (1) are defined by

$$H = \langle \phi^\dagger, \mathscr{H} \phi \rangle \qquad \text{and} \qquad S = \langle \phi^\dagger, \phi \rangle, \qquad (2)$$

where the row vector $\phi = (\phi_1, \phi_2, ..., \phi_n)$. Let G be the symmetry group of order g, and with h classes, associated with the system of interest. By definition the Hamiltonian commutes with all the symmetry operators R belonging to the group,

$$\mathscr{R}\mathscr{H} = \mathscr{H}\mathscr{R}. \qquad (3)$$

It will be assumed that the space of the functions ϕ is closed under the operations of the group, so that ϕ forms the basis for a matrix representation Γ, in general reducible, of G. The matrices $\Gamma(R)$ are defined in the usual way by

$$\mathscr{R}\phi = \phi\Gamma(R). \qquad (4)$$

The completely reduced form of Γ may be written formally as

$$\Gamma = \sum_{\alpha=1}^{h} m_\alpha \Gamma^{(\alpha)}, \qquad (5)$$

where $\Gamma^{(\alpha)}$ is the αth irreducible representation of dimension l_α.

The essential step in solving Eq. (1) is to find the n roots (eigenvalues) of the determinantal equation

$$\det(H - ES) = 0. \qquad (6)$$

Equation (1) may then be solved for the corresponding eigenvectors c. The structure of Γ implies that there are m_α distinct eigenvalues $E_i^{(\alpha)}(i = 1, 2, ..., m_\alpha)$, each l_α-fold degenerate, belonging to the representation $\Gamma^{(\alpha)}$; the total number of eigenvalues is

$$n = \sum_{\alpha=1}^{h} m_\alpha l_\alpha. \tag{7}$$

It follows that a transformation matrix $\mathbf{U}$ exists, depending only on the properties of G, which will reduce the determinant of Eq. (6) to a block diagonal form* which can be factored in the following manner:

$$\det(\mathbf{U}\mathbf{H}\mathbf{U}^\dagger - E\mathbf{U}\mathbf{S}\mathbf{U}^\dagger) = \prod_{\alpha=1}^{h} \{\det(\mathbf{H}_\alpha - E\mathbf{S}_\alpha)\}^{l_\alpha}, \tag{8}$$

where the matrices $\mathbf{H}_\alpha$ and $\mathbf{S}_\alpha$ are of order $m_\alpha \times m_\alpha$. The roots of Eq. (6) are unaltered by the transformation, and the m_α eigenvalues $E_i^{(\alpha)}$ are therefore given by the factor determinantal equation

$$\det(\mathbf{H}_\alpha - E\mathbf{S}_\alpha) = 0. \tag{9}$$

The aim of the present paper is to construct irreducible factor equations (9) involving only the characters $\chi^{(\alpha)}$ of the irreducible representations $\Gamma^{(\alpha)}$ of G. It is not feasible in general to determine a transformation matrix $\mathbf{U}$ which will do the job directly. The first step is to use the well-known procedure of projecting symmetry adapted functions $\Phi^{(\alpha)}$ out of the basis ϕ. The number of sets of such functions required is equal to the number of generators p in the basis. From the new (redundant) basis Φ, matrixes $\mathbf{H}^{(\alpha)}$ and $\mathbf{S}^{(\alpha)}$ of order $pl_\alpha \times pl_\alpha$ and rank m_α are constructed; these involve the irreducible matrixes $\Gamma^{(\alpha)}$. The final step is to sum over the appropriate principal minors of order m_α of $\mathbf{H}^{(\alpha)} - E\mathbf{S}^{(\alpha)}$, which yields the explicitly invariant form of Eq. (9).

III. Factorization with Simple Basis

Consider first the simplest case in which the space of the basis ϕ can be generated by the action of the g symmetry operators $\mathcal{R}$ of the group on one member, say ϕ_1. This is only possible if $n \leqslant g$, or more precisely $m_\alpha \leqslant l_\alpha$. A new basis, $\Phi^{(1)}, \Phi^{(2)}, \ldots, \Phi^{(h)}$ of g symmetry functions may then be defined by†

$$\Phi_{ik}^{(\alpha)} = g^{-1} \sum_R \Gamma_{ik}^{(\alpha)}(R)\mathcal{R}\phi_1, \tag{10}$$

where the sum is over all elements R of G. The significance of the Φ's follows from the orthogonality theorem for irreducible representations (Wigner, 1959),

---

* Note that $\mathbf{U}$ is not the same as the matrix which reduces the matrixes of Γ simultaneously to block form (5).

† The usual definition involves the complex imaginary of the matrix element Γ, which is a nuisance in the present work.

which leads to the result

$$\langle \Phi_{ik}^{(\alpha)}, \mathscr{D}\Phi_{jl}^{(\beta)} \rangle = \delta_{\alpha\beta}\delta_{ij}(gl_\alpha)^{-1} \sum_R \Gamma_{kl}^{(\alpha)}(R)D_R, \tag{11}$$

where $\mathscr{D}$ is any operator which commutes with the operators of G, and

$$D_R = \langle \phi_1, \mathscr{D}\mathscr{R}\phi_1 \rangle. \tag{12}$$

Let the members Φ_{ik}^α of the new basis be ordered lexicographically, first by the representation superscript α, then by the row suffix i, and finally by the column suffix k. Then it follows from Eq. (11) that the new $g \times g$ matrix representative of $\mathscr{D} = \mathscr{H} - E$, which commutes with G, will have a block form of the kind illustrated in Fig. 1. The l_α blocks $\mathbf{D}^{(\alpha)} = \mathbf{H}^{(\alpha)} - E\mathbf{S}^{(\alpha)}$ of order

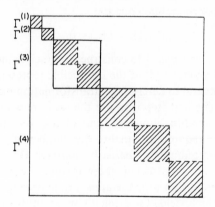

Fig. 1.   Block form of $\mathbf{D} = \mathbf{H} - E\mathbf{S}$ in the symmetry basis Φ for a group of order 15 with 4 irreducible representations with dimensions 1, 1, 2, and 3. Nonzero matrix elements are shaded.

$l_\alpha \times l_\alpha$, belonging to representation $\Gamma^{(\alpha)}$, are identical, since the expression on the right-hand side of Eq. (11) is independent of i for $i = j$. The block submatrix $\mathbf{D}^{(\alpha)}$ may be conveniently defined by summing Eq. (11) over i and j to give*

$$\mathbf{D}^{(\alpha)} = \langle \mathbf{\Phi}^{(\alpha)}, (\mathscr{H} - E)\mathbf{\Phi}^{(\alpha)} \rangle = g^{-1} \sum_R \mathbf{\Gamma}^{(\alpha)}(R)D_R \tag{13}$$

where

$$D_R = \mathbf{H}_R - E\mathbf{S}_R. \tag{14}$$

The matrix $\mathbf{D}^{(\alpha)}$ of order $l_\alpha \times l_\alpha$ is of rank m_α. This follows from the fact that the l_α^2 functions $\mathbf{\Phi}^{(\alpha)}$ span a subspace of dimension $m_\alpha l_\alpha$, belonging to $\Gamma^{(\alpha)}$, of

---

* The notation in Eq. (13) requires that the adjoint be taken of a matrix in the left half of a bracket expression. This definition of $\mathbf{D}^{(\alpha)}$ is l_α times that occurring in Fig. 1.

the n-dimensional space of the basis Γ. Since functions belonging to different rows of $\mathbf{\Phi}^{(\alpha)}$ are orthogonal, only m_α functions in any row are linearly independent. Nevertheless, the m_α roots $E_i^{(\alpha)}$ could be obtained from the determinantal equation

$$\det(\mathbf{D}^{(\alpha)}) \equiv \det(\mathbf{H}^{(\alpha)} - E\mathbf{S}^{(\alpha)}) = 0. \tag{15}$$

This has two disadvantages, however. In the first place, if $m_\alpha < l_\alpha$ Eq. (15) will have $l_\alpha - m_\alpha$ irrelevant zero roots. Secondly, to construct $\mathbf{D}^{(\alpha)}$ it is necessary to have particular realizations of the $\Gamma^{(\alpha)}(R)$. These disadvantages are removed in the next section.

IV. Invariant Factor Equations

Possible forms for the irreducible factor equations (9) are obtained by equating to zero any nonvanishing minor of $\mathbf{D}^{(\alpha)}$ of order m^α. However, such forms contain the elements of the irreducible matrixes $\Gamma^{(\alpha)}(R)$ explicitly. A form involving only the group characters can be obtained by equating to zero the *sum* of all the principal minors of $\mathbf{D}^{(\alpha)}$ of order m_α. Since $\mathbf{D}^{(\alpha)}$ is hermitian, at least one of the principal minors must be nonvanishing ($m_\alpha \neq 0$). Furthermore, the nonvanishing minors must be proportional to each other, since they all yield the same roots.

For convenience in deriving the explicitly invariant form, the representation number α will be dropped everywhere temporarily. The matrix $\mathbf{D}^{(\alpha)}$ given by Eq. (13) will therefore be written, ignoring the factor g^{-1},

$$\mathbf{D} = \sum_R \Gamma(R) D_R. \tag{16}$$

A typical principal minor of $\mathbf{D}$ of order m is

$$M_{ij\cdots k} \equiv \begin{vmatrix} \sum_R D_R \Gamma_{ii}(R) & \sum_R D_R \Gamma_{ij}(R) & \cdots & \sum_R D_R \Gamma_{ik}(R) \\ \sum_R D_R \Gamma_{ji}(R) & \sum_R D_R \Gamma_{jj}(R) & \cdots & \cdots\cdots\cdots \\ \cdots\cdots\cdots & \cdots\cdots\cdots & \cdots & \cdots\cdots\cdots \\ \sum_R D_R \Gamma_{ki}(R) & \cdots\cdots\cdots & \cdots & \sum_R D_R \Gamma_{kk}(R) \end{vmatrix} \tag{17}$$

By the rule for addition of determinants this may be written

$$M_{ij\cdots k} = \sum_R \sum_Q \cdots \sum_K D_R D_Q \cdots D_K \begin{vmatrix} \Gamma_{ii}(R) & \Gamma_{ij}(R) & \cdots & \Gamma_{ik}(R) \\ \Gamma_{ji}(Q) & \Gamma_{jj}(Q) & \cdots & \cdots \\ \cdots & \cdots & \cdots & \cdots \\ \Gamma_{ki}(K) & \cdots & \cdots & \Gamma_{kk}(K) \end{vmatrix} \tag{18}$$

The sum of the principal minors is

$$\sum_{i>j>}^{l}\sum_{>k=1}^{l}\cdots\sum^{l} M_{ij\cdots k} = \sum_{R}\sum_{Q}\cdots\sum_{k} D_R D_Q \cdots D_K X_m(R, Q, ..., K) \tag{19}$$

where

$$X_m(R, Q, ..., K) = (m!)^{-1}\sum_{i=1}^{l}\sum_{j=1}^{l}\cdots\sum_{k=1}^{l}
\begin{vmatrix}
\Gamma_{ii}(R) & \Gamma_{ij}(R) & \cdots & \Gamma_{ik}(R) \\
\Gamma_{ji}(Q) & \Gamma_{jj}(Q) & \cdots & \cdots\cdots \\
\cdots\cdots & \cdots\cdots & \cdots & \cdots\cdots \\
\Gamma_{ki}(K) & \cdots\cdots & \cdots & \Gamma_{kk}(K)
\end{vmatrix}_m . \tag{20}$$

The importance of the coefficients X defined above lies in the fact that they can be expressed directly in terms of the characters $\chi(R)$, $\chi(RQ)$, etc., of the αth irreducible representation. That this is possible can be seen immediately by comparing a typical term from the determinant of Eq. (20) with the formulas for the characters:

$$\chi(R) = \sum_i \Gamma_{ii}(R),$$

$$\chi(RQ) = \sum_i \sum_j \Gamma_{ij}(R)\Gamma_{ji}(Q),$$

$$\chi(RQK) = \sum_i \sum_j \sum_k \Gamma_{ij}(R)\Gamma_{jk}(Q)\Gamma_{ki}(K), \quad \text{etc.}$$

Every term in the *compound character* X_m, as it may be called, corresponds to a permutation belonging to the symmetric group of degree m. Therefore

$$X_m(R_1, R_2, ..., R_m) = (m!)^{-1}\sum_P \pm T_P(R_1, R_2, ..., R_m), \tag{21}$$

where the summation is over all $m!$ permutations, and the $+$ or $-$ sign is taken according to whether P is even or odd. The correspondence between the permutations P and the individual terms of Eq. (21) is illustrated by the following example: if $m = 5$ and $P = (1)(3)(254)$, then

$$T_P(R_1, ..., R_2) = \chi(R_1)\chi(R_3)\chi(R_2R_5R_4);$$

the form of T_P in the general case is clear from this example. The first three compound characters are

$$X(R) = \chi(R),$$

$$X(R, Q) = \tfrac{1}{2}[\chi(R)\chi(Q) - \chi(RQ)],$$

$$X(R, Q, K) = \tfrac{1}{6}[\chi(R)\chi(Q)\chi(K) - \chi(R)\chi(QK) - \chi(Q)\chi(KR) - \chi(K)\chi(RQ)$$
$$+ \chi(RQK) + \chi(QRK)]. \tag{22}$$

The X_m are not defined for $m > l$, the dimension of the representation. Some elementary properties are as follows:

(a) $X_m(R, Q, ..., K)$ is symmetric in $R, Q, ..., K$.

(b) $\sum_R X_m(R, Q, ..., K) = 0$, except for the unit representation.

(c) $X_l(R, R, ..., R] = \det\{\Gamma(R)\} = \pm 1$, since Γ is unitary.

The explicitly invariant form of the irreducible factor equations can be obtained by equating (19) to zero. By substituting for D_R from Eq. (14), introducing $R_1, R_2, ..., R_m$ as the element summation symbols and restoring the representation number α, Eq. (19) can be written in the polynomial form:

$$\sum_{r=0}^{m_\alpha} \binom{m_\alpha}{r}(-E)^{m_\alpha - r} \sum_{R_1} \sum_{R_2} \cdots \sum_{R_m} H_{R_1} H_{R_2} \cdots H_{R_r} S_{R_{r+1}} \cdots S_{R_m} \chi_m^{(\alpha)}(R_1, ..., R_m) = 0$$

$$(23)$$

For the cases $m_\alpha = 1$, 2, and 3, Eq. (23) for the $E_i^{(\alpha)}$ has the form

$$\sum_R (H_R - E S_R) X^{(\alpha)}(R) = 0,$$

$$\sum_R \sum_Q (H_R H_Q - 2 E H_R S_R + E^2 S_R S_Q) X^{(\alpha)}(R, Q) = 0, \qquad (24)$$

$$\sum_R \sum_Q \sum_K (H_R H_Q H_K - 3 E H_R H_Q S_K + 3 E^2 H_R S_Q S_K - E^3 S_R S_Q S_K) X^{(\alpha)}(R, Q, K) = 0,$$

where $X^{(\alpha)}(R, Q)$ and $X^{(\alpha)}(R, Q, K)$ are given by Eq. (22).

V. General Basis

Consider now the general case in which the basis ϕ possesses p generators, say, $\phi_1, \phi_2, ..., \phi_p$. That is, the gp functions $R\phi_1, R\phi_2, ..., R\phi_p$ where R ranges over the group G, span the n-dimensional space of the basis. The functions produced from the generators may be linearly dependent $(n \leqslant gp)$. Let the subbasis $^\mu\phi$, consisting of the g functions $R\phi_\mu (R \subset G)$, be of rank $^\mu m$, so that

$$n = \sum_{\mu=1}^{p} {}^\mu m.$$

The $^\mu\phi$ form the basis for a representation $^\mu\Gamma$ of the group of order $^\mu m$, in general reducible. Let

$$^\mu\Gamma = \sum_{\alpha=1}^{h} {}^\mu m_\alpha \Gamma^{(\alpha)}. \qquad (25)$$

Then it follows from Eq. (5) that

$$m_\alpha = \sum_{\mu=1}^{p} {}^\mu m_\alpha \quad \text{and} \quad {}^\mu m = \sum_{\alpha=1}^{h} {}^\mu m_\alpha l_\alpha. \tag{26}$$

To factorize the secular equation (1) in the general case it is necessary to introduce a set of g symmetry functions ${}^\mu\Phi = {}^\mu\Phi^{(1)}, {}^\mu\Phi^{(2)}, \ldots, {}^\mu\Phi^{(h)}$ for each subbasis ${}^\mu\phi$, defined by

$$^\mu\Phi^{(\alpha)} = g^{-1} \sum_R \Gamma^{(\alpha)}(R)\, \mathscr{R}\phi_\mu. \tag{27}$$

Let the new basis of gp functions ${}^\mu\Phi^{(\alpha)}_{ik}$ be ordered lexicographically by α, μ, i, k. The matrix representative of the operator $\mathscr{D} = \mathscr{H} - E$ will consist of l_α diagonal blocks $\mathbf{D}^{(\alpha)}$ for each representation $\Gamma^{(\alpha)}$, as in the simple case of Section III. However, the $\mathbf{D}^{(\alpha)}$ are now of order $pl_\alpha \times pl_\alpha$, and consist of submatrixes ${}^{\mu\nu}\mathbf{D}^{(\alpha)}$,

$$\mathbf{D}^{(\alpha)} = [{}^{\mu\nu}\mathbf{D}^{(\alpha)}]. \tag{28}$$

The submatrices may be defined, by analogy with Eq. (13), by

$$^{\mu\nu}\mathbf{D}^{(\alpha)} = \langle {}^\mu\Phi^{(\alpha)}, \mathscr{D}^\nu\Phi^{(\alpha)} \rangle,$$

$$= g^{-1} \sum_R \Gamma^{(\alpha)}(R){}^{\mu\nu}D_R, \tag{29}$$

where

$$^{\mu\nu}D_R = \langle \phi_\mu, \mathscr{D}\mathscr{R}\phi_\nu \rangle,$$

$$= {}^{\mu\nu}H_R - E^{\mu\nu}S_R. \tag{30}$$

By introducing new $p \times p$ matrixes $\mathbf{D}_R$, whose elements are the ${}^{\mu\nu}D_R$, the matrix $\mathbf{D}^{(\alpha)}$ may be defined succinctly by

$$\mathbf{D}^{(\alpha)} = \sum_R \Gamma^{(\alpha)}(R) \times \mathbf{D}_R, \tag{31}$$

where $\times$ indicates a direct product.

The required form of the irreducible factor equations is obtained by taking the sum of certain of the principal minors of $\mathbf{D}^{(\alpha)}$ of order m_α. These minors must contain ${}^\mu m_\alpha$ rows and columns from the submatrix ${}^{\mu\mu}\mathbf{D}^{(\alpha)}$ of rank ${}^\mu m_\alpha$, as any nonvanishing minor of $\mathbf{D}^{(\alpha)}$ of order m_α must consist of linearly independent rows and columns. Let $M_{ij\ldots k}({}^1m, {}^2m, \ldots, {}^pm)$ be a principal minor of $\mathbf{D}^{(\alpha)}$ of order $m = {}^1m + {}^2m + \cdots + {}^pm$ which satisfies the above condition. By the rule for the addition of determinants, it can be written

$$M_{ij\ldots k}(^1m, {}^2m, \ldots, {}^pm) =$$

$$\sum_R \sum_Q \cdots \sum_K \begin{vmatrix} {}^{11}D_R\Gamma_{ii}(R) & {}^{11}D_R\Gamma_{ij}(R) & \cdots & \vdots & \cdots & \vdots & \cdots & {}^{1p}D_R\Gamma_{ik}(R) \\ {}^{11}D_Q\Gamma_{ji}(Q) & {}^{11}D_Q\Gamma_{jj}(Q) & \cdots & \vdots & \cdots & \vdots & \cdots & \cdots \\ \cdots & \cdots & \cdots & \vdots & \cdots & \vdots & \cdots & \cdots \\ \hline \cdots & \cdots & \cdots & \vdots & \cdots & \vdots & \cdots & \cdots \\ \hline \cdots & \cdots & \cdots & \vdots & \cdots & \vdots & \cdots & \cdots \\ {}^{p1}D_K\Gamma_{ki}(K) & \cdots & \cdots & \vdots & \cdots & \vdots & \cdots & {}^{pp}D_K\Gamma_{kk}(K) \end{vmatrix}, \quad (32)$$

where the representation superscript α has been dropped from Γ. The determinant in Eq. (32) differs from that in the corresponding Eq. (18) of the previous section, in that it is not possible to factor the ${}^{\mu\nu}D_R$'s out of it. An explicitly invariant form of the irreducible factor equation is still obtained by taking the sum over all such minors, but in this general case must be left in the form*

$$\sum_{i=1}^{l} \sum_{j=1}^{l} \cdots \sum_{k=1}^{l} M_{ij\ldots k}(^1m, \ldots, {}^pm) = 0. \quad (33)$$

It can be seen, however, that the coefficient of any product of the ${}^{\mu\nu}D_R$'s will be directly expressible in terms of the simple characters $\chi^{(\alpha)}$; the compound characters $X_m^{(\alpha)}$ do not appear in general. The invariant form of the factor equations can be illustrated best by means of simple examples in which the basis ϕ possesses $p = 2$ generators, ϕ_1 and ϕ_2.

(a) Consider the case $^1m = {}^2m = 1$. The general principal minor of $\mathbf{D}^{(\alpha)}$ of order 2 is

$$M_{ij}(1, 1) = \sum_R \sum_Q \begin{vmatrix} {}^{11}D_R\Gamma_{ii}(R) & {}^{12}D_R\Gamma_{ij}(R) \\ {}^{21}D_Q\Gamma_{ji}(Q) & {}^{22}D_Q\Gamma_{jj}(Q) \end{vmatrix}$$

Taking the sum of the principal minors, Eq. (33) is

$$\sum_R \sum_Q [{}^{11}D_R{}^{22}D_Q\chi(R)\chi(Q) - {}^{12}D_R{}^{21}D_Q\chi(RQ)] = 0. \quad (34)$$

---

* Equation (33) is actually $(^1m! \, {}^2m! \ldots {}^pm!)$ times the sum of the appropriate principal minors of $\mathbf{D}^{(\alpha)}$.

(b) Consider the case $^1m = 1$, $^2m = 2$. The principal minor is

$$
M_{ijk}(1, 2) = \sum_R \sum_Q \sum_K
\begin{vmatrix}
^{11}D_R\Gamma_{ii}(R) & ^{12}D_R\Gamma_{ij}(R) & ^{12}D_R\Gamma_{ik}(R) \\
^{21}D_Q\Gamma_{ji}(Q) & ^{22}D_Q\Gamma_{jj}(Q) & ^{22}D_Q\Gamma_{jk}(Q) \\
^{21}D_k\Gamma_{ki}(Q) & ^{22}D_k\Gamma_{kj}(K) & ^{22}D_k\Gamma_{kk}(K)
\end{vmatrix}
$$

Expanding the determinant and taking the sum over all i, j, k this becomes

$$
\sum_R \sum_Q \sum_K {}^{22}D_K\{^{11}D_R{}^{22}D_Q[\chi(Q)\chi(K) - \chi(QK)]\chi(R)
$$

$$
+ 2{}^{12}D_R{}^{21}D_Q[\chi(RQK) - \chi(RQ)\chi(K)]\} = 0. \tag{35}
$$

These equations may be put in the form of polynomials in E by substituting for $^{\mu\nu}D_R$ from Eq. (30).

VI. Epilogue

It would seem incredible if the mathematical problem solved in this paper had not been tackled and solved at least fifty years ago by the mathematicians of group representation theory. However, a reasonably diligent search of the literature, and much questioning of mathematicians, has not yet brought such a discussion to light. Rather than engage in further historical research, it seemed more sensible to publish the author's treatment of the problem within the context of quantum mechanics.

ACKNOWLEDGMENTS

I would like to thank Professor H. C. Longuet-Higgins for suggesting the problem discussed in this paper, and for supervising my work on it some years ago. I am also very grateful to Professor P.-O. Löwdin, whose interest and enthusiasm have led to its resuscitation, for valuable discussion and criticism. Lastly, I would like to thank the Department of Scientific and Industrial Research (U.K.) for a grant, during the tenure of which most of the work was carried out.

REFERENCES

Slater, J. C. (1929). *Phys. Rev.* **34**, 1293.
Slater, J. C. (1960). *In* "Quantum Theory of Atomic Structure," Vol. II. McGraw-Hill, New York.
Wigner, E. P. (1959). "Group Theory and Its Applications to the Quantum Mechanics of Atomic Spectra." Academic Press, New York.

On the Existence of a Maximum in the Interaction between He(1s2s; ^3S) and He(1s²; ^1S)*

F. A. MATSEN and D. R. SCOTT†

MOLECULAR PHYSICS GROUP
THE UNIVERSITY OF TEXAS, AUSTIN, TEXAS

I. Introduction

The techniques for performing *ab initio* quantum mechanical calculations have now developed to the stage where accurate predictions can be made of the interaction between simple atoms. Except for the Born-Oppenheimer condition, no assumptions or approximations are made in these calculations. The accuracy of the results is limited only by the relative completeness of the basis set. Further, meaningful bounds can often be put on the results. Professor Slater, to whom this volume is dedicated, has played a leading role in the development of the technique of *ab initio* quantum mechanical prediction.

The accurate prediction of an atom–atom interaction is often of considerable interest to the experimentalist. His experiment does not directly measure the interaction, yet the interpretation of his results often requires a knowledge of the interaction. Without this knowledge, he may be unable to judge the validity of his interpretation of the results. Further, his experiments often cannot decide among a number of different interactions, let alone determine the interactions with accuracy. The *ab initioist* can assist the experimentalist in distinguishing between possible interactions and, less frequently, delineate the interactions in detail.

* Supported by the Robert A. Welch Foundation, Houston, Texas, and by the National Aeronautical and Space Administration.

† *Present address:* Department of Chemistry, Texas Technological College, Lubbock, Texas.

133

In this paper, we review the history of the $^3\Sigma_u^+$ interaction* between $He(1s2s, {}^3S)$ and $He(1s^2, {}^1S)$. This interaction provides an ideal case history of the interplay between the experimentalist and the *ab initioist*. A wide variety of experiments have been used for the experimental study of this interaction; spectroscopy, scattering, gaseous electronics and isotope exchange. The important issue in our discussion is the existence of a maximum in the interaction. The existence of a maximum in this system is not intuitively obvious, but experiment and theory have combined to establish its existence and size beyond reasonable doubt. Included in this discussion are the latest, and heretofore unpublished, calculations performed on this system by the Molecular Physics Group. In our discussion we will have need to refer to the following states of He_2 and He_2^+ :

$$^2\Sigma_g^+ \equiv He_2^+[He^+(1s)^2S, He(1s^2)^1S; \, ^2\Sigma_g^+]$$

$$^1\Sigma_g^+ \equiv He_2[He(1s^2)^1S, He(1s^2)^1S; \, ^1\Sigma_g^+]$$

$$^1\Sigma_u^+ \equiv He_2[He(1s2s)^1S, He(1s^2)^1S; \, ^1\Sigma_u^+]$$

$$^3\Sigma_u^+ \equiv He_2[He(1s2s)^3S, He(1s^2)^1S; \, ^3\Sigma_u^+]$$

To place the problem in proper perspective, the energies of these states are plotted as a function of internuclear distance in Fig. 1. These interactions have been computed at various times by the Molecular Physics Group of the University of Texas.

II. The Evidence

The earliest suggestion of a maximum in a He_2 state was made in 1935 by Nickerson. He attributed the diffuse 600 Å band in a helium discharge to the $^1\Sigma_u^+ \rightarrow {}^1\Sigma_g^+$ transition of He_2. Since the highest frequencies in the band were greater than the differences in the separated atom energies, it was inferred that there existed a maximum in the $^1\Sigma_u^+$ interaction.

In 1952, Buckingham and Dalgarno made *ab initio* quantum mechanical calculations on the interactions of $He(1s^2, {}^1S)$ with $He(1s2s, {}^1S)$ and with $He(1s2s, {}^3S)$. These authors used a single term Heitler-London wave function with unoptimized orbital exponents. The orbitals employed were the hydrogenic 1s and 2s functions of Morse *et al.* (1935). In the $^1\Sigma_u^+$ and $^3\Sigma_u^+$ states they found maxima at about 4 a_0 with heights of 0.26 and 0.29 eV respectively. Both of these states were also found to have binding minima at about 2.1 a_0. This classic calculation supported Nickerson's conjecture about the $^1\Sigma_u^+$ state of He_2 and, in addition, suggested the existence of a maximum in the

---

* The state $^3\Sigma_g^+ \equiv He_2[He(1s2s)^3S, He(1s^2)^1S; \, ^3\Sigma_g^+]$ which also results from the interaction of $He(1s2s; {}^3S)$ with $He(1s^2, {}^1S)$, is not considered here. However, see Mulliken (1965), Browne (1965) and Buckingham and Dalgarno (1952).

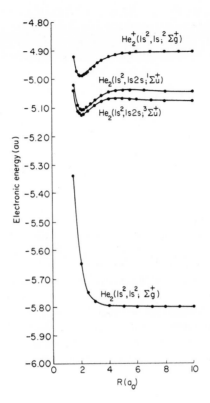

FIG. 1.   *Ab Initio* computed potential energy curves for various states of He$_2$ and He$_2^+$. Computations done by Molecular Physics Group, University of Texas: He$_2^+$, $^2\Sigma_g^+$ (Reagan, Browne, and Matsen, 1963); He$_2$, $^1\Sigma_u^+$ (Scott, Greenawalt, Browne, and Matsen, 1966); He$_2$, $^3\Sigma_u^+$ (Rodriguez, Browne, and Matsen, 1965).

$^3\Sigma_u^+$ state of He$_2$. This latter system is of particular interest experimentally because one of the separated atom states, He(1s2s; ^3S), is metastable with natural lifetime estimated to be 10^5 seconds (Mathis, 1957). Such a long life-time permits a direct study of the metastable atom and its reactions.

The first experimental evidence of a maximum in the $^3\Sigma_u^+$ interaction came from a study of Molnar and Phelps (1953), who used optical techniques in an electrical discharge and showed that the destruction of the ^3S helium atoms at low metastable densities was by diffusion to the walls at low helium pressure and by three-body molecular formation

$$He(^1S) + He(^1S) + He^*(^3S) \rightarrow He(^1S) + He_2(^3\Sigma_u^+)$$

at higher helium pressures. Their studies of the diffusion coefficient and molecular formation at 300° and 77°K suggested that the interaction had a maximum with a height of the order of 0.03 eV. The authors also suggested that a maximum existed in the interaction between a normal Ne atom and a ^3P metastable Ne atom with a height greater than 0.05 eV. This seems to provide a lower limit for the $^3\Sigma_u^+$ maximum since the observation of the three-body collision coefficient of neon (Phelps, 1959) indicates that the height of the maximum for Ne is less than that for helium.

Burhop (1954) obtained a maximum of 0.12 eV at 4.2 a_0 in the $^3\Sigma_u^+$ interaction by applying scattering theory to the data of Phelps and Molnar.

A later investigation (Phelps, 1955) of the diffusion coefficients for He(1s2s, ^1S) and He(1s2s, ^3S) in normal helium by optical methods gave additional experimental support for the potential maximum in the $^3\Sigma_u^+$ curve of He$_2$. These results showed that the diffusion coefficients for the He(1s2s, ^1S) and He (1s2s, ^3S) atoms were almost equal at 300°K with an indication that the former diffusion coefficient was slightly larger.

At this point in the case history, an *ab initio* calculation had predicted the existence of a maximum in the $^3\Sigma_u^+$ interaction, and several lines of experimental evidence tended to substantiate the prediction. However, the interpretation of the results were not unambiguous and the experiments not definitive. Further, the possibility existed that the *ab initio* calculation made an incorrect prediction.* For example, the calculations could have contained numerical errors, or the predictions could be invalid because of the choice and the size of the basis set. (The authors' choice of a hydrogenic 2s function gave rise to the possibility that the maximum was an artifact due to the presence of the node in that function.) Further, the Buckingham and Dalgarno results lay 2.25 eV above the sum of the experimental separated atom energies. With such an error, the probability is high that the fine features of the interaction would not be reproduced with accuracy.

This problem is relevant to a broad spectrum of experiments; it is an important interaction. Further, as a four-electron two-center problem it was susceptible to the same type of calculational techniques used in previous investigations of lithium hydride.† For these reasons, the Molecular Physics Group initiated a series of *ab initio* valence bond calculations with the aim of providing the most accurate predictions possible for this interaction.

The first of these (Brigman *et al.* (1961)) was a single configuration variation calculation with a basis set of Slater orbitals and was carried out on an IBM 650. The important features of this calculation are the optimization of orbital exponents at each internuclear separation, the use of an open shell He(1s, 1s' ^1S) function, and a nodeless 2s function in He(1s2s, ^3S). The calculated separated atoms energy lay 1.358 eV below that of Buckingham and

---

* In fact, the calculations of Buckingham and Dalgarno predicted that the He$_2$ states of $^1\Sigma_g^+$ and $^3\Sigma_g^+$ were not bound. Both of these states have been found to possess binding minima in later calculations (Browne, 1965).

† For the latest paper in this series, see Browne and Matsen (1964).

Dalgarno. The calculated interaction showed a maximum of 0.19 eV at 4.5 a_0. Thus, a second *ab initio* calculation exhibited a maximum.

However, the height of the maximum decreased from 0.29 eV in the Buckingham and Dalgarno calculation to 0.19 eV in the latter study. This suggested the possibility that more refined calculations would reduce or even eradicate the maximum. To test this possibility, a new calculation was made on a larger computer (CDC 1604) with a larger basis set (Matsen and Poshusta, 1963). This calculation employed a twelve-term valence bond wave function constructed from 1s, 2s, 3s, 2p, and 3d Slater orbitals. The orbital exponents were determined from partial optimization and from helium atom calculations. A calculated maximum of 0.14 eV was found at 4.7 a_0. Thus, a third *ab initio* calculation exhibited a maximum. However, the computed height of the maximum again decreased from the earlier calculated values.

In the meantime, experimental evidence for a maximum in the closely related He_2 $^1\Sigma_u^+$ state appeared in a spectroscopic reinvestigation of the 600 Å band of helium (Tanaka and Yoshino, 1963). The authors concluded that the 600 Å spectrum arises from transitions $^1\Sigma_u^+$ to $^1\Sigma_g^+$ and that the $^1\Sigma_u^+$ state possesses a maximum. More recent evidence for the maximum in the curve of the $^3\Sigma_u^+$ state of He_2 has been obtained from a study of the scattering of metastable helium atoms by normal helium atoms (Muschlitz and Richards, 1964). It was found that the scattering of the triplet atoms was larger than that of the singlet atoms. This was attributed to the presence of a larger maximum in the $^3\Sigma_u^+$ interaction.

The most direct evidence for the potential maximum in the $^3\Sigma_u^+$ curve of He_2 should come from a study of the temperature dependence of collision processes. In the case of interaction of two atoms with no potential maximum in their interaction curve, it is expected that the cross sections will increase with decreasing temperature with a maximum cross section near absolute zero. However, for an interaction curve having a maximum, the cross section should decrease rapidly at low temperatures, approaching zero as the temperature decreases to absolute zero. The temperature variation of the exchange cross section for metastability of He* with He (Colegrove *et al.*, 1964) was expressly undertaken to experimentally test for the existence of a maximum in the $^3\Sigma_u^+$ interaction. The experimental results, obtained by optical pumping techniques, definitely show that the cross section decreases with decreasing temperature, approaching zero as the temperature approached absolute zero.

Shortly before the publication of these important experimental papers, the Molecular Physics Group had begun another *ab initio* calculation on the $^3\Sigma_u^+$ state of He_2 using a mixed basis set of elliptical and Slater orbitals of the type developed by Browne and Matsen (1964). The elliptical orbitals were introduced in order to better represent polarization effects in the region of the maximum. The details of this computation are given in the appendix. The computed potential energy curve from this study as well as those of previous investigations are illustrated in Figs. 2 and 3. A maximum in the $^3\Sigma_u^+$ curve

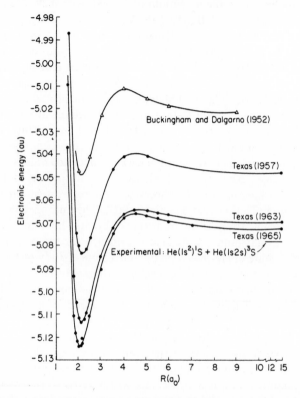

FIG. 2. Successively improved *ab initio* curves for the interaction He(1s², ¹S) + He(1s2s, ³S). Texas, 1961 (Brigman, Brient, and Matsen, 1961); Texas, 1963 (Matsen and Poshusta, 1963); Texas, 1965 (Matsen and Scott, 1965).

of 0.16 eV was found at 4.7 a_0. The difference between the calculated separated atom energies and the experimental value was only 0.17 eV, and a rigorous upper bound of 0.33 eV for the maximum was established. Thus, a fourth *ab initio* calculation exhibited a maximum. Of particular importance was the fact that the height of the maximum had stabilized between the third and fourth calculation and that refinement of the calculation did not necessarily decrease the barrier height. This computation lies at the limit of the CDC 1604 computer.

A similar *ab initio* computation on the closely related $^1\Sigma_u^+$ state of He$_2$ has also recently been completed (Scott *et al.*, 1966). This is of interest to the discussion of the $^3\Sigma_u^+$ curve since the $^1\Sigma_u^+$ state arises from similar atomic states, He(1s², ¹S) and He(1s2s, ¹S) and because the calculations of Buckingham

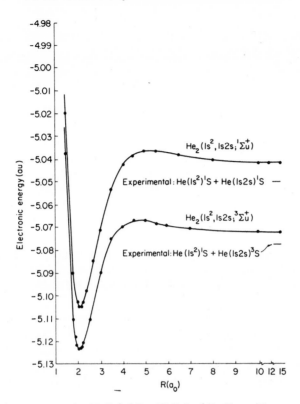

FIG. 3. *Ab initio* curves for He(1s², ¹S) + He(1s2s, ¹S), (Scott, Greenawalt, Browne, and Matsen, 1965) and forHe(1s², ¹S) + He(1s2s, ³S) (Matsen and Scott, 1965).

and Dalgarno indicated a maximum in the $^1\Sigma_u^+$ state as well as in the $^3\Sigma_u^+$ state. Clearly, for the results of the *ab initio* calculations on the $^3\Sigma_u^+$ curve to be trustworthy, it should be shown that the maxima which are predicted by the early computations on the other states of He$_2$ are verified by more refined calculations. Also, there is experimental evidence for the maximum in the $^1\Sigma_u^+$ curve from spectroscopic and scattering studies as mentioned previously. The results of the computation using seventeen terms constructed from Slater orbitals; 1s, 2s, 3s, 2p$_0$, 2p$_+$, 2p$_-$, 3p$_0$, 3p$_+$, 3p$_-$, 3d$_0$; gave a maximum of 0.15 eV at 5.2 a_0. The height of the maximum is the same as that found for the $^3\Sigma_u^+$ curve in the most recent computation, although its location is at 0.5 a_0 larger internuclear separation.

The University of Texas is now contracting for a new computer with which a fifth *ab initio* calculation of this type will be carried out. With the new computer one can employ a larger basis set and more extensive orbital exponent optimization. It is estimated that the results will lie within 0.1 eV of the true one. This calculation should provide a representation of the interaction which is accurate enough for the experimentalist.

III. Conclusions

The results of the *ab initio* calculations are summarized in Table 1 and Figs. 2 and 3. There is definite evidence from all of these computations that a maximum does exist in the $^3\Sigma_u^+$ curve. In the latest and more extended calculations the height of the maximum has leveled off to a value of about 0.15 eV which is probably a good estimate. The location of the broad maximum is 4.6–4.7 a_0. The validity of the calculations is supported by the fact that a maximum is also found in the $^1\Sigma_u^+$ curve calculated to the same level as the $^3\Sigma_u^+$ curve. The maximum in the $^1\Sigma_u^+$ curve is also supported by experiment.

This theoretical evidence coupled with the experimental studies, particularly the study of the temperature dependence of the metastability exchange cross section, prove beyond any reasonable doubt that a maximum does exist in the $^3\Sigma_u^+$ curve of He_2.

A fact of considerable significance is that no elementary physical basis for the maximum in the interaction has yet been proposed. This important feature of the interaction is the consequence of subtle dynamic effects which are revealed only by the intensive *ab initio* treatment of the type described here.

We wish to express our appreciation to Dr. J. C. Browne for his many helpful suggestions and criticisms.

Appendix. Potential Curve for Lowest $^3\Sigma_u^+$ State of He_2

The wave functions used in these computations were of the generalized valence bond type (Browne and Matsen, 1962). The basis set was composed of both Slater orbitals as defined by Browne and Miller (1962) and elliptic orbitals defined as follows:

$$\phi(n, l, m; j) = (2\pi)^{1/2}(-1)^{(|m|-m)/2}\lambda^n\mu^l \exp[-(\alpha\lambda + \beta\mu)]$$
$$[(\lambda^2 - 1)(1 - \mu^2)]^{|m|/2} \exp(im\phi)$$

α_j and β_j are the variable orbital exponents, and the elliptic coordinates, λ and μ, are defined by Miller *et al.* (1959). Harris (1960), Harris and Taylor (1963), and Browne (1964) describe the properties of these orbitals. Orbital exponents were varied independently at each internuclear separation to obtain the lowest energy with the following wave function:

$$\Psi_1 = C_1[1s_A^2 1s_B' \phi_B(1, 0, 0; 2)] + C_2[1s_A^2 1s_B' \phi_B(0, 1, 0; 2)].$$

TABLE 1

SUMMARY OF *Ab Initio* VALENCE BOND CALCULATIONS OF $^3\Sigma_u^+$ STATES OF He$_2$

Calculation	Type	R_e (a_0)	D_e (eV)	Lowest bound on D_e (eV)	R_m^a (a_0)	Barrier (eV)	Upper bound on barrier (eV)
Buckingham and Dalgarno	Single term (1s², 1s2s); hydrogenic functions of Morse, Young, and Haurwitz; no orbital exponent variation.	2.1	1.0–1.2		4.0	0.29	
Texas, 1961[b]	Single term (1s1s′, 1s″2s); open shell, Slater orbitals; orbital exponent optimization.	2.18	1.01	0.12	4.5	0.19	
Texas, 1963[c]	Twelve terms, Slater orbitals; partial orbital exponent optimization.	2.14	1.24	0.939	4.7	0.14	
Texas, 1965[d]	21 terms, ellipticals and Slater orbitals; partial orbital optimization.	2.08	1.39	1.22	4.6	0.16	0.33

[a] Internuclear separation at which barrier maximum occurs.
[b] Brigman, Brient, Matsen (1961). These results are corrected for numerical errors noted by Matsen and Poshusta (1963).
[c] Matsen and Poshusta, 1963. Terms were: 1s²1s′2s′; 1s$\widehat{2}$s1s′2s′; 2s²1s′2s′; 2p$\widehat{0}$1s′2s′; 2p$_{+1}$2p$_{-1}$1s′2s′; 1s²2s′3s′; 1s²1s′2p6; 3d$\widehat{0}$²1s′2s′; 3d$_{+1}$3d$_{-1}$1s′2s′; 3d$_{+2}$3d$_{-2}$1s′2s′; 1s$\widehat{2}$p$_0$1s′; 1s²2s,1s′; 1s²2p$_0$,1s′.
[d] Matsen and Scott (1965). Unpublished work. See appendix for details of computations.

After obtaining these orbital exponents, additional terms composed of Slater orbitals were added to give the twenty-one term wave function below:

$$\Psi_2 = \Psi_1 + C_3[\overbrace{2p_{+A}2p_{-A}}1s'_B2s_B] + C_4[2s'^2_A1s'_B2s_B] + C_5[2p^2_{0A}1s'_B2s_B]$$
$$+ C_6[3s'^2_A1s'_B2s_B] + C_7[1s^2_A1s'_B2p'_{0B}] + C_8[1s^2_A2s_A1s'_B]$$
$$+ C_9[\overbrace{3p_{+A}3p_{-A}}1s'_B2s_B] + C_{10}[\overbrace{1s_A2s'_A}1s'_B2s_B] + C_{11}[2s'_A3s_A1s'_B2s_B]$$
$$+ C_{12}[1s_A3s_A1s'_B2s_B] + C_{13}[\overbrace{2p_{+A}3p_{-A}}1s'_B2s_B] + C_{14}[1s^2_A2p'_{0A}1s'_B]$$
$$+ C_{15}[1s_A2p_{0A}1s'_B2s_B] + C_{16}[1s^2_A1s'_B2s_B] + C_{17}[3p^2_{0A}1s'_B2s_B]$$
$$+ C_{18}[\overbrace{2p_{0A}3p_{0A}}1s'_B2s_B] + C_{19}[1s^2_A1s'_B3s'_B] + C_{20}[1s^2_A2s_A2s_B]$$
$$+ C_{21}[2s'^2_A1s'_B2p'_{0B}]$$

The carats indicate the pairing between the orbitals. The orbital exponents for the added terms were obtained from a similar computation on the $^1\Sigma^+_u$ state (Scott $et\ al.$, 1965), previous computations on the $^3\Sigma^+_u$ state (Matsen and Poshusta, 1963), a computation on the helium atom (Matsen and Stuart, 1964), and from numerical experimentation with Ψ_1 and added terms. The orbital exponents are listed in Table 2. The numerical potential energy data

TABLE 2

ORBITAL EXPONENTS FOR Ψ_2

R (a_0)	$\alpha(0, 1, 0)$	$\beta(0, 1, 0)$	$\alpha(1, 0, 0)$	$\beta(1, 0, 0)$	1s	1s'
1.5	0.9363	1.2632	0.4026	0.0718	1.8244	2.0015
1.8	1.6234	1.2691	0.4611	0.1405	1.7715	2.0174
1.9	0.7510	1.3300	0.4625	0.0654	1.7527	2.0135
1.982	0.5223	1.2224	0.4847	0.0342	1.7444	2.0182
2.08	0.6834	1.1000	0.5015	0.0834	1.7329	2.0148
2.13	0.6766	1.1600	0.5106	0.0934	1.7264	2.0136
2.17	0.6466	1.1000	0.5147	0.0765	1.7253	2.0172
2.20	0.7156	1.100	0.5228	0.1229	1.7206	2.0144
2.50	0.7045	1.200	0.5842	0.2776	1.7004	2.0124
3.00	0.3152	1.0800	0.6861	0.7147	1.6838	2.0040
3.50	0.7061	1.2100	0.7953	0.8889	1.6816	1.9915
4.00	2.4050	1.6359	1.0273	1.1352	1.6818	2.0018
4.50	2.7079	1.9032	1.1874	1.2679	1.6834	2.0014
5.00	2.9766	2.0675	1.3541	1.4373	1.6849	2.0008
5.50	3.1736	2.3445	1.5197	1.5143	1.6859	2.0010
6.00	3.2089	2.4711	1.6988	1.6240	1.6864	2.0008
7.00	3.4439	2.7799	2.0294	1.7931	1.6870	2.0008
10.00	3.5825	3.4548	2.8917	2.4342	1.6875	1.9994
15.00	6.1008	5.2296	4.4623	3.9095	1.6647	2.0009

TABLE 2 (Cont.)

R (a_0)	2s	2s′	3s	3s′	$2p_0$, $2p_+$, $2p_-$	$2p_0'$	$3p_0$, $3p_+$, $3p_-$
1.5	0.4500	3.5801	2.175	1.227	2.4700	0.4500	3.000
1.8	0.4600	2.8582	2.170	1.227	2.4700	0.4600	3.000
1.9	0.4650	2.7500	2.170	1.227	2.4750	0.4650	3.000
1.982	0.4650	2.6343	2.170	1.227	2.4800	0.4650	3.000
2.08	0.4700	2.7000	2.164	1.227	2.4800	0,4700	3.000
2.13	0.4700	2.7675	2.164	1.227	2.4800	0.4700	3.000
2.17	0.4750	2.7280	2.164	1.227	2.4800	0.4750	3.000
2.20	0.4800	2.6888	2.164	1.227	2.4800	0.4800	3.000
2.50	0.4900	2.6780	2.160	1.227	2.4850	0.4900	3.000
3.00	0.5000	2.5708	2.160	1.227	2.4900	0.5000	3.000
3.50	0.5200	2.5562	2.160	1.227	2.4950	0.5200	3.000
4.00	0.5300	2.4954	2.160	1.227	2.5000	0.5300	3.000
4.50	0.5600	2.5622	2.159	1.227	2.500	0.5600	3.000
5.00	0.5600	2.5327	2.155	1.227	2.500	0.5600	3.000
5.50	0.5600	2.5584	2.150	1.227	2.500	0.5600	3.000
6.00	0.5650	2.5550	2.150	1.227	2.500	0.5650	3.000
7.00	0.5650	2.5500	2.140	1.227	2.500	0.5650	3.000
10.00	0.5700	2.4479	2.130	1.227	2.5000	0.5700	3.000
15.00	0.5700	2.4473	2.099	1.227	2.5000	0.5700	3.000

are collected in Table 3 and illustrated in Figs. 2 and 3. Table 4 contains the computed spectroscopic constants. These computations were performed on the CDC 1604 at the University of Texas using programs written by the Molecular Physics Group.

TABLE 3

POTENTIAL ENERGY DATA FOR $^3\Sigma_u^+$ STATE OF He_2 FROM Ψ'_2

R (au)	$-E$ (au)	R (au)	$-E$ (au)
1.50	5.03724	3.50	5.07490
1.80	5.11073	4.00	5.06787
1.90	5.11829	4.50	5.06694
1.982	5.12202	5.00	5.06693
2.08	5.12373	5.50	5.06807
2.13	5.12360	6.00	5.06913
2.17	5.12279	7.00	5.07071
2.20	5.12097	10.00	5.07234
2.50	5.11084	15.00	5.07266
3.00	5.09031		

TABLE 4

COMPUTED SPECTROSCOPIC CONSTANTS FOR
$^3\Sigma_u^+$ STATE OF He_2 FROM Ψ'_2

R_e (a_0)	ω_e (cm^{-1})	$\omega_e x$ (cm^{-1})	α_e (cm^{-1})	B_e (cm^{-1})
		Experimental[a]		
1.975	1809.91	38.8$_9$	0.243$_8$	7.710$_3$
		Calculated		
2.08[b]	2051.73[c]	37.17[c]	0.095[c]	6.78[c]

[a] Ginter, 1965.
[b] Obtained by fitting a cubic through computed points at 1.982, 2.08, 2.13, and 2.20 a_0.
[c] Obtained by fitting a cubic by least squares through computed points at 1.5, 1.8, 1.9, 1.982, 2.08, 2.13, 2.50, and 3.00 a_0 and applying the formulas of Dunham (1932).

The results of this calculation show a maximum in the curve at 4.6 a_0 with a computed height of 0.16 eV. From the experimental separated atom energies and the computed energy at an internuclear separation of 4.5 a_0, a rigorous upper bound of 0.33 eV may be set on the height of the maximum. The minimum in the curve occurs at $R = 2.08 \, a_0$, and the calculated value for the rationalized binding energy, D_e, is 1.39 eV. A new rigorous lower bound on D_e is calculated to be 1.22 eV. From an energy cycle involving the ionization energy of He(1s2s; ^3S) and the ionization energy of the $^3\Sigma_u^+$ state of He_2 (Reagan et al., 1963) a lower limit of 1.76 eV may be set for D_e. Therefore, the wave function still needs to be improved in the vicinity of the minimum. The difference between the sum of the experimental separated atom energies and the calculated value at 15 a_0 is only 0.17 eV. The agreement between the computed and experimental spectroscopic constants is good.

REFERENCES

Brigman, G. H., Brient, S. J., and Matsen, F. A. (1961). J. Chem. Phys. 34, 958. (Some numerical errors in this work are corrected in Matsen and Poshusta, 1963).
Browne, J. C. (1964). J. Chem. Phys. 40, 48.
Browne, J. C. (1965). J. Chem. Phys. 42, 2826.
Browne, J. C., and Matsen, F. A. (1962). J. Phys. Chem. 66, 2332.
Browne, J. C., and Matsen, F. A. (1964). Phys. Rev. 135, 1227.
Browne, J. C., and Miller, J. M. (1962). Technical Report, Molecular Physics Group, University of Texas, Austin, Texas.
Buckingham, R. A., and Dalgarno, A. (1952). Proc. Roy. Soc. (London) A213, 327.
Burhop, E. H. S. (1954). Proc. Phys. Soc. (London) A67, 276.
Colegrove, F. D., Schearer, L. D., and Walter, G. K. (1964). Phys. Rev. 135, 353.

Dunham, J. L. (1932). *Phys. Rev.* **41**, 721.

Ginter, J. (1965). *J. Chem. Phys.* **42**, 561.

Harris, F. E. (1960). *J. Chem. Phys.* **32**, 3.

Harris, F. E., and Taylor, H. E. (1963). *J. Chem. Phys.* **38**, 2591.

Mathis, J. C. (1957). *Astrophys. J.* **125**, 318.

Matsen, F. A., and Poshusta, R. D. (1963). *Phys. Rev.* **132**, 307.

Matsen, F. A., and Scott, D. R. (1965). Unpublished studies at Molecular Physics Group, University of Texas, Austin, Texas.

Matsen, F. A., and Stuart, J. D. (1964). *J. Chem. Phys.* **41**, 1646.

Miller, J. M., Gerhauser, J. M., and Matsen, F. A. (1959). "Quantum Chemistry Integrals and Tables." Univ. of Texas Press, Austin, Texas.

Molnar, J. B., and Phelps, A. V. (1953). *Phys. Rev.* **98**, 120.

Morse, P. M., Young, L. A., and Haurwitz, E. S. (1935). *Phys. Rev.* **48**, 948.

Mulliken, R. S. (1965). *Phys. Rev.* **136**, 962.

Muschlitz, E. E., and Richards, H. L. (1964). *J. Chem. Phys.* **41**, 559.

Nickerson, J. L. (1935). *Phys. Rev.* **47**, 707.

Phelps, A. V. (1955). *Phys. Rev.* **99**, 1307.

Phelps, A. V. (1959). *Phys. Rev.* **114**, 1011.

Reagan, P. N., Browne, J. C., and Matsen, F. A. (1963). *Phys. Rev.* **132**, 304.

Rodriguez, C. E., Browne, J. C., and Matsen, F. A. (1965). Unpublished work at the Molecular Physics Group, University of Texas, Austin, Texas.

Scott, D. R., Greenawalt, E. M., Browne, J. C., and Matsen, F. A. (1966). *J. Chem. Phys.* **44**, 2981.

Tanaka, Y., and Yoshino, K. (1963). *J. Chem. Phys.* **39**, 3081.

Recursion Formula Method for Three-Particle Problems

ARTHUR A. FROST and JASHBHAI C. PATEL

DEPARTMENT OF CHEMISTRY
NORTHWESTERN UNIVERSITY
EVANSTON, ILLINOIS

I. Introduction

This discussion will relate particularly to the approximate solution of the Schrödinger equation for the helium atom and other three-particle Coulombic systems. These problems form the simplest examples of incompletely separable Schrödinger equations where recursion formula methods have been used.

Slater (1927) was one of the first to consider the quantum mechanics of the He atom. The early results of Hylleraas (1929, 1964) served not only to provide a good theoretical ground-state energy of He but also to confirm the essential validity of quantum mechanics. Kato (1951a,b) proved the existence of solutions to the problem and Kinoshita (1957, 1959) and especially Pekeris (1958, 1959) produced results of unusual accuracy.

Recursion formulas in the He problem were first considered by Bartlett et al. (1935) and later by Kinoshita (1957), Pekeris (1958) and Munschy and Pluvinage (1962).

The He calculation has been reviewed by Bethe and Salpeter (1957) and by Hylleraas (1964).

The purpose of the present article is to discuss the relation between recursion formula methods and the variation method ordinarily used for He and similar problems.

II. Coordinates and Function Sets

Restricting the discussion to S states of a general three-particle Coulombic system in the nonrelativistic approximation and with neglect of magnetic interactions it is well known that the wave function involves three nonseparable internal coordinates. Two sets of coordinates will be emphasized in this discussion; interparticle coordinates and perimetric coordinates. For each set of coordinates two or more function sets will be considered.

A. COORDINATES

1. Interparticle Coordinates r_1, r_2, r_{12}. The distances of electrons number 1 and 2 from the nucleus are r_1 and r_2 while r_{12} is the interelectronic distance. If the nucleus or other particle is called particle number 3 a more symmetrical notation may be used:

$$r_1 = r_{13}$$

$$r_2 = r_{23}.$$

2. Hylleraas Coordinates s, t, u. For systems with two like particles such as two electrons the symmetry of the wave function is most easily handled with coordinates defined as:

$$s = r_1 + r_2$$

$$t = -r_1 + r_2$$

$$u = r_{12}.$$

3. Kinoshita Coordinates s, p, q. Kinoshita (1957) showed the advantage to be gained by defining:

$$s = r_1 + r_2 \text{ as before,}$$

$$p = u/s$$

$$q = t/u.$$

In particular a series using positive powers of s, p, q, which bring in negative powers of s and u, can result in a formal solution.

4. Perimetric Coordinates u, v, w. These coordinates were originally defined by Coolidge and James (1937) as:

$$u = r_2 + r_{12} - r_1$$
$$v = r_1 + r_{12} - r_2$$
$$w = r_1 + r_2 - r_{12}.$$

Pekeris (1958) made use of similar coordinates differing by a common scale factor and a factor of 2 in w:

$$w = 2(r_1 + r_2 - r_{12}).$$

The Kinoshita and perimetric coordinates both have an advantage over the other systems mentioned above in that the ranges of the separate coordinates are independent of each other. In interparticle coordinates, for example, the triangular condition

$$|r_1 - r_2| \leq r_{12} \leq r_1 + r_2$$

must be satisfied.

B. FUNCTION SETS

This discussion will involve, and attempt to interrelate, power series, exponential power series, and the series in Laguerre functions as used by Pekeris. Other important function sets have been put forth by Fock (1954) and by Pluvinage (1955) and Munschy and Pluvinage (1957).

1. Power Series. The simple power series in interparticle coordinates

$$\Psi = \sum_{l,m,n} c_{l,m,n} r_1^l r_2^m r_{12}^n \tag{1}$$

was considered by Bartlett *et al.*, (1935). This series yields the simplest recursion formula and is useful in discussing the possibility of a formal solution. Of course it is of no value for a variation method calculation since the separate terms do not satisfy boundary conditions.

2. Exponential Power Series.

$$\Psi = \sum_{l,m,n} c'_{l,m,n} e^{-\zeta(r_1+r_2)} r_1^l r_2^m r_{12}^n. \tag{2}$$

This series and similar series in the other coordinate systems are particularly useful in variation method calculations. Recursion formulas are easily derived.

3. Laguerre Function Series in Perimetric Coordinates.

$$\Psi = \sum_{l,m,n} c''_{l,m,n} \exp[-(u + v + w)/2] L_l^{(u)} L_m^{(v)} L_n^{(w)}. \tag{3}$$

This is the series used by Pekeris.

III. Recursion Formulas

Bartlett *et al.*, (1935) derived the nine-term recursion formula for the simple power series in interparticle coordinates, Eq. (1):

$$
\begin{aligned}
&(l + 2)(l + 3 + n)c_{l+2,m,n} + (m + 2)(m + 3 + n)\,c_{l,m+2,n} \\
&+ (n + 2)(2n + 6 + l + m)\,c_{l,m,n+2} - (l + 2)(n + 2)\,c_{l+2,m-2,n+2} \\
&- (m + 2)(n + 2)\,c_{l-2,m+2,n+2} + (\lambda/4)\,c_{l,m,n} \\
&+ c_{l+1,m,n} + c_{l,m+1,n} - \tfrac{1}{2}c_{l,m,n+1} = 0
\end{aligned}
\tag{4}
$$

Other published recursion formulas for the He problem are the twelve-term formula for the exponential-power series in Kinoshita (1957) coordinates and the 33-term formula of Pekeris (1958) for the series of Eq. (3).

A. The Question of Formal Solutions

Bartlett *et. al.*, (1935) showed that the recursion formula of Eq. (4) does not permit a formal solution. In particular by inserting the sets of values for l, m, and n of $(-1, 2, -1)$, $(-1\ 0, 0)$, and $(1, 0, -1)$, an inconsistent set of equations result for the calculation of $C_{1,0,1}$ in terms of $C_{0,0,0}$. In the same way it can be shown that power series or exponential-power series in any of the coordinate systems 1, 2, or 4 or Section II,A. above do not provide formal solutions.

On the other hand, Kinoshita (1957) proved that the exponential-power series in his coordinate system [Eq. (3) of Section II,A] does give the possibility of a formal solution. This was accomplished by arranging the coefficients, $c_{l,m,n}$, is such an order that each succeeding coefficient could be calculated in terms of the preceding coefficients. That this series forms a formal solution whereas the corresponding Hylleraas series does not was explained by noting that the former differs from the latter by the inclusion of terms with negative exponents on Hylleraas coordinates.

Whether the Pekeris series, Eq. (3), can or cannot be a formal solution seems to be an open question. The 33-term recursion formula is sufficiently complicated so that it is not easy to find an inconsistency by the method of Bartlett, Gibbons, and Dunn nor does it seem likely to be able to put the recursion formula in a form to prove positively that a formal solution exists.

Although Kinoshita presented and discussed the recursion formula for his series he did not make use of it in his numerical calculations. However in the Pekeris calculation the recursion formula was a central feature in the numerical work in that the formula essentially provided all of the matrix components for the variation method secular equation without the direct evaluation of any integrals. In this way, Pekeris (1959) obtained the remarkable precision of ten significant figures for the He atom energy while using up to 1078 terms in the series. This might lead one to believe that the Pekeris series could be a formal solution. This is not necessarily the case since the Pekeris method involves solving a finite secular equation obtained by truncating the infinite matrix resulting from the application of the recursion formula. Even if a formal solution exists the coefficients obtained in the Pekeris calculation will not all satisfy the recursion formula.

B. A PARADOX

The unusual accuracy of the Pekeris calculation might lead one to surmise that his series can be a formal solution. If it be assumed that this is the case then the following paradox would seem to exist. The function $L_l(u)$, for example, is a polynomial of degree l in the variable u. If the Pekeris series, Eq. (3), with terms up through a certain maximum degree $l + m + n$ is expanded it will be in the form of an exponential-power series in perimetric coordinates with terms to this same highest degree. This finite series in turn is equivalent to an exponential-power series in interparticle coordinates to this same degree. Up to this given degree each set of basis functions can be written in terms of any of the other sets. Therefore since both exponential-power series are known to lack formal solutions doubt is cast on the Pekeris series as a formal solution.

The resolution of the paradox, if indeed it actually exists, can be found in terms of transformations between basis sets of functions, in particular between the set of Laguerre functions of perimetric coordinates and the set of functions of the exponential power series in perimetric coordinates. If $\{\varphi_{l,m,n}\}$ and $\{\varphi'_{l,m,n}\}$ are the two basis sets of exponential powers and exponential Laguerre functions as used in Eqs. (2) and (3) which can be represented by infinite row vectors $\boldsymbol{\Phi}$ and $\boldsymbol{\Phi}'$, respectively, an infinite series wave function ψ can be written as

$$\psi = \boldsymbol{\Phi}\mathbf{c} = \boldsymbol{\Phi}'\mathbf{c}' \tag{5}$$

where $\mathbf{c}$ and $\mathbf{c}'$ are column vectors formed from the coefficients in the two series.

Let $\mathbf{T}$ be a transformation matrix such that

$$\boldsymbol{\Phi}' = \boldsymbol{\Phi}\mathbf{T} \quad \text{and} \quad \boldsymbol{\Phi} = \boldsymbol{\Phi}'\mathbf{T}^{-1}. \tag{6}$$

Each column of $\mathbf{T}$ contains a finite set of nonzero numbers which are coefficients in the corresponding product of Laguerre polynomials. Conversely the columns of $\mathbf{T}^{-1}$ are coefficients of exponential powers expressed as linear combinations of Laguerre polynomials. Both $\mathbf{T}$ and $\mathbf{T}^{-1}$ are approximately upper triangular matrixes in that zero elements occur if one goes sufficiently below the main diagonal.

In order for Eq. (5) and Eq. (6) to be satisfied the coefficient vectors must transform as

$$\mathbf{c}' = \mathbf{T}^{-1}\mathbf{c} \quad \text{and} \quad \mathbf{c} = \mathbf{T}\mathbf{c}'. \tag{7}$$

Because of the upper triangular nature of $\mathbf{T}^{-1}$ and $\mathbf{T}$ and the involvement of rows of $\mathbf{T}^{-1}$ and $\mathbf{T}$ in Eq. (7) instead of columns the elements of $\mathbf{c}$ and $\mathbf{c}'$ are related through infinite rather than finite series. It is uncertain in general whether such series converge. If the Pekeris-type infinite series is a formal solution there should be a well-defined vector of coefficients $\mathbf{c}'$. But the infinite series $\mathbf{c} = \mathbf{T}\mathbf{c}'$ may diverge or oscillate, therefore the exponential power series can be understood to lack a formal solution even though the Pekeris series may be a formal solution.

IV. Matrix Formulation

In considering the general three-particle problem in which no one particle is held fixed it has been found useful to use a matrix formulation (Frost, 1964). Allowing all three particles to move relative to the center of mass the Pekeris series recursion formula would expand to 55 terms. Using a simpler exponential-power series in perimetric coordinates yields a 25-term recursion formula (Frost et al., 1964a). After first setting up the 25 term recursion formula matrix it was then easily transformed to what would have been obtained directly from the 55-term recursion formula. The computer programming of the calculation was easier to accomplish by this method than if the 55-term formula had been used directly.

A. Recursion Formulas in Matrix Form

Consider a general series solution of an arbitrary Schrödinger equation in the form

$$(\mathcal{H} - E)\psi = 0 \tag{8}$$

where

$$\psi = \sum_j \varphi_j c_j. \tag{9}$$

By substitution

$$\sum_j (\mathcal{H}\varphi_j - E\varphi_j)c_j = 0 \tag{10}$$

$\mathcal{H}\varphi_j$ can in principle be expanded as a series in φ_i. This series will in general be infinite. However if Eq. (10) is multiplied by a carefully chosen function g, which for the three-particle problem is

$$g = r_{12}r_{13}r_{23},$$

the necessary expansions have a finite number of terms:

$$g\mathscr{H}\varphi_j = \sum_i \varphi_i H_{ij} \tag{11}$$

$$g\varphi_j = \sum_i \varphi_i S_{ij} \tag{12}$$

The expansion coefficients are elements of matrixes defined as **H** and **S**, respectively.

After multiplying by g, Eq. (10) can then be written in matrix form as

$$\mathbf{\Phi}(\mathbf{H} - E\mathbf{S})\mathbf{c} = 0. \tag{13}$$

The recursion formula in matrix form follows from the requirement that the coefficient of each element of $\mathbf{\Phi}$ must be zero, therefore,

$$(\mathbf{H} - E\mathbf{S})\mathbf{c} = 0. \tag{14}$$

That the recursion formula has a finite number of terms corresponds to the matrixes **H** and **S** having only a finite number of nonzero elements in each column even though the matrixes are infinite.

Equation (14) amounts to an infinite number of linear equations in an infinite number of unknowns c_j. To get an approximate solution of the problem it seems necessary to truncate the system of equations to finite size, say n by n, and solve the usual secular equation

$$|\mathbf{H} - E\mathbf{S}|_{n \times n} = 0. \tag{15}$$

In general this does not seeem possible since the matrixes **H** and **S** are not necessarily Hermitian or symmetrical and therefore the eigenvalues E are not necessarily real. Pekeris was successful because with his choice of basis functions which are orthogonal with a weighting factor $1/g$ the matrixes are necessarily symmetrical. It is this truncation of Eq. (14) with symmetrical matrixes that causes the result to be equivalent to the use of the variation method.

This matrix formulation of the quantum mechanical problem has a relation to the linear algebra treatment by Löwdin (1964).

B. Transformation of Recursion Formula Matrixes

By insertion of the product $\mathbf{TT}^{-1}$ both in front of and behind the parenthesis in Eq. (13) and realizing the transformation properties of $\mathbf{\Phi}$ and $\mathbf{c}$ [Eqs. (6) and (7)] it follows that the transformation of **H** and **S** from a basis $\mathbf{\Phi}$ to a basis $\mathbf{\Phi}'$ results in

$$\mathbf{H}' = \mathbf{T}^{-1}\mathbf{HT}$$
$$\mathbf{S}' = \mathbf{T}^{-1}\mathbf{ST}. \tag{16}$$

If a T is known or can be determined such that H' and S' are symmetric where the original H and S are not, a truncated solution can surely be obtained. It is important to note that while for given size matrixes a similarity transformation such as Eq. (16) does not modify eigenvalues this rule does not apply here since the H' and S' are to be truncated after the transformation not before. This procedure was used successfully in the work mentioned in the introduction of Section IV.

V. Extension of Recursion Formula Methods

Following Pekeris' lead it would be desirable for general atomic and molecular problems to be able to choose a reasonably simple set of functions in some suitable coordinate system such that matrixes H and S can be calculated according to the definitions in Eqs. (11) and (12). The procedure would be to find a transformation T such that H' and S' would be symmetrical.

The first part of this procedure has been accomplished with exponential-power functions in interparticle coordinates (Frost *et al.*, 1964b). Unfortunately neither the similarity transformation nor an alternate method of symmetrization which was tried has been sufficiently successful. Not all conceivable schemes for symmetrization have been exhausted so there may still be a prospect.

It has occurred to several workers that the original typically unsymmetrical matrixes might still yield a practical solution by some limiting process as the size of the truncation is increased. So far, only trivial cases where the recursion formula has no more than three terms has been successful by this method.

ACKNOWLEDGMENT

This research has been supported by a grant from the National Science Foundation.

REFERENCES

Bartlett, J. H., Gibbons, J. J., and Dunn, C. G. (1935). *Phys. Rev.* **47**, 679.
Bethe, H. A., and Salpeter, E. E. (1957). *In* "Quantum Mechanics of One- and Two-Electron Atoms." Academic Press, New York.
Coolidge, A. S., and James, H. M. (1937). *Phys. Rev.* **51**, 855.
Fock, V. A. (1954). *Izv. Akad. Nauk. SSSR, Ser. Fiz.* **18**, 161 (National Research Council of Canada, Technical Translation, TT-503).
Frost, A. A. (1964). *J. Chem. Phys.* **41**, 478.
Frost, A. A., Inokuti, M., and Lowe, J. P. (1964a). *J. Chem. Phys.* **41**, 482.
Frost, A. A., Harriss, D. K., and Scargle, J. D. (1964b). *J. Chem. Phys.* **41**, 489.
Hylleraas, E. A. (1929). *Z. Physik* **54**, 347.
Hylleraas, E. A. (1964). *Advan. Quan. Chem.* **I**, 1–33.
Kato, T. (1951a). *Trans. Am. Math. Soc.* **70**, 195.
Kato, T. (1951b). *Trans. Am. Math. Soc.* **70**, 212.

Kinoshita, T. (1957). *Phys. Rev.* **105**, 1490.
Kinoshita, T. (1959). *Phys. Rev.* **115**, 366.
Löwdin, P.-O. (1964). Quantum Chemistry Group, Scientific Report No. 20. University of Uppsala, Sweden.
Munschy, G., and Pluvinage, P. (1957). *J. Phys. Radium* **18**, 157.
Munschy, G., and Pluvinage, P. (1962). *J. Phys. Radium* **23**, 184.
Pekeris, C. L. (1958). *Phys. Rev.* **112**, 1649.
Pekeris, C. L. (1959). *Phys. Rev.* **115**, 1216.
Pluvinage, P. (1955). *J. Phys. Radium* **16**, 675.
Slater, J. C. (1927). *Proc. Natl. Acad. Sci. U.S.* **13**, 423.

Computation of the Magnetic Hyperfine Structure of Atomic S-States

R. K. NESBET

IBM RESEARCH LABORATORY
SAN JOSE, CALIFORNIA

I. Introduction

It was first pointed out by Slater (1951) that solutions of the ordinary Hartree-Fock equations must exist in which electrons of different spin, $m_s = \pm 1/2$, are described by significantly different one-electron Hamiltonian operators. This is obviously true for a molecule such as H_2 at large internuclear separation, and can be expected to be true for antiferromagnetic materials (Slater, 1951). An analysis of the Hartree-Fock equations obtained by requiring the energy of a single Slater determinant to be stationary, with no constraint other than normalization, shows that for general open-shell configurations the effective one-electron Hamiltonian necessarily has symmetry lower than that of the many-electron Hamiltonian (Nesbet, 1955). For atoms, unless $L = 0$, the equations differ for different values of m_l and mix different values of l, and unless $S = 0$, the equations depend on m_s. The ground states of $B(^2P)$ and $Li(^2S)$ were discussed in this reference as examples, respectively, of reduced orbital and spin symmetry of the one-electron Hamiltonian. The theorems of Brillouin (1934) and of Møller and Plesset (1934), which show that Hartree-Fock one-electron properties of many-electron systems are subject to corrections only of second order and higher in the many-particle perturbation theory, are valid only when such properties are calculated in the *unrestricted* Hartree-Fock (UHF) approximation, with a one-electron Hamiltonian of reduced symmetry for an open-shell configuration. Conversely,

157

if the variational equations are constrained by a *symmetry* restriction (not allowing different l values to mix) or by an *equivalence* restriction (using the same one-electron Hamiltonian for all m_l values or for both m_s values), one-electron properties are subject to first-order corrections. This is the usual situation for traditional Hartree-Fock calculations in open-shell configurations (Nesbet, 1955, 1961). The m_s equivalence restriction in $Li(^2S)$ has also been discussed by Pratt (1956).

Relaxation of the m_s equivalence restriction is especially important in calculating the Fermi contact term (Fermi, 1930) in magnetic hyperfine structure,

$$a_s = \frac{8\pi}{3}\left(\frac{\mu_I}{I}\right)\left(\frac{\mu_B}{J}\right)[\rho_+(0) - \rho_-(0)]. \tag{1}$$

Here μ_I is the nuclear magnetic moment, I the nuclear spin, μ_B the Bohr magneton, J the total electronic angular momentum, $\rho_+(0)$ the $m_s = +1/2$ electron density at the nucleus, and $\rho_-(0)$ the $m_s = -1/2$ density at the nucleus. In atomic S-states ($L = 0$) this is the only contribution to the magnetic hyperfine structure. Since one-electron wave functions (orbitals) with l greater than zero vanish at the nucleus, a_s depends only on the atomic s-orbitals. Under m_s equivalence restriction, inner closed-shell orbitals are doubly occupied, and contributions to Eq. (1) cancel out identically. If s-orbitals of different spin are allowed to have different radial functions there can be a net contribution from the inner shell orbitals, induced by an incomplete outer shell. When the incomplete shell contains no s-orbitals, as in the $1s^2 2s^2 2p^3 (^4S)$ ground state configuration of nitrogen, the Fermi contact term vanishes in the traditional Hartree-Fock approximation, although a quite large magnetic hyperfine splitting is observed for $N(^4S)$. To compute this splitting it is necessary to take into account the polarization of the nominally closed inner shells by the unsymmetrical exchange interaction with the half-filled $2p^3$ shell.

This paper will be concerned with calculations of a_s for atoms in S-states, in particular for the ^2S ground states of Li and Na and for the ^4S ground states of N and P. Since L vanishes, the UHF method for these states is equivalent to the spin-polarized Hartree-Fock (SPHF) method, in which the m_s equivalence restriction is relaxed without reference to other symmetry or equivalence restrictions. The matrix form of the SPHF equations is due to Pople and Nesbet (1954) and to Berthier (1954), and these equations have been used for calculations reported here. The terminology "spin-polarized" was suggested by Watson and Freeman (1960), who carried out SPHF calculations on the $3d^8(^3F)$ ground state of Ni^{++}. No true UHF calculation has yet been published except for atomic S-states.

While, by the usual variational criterion, the UHF equations lead to a better wave function than does the traditional Hartree-Fock method, the UHF function is in general a mixture of states of definite symmetry (^2S and ^4S for the ground state of Li), and the dependence of orbital radial factors on m_s and m_l makes the calculation of corrections to the UHF approximation considerably more awkward than in the traditional theory. To avoid these difficulties, it was suggested that it might be more convenient to use perturbation theory to evaluate effects of the one-particle excitation matrix elements that occur as a consequence of symmetry and equivalence restrictions than to use the UHF method directly (Nesbet, 1955). More detailed arguments (Marshall, 1961; Bessis *et al.*, 1961) have shown that these alternative approaches should lead to essentially identical results, although in the UHF method the trial wave function is not an angular momentum eigenfunction, while it is in the perturbation method. The value of a_s obtained by projecting an angular momentum eigenfunction out of the UHF function is substantially different from the UHF or perturbation theory value. Without a direct variational calculation of the projected function, the projected value of a_s has little theoretical justification.

In the case of $^{31}P(^4S)$ a very serious disagreement exists between the experimental value of a_s and theoretical values computed by the UHF or perturbation methods (Bessis *et al.*, 1964). Theoretical results on atoms with ^2S or ^4S ground states are reviewed in Section II, below, and some new UHF calculations are reported which confirm the previously published work. In Section III, a new method is proposed for computing one-electron properties of atoms to high accuracy, and preliminary results on Li(^2S) are reported.

II. Unrestricted Hartree-Fock Calculations for Li, N, Na, and P

Since Eq. (1) contains two experimental quantities, a_s and μ_I, it is convenient to define the experimental Fermi contact parameter

$$f = 4\pi(\rho_+(0) - \rho_-(0)) \tag{2}$$

$$= IJa_s/31.8027 \, \mu_I \tag{3}$$

in units a_0^{-3} if a_s is given in megacycles per second and μ_I in nuclear magnetons. The constant in Eq. (3) is computed from Eq. (1), using recently tabulated values of fundamental constants (NAS-NRC Committee, 1964). The parameter f computed for a single determinant wave function is the sum of squared amplitudes of radial factors of s-orbitals with spin $m_s = +1/2$ minus the corresponding sum for spin $m_s = -1/2$, evaluated at $r = 0$.

In Li(^2S) the value of f computed in the traditional Hartree-Fock approximation is only $2.07 \, a_0^{-3}$, compared with the observed value, $2.91 \, a_0^{-3}$. Calculations by both the perturbation (Nesbet, 1956, 1960) and UHF (Sachs, 1960) methods are in reasonable agreement with experiment, showing that the relatively large correction to the traditional Hartree-Fock result is almost entirely due to the exchange polarization effect. A similar result is obtained by Cohen et al. (1959), who treat the unbalanced exchange integral as a perturbation in the ordinary Hartree-Fock equations, solved by numerical methods.

To verify this work, and to provide computations of comparable accuracy for $Li(^2S)$, $N(^4S)$, $Na(^2S)$, and $P(^4S)$, new UHF calculations have been carried out using orbital basis sets that give accurate traditional Hartree-Fock functions (Clementi, 1965). Results are tabulated in Table 1. It can be seen that there is a striking disagreement with experiment for both $N(^4S)$ and $P(^4S)$, and that the error in f for $Na(^2S)$ is considerably larger than that for $Li(^2S)$.

SPHF calculations, using Hartree's numerical integration method, were carried out on a number of atoms by Goodings (1961). It was found that f for $N(^4S)$ is much greater than the observed value, and is comparable to the computed value given in Table 1. Results for Li and Na are similar to those given here.

A number of calculations on $N(^4S)$ were reported by Bessis et al. (1961). The best UHF result for f (lowest variational energy) agrees with the result in Table 1, three times greater than the observed Fermi contact parameter. However, several different perturbation calculations gave results much closer to experiment. Configuration interaction calculations that included pair

TABLE 1

FERMI CONTACT PARAMETERS $f(a_0^{-3})$ AND COMPUTED HARTREE-FOCK ENERGIES
E(HARTREE ATOMIC UNITS, e^2/a_0)

Atomic state	$E(HF)^a$	$E(UHF)^b$	$f(UHF)^b$	$f(obs)^c$
Li (^2S)	-7.432726	-7.432745	2.923	2.90960
N (^4S)	-54.400904	-54.403838	3.753	1.22099
Na(^2S)	-161.85857	-161.85857	8.210	9.42027
P (^4S)	-340.71857	-340.71878	-2.240	1.14736

[a] Clementi (1965). HF refers to the traditional Hartree-Fock method.
[b] Computed with same orbital basis set as Clementi (1965).
[c] Obtained by Eq. (3) from the following data:

$\mu_1(^7Li) = 3.256310$ nm (Ramsey, 1956)
$a(^7Li; {}^2S) = 401.756$ Mc/sec (Kusch and Taub, 1949)
$\mu_1(^{14}N) = 0.40371$ nm (Ramsey, 1956)
$a(^{14}N; {}^4S) = 10.45091$ Mc/sec (Anderson et al., 1959)
$\mu_1(^{23}Na) = 2.21753$ nm (Ramsey, 1956)
$a(^{23}Na; {}^2S) = 885.80$ Mc/sec (Kusch and Taub, 1949)
$\mu_1(^{31}P) = 1.13162$ nm (Ramsey, 1956)
$a(^{31}P; {}^4S) = 55.0557$ Mc/sec (Lambert and Pipkin, 1962)

correlation terms as well as the exchange polarization effect appeared to give a value of f close to experiment.

Calculations on Na(^2S) by Cohen *et al.* (1959) and by Goodings (1961) give a result for f similar to that in Table 1. The disagreement with experiment is greater for Na than for Li, but not so striking as it is for N and P. Calculations on P(^4S) by both the perturbation and UHF methods (Bessis *et al.*, 1964) consistently give negative values of f. The experimental sign of a_s for ^{31}P(^4S) has recently been redetermined (Pendlebury and Smith, 1964), verifying the positive sign of f indicated in Table 1.

There appears to be a large qualitative difference between the accuracy of the UHF results for s(^2S) and p^3(^4S) electronic configurations. In view of the serious disagreement with experiment for both N(^4S) and P(^4S), it is reasonable to look for correlation corrections to f (improvements beyond the UHF approximation) that are sensitive to the structure of the electronic valence shell. A new method for analysis and computation of such corrections is presented in the following section.

III. Use of Bethe-Goldstone Equations to Compute One-Electron Properties of Atoms

In principle one can represent a stationary state many-electron wave function to arbitrary accuracy as a linear combination of the complete orthonormal set of Slater determinants

$$\Phi_{ijk\cdots}^{abc\cdots}, \qquad i < j < k < \cdots \leq N < a < b < c < \cdots, \qquad (4)$$

constructed from a complete orthonormal set of orbital functions that includes the N occupied orbitals ϕ_i of a reference state Slater determinant

$$\Phi_0 = \det \phi_1(1) \cdots \phi_i(i) \cdots \phi_N(N), \qquad (5)$$

where det represents the total antisymmetrizing operator, with a normalization factor $(N!)^{-1/2}$. The Slater determinant indicated in Eq. (4) is obtained from Φ_0 by replacing occupied orbitals ϕ_i, ϕ_j, ..., by unoccupied orbitals ϕ_a, ϕ_b, ... from the complete set. If the Slater determinants of Eq. (4) are denoted in general by Φ_μ, the coefficients c_μ in the expansion of an exact wave function

$$\Psi = \sum_\mu \Phi_\mu c_\mu \qquad (6)$$

are obtained by the Rayleigh-Ritz variational principle, and occur as components of eigenvectors of the configuration interaction matrix

$$H_{\mu\nu} = (\Phi_\mu, H\Phi_\nu), \qquad (7)$$

where H is the many-electron Hamiltonian. The same formalism applies in a finite orbital basis, and Ψ approaches an exact wave function as such a basis is extended to become complete.

The Bethe-Goldstone equation (Bethe and Goldstone, 1957) is the time independent Schrödinger equation for two particles of an N-particle system. The interaction with the remaining N-2 particles is represented by a self-consistent field analogous to that of the Hartree-Fock theory, and by an orthogonality constraint. In the theory of Brueckner (Brueckner et al., 1954; Brueckner, 1954, 1955; Brueckner and Levinson, 1955; Brueckner and Wada, 1956) the equivalent integral equations are derived from multiple scattering formalism. Given N orthonormal orbitals for an N-particle system, Bethe-Goldstone equations are solved independently for each possible pair of orbitals.

In terms of configuration interaction, with reference state Φ_0 determined by N specified occupied orbitals, the Bethe-Goldstone equation for pair ij is just the variational equation for a trial wave function.

$$\Psi_{ij} = \Phi_0 + \sum_a \Phi_i^a c_i^a + \sum_b \Phi_j^b c_j^b + \sum_{ab} \Phi_{ij}^{ab} c_{ij}^{ab}. \qquad (8)$$

The configuration interaction matrix is diagonalized over the set of Slater determinants Φ_0, Φ_i^a, Φ_j^b, Φ_{ij}^{ab} for a specified pair ij. The energy eigenvalue is expressed as $H_{00} + E_{ij}$, defining an energy increment or pair correlation energy for orbital pair ij. If Φ_0 is a Hartree-Fock function (Nesbet, 1958), the total correlation energy is approximated by $\sum_{ij} E_{ij}$.

When expressed in this form, it is clear that the Bethe-Goldstone equation is a special case of a more general concept, which might be characterized as Bethe-Goldstone equations of order n, referring to the exact solution of an n-particle problem, subject to the constraint of strong orthogonality to N-n orbitals of a specified orthonormal set. Thus, in matrix form, the third order Bethe-Goldstone equation for triplet ijk is equivalent to diagonalization of the configuration interaction matrix over the set of determinants Φ_0, Φ_i^a, Φ_j^b, Φ_k^c, Φ_{ij}^{ab}, Φ_{ik}^{ac}, Φ_{jk}^{bc}, Φ_{ijk}^{abc} for a specified set of three orbitals ϕ_i, ϕ_j, ϕ_k. By definition orbitals ϕ_a, ϕ_b, ϕ_c are orthogonal to the N orbitals $\{\phi_i\}$ occupied in Φ_0. The sequence of calculations indicated by solving Bethe-Goldstone equations of successively higher order eventually terminates in an exact solution of the N-particle problem. The increments of energy or any other physical quantity obtained in successively higher orders form a series whose sum is the exact value for a stationary state wave function. If this series converges sufficiently rapidly (to 2nd or 3rd order terms) this procedure would provide a practicable computational method.

Preliminary results for the Fermi contact parameter f for Li(^2S) obtained by this method are given in Table 2. The orbital basis set used is extremely limited, consisting only of the five s-orbitals used by Clementi (1965) to

TABLE 2

ANALYSIS OF FERMI CONTACT PARAMETER FOR Li(^2S)

Indices 1, 2, 3 denote $1s\beta$, $1s\alpha$, $2s\alpha$, respectively.		
$f_0 = F_0$	2.066865	a_0^{-3}
$f_1 = F_1 - f_0$	0.707176	
$f_2 = F_2 - f_0$	0.000013	
$f_3 = F_3 - f_0$	0.000007	
$f_{12} = F_{12} - f_0 - f_1 - f_2$	0.090140	
$f_{13} = F_{13} - f_0 - f_1 - f_3$	0.060908	
$f_{23} = F_{23} - f_0 - f_2 - f_3$	-0.000187	
$f_{123} = F_{123} - f_0 - f_1 - f_2 - f_3$		
$\quad\quad\quad - f_{12} - f_{13} - f_{23}$	-0.066832	
f	2.858090	
f_{exp}	2.90960	

expand the occupied Hartree-Fock orbitals. In Table 2, the notation $F_{ij\ldots}$ is used for the computed mean value of the one-electron operator F whose mean value for a single Slater determinant is the parameter f of Eq. (2). $F_{ij\ldots}$ is computed in principle from the Bethe-Goldstone wave functions $\Psi_{ij\ldots}$, analogous to Eq. (8). Because all coefficients c_μ ($\mu \neq 0$) are small in the present calculations, squares of these coefficients have been neglected, giving the approximate formula, if all numbers are real,

$$F_{ij\ldots} - F_0 \cong 2\sum{}'_\mu F_{0\mu} c_\mu, \tag{9}$$

where $\mu \neq 0$ in the primed summation. Equation (9) is used to compute the quantities in Table 2.

It is clear from Table 2 that the present method provides a very detailed analysis of properties of a many-electron system. The dominant correction to the traditional Hartree-Fock value, f_0, is the exchange polarization term, f_1. The two significant pair-correlation terms f_{12} and f_{13} are an order of magnitude smaller.

IV. Discussion

Although the calculation on Li(^2S) reported in Table 2 is incomplete, using only a limited basis set of s-orbitals, the method used is capable of giving definitive results. Each of the quantities $F_{ij\ldots}$ is obtained from a wave function $\Psi_{ij\ldots}$ that is obtained variationally. For this reason each of the quantities $f_{ij\ldots}$ has a well-defined limit that can be approached by a series of variational calculations. In terms of matrix calculations with limited orbital basis sets, a separate basis set can be chosen for each of these variational calculations, if necessary, and a given $f_{ij\ldots}$ will be known to have converged to a specified accuracy if further additions to the orbital basis sets do not influence a specified significant digit. In this way the work of computation can be concentrated on the particular $f_{ij...}$ values that are largest or most sensitive to changes in the orbital basis set.

For $\text{Li}(^2S)$, orbitals with $l > 0$ can contribute only to second- or third-order Bethe-Goldstone equations. With the basis set used here (all s-orbitals), f_0 and f_1 should be close to their limiting values. f_2 and f_3 can be made to vanish identically by tightening the convergence criterion of the Hartree-Fock calculation. Further changes due to electronic correlation will occur in f_{12}, f_{13}, f_{23}, and f_{123}. It seems very likely that f_1 will continue to dominate the final values of these quantities.

This conclusion is in apparent disagreement with Berggren and Wood (1961), who argue on the basis of calculations with nonorthogonal three-electron functions that correlation effects are more important than exchange polarization in determining f for $\text{Li}(^2S)$. This perhaps is only a question of terminology, since there is no simple way to analyze the wave functions of Berggren and Wood to give terms analogous to those in Table 1. The characterization of f_1 as an exchange polarization effect and of f_{12} and f_{13} as pair correlation effects is based on Brillouin's theorem, discussed in Section I, above.

A method of computation of correlation energy closely related to the method of Brueckner, Bethe, and Goldstone has been proposed by Sinanoğlu (1962a,b, 1964). The method proposed here, which is based directly on nth order Bethe-Goldstone equations, has the advantage of defining a computational procedure with an exact solution of the Schrödinger equation as the nth order limit, and of providing an algorithm for the computation of physical properties other than the energy.

Results of calculations on Li, N, Na, and P by the method of Section III will be reported in a subsequent publication.

REFERENCES

Anderson, L. W., Pipkin, F. M., and Baird, Jr., J. C. (1959). *Phys. Rev.* **116**, 87.
Berggren, K. F., and Wood, R. F. (1961). *Phys. Rev.* **130**, 198.
Berthier, G. (1954). *J. Chim. Phys.* **51**, 363.
Bessis, N., Lefebvre-Brion, H., and Moser, C. M. (1961). *Phys. Rev.* **124**, 1124.
Bessis, N., Lefebvre-Brion, H., Moser, C. M., Freeman, A. J., Nesbet, R. K., and Watson, R. E. (1964). *Phys. Rev.* **135**. A588.
Bethe, H. A., and Goldstone, J. (1957). *Proc. Roy. Soc. (London)* **A238**, 551.
Brillouin, L. (1934). *Actualités Sci. Ind.* **159**. Hermann et Cie., Paris.
Brueckner, K. A. (1954). *Phys. Rev.* **96**, 508.
Brueckner, K. A. (1955). *Phys. Rev.* **97**, 1353.
Brueckner, K. A., and Levinson, C. A. (1955). *Phys. Rev.* **97**, 1344.
Brueckner, K. A., and Wada, W. (1956). *Phys. Rev.* **103**, 1008.
Brueckner, K. A., Levinson, C. A., and Mahmoud, H. M. (1954). *Phys. Rev.* **95**, 217.

Clementi, E. (1965). *IBM J. Res. Develop.* **9**, 2. *Suppl.* Tables 4-1, 10-1, 18-1, 24-1.
Cohen, M. H., Goodings, D. A., and Heine, V. (1959). *Proc. Phys. Soc.* (*London*) **73**, 811.
Fermi, E. (1930). *Z. Physik* **60**, 320.
Goodings, D. A. (1961). *Phys. Rev.* **123**, 1706.
Kusch, P., and Taub, H. (1949). *Phys. Rev.* **75**, 1477.
Lambert, R. H., and Pipkin, F. M. (1962). *Phys. Rev.* **128**, 198.
Marshall, W. (1961). *Proc. Phys. Soc.* (*London*) **A78**, 113.
Møller, C., and Plesset, M. S. (1934). *Phys. Rev.* **46**, 618.
NAS-NRC Committee (1964). *Physics Today* **17**, 48.
Nesbet, R. K. (1955). *Proc. Roy. Soc.* (*London*) **A230**, 312.
Nesbet, R. K. (1956). *Quarterly Progress Report, Solid State and Molecular Theory Group*, MIT. July 15, p. 3, Oct. 15, p. 47. Unpublished.
Nesbet, R. K. (1958). *Phys. Rev.* **109**, 1632.
Nesbet, R. K. (1960). *Phys. Rev.* **118**, 681.
Nesbet, R. K. (1961). *Rev. Mod. Phys.* **33**, 28.
Pendlebury, J. M., and Smith, K. F. (1964). *Proc. Phys. Soc.* (*London*) **84**, 849.
Pople, J. A., and Nesbet, R. K. (1954). *J. Chem. Phys.* **22**, 571.
Pratt, Jr., G. W. (1956). *Phys. Rev.* **102**, 1303.
Ramsey, N. F. (1956). "Molecular Beams," p. 172. Oxford Univ. Press, London and New York.
Sachs, L. M. (1960). *Phys. Rev.* **117**, 1504.
Sinanoğlu, O. (1962a). *J. Chem. Phys.* **36**, 706.
Sinanoğlu, O. (1962b). *J. Chem. Phys.* **36**, 3198.
Sinanoğlu, O. (1964). *Adv. Chem. Phys.* **6**, 315.
Slater, J. C. (1951). *Phys. Rev.* **82**, 538.
Watson, R. E., and Freeman, A. J. (1960). *Phys. Rev.* **120**, 1125.

Application of Quantum Theory to Atomic Processes Occurring in Planetary Nebulae

S. J. CZYZAK and T. K. KRUEGER

GENERAL PHYSICS LABORATORY, AEROSPACE RESEARCH LABORATORIES
WRIGHT-PATTERSON AIR FORCE BASE, DAYTON, OHIO

I. Introduction

Considerable progress has been made in recent years on the understanding of nebulae, especially the planetaries; this is due, in some measure, to the advances made in the theoretical investigation of atomic processes which occur in nebulae. We shall not attempt to discuss what is already known about these objects because this material has been thoroughly covered in the literature and summarized in a number of reviews (see Aller, 1956; Dufay, 1954; Osterbrock, 1964; Seaton, 1960; Wurm, 1951; Vorontsov-Velyaminov, 1953); but, instead we shall be primarily concerned with the advances that have been made in calculating atomic parameters which are used in determining some of the properties of nebulae, i.e., the emphasis will be on the spectroscopic and hence the atomic structure problems.

Interstellar matter may be divided, somewhat superficially, into three general categories, namely, interstellar matter, dark nebulae, and luminous nebulae. The last of these can be further separated into diffuse (or irregular) and planetary nebulae. Interstellar matter consists of gas and dust in interstellar space, the gas being primarily hydrogen and helium (approximately 96% by mass) and the dust consists of microscopic solid grains (of the order of 10^{-5} cm) believed to be mostly dielectric compounds of hydrogen and other common elements. The interstellar matter is not homogeneously distributed (patchy) throughout space, but instead tends to be more dense in some areas than in others, i.e., it tends to form clouds or nebulae. These nebulae may or may not be visible. This depends on whether there are stars imbedded in the nebula to supply the light source, as for example in Orion nebula, or whether a strong star field is in the region to silhouette the nebula against the star field, as in the case of the Horsehead nebula.

The existence of interstellar gas and dust has been abundantly confirmed by the analysis of the spectra and luminosity of certain B stars. By using distant B stars near the galactic plane, analysis reveals that the B stars are redder than they should be and also show a few very sharp, but faint, lines that are due to the interstellar gas. These lines were first noted in the spectra of spectroscopic binaries because such lines did not take part in the periodic oscillation of the stellar lines. Common interstellar lines are due to the H and K lines of Ca^+, Ca, K, Na, and Ti^+. There are also interstellar molecular bands some of which have been identified as CH, CN, and CH^+. The reddening, on the other hand, is caused by the interstellar dust, which scatters the star light before it reaches the observer.

As implied above, nonluminous clouds of solid dustlike material and gas occur between the stars in many parts of the spiral arms of our galaxy and other galaxies. If a cloud lies in front of a dense star field it shows up as a silhouette which is a dark nebula. Dark nebulae reflect some light of the very distant stars but the reflected light intensity is so low that they are black for all practical purposes. Their existence is determined by the fact that they partially conceal luminous objects behind them. There is also evidence of the coexistence of dark and bright nebulae in the same region, as for example in the region of the star Rho Ophiuchi.

The luminous nebulae as well as the dark nebulae are not self-luminous; it is the stars imbedded in the nebula that are the primary source for illumination. Diffuse nebulae are associated with fairly luminous stars, and it is through one of two processes caused by the emission of light from a star or stars that cause the nebula to appear as a bright object. These nebulae are associated with Type I population and they are normally irregular in form, often of low density and sometimes of considerable size, such as Orion, 30 Doradus in the Large Magellanic Cloud and NGC 604 in the Triangulum Spiral. The two processes, either of which will illuminate a nebula are: (1) reflection of starlight and (2) fluorescence. Those nebulae that are illuminated by the reflection of starlight normally have stars of the B2 or later spectral class imbedded in them. These stars emit radiation whose energy maximum is insufficient to excite or ionize the nebular atoms, i.e., they have too little radiation beyond the Lyman limit to ionize hydrogen and the other atoms in the large volume of the surrounding nebula. Hence, the light from these stars is reflected by the nebula as is indicated by the spectrograms in that they show a typical absorption line spectra that would be observed in stars. These nebulae are often referred to as reflection nebulae. Thus if stars of this type were imbedded in a dark nebula it would appear as a reflection nebula. Some of these nebulae are very large so that only the central parts are illuminated by stars. Reflection nebulae which are star-illuminated dark nebulae have been identified; an example of these is the nebula NGC 7023. For this case, the outer region appears as a dark nebula that almost completely masks the stars beyond it. There are of course no known totally opaque nebulae; the absorption range varies from 30 to 95 %. The illumination process causing fluorescence is due to the light from B1 or earlier spectral class stars and if the nebula is examined spectro-scopically a bright line spectrum is obtained. These stars are very hot ($\geq 25{,}000°K$), and starlight emitted from them is largely in the ultraviolet region (energy peak at approximately 900 Å). Here enough energy radiation beyond the limit of the Lyman series is available to excite or ionize hydrogen and the other nebular atoms. The atoms either absorb this radiation and emit light of longer wavelengths by variously cascading from one energy level to another and finally to the ground state yielding the characteristic emission spectrum, or else if the energy available is sufficiently high the atoms may be ionized one or more times. The latter, a photoionization process, is one of the most important atomic processes that occurs in the nebula. Nebulae in which the fluorescence process occurs are often referred to as emission nebulae.

Planetary nebulae are associated with Type II population and are often symmetrical in form and smaller than the diffuse nebulae. Many have a higher surface brightness and higher density than the better known diffuse nebulae. Just as in the case of diffuse nebulae illumination is due to the fluorescence process. Of the approximately 700 planetary nebulae known in our galaxy, spectra and direct photographs are available for about half of them. Detailed investigations have been carried out on approximately 30 of them.

II. Planetary Nebulae

Planetary nebulae, as indicated earlier, are clouds of ionized gas which receive their radiation from certain hot central stars contained within them. The ultraviolet radiation from the central star is absorbed by the surrounding gas exciting and/or ionizing the atoms within the nebula which then emit light. The emitted light gives the nebula a pale green disklike appearance resembling that of the planets Uranus and Neptune, hence the name planetary. Planetary nebulae are Type II population objects, although not members of the extreme halo branch, which are fairly small masses of gas, i.e., the masses vary over a wide range (probably 0.01 to 0.3 solar masses) but never exceed one solar mass, and are not strongly concentrated towards the galactic plane. The physical dimensions of these nebulae are of the order of 10^{17} cm or 10^6 solar radii. The radiation from the star is diluted by a factor of $(r_*/2R)^2$, where r_* is the radius of the star and R is the distance from the star to nebula. The electron temperatures T_ε are of the order of $10^{4\circ}$K, and the electron densities are of the order of 10^4 cm^{-3}. Chemically, the nebula consists mainly of hydrogen with helium being the next most abundant element (approximately 1/6 that of hydrogen) and all other elements being even less abundant, as for example the important element oxygen which is present in a ratio of 1/1000 to that of hydrogen. The atomic processes occurring in planetary nebulae are quite similar to those in diffuse nebulae. The spectrum of a planetary contains emission lines and a background continuum. Thus, in a study of a planetary nebular spectrum one would hope to obtain information about the temperature, density, and chemical composition of the object, as well as the nature of the diluted radiation received from the central star, based on the atomic processes taking place in the nebula (a low-density plasma). The unique feature of planetary nebulae is the close relation between the central star and the nebula. Unlike the other types of nebulae, the nebular gas most probably has been ejected from the central star, with its mass being a small fraction of that of the star, and having an expansion velocity of the order of 20 km/sec.

The central stars or nuclei in planetaries cover a wide range of surface temperatures, hence very little information can be obtained regarding their true luminosities from their magnitudes alone. These nuclei are all hot stars with the temperatures ranging upwards from 25,000°K. The spectra of these nuclei appear to be similar to certain stars of the Type I population although they themselves belong to the Type II population. Their spectra may be divided into four main groups, namely the Wolf-Rayet type, the Of type with combined emission and absorption lines, the O-type with absorption lines only, and continuous spectra without absorption or emission lines observed. A very thorough and detailed exposition of stars in nebulae has been given by Aller (1956).

To interpret the central stars in nebulae, it is necessary to obtain quantitative spectrophotometric data in order to study the profiles and intensities of the absorption and emission lines in the spectra of these nuclei. Excitation temperatures and chemical composition of these nuclei can then be estimated from the absorption or emission lines. One may also deduce the central star temperatures from the nebular spectrum using both allowed and forbidden nebular lines (see Menzel, 1962).

If the nuclei of the planetary nebulae are assumed to radiate as black bodies, then the density of radiation ρ_v^* in the thermodynamic equilibrium at the star temperature T_* is

$$\rho_v^* = \frac{8\pi h v^3}{c^3} \frac{1}{\exp(hv/kT_*) - 1}. \tag{1}$$

At the surface of the star the density of radiation is $\frac{1}{2}\rho_v^*$, but as the distance from the surface of star is increased the radiation is diluted by a ratio of $\frac{1}{4}(r^*/R)^2$ for a nebula, so that Eq. (1) becomes

$$\rho_v^* = \frac{2\pi h v^3}{c^3} \left(\frac{r_*}{R}\right)^2 \frac{1}{\exp(hv/kT_*) - 1} \tag{2}$$

Thus, on the basis of this equation there are three parameters to determine, namely, the star radius r_*, star temperature T_*, and the distance R from the center. It is still necessary to take into account the direction in which the radiation process takes place. Rosseland's theorem states that, for a dilution of radiation, quanta of high frequency are more likely to transform into quanta of low frequency than the converse. In a nebula the converse may be completely neglected and only transformation from high to low frequency need be considered. Since central stars are very hot, part of the energy in the ultraviolet region which is transformed into visible radiation by the nebula exceeds the energy that is emitted by the central star in the visible region, so that the nebulae have greater visual luminosities than their nuclei.

It has been assumed in Eq. (2) that the nebula does not contribute anything to the radiation, whereas it is the nebula that supplies the diffuse radiation from the hydrogen, helium, and other elements within it, by photoionization and recombination of H I, He I, and He II and by the forbidden transitions of the heavier elements. As a matter of fact, the temperatures of planetary nuclei were first estimated on theories of excitation of the nebula. If a nebular shell is optically thick* then the radiation beyond the Lyman limit emitted by the nucleus would be absorbed. Zanstra (1927, 1931a,b) showed that for H I each Lyman continuum quanta would be transformed into a Lyman α (Ly_α^*) quantum and a Balmer series quantum or continuum. Thus the total number of quanta emitted by the central star beyond the Lyman limit (Ly_c^*) must equal the total number of quanta in the Balmer series plus the continuum, i.e., $N_{Ba+Ba_c} = N_{Ly_c}^*$. In general it can be stated that the number of Balmer quanta emitted by the nebula does not exceed the number of Ly_c^* quanta emitted by the central star, or $N_{Ba} \leq N_{Ly_c}^*$. The N_{Ba+Ba_c} then gives a lower limit to the number of $N_{Ly_c}^*$. By comparing the intensities of nebular Balmer lines with that of the underlying stellar continuum the temperature of the central star can be estimated, assuming that it radiates as a black body. Analogous reasoning may be employed for cases where He II lines are observed except, of course, here the Paschen and Brackett series are observed rather than the Lyman and Balmer ones. Thus the temperatures may be obtained from both H I and He II.

---

* Optical thickness is defined as $\tau = \int k_v \rho \, ds$, when k_v is the absorption coefficient, ρ is the density of the absorbing material, and s is the thickness of the absorbing layer.

The total number of quanta emitted by the star beyond the Lyman limit is

$$N_{\mathrm{Ly}_c} = \frac{8\pi^2 r_*^2}{c^2} \int_{v_0}^{\infty} \frac{v^2 dv}{\exp(hv/kT_*) - 1}, \tag{3}$$

where v_0 is the frequency of the Lyman series limit. From observations one can determine the quantity

$$A_i = \frac{E_i}{v_i(\partial E_*/\partial v)_i}, \tag{4}$$

where E_i is the total amount of energy emitted per unit time by the entire nebula in the ith Balmer line, and $(\partial E_*/\partial v)_i$ is the total amount of energy emitted per unit time and frequency by the underlying stellar continuum at the same frequency. From these quantities the dimensionless quantity A_i is obtained.

Since

$$\left(\frac{\partial E_*}{\partial v}\right)_i = \frac{8\pi^2 r_*^2 h v_i^3}{c^2} \cdot \frac{1}{\exp(hv_i/kT_*) - 1}, \tag{5}$$

the total number of Balmer quanta emitted by the nebula is:

$$N_{\mathrm{neb}} = \sum \frac{E_i}{hv_i} = \frac{1}{h} \sum A_i \left(\frac{\partial E_*}{\partial v}\right)_i = \frac{8\pi^2 r_*^2}{c^2} \sum \frac{v_i^3 A_i}{\exp(hv_i/kT_*) - 1}. \tag{6}$$

From the expression $N_{Ba+Ba_c} \leqq N_{\mathrm{Ly}_c}$ we get:

$$\sum \frac{v_i^3 A_i}{\exp(hv_i/kT_*) - 1} \leq \int_{v_0}^{\infty} \frac{v^2 dv}{\exp(hv/kT_*) - 1} \tag{7}$$

or

$$\sum \frac{x_i^3 A_i}{e^{x_i} - 1} \leq \int_{x_0}^{\infty} \frac{x^2 dx}{e^x - 1}, \tag{8}$$

where

$$x = hv/kT_*; \qquad x_0 = hv_0/kT_*; \qquad x_i = hv_i/kT_*$$

and the summation of the left side is over the Balmer lines and continuum.

If the temperature is to be determined from the forbidden lines, as for example the two nebulium lines (N_1 and N_2), the expression is analogous to Eq. (8) and was obtained by Zanstra in essentially the following way:

Suppose that free electrons are obtained by the ionization of hydrogen atoms. If this is the case then the electron will acquire a kinetic energy of

$$\tfrac{1}{2}mv^2 = hv - hv_0 \tag{9}$$

by the absorption of a quantum of frequency v where the H ionization frequency is v_0. In a frequency interval v to $v + dv$ the total quanta emitted per unit time will be

$$8\pi^2 \frac{r_*^2 v^2}{c^2} \frac{dv}{\exp(hv/kT_*) - 1}.$$ (10)

On the other hand the total amount of kinetic energy obtained by the electrons per unit time by the absorption of all the Ly_c^* quanta from the star becomes

$$8\pi^2 \frac{r_*^2 h}{c^2} \int_{v_0}^{\infty} \frac{(v - v_0)v^2}{\exp(hv/kT_*) - 1} dv.$$ (11)

From the forbidden O III lines (N_1 and N_2) in the nebula the energy emitted is

$$\frac{8\pi^2 r_*^2 h}{c^2} \sum \frac{v_i^4}{\exp(hv_i/kT_*) - 1} A_i,$$ (12)

where the summation is over the nebulium lines and A_i is determined from observation [see Eq. (4)]. By Zanstra's theorem the energy acquired to excite the forbidden O III lines ≤ the kinetic energy obtained by the electrons; therefore

$$\sum \frac{v_i^4 A_i}{\exp(hv_i/kT_*) - 1} \leq \int_{v_0}^{\infty} \frac{(v - v_0)v^2}{\exp(hv/kT_*) - 1} dv$$ (13)

or

$$\sum \frac{x_i^4}{e^{x_i} - 1} A_i \leq \int_{x_0}^{\infty} \frac{(x - x_0)x^2}{e^x - 1} dx.$$ (14)

Thus by means of Eqs. (2), (8), or (14) the temperature of the central star may be determined. In addition to these there are several additional techniques for determining central star temperatures, namely, the method of Stoy (1933), Wurm's (1951) Balmer continuum method, and the spectral class method. In Stoy's method a comparison is made of the intensities of the Balmer nebular lines and forbidden lines. The basic assumption is the same as that made by Zanstra [which yields Eq. (14)] in his "nebulium" method, i.e., the energy brought into the continuum by the electrons photoelectrically detached from hydrogen is all dissipated in inelastic collisions with ions of O III, N II, S II, etc. Wurm, on the other hand, derived the temperature of the central star from the ratio of the intensity in the nebular continuum at the Balmer limit to that of the continuum of the central star. The ratio depends on the central star temperature, the fraction of the captures on the second level, and on the optical thickness of the nebula. Petrie (1947) applied the spectral class method to

Population Type I stars and Wilson and Aller (Aller, 1948; Wilson, 1948; Wilson and Aller, 1954) to nebulae. For this method equivalent widths W_λ's of hydrogen and helium lines are used to determine the spectral classes, i.e., by measuring the W_λ's one can read off the spectral classes. For most central stars in planetary nebulae the He I/He II or the He II/H ratios may be employed provided the blending effects with nebular lines is taken into account. In this method, in which Petrie calibrated the excitation temperatures of normal O-type stars, it is assumed that the helium/hydrogen ratio is the same in all stars. Of the various methods which are available for determining the temperature of the central star the methods of Zanstra, Stoy, and Petrie are used most often.

The spectral lines arising in the nebula are due to the following three mechanisms:

(a) The primary physical process that occurs in the nebula itself is the photoionization mechanism due to the absorption of stellar ultraviolet radiation by the surrounding gas cloud, i.e.,

$$H + h\nu \rightarrow H^+ + e^-, \tag{15}$$

and occurs in atoms in the ground state. The electrons are then recaptured leaving the atoms in highly excited levels from which they cascade to lower levels emitting lines of allowed transitions. While this recombination occurs primarily in hydrogen and helium, it also has been observed in the heavier elements such as oxygen, carbon, and nitrogen.

The emission per unit volume for an $n \rightarrow n'$ transition in hydrogen or ionized helium may be written in the following form:

$$E(n \rightarrow n') = 2kh \frac{Z^6 g(n \rightarrow n') N_i N_\varepsilon b_n(T_\varepsilon)}{n'^3 n^3 T_\varepsilon^{3/2}} e^{\chi_n}$$

or

$$E(n \rightarrow n') = 1.42 \times 10^{-16} \frac{Z^6 g(n \rightarrow n') N_i N_\varepsilon b_n(T_\varepsilon)}{n'^3 n^3 T_\varepsilon^{3/2}} e^{157,000/n^2 T_\varepsilon}. \tag{16}$$

Here n and n' denote the upper and lower levels, respectively, N_i the number of ions of hydrogen or doubly ionized helium per cm^3, N_ε the electronic concentration, Z the nuclear charge, T_ε the electron temperature, $g(n \rightarrow n')$ the Gaunt correction factor, which for most applications may be taken as unity, and $b_n(T_\varepsilon)$ is a measure of the deviation from thermodynamic equilibrium (see Seaton, 1960; Baker and Menzel, 1938; Burgess, 1958). The T_ε and N_ε of the gas usually can be determined from the relative forbidden line intensities. By measuring the surface brightness of a nebula at a known distance an estimate of the energy, electron, or ion density can be obtained. Usually it is possible to equate the N_i of hydrogen with the N_ε without too much loss in accuracy, since the hydrogen is very abundant in relation to helium and the other ions.

A similar theory of recombination has been developed for helium and other ions by Mathis (1957) and Seaton (1964) and by Burgess and Seaton (1960), respectively.

(b) Collisional excitations are responsible for the strongest lines in most planetary nebulae. These lines are due to the well-known forbidden transitions, first explained by Bowen (1928), which arise from the collisional excitation of the metastable levels that lie in a few electron volts above the ground level. After the electrons have been excited to the metastable levels by inelastic collisions they cascade back to a lower level with the emission of a forbidden quanta of the magnetic dipole or electric quadrupole type or both; or by a collision of the second kind.

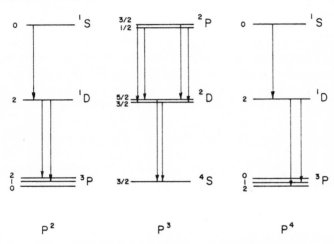

FIG. 1.   The forbidden transitions for p^q configurations.

In Fig. 1 the forbidden transition scheme is shown for the p^q type configurations ($q = 2$, 3, and 4) which are some of the important ones in astrophysics.

The number of collisional excitations/cm³/ sec from a lower level n' to an upper level n depends on the ion density in level n', the electron density, the electron temperature, the excitation potential, $\chi_{n'n}$, of the upper level, the statistical weight, $\tilde{\omega}_{n'}$, of the lower level, and the collision strength, $\Omega(n, n')$, of the particular ion and the transition involved, viz.,

$$\mathscr{F}_{n'n} = 8.63 \times 10^{-6} N_{n'} N_\varepsilon T_\varepsilon^{-1/2} \frac{\Omega(n', n)}{\tilde{\omega}_{n'}} e^{-\chi_{n'n}/kT\varepsilon}. \tag{17}$$

The corresponding number of collisions of the second kind per cm³ per sec is:

$$\mathscr{F}_{nn'} = 8.63 \times 10^{-6} N_n N_\varepsilon T_\varepsilon^{-1/2} \frac{\Omega(n, n')}{\tilde{\omega}_n} \tag{18}$$

and under conditions of thermodynamic equilibrium $\mathscr{F}_{n'n} = \mathscr{F}_{nn'}$. However for a steady-state condition the number of collisional excitations $\mathscr{F}_{n'n}$ equals the number of collisional de-excitations $\mathscr{F}_{nn'}$ plus the number of radiative de-excitations $N_n A_{nn'}$, i.e., $\mathscr{F}_{n'n} = \mathscr{F}_{nn'} + N_n A_{nn'}$ where $A_{nn'}$ is the Einstein probability coefficient for the radiative transition. Thus the emission per unit volume for the forbidden line radiation is

$$E_{nn'} = N_n A_{nn'} h\nu_{nn'}. \tag{19}$$

If Eqs. (17) and (18) and the steady-state condition are introduced into Eq. (19), we then obtain a complex expression which contains two very important atomic parameters, i.e., $\Omega(n, n')$ and $A_{nn'}$, whose accuracy can seriously affect the T_ε and N_ε and hence the chemical abundances in a nebula.

(c) A fluorescence mechanism due to Bowen (1935) shows that a number of strong lines should appear in the near ultraviolet, and these have been observed in nitrogen and oxygen in high-excitation planetaries. This effect is due to the absorption of the He II (resonance Ly_α line) by O III, raising it to the 2p3d $^3P_2$ level which then either returns to the ground level 2p^2 $^3P_2$ or cascades through the 2p3p and 2p3s levels emitting radiation in the process. A similar cycle occurs for N III wherein lines are produced by cascades from 3d ^2D to 3p ^2P and from 3p^2P to 3s^2S, respectively. Thus the He II resonance Ly_α radiation provides the source of energy to O III and N III ions, and these lines appear only in nebulae with a strong He II $\lambda4686$ line. The Bowen fluorescence is identified by the conspicuous intensities of the lines in the ultraviolet region of O III which arise by cascade from a single upper level.

In addition to the spectral lines observed in planetary nebulae there also exists an underlying continuum apparently due to three processes, namely, (1) recombination of ions and electrons to excited levels, (2) free–free transitions in the fields of ions and electrons, and (3) two-quantum emissions from the 2s level of hydrogen.

One of the most difficult problems that still exists in the estimation and interpretation of forbidden line intensities [see (b) above] is the calculation of the collisional cross-section parameters and to some degree the transition probabilities. For the calculation of both parameters accurate atomic wave functions are required.

III. Forbidden Transitions and the Calculation of Atomic Parameters

Electron temperature T_ε estimates were originally obtained from the study of the relative intensities of the hydrogen recombination spectrum (see Page, 1935, 1942). However, by this method only order of magnitude estimates can be obtained because the relative intensities are insensitive to T_ε. Likewise, the early predictions of the electron density N_ε (see Menzel and Aller, 1941; Page and Greenstein, 1951) were obtained by estimating the absolute emission rate in the hydrogen recombination spectrum. But, in order to use this procedure it was necessary to determine the absolute surface brightness and the absolute nebular dimensions. Unfortunately, both properties are difficult to determine to the high precision required, i.e., to determine the dimensions and N_ε from the surface brightness in H_β one must assume that the nebula is uniform. This presumes that there are no large density fluctuations, a situation which is often not true. In principle it should be possible to obtain more reliable N_ε and T_ε values from the relative intensities of the forbidden lines of the various ions. For a particular ion the relative intensities are determined from the excitation, deactivation, and spontaneous emission rates. Thus, if the excitation and deactivation cross sections Q or collision strengths Ω and the transition probabilities A are known, then the T_ε and N_ε may be determined as can be seen from Eqs. (17), (18), and (19). Figure 1 shows that the ions giving the forbidden transitions contain two metastable levels.

For ions with sufficiently large transition probabilities from the metastable levels, it is possible for the electron deactivation of the levels to be negligible; this occurs when the electron density is low. The ratio of the emission rates then will be proportional to the ratio of the excitation rates for the two levels, and the ratio of the excitation rates will be a function of the T_ε only. Thus, the intensity ratios may be used to determine the T_ε. Where the N_ε is high enough for the deactivation to be important, the intensity ratio becomes a function of the T_ε and N_ε, and consequently observations on the relative intensities of at least two ions are necessary. However, it is desirable to have data on several ions all of which should yield the same value for T_ε and N_ε, provided it is assumed that the distribution of the ions throughout the nebula is homogeneous. Whether or not identical results are obtained will depend primarily on the accuracy of the atomic parameters. When the N_ε is high, the electron excitation and deactivation of the metastable levels lead to a Boltzmann distribution among the levels of the ion. The intensity ratio for the forbidden lines is then a function of the radiative transition probabilities and the T_ε, but not the N_ε.

The explicit dependence of the intensity ratio on the T_ε and N_ε can be obtained by mathematically formulating the steady-state condition referred to previously. For an ion with two metastable levels, say ^1S and ^1D, with the ^3P being the ground term and referred to hereafter as states " 3 ", " 2 ", and " 1 ", respectively, we have, following the procedure of Aller (1956) for state 3

$$N_1 N_\varepsilon q_{13} + N_2 N_\varepsilon q_{23} = N_3 [N_\varepsilon q_{32} + N_\varepsilon q_{31} + A_{32} + A_{31}], \qquad (20)$$

and for state 2

$$N_1 N_\varepsilon q_{12} + N_3 N_\varepsilon q_{32} + N_3 A_{32} = N_2 N_\varepsilon (q_{23} + q_{21}) + N_2 A_{21}, \tag{21}$$

where

$$q_{mn} = q_{nm} \frac{\tilde{\omega}_n}{\tilde{\omega}_m} \exp\left(-\frac{\chi_{mn}}{kT_\varepsilon}\right)$$

and

$$q_{nm} = \frac{8.63 \times 10^{-6}}{\tilde{\omega}_n \sqrt{T_\varepsilon}} \left\{ \int_0^\infty \Omega_{nm} \exp\left(-\frac{E}{kT_\varepsilon}\right) \frac{dE}{kT_\varepsilon} \right\}$$

are the activation and deactivation coefficients, respectively. The quantities N_1, N_2, and N_3 represent the number of atoms in each of the respective levels, the A's the transition probabilities, the $\tilde{\omega}$'s the statistical weights of the levels the χ_{mn}'s the difference in the excitation potential between states m and n, E the kinetic energy of the free electron, and Ω_{nm} the collision strength.

The deviation from thermodynamic equilibrium of states 1, 2, and 3, may be expressed as follows:

$$\frac{N_2}{N_1} = \frac{b_2}{b_1} \frac{\tilde{\omega}_2}{\tilde{\omega}_1} \exp\left(-\frac{\chi_{12}}{kT_\varepsilon}\right) \tag{22}$$

and

$$\frac{N_3}{N_2} = \frac{b_3}{b_2} \frac{\tilde{\omega}_3}{\tilde{\omega}_2} \exp\left(-\frac{\chi_{23}}{kT_\varepsilon}\right). \tag{23}$$

The ratios b_3/b_2 and b_2/b_1 represent the deviation from thermodynamic equilibrium, which have been rigorously developed by Menzel et al. (1941) and are

$$\frac{b_3}{b_2} = \frac{1 + \dfrac{\Omega_{23}}{\Omega_{12}} \dfrac{\exp(-\chi_{23}/kT_\varepsilon)}{(1 + \Omega_{23}/\Omega_{13})} + \dfrac{A_{21}\tilde{\omega}_2}{C\Omega_{12}(1 + \Omega_{23}/\Omega_{13})}}{1 + \dfrac{(A_{32} + A_{31})\tilde{\omega}_3}{\Omega_{13}C(1 + \Omega_{23}/\Omega_{13})} + \left[\Omega_{23} + \dfrac{A_{32}\tilde{\omega}_3}{C}\right] \dfrac{\exp(-\chi_{23}/kT_\varepsilon)}{\Omega_{12}(1 + \Omega_{23}/\Omega_{13})}} \tag{24}$$

and

$$\frac{b_2}{b_1} = \frac{\Omega_{12} + \Omega_{13}d \exp(-\chi_{23}/kT_\varepsilon)}{(\Omega_{12} + A_{21}\tilde{\omega}_2/C) + \Omega_{23}(1 - d) \exp(-\chi_{23}/kT_\varepsilon)} \tag{25}$$

where

$$C = 8.63 \times 10^{-6} N_\varepsilon / T_\varepsilon^{1/2}$$

and

$$d = \frac{\Omega_{32} + (A_{32}/C)\tilde{\omega}_3}{\Omega_{13} + \Omega_{23} + (A_{32} + A_{31})\tilde{\omega}_3/C}$$

In order to get some idea as to which of the atomic parameters, i.e., Ω_{mn} or

A_{mn}, predominates, let us consider a high density and a low density nebula. If then N_ε is allowed to increase, then C increases and in the limit $b_3/b_2 \to 1$ so that

$$\frac{N_3}{N_2} = \frac{\tilde{\omega}_3}{\tilde{\omega}_2} \exp\left(-\frac{\chi_{23}}{kT_\varepsilon}\right);$$

the ratio of the intensities becomes

$$\frac{I_{32}}{I_{21}} = \frac{\tilde{\omega}_3}{\tilde{\omega}_2} \frac{\bar{\nu}_{32}}{\bar{\nu}_{21}} \frac{A_{32}}{A_{21}} \exp\left(-\frac{\chi_{23}}{kT_\varepsilon}\right), \tag{26}$$

where the $\bar{\nu}$'s are transition values in wave numbers. Similarly if N_ε decreases then C decreases and in the limit

$$\frac{I_{32}}{I_{21}} = \frac{\bar{\nu}_{32}}{\bar{\nu}_{21}} \exp\left(-\frac{\chi_{23}}{kT_\varepsilon}\right) \left\{ \frac{\Omega_{12}}{\Omega_{13}}\left[1 + \frac{A_{31}}{A_{32}}\right] + \exp\left(-\frac{\chi_{23}}{kT_\varepsilon}\right)\right\}^{-1} \tag{27}$$

It can be seen that in Eq. (26) transition probabilities play an important part in the determination of T_ε, whereas in Eq. (27) it is collision strengths that predominate, since the contribution from A_{31}/A_{32} is small. A very thorough exposition of such calculations has been given by Aller (1954, 1956), Aller *et al.* (1949), Shortly *et al.* (1941), Osterbrock (1955), Seaton (1958, 1959, 1960, 1962), Seaton and Osterbrock (1957), Garstang (1951, 1952, 1956, 1962), Czyzak and Krueger (1963), and Krueger and Czyzak (1965). However, what is more important is that in order to determine the T_ε and N_ε accurately, precise values of the collision strengths Ω and the transition probabilities A are necessary. For the calculation of both of these parameters it is necessary to use atomic wave functions, and the accuracy of these wave functions indirectly plays a significant role in the determination of not only the T_ε and N_ε but also the estimation of the chemical abundances.

The dependence of the T_ε and the N_ε on the transition probabilities and the collision strengths may be illustrated in the following way. Let us consider two nebulae, one of high density (NGC II 4997) and the other of low density (NGC 6720). If we employ Eqs. (26) and (27), respectively, we shall be able to determine the importance of accurate transition probability and collision strength values. It must be emphasized that the numerical values of the T_ε will be only of the right order of magnitude since it would depend on how well a high or low density nebula approaches the limiting conditions that were imposed to obtain Eqs. (26) and (27). For observed nebulae this limiting condition has never been obtained. However, there exist nebulae to which the low density approximation may be applied to obtain rough estimates; although the high density approximation is poor for nebulae, it is more useful in getting estimates of the electron temperature in the shells of novae. The purpose in obtaining these equations is only to indicate the importance of the A and Ω parameters. In Table 1 the values are shown for the transition probabilities

TABLE 1

TRANSITION PROBABILITIES

Ion	Transition Symbol	$\lambda(\text{Å})$	$A^{(M)}$	$A^{(Q)}$	A_{mn}	Remarks
Values calculated by Garstang (1951)						
O III	$^1D_2 - {}^1S_0$ A_{32}	4363	0·	1·60	1·600	For the electric-quad-
	$^3P_1 - {}^1D_2$ A_{21}	4959	0·0071	0·0^5 52	0·028	rupole moment $s_q =$
	$^3P_2 - {}^1D_2$	5007	0·021	0·0^4 41		$e\int r^2 P(nl;r)P(n'l';r)\,dr$
	$^3P_1 - {}^1S_0$ A_{31}	2321	0·230	0·	0·237	Garstang used HFSCF
	$^3P_2 - {}^1S_0$	2332	0·	0·0071		wave functions with
						exchange which were
						used to obtain the $A^{(Q)}$
						component of A_{mn}.
Values calculated by Pasternack (1940)						
O III	$^1D_2 - {}^1S_0$ A_{32}	4363	0·0	2·80	2·80	For the electric-quad-
	$^3P_2 - {}^1D_2$ A_{21}	4959	0·0056	0·0^4 86	0·0217	rupole moment Paster-
	$^3P_2 - {}^1D_2$	5007	0·016	0·0^4 57		nack used hydrogenic
	$^3P_1 - {}^1S_0$ A_{31}	2321	0·190	0·	0·200	wave functions which
	$^3P_2 - {}^1S_0$	2332	0·	0·001		were used to obtain
						the $A^{(Q)}$ component of
						A_{mn}.

of O III as determined by Pasternack (1940) using hydrogenic wave functions and those determined by Garstang (1951) using Hartree-Fock self-consistent field wave functions with exchange. If the A values of Garstang and Pasternack are introduced into Eq. (26) for the high density nebula NGC II 4997, whose intensity ratio from observational data for $\dfrac{I_{21} (\lambda\,4959 + \lambda\,5007)}{I_{32} (\lambda\,4363)} = 9.2$, the electron temperatures T_ε turn out to be 6890° and 5890°K, respectively. This represents a difference of approximately 15%, which is sizable. In a similar manner a comparison of the T_ε's for a low density nebula may be made. In Table 2 we have the appropriate collision strengths required by Eq. (27) as determined by Hebb and Menzel (1940), Seaton (1953), and Billings et al. (1965). It will be observed there is a sizable discrepancy between the results of Hebb and Menzel, those of Seaton, and the very recent values obtained by Seaton and his co-workers. The major difficulty in the Coulomb wave approximation as developed by Hebb and Menzel is that it violates the conservation theorem due to Mott et al. (1933) which states that $\sum \Omega/(2J + 1) \leq (2l + 1)$, where $(2J + 1)$ is the statistical weight of the lower level from which the collision excitation takes place and l is the azimuthal quantum number of the partial

TABLE 2

COLLISION STRENGTHS FOR O III

	Seaton (1953)	Billings *et al.* (1965)	Hebb and Menzel (1940)
Ω^{12}	1·73	2·24	19·08
Ω^{13}	0·195	0·29	3·37
Ω^{12}/Ω^{13}	8·87	7·38	5·66

wave that contribute the largest share to the cross section. Hence, the cross-section values obtained by this method may be in error by as much as one or two orders of magnitude. The variation between the Seaton (1953) results and his latest data (Billings *et al.*, 1965) is due to the availability of better wave functions and the further development of theory and mathematical techniques. The values of T_ε obtained using the three sets of Ω's in Eq. (27) are 14,300°K (Hebb and Menzel, 1940), 17,500°K (Seaton, 1953), and 16,000°K (Billings *et al.*, 1965). Here as in the case of the high density nebula the difference is also sizable. Thus, if one has a T_ε which is in error then one also obtains a large error in the N_ε which in turn gives an equally large error in the calculation of the ionic abundances, as can be seen from the following expression for the abundance of O III; i.e., for $N(O^{++})$ we get

$$N(O^{++}) = 3.7 \times 10^{-6} \frac{b_4(T_\varepsilon)\exp(-\chi/kT_\varepsilon)}{T_\varepsilon^{3/2}} N_\varepsilon^2 \left[1 + 9380 \frac{T_\varepsilon^{1/2}}{N_\varepsilon} \right] \frac{I(N_1 + N_2)}{I(H_\beta)}$$

(28)

where $b_4(T_\varepsilon)$ is a temperature dependent factor that denotes the departure of the assembly from thermodynamic equilibrium, $I(N_1 + N_2)$ is the intensity of λ 5007 and λ 4959 forbidden lines, and $I(H_\beta)$ is the intensity of the hydrogen λ 4863 line. The seriousness of such discrepancies becomes even more apparent when Ne IV is considered, an ion often found in nebulae. It has an ionization potential of 7.3 eV, and if we use the electron temperatures of 16,000° and 17,500°K, a difference in ion concentration of 33% is obtained. It is quite apparent from the foregoing discussion that the atomic parameters A and Ω play an important role in the study of the atomic processes that occur in a nebula.

In summarizing, it may be stated that all that can be deduced about a nebula or a star is obtained from the light that the object emits. From the light that is received we can obtain information as to its direction, amount, and type, i.e., its color and spectrum. As can be seen from our foregoing discussion the structure of a nebula or the atmosphere surrounding a star depends to a large extent on the interpretation of its spectrum. To make such an assessment it is necessary to determine from the spectra the observed wavelengths of the elements in the various stages of ionization and also the transition probabilities for these lines. For the calculation of the latter a knowledge of the matrix components of the electric moments is required, and these components are very sensitive to small errors in wave functions. This is due to the fact that in a large number of cases they are of the form of integrals, over r, of functions which are almost as often positive as negative, and the small difference which represents the whole effect can be affected greatly by small changes in the wave functions. Likewise in collision cross-section calculations the atomic wave functions are important. Since the wave functions represent the electron configuration that the colliding electron would observe, the changes in the electronic density affect the form of the wave function for the scattered electron and hence the collision strength.

It is for these reasons that an intensive effort has been made in the past decade to obtain accurate atomic wave functions and wave functions best suited for this purpose are the Hartree-Fock type. For a comprehensive exposition of the theory the reader is referred to the textbooks by Hartree (1958) and Slater (1960). In general two basic procedures for calculating Hartree-Fock Self-Consistent Field (HFSCF) wave functions are used, namely, one employing analytical techniques and the other using numerical ones. The HFSCF method of calculating the wave functions still gives the best one-electron representation of a many-electron atomic configuration. Within the past few years many of these functions have appeared in the literature, and more recently programs for calculating them have become available. Iterative programs have been developed and also calculation of various atomic wave functions have been made by Douglas (1954), Piper (1961), Froese (1957, 1958, 1963a,b), Mayers and Hirsh (1965), Czyzak (1962), Herman and Skillman (1963), Clementi (1962, 1963a,b), Krueger et al. (1965, 1966), and Chapman and Clarke (1966). Analytical programs have been developed by Boys and Price (1954), Nesbet (1955), Nesbet and Watson (1960), Roothaan (1960), and Watson and Freeman (1961).

While some of the methods may be regarded as superior to others, further work is still necessary since the majority of the programs do not take into account configuration interaction. Those that do have been used for the light elements only and have given more accurate results. However, very recently Froese (1965), as well as Mayers and O'Brien (1965) have further developed their programs to include configuration interaction. This should improve the accuracy of the wave functions. Still lacking is a program for a completely relativistic treatment of the wave functions, which is somewhat urgently needed for calculating accurate atomic parameters of the heavier elements of astrophysical interest, i.e., those elements of $Z \geq 38$.

It is our pleasure to honor Professor Slater on his 65th birthday by showing in this paper how the application of the quantum theory of atomic structure plays an important role in the calculation of atomic processes occurring in planetary nebulae. While our emphasis here has been on the importance of accurate atomic wave functions, this represents but a part of Professor Slater's contribution to the quantum theory of matter. For, as is well known, Professor Slater's contributions in this area are many and outstanding. His work spans a period of approximately four decades during which he has continuously been on the forefront in development and exposition of quantum theory for atoms, molecules, and solids.

REFERENCES

Aller, L. H. (1948). *Astrophys. J.* **108**, 462.
Aller, L. H. (1954). *Astrophys. J.* **120**, 401.
Aller, L. H. (1956). "Gaseous Nebulae." Chapman and Hall, London.
Aller, L. H., Ufford, C. W., and Van Vleck, J. H. (1949). *Astrophys. J.* **109**, 42.
Baker, J. G., and Menzel, D. J. (1938). *Astrophys. J.* **88**, 52.
Billings, A., Czyzak, S. J., Krueger, T. K., Saraph, H. E., Seaton, M. J., and Shemming, J. (1965). *Phys. Electron. and At. Collisions, IVth Intern. Conf., Quebec, 1965.*
Bowen, I. S. (1928). *Astrophys. J.* **67**, 1.
Bowen, I. S. (1935). *Astrophys. J.* **81**, 4.
Boys, S. F., and Price, V. E. (1954). *Phil. Trans. Roy. Soc. London* **A246**, 451.
Burgess, A. (1958). *Monthly Notices Roy. Astron. Soc.* **118**, 477.
Burgess, A., and Seaton, M. J. (1960) *Monthly Notices Roy. Astron. Soc.* **120**, 121.
Chapman, R. D., and Clarke, W. H. (1966). Table of Hartree-Fock self-consistent field wave functions with exchange, ARL report of work accomplished at UCLA, Dept. of Astronomy, Suppl. II, ARL 66—0018.
Clementi, E. (1962). *J. Chem. Phys.* **36**, 33.
Clementi, E. (1963a). *J. Chem. Phys.* **38**, 2248.
Clementi, E. (1963b). *J. Chem. Phys.* **39**, 175.
Czyzak, S. J. (1962). *Astrophys. J. Suppl. VII* **65**, 53.
Czyzak, S. J., and Krueger, T. K. (1963). *Monthly Notices Roy. Astron. Soc.* **126**, 177.
Douglas, A. S. (1954). Computer methods and programs, unpublished.
Dufay, J. (1954). "Nebeleuses Galactiques et Matiere Interstellaire." Abbin Michel, Paris.
Froese, C. (1957). *Proc. Roy. Soc. (London)* **A239**, 311.
Froese, C. (1958). *Proc. Roy. Soc. (London)* **A244**, 390.
Froese, C. (1963a). *Can. J. Phys.* **41**, 50.
Froese, C. (1963b). *Can. J. Phys.* **41**, 1895.
Froese, C. (1965). Private communication.
Garstang, R. H. (1951). *Monthly Notices Roy. Astron. Soc.* **111**, 115.
Garstang, R. H. (1952). *Astrophys, J.* **115**, 506.
Garstang, R. H. (1956). *Proc. Cambridge Phil. Soc.* **52**, 107.
Garstang, R. H. (1962). *In* "Atomic and Molecular Processes," (D. R. Bates, ed.), pp. 1–46. Academic Press, New York.
Hartree, D. R. (1958). "The Calculation of Atomic Structure." Wiley, New York.
Hebb, M. N., and Menzel, D. H. (1940). *Astrophys. J.* **92**, 129.
Herman, F., and Skillman, S. (1963). "Atomic Structure Calculations." Prentice-Hall, Englewood Cliffs, New Jersey.

Krueger, T. K., and Czyzak, S. J. (1965). *Mem. Roy. Astron. Soc.* **69**, 145.

Krueger, T. K., McDavid, W. L., and Czyzak, S. J. (1965). Table of Hartree-Fock self-consistent feld wave functions with exchange, ARL 65-10.

Krueger, T. K., McDavid, W. L., and Czyzak, S. J. (1966). Table of Hartree-Fock self-consistent field wave functions with exchange, Suppl. I, ARL 66-0014.

Mathis, J. (1957). *Astrophys. J.* **125**, 328.

Mayers, D., and Hirsh, A. (1965). The Calculation of Atomic Wave Functions by Solution of the Hartree-Fock Equations. ARL 65-62.

Mayers, D., and O'Brien, F. (1965). Private communication.

Menzel, D. H. (1962). ed. "Selected Papers on Physical Processes in Ionized Plasma." Dover, New York.

Menzel, D. H., and Aller, L. H. (1941). *Astrophys. J.* **93**, 195.

Menzel, D. H., Hebb, M. N., and Aller, L. H. (1941). *Astrophys. J.* **93**, 230.

Mott, N. F., Bohr, N., Peierls, R. E., and Placzek, G. (1933). *Proc. Roy. Soc. (London).* **A133**, 228.

Nesbet, R. K. (1955). *Proc. Roy. Soc. (London)* **A230**, 312.

Nesbet, R. K., and Watson, R. E. (1960). *Ann. Phys. (N.Y.)* **9**, 260.

Osterbrock, D. E. (1955). *Astrophys. J.*, **122**, 235.

Osterbrock, D. E. (1964). *Ann. Rev. Astron. Astrophys.* **2**, 95-120.

Page, T. L. (1935). *Monthly Notices Roy. Astron. Soc.* **96**, 604.

Page, T. L. (1942). *Astrophys. J.* **96**, 78.

Page, T. L., and Greenstein, T. L. (1951). *Astrophys. J.* **114**, 98.

Pasternack, S. (1940). *Astrophys. J.* **92**, 129.

Petrie, R. M. (1947). *Publ. Dominion Astrophys. Obs. Victoria, B.C.* **7**, 321.

Piper, W. W. (1961). *Phys. Rev.* **123**, 1281.

Roothaan, C. C. J. (1960). *Rev. Mod. Phys.* **32**, 179.

Seaton, M. J. (1953). *Proc. Roy. Soc. (London)* **A245**, 469.

Seaton, M. J. (1958). *Rev. Mod. Phys.* **30**, 979.

Seaton, M. J. (1959). *Monthly Notices Roy. Astron. Soc.* **119**, 81.

Seaton, M. J. (1960). *Rep. Prog. Phys.* **23**, 313-354.

Seaton, M. J. (1962). *In* " Atomic and Molecular Processes " (D. R. Bates, ed.), pp. 374-420. Academic Press, New York.

Seaton, M. J., and Osterbrock, D. E. (1957). *Astrophys. J.* **125**, 66.

Shortley, G. H., Aller, L. H., Baker, J. O., and Menzel, D. H. (1941). *Astrophy. J.* **93**, 178.

Slater, J. C. (1960) " Quantum Theory of Atomic Structure," Vols. I and II. McGraw-Hill, New York.

Stoy, R. (1933). *Monthly Notices Roy. Astron. Soc.* **93**, 588.

Vorontsov-Velyaminov, B. A. (1953). "Gas Nebulae and Neue Sterne." Verlag Kultur und Forschritt, Berlin.

Watson, R. E., and Freeman, A. J. (1961). *Phys. Rev.* **123**, 521, 1117.

Wilson, O. C. (1948). *Astrophys. J.* **108**, 201.

Wilson, O. C., and Aller, L. H. (1954). *Astrophys. J.* **119**, 243.

Wurm, K. (1951). "Die Planetarischen Nebel." Academie Verlag, Berlin.

Zanstra, H. (1927). *Astrophys. J.* **65**, 50.

Zanstra, H. (1931a). *Publ. Dominion Astrophys. Obs. Victoria, B.C.* **4**, 209.

Zanstra, H. (1931b). *Z. Astrophys.* **2**, 1.

Spin-Orbit Interaction In Self-Consistent Fields

E. U. CONDON and H. ODABASI

JOINT INSTITUTE FOR LABORATORY ASTROPHYSICS
BOULDER, COLORADO

Although much effort has gone into the calculation of self-consistent fields by the Hartree, Hartree-Fock, and Hartree-Fock-Slater methods (*1*) since the advent of automatic digital computers, little attention has thus far been paid to the use of such solutions for fields and radial functions to calculate spin-orbit interaction parameters. This paper is a report on some calculations we are making on this subject.

In the older accounts (*2*) the magnetic spin-orbit interaction is represented by a term in the Hamiltonian

$$\mathcal{H}^I = \frac{e^2 \hbar^2}{2m^2 c^2} \sum_{i=1}^{N} \xi(r_i) \mathbf{L}_i \cdot \mathbf{S}_i, \tag{1}$$

the sum being over the N electrons in the atom or ion. Here $\mathbf{L}_i$ and $\mathbf{S}_i$ are the orbital and spin-angular momenta of each electron in units of $\hbar$, and $\xi(r_i)$ is commonly taken as

$$\xi(r_i) = \frac{1}{r_i} \frac{\partial U}{\partial r_i}, \tag{2}$$

in which $-e^2 U(r_i)$ is the potential energy at distance r_i from the nucleus of the effective central field in which the ith electron moves.

Measuring energy in Rydbergs, $e^2/2a$, and length in atomic units, $a = \hbar^2/me^2$, the coefficient in front of the sum in Eq. (1) becomes α^2 where $\alpha = e^2/\hbar c$, the fine structure constant. That is,

$$\mathcal{H}^I = \sum_i \alpha^2 \xi(r_i) \mathbf{L}_i \cdot \mathbf{S}_i. \tag{1'}$$

Calculation of matrix elements of $\mathcal{H}^I$ in the $SLM_S M_L$ scheme of zero-order states leads to (*2*, p. 196)

$$(\gamma SLM_S M_L | \mathcal{H}^I | \gamma SLM_S M_L) = \zeta(\gamma SL) M_S M_L$$

$$= \sum_i \xi_{nl}^{(i)} m_{si} m_{li} \tag{3}$$

185

in which $(2, \text{p. } 122)$

$$\zeta_{nl} = \int_0^\infty \alpha^2 \xi(r) P_{nl}^2(r) \, dr \qquad (4)$$

and $P_{nl}(r)$ is written for r times the radial wave function as in Ref. (1).

In Eq. (3) the sum of m_{si} and m_{li} over the states of electrons in a closed shell gives zero, so the sum can be restricted to the electrons not in closed shells.

When hydrogenic radial functions are used in Eq. (4), the integral can be evaluated exactly to give

$$\zeta_{nl} = \frac{\alpha^2 Z^4}{n^3 l(l + \frac{1}{2})(l + 1)} \qquad (l \neq 0). \qquad (5)$$

In the pre-quantum-mechanical period much of the empirical analysis of spin-orbit interaction was expressed in terms of a semiempirical formula due to Lande (3) which can be obtained from Eq. (5) by replacing n by n^* in which n^* is the effective total quantum number calculated from the observed term energy by $E_{nl} = -Z_0^2/2n^{*2}$ and by replacing Z^4 by $Z_i^2 Z_0^2$ in which $Z_0 = (Z - N + 1)$ and Z_i is an empirically adjusted effective nuclear charge for the inner part of the orbital.

For Russell-Saunders terms the spin-orbit factors $\zeta(\gamma SL)$ can be expressed in terms of the ζ_{nl} for electrons outside closed shells in the configuration γ. The contribution of spin-orbit interaction energy $\mathscr{H}^I$ to the energy levels is then $(2, \text{p. } 194)$

$$E^I(\gamma SLJ) = \tfrac{1}{2}\zeta(\gamma SL)[J(J + 1) - L(L + 1) - S(S + 1)]. \qquad (6)$$

This result gives the theoretical basis of the Landé interval rule according to which inside the same term $E(\gamma, S, L, J) - E(\gamma SL, J - 1) = \zeta(\gamma SL)J$, and so is proportional to the higher of the two J values involved. This result affords the basis for estimation of empirical values of the $\zeta(\gamma SL)$ from observed spectra, from which one obtains empirical values of the ζ_{nl} by using the theoretical connections between the $\zeta(\gamma SL)$ and the individual ζ_{nl}.

In the simplest case of doublet spectra due to a single electron outside of closed shells the doublet interval gives the ζ_{nl} directly,

$$E(\gamma^2 L_{l+1/2}) - E(\gamma^2 L_{l-1/2}) = (l + \tfrac{1}{2})\zeta_{nl}. \qquad (7)$$

In other cases the $\zeta(\gamma SL)$ are expressed in terms of the ζ_{nl}. Examples of such relations are given in Chap. VII of (2) and a more complete collection of them is given by Edlén (4).

Before extensive calculations of self-consistent fields became possible, little use could be made of Eq. (4) to compute theoretical values of the ζ_{nl} because of lack of knowledge of the $U(r)$ and of the radial wave functions $P_{nl}(r)$. Now an abundance of such material is available, especially through the work of Herman and Skillman (5). They have calculated the effective central fields and the radial wave functions for the ground-state configurations of all the neutral atoms from $_2$He to $_{103}$Lw. They have also calculated the ζ_{nl} involved in the ground states of the elements of even Z. Dependence on Z is sufficiently smooth that those for odd Z can be found by interpolation.

In the Herman and Skillman work the same radial potential energy function $V(r)$ is used for each electron. This is defined as

$$V(r) = -2(Z - N + 1)/r, \quad r \geqslant r_0, \tag{8}$$
$$= V_0(r), \quad r \leqslant r_0,$$

where r_0 is defined as that value of r for which these two expressions are equal, a procedure originally introduced by Latter (6), and

$$V_0(r) = -\frac{2Z}{r} + \frac{2}{r}\left[\sum_{nl} \omega_{nl} \int_0^r P_{nl}^2(s)\, ds + \sum_{nl} \omega_{nl} \int_r^\infty \frac{P_{nl}^2(s)}{s}\, ds - \frac{9}{8\pi}[\rho(r)]^{1/3} \right]. \tag{9}$$

Here ω_{nl} is the number of electrons occupying the nl orbital in the ground state so that

$$\sum \omega_{nl} = N \tag{10}$$

and $\rho(r)$ is the total charge density

$$\rho(r) = (4\pi r^2)^{-1} \sum \omega_{nl} P_{ln}^2(r). \tag{11}$$

The term in Eq. (9) involving $\rho(r)$ is Slater's effective potential energy correction for the exchange terms of the Hartree-Fock equations (1, Vol. 2, pp. 10–14). Wave functions based on the use of Eq. (9) in (8) are customarily referred to as the Hartree-Fock-Slater approximation.

Herman and Skillman use the $V(r)$ so defined in determining the energy parameters E_{nl} and the radial wave function $P_{nl}(r)$ for each type of occupied orbital in the ground states of the neutral elements. Their same computer program can also be used for the ground-state configuration of various stages of ionization for which $N < Z$.

For a given (Z, N) one can also calculate the radial wave functions for excited states. Strictly speaking, this ought to involve a complete recalculation of the $P_{nl}(r)$ for all of the electrons, because excitation of one of them alters $V_0(r)$ which alters each $P_{nl}(r)$. However, experience has shown, as was first pointed out to us by R. N. Zare, that the gain in accuracy is too small to justify the considerable extra computing effort. Therefore, we use the $V(r)$ as found by a self-consistent solution for the ground state also to determine the $P_{nl}(r)$ for excited states. This approximation has the added advantage that the $P_{nl}(r)$ for excited states that are so determined form an orthonormal set with that of the ground state.

Whether fully justifiable or not, what we have done for excited states of the (Z, N) ion is to use the $V(r)$ determined by Eq. (8) using the occupation numbers ω_{nl} that are appropriate to the ground configuration of that ion.

We consider next the question of what $U(r)$ should be used in Eq. (2) for calculation of the ζ_{nl} by (4). Herman and Skillman simply identify $U(r)$ with $V(r)$ to obtain the ζ_{nl} which they tabulate on pages 2–6 through 2–16 of their book. We followed the same procedure in calculating ζ_{2p}, ζ_{3p} in the $N = 3$(Li) isoelectronic sequence, and ζ_{3p}, ζ_{3p} in the $N = 11$ (Na) sequence, and also for ζ_{3d} for both of these sequences.

But there is considerable question as to whether this procedure represents a good approximation because $V(r)$ includes all N of the electrons and even includes the $\rho^{1/3}$ term which Slater introduced to represent the effective central field of the exchange energy.

Instead of starting with Eq. (1) as is usually done, it seems more appropriate to follow the discussion given by Slater (1, Vol. 2, Chap. 24), which leads to the conclusion (his Eqs. 24–18) that the spin-orbit interaction energy is a sum over the $i = 1, \ldots, N$ electrons of

$$\alpha^2 \mathbf{S}_i \cdot \left[\frac{Z\mathbf{r}_i}{r_i^3} - \sum_j{}' \frac{\mathbf{r} - \mathbf{r}_j}{r_{ij}^3} \right] \times (-i\nabla_i), \tag{12}$$

in which the prime on $\sum'$ calls for the omission of the $i = j$ term. The quantity in brackets is the electric field at the ith electron due to the combined influence of the nucleus and the other $(N - 1)$ electrons.

The contribution of closed shells to this is spherically symmetrical. We may also make the usual spherical average approximation for the other electrons. Accordingly the field at r_i, due to the nucleus and the other electrons, is $Z_{fi}(r_i)/r_i^2$ in which

$$Z_{fi} = Z - \sum_{nl}{}' \omega_{nl} \int_0^{r_i} P_{nl}^2(s)\, ds, \tag{13}$$

since, from elementary electrostatics, the field at r_i due to a spherical charge distribution is determined by the total charge within a sphere of radius r_i.

This treatment leads to an altered spin-orbit interaction term, in place of Eq. (1),

$$\mathscr{H}^I = \sum_i \frac{\alpha^2 Z_{fi}(r_i)}{r_i^3} \mathbf{L}_i \cdot \mathbf{S}_i. \tag{14}$$

This is close to the usual form but with the ζ_{nl} to be calculated by

$$\zeta_{nl} = \int_0^\infty \frac{\alpha^2 Z_{fi}(r)}{r_i^3} P_{nl}^2(r)\, dr, \tag{15}$$

instead of (4). Eq. (15) has a more secure theoretical basis than (4) when U is replaced by V_0, and so we have also calculated some values of ζ_{nl} this way.

We have calculated a value of ζ_{nl} for several values of (nl) and for several isoelectronic sequences of low values of N, both by Eq. (4) and by Eq. (15). We have also made a systematic collection of the corresponding "observed" values of these ζ_{nl}'s by calculating them from the doublet intervals. In the case of optical spectra the observed intervals are taken from the compilation of Moore (7), and in the case of X-ray spectra from the compilation of Sandström (8).

The results of this work are shown in Tables 1–5 and also in Figs. 1–7. In Table 1, the observed and calculated values of ζ_{2p} in Rydbergs are given for the isoelectronic sequences $N = 3$, 5, and 9. In the $N = 3$(Li) sequence, the $P_{2p}(r)$ is an excited state in the configuration $1s^2 2p$, the ground state being $1s^2 2s$. So, as already mentioned, the $P_{2p}(r)$ is the one obtained by solving for $P_{2p}(r)$ using the potential function $V(r)$ derived from the self-consistent field for the $1s^2 2s$ configuration.

In the $N = 5$(B) sequence, the $P_{2p}(r)$ refers to the ground configuration, $1s^2 2s^2 2p$ and in the $N = 9$ sequence, it also refers to the ground configuration which is $1s^2 2s^2 2p^5$, giving an inverted ^2P ground term. In Table 1 the values as calculated both by Eq. (4) and by (15) are given, showing that (15) gives somewhat better agreement with observed values than (4), although the difference of the two methods is rather small. For $N = 5$ and 9 we calculated the ζ_{nl} values only on the basis of Eq. (15).

In every case the ζ_{nl} is smaller than the hydrogenic value (5) because of the screening by the other electrons. As the hydrogenic values increase with Z^4, we found it convenient to exhibit the numerical results graphically by plotting ζ_{nl}/Z^4 against Z, choosing the hydrogenic value for the top of the figure in each case. Figure 1 is such a plot for ζ_{2p}/Z^4 against Z on log-log scales, squares showing values inferred from observed intervals. The curves connect points of the same isoelectronic sequence.

The general trend is as expected: for constant N increasing Z gives approach toward the hydrogenic value, and for constant Z increasing N gives a decrease of ζ_{2p} as more electrons produce more screening. Figure 1 includes the observed values for the $N = 6$ and 7 sequences showing clearly how they fit in with the others, but we did not calculate theoretical ζ_{2p} for them.

Table 2 and Fig. 2 are similar presentations of the results for ζ_{3p}. Here the doublet in question for $N = 3$, 5, and 9 corresponds to excited terms. Observations are lacking for $N = 9$ where the ζ_{3p} would have to be inferred from the complex $2p^4 3p$ structure. For the $N = 11$(Na) sequence we calculated ζ_{3p} by both methods, and again we see that Eq. (15) gives better agreement than (4). Also here we see that the agreement of the calculated and observed values is considerably better than in the other instances covered so far.

TABLE 1

ζ_{2p} (in Rydbergs)

		N = 3					N = 5				N = 9	
			Calculated									
Z		Observed	(4)	(15)	Z		Observed	Calculated (15)	Z		Observed	Calculated (15)
3	Li	0.000002066	0.00000710	0.00000562	5	B	0.000097202	0.00017107	9	F	0.002454344	0.00337137
4	Be	0.000040096	0.00008654	0.00007432	6	C	0.000388807	0,00060938	10	Ne	0.004750734	0.00619540
5	B	0.00020716	0.00036336	0.00032438	7	N	0.001060106	0.00153294	11	Na	0.008286447	0.01046786
6	C	0.000650644	0.00101224	0.00092537	8	O	0.002348029	0.00319950	12	Mg	0.0135231904	0.01661275
7	N	0.001569808	0.00226348	0.00209982	9	F	0.0045320306	0.00591982	13	Al	0.0208983714	0.02510470
8	O	0.003234995	0.0043939	0.00412358	10	Ne	0.007794842	0.01005795	14	Si	0.030983051	0.03647289
9	F	0.005935381	0.00774354	0.00732525	11	Na	0.012994656	0.01603099	15	P	0.0441538848	0.05129898
10	Ne	—	0.01268848	0.01208730	12	Mg	0.020072157	0.02430914	16	S	0.061540844	0.07021835
11	Na	0.016099036	0.01969656	0.01884492	13	Al	0.029707278	0.03541674	17	Cl	0.082621468	0.09392031
12	Mg	0.02458596	0.02920308	0.02808797	14	Si	0.0424650	0.04992909	18	Ar	0.109734674	0.12314656
13	Al	0.03596464	0.0418719	0.04035757	15	P	0.058928548	0.06847842	19	K	—	0.15869125
14	Si	0.05097016	0.05822746	0.05624969	16	S	0.080592382	0.09174777	20	Ca	—	0.20140271
15	P	0.07004599	0.07888952	0.07641298	17	Cl	—	0.12047313	21	Sc	—	0.25217713
16	S	—	0.10453448	0.10154908	18	Ar	—	0.15544507	22	Ti	—	0.31197428

TABLE 2a

ζ_{3p} (in Rydbergs)

N = 3

Z		Observed	Calculated (4)	Calculated (15)
3	Li	—	0.00000230	0.0000018
4	Be	0.000010935	0.00002688	0.00002291
5	B	0.000061966	—	0.00009828
6	C	0.0001913659	—	0.00027797
7	N	0.000450773	0.00067916	0.00062780
8	O	0.000951362	0.00131386	0.00122942
9	F	0.0017131804	0.00231078	0.00218011
10	Ne	—	—	0.00359309
11	Na	0.0046292322	—	0.00559728
12	Mg	0.0079766167	—	0.00833753
13	Al	0.010631439	0.01244394	0.01197438
14	Si	—	0.0172972	0.01668412
15	P	0.03499262	0.02342732	0.02265894
16	S	—	0.03103220	0.03010665

N = 5

Z		Observed	Calculated (15)
5	B	—	0.00002017
6	C	0.000067616	0.00009741
7	N	0.0002187039	0.00028567
8	O	0.0005291419	0.00065386
9	F	0.0010752941	0.00128662
10	Ne	0.0017557062	0.00228435
11	Na	—	0.00376329
12	Mg	—	0.00585538
13	Al	—	0.00870839
14	Si	—	0.01248547
15	P	—	0.01736639
16	S	—	0.02354649
17	Cl	—	0.03123594
18	Ar	—	0.04066303

N = 9

Z		Calculated (15)
9	F	0.00008458
10	Ne	0.00038563
11	Na	0.00097265
12	Mg	0.00194808
13	Al	0.00343283
14	Si	0.00556395
15	P	0.00849491
16	S	0.01239577
17	Cl	0.01745087
18	Ar	0.02386166
19	K	0.03184432
20	Ca	0.04163288
21	Sc	0.05347656
22	Ti	0.06763368

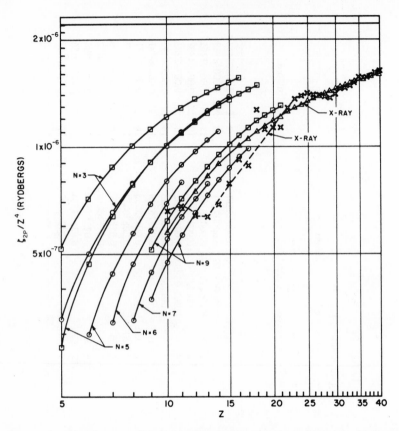

FIG. 1. ζ_{2p}/Z^4 (Rydbergs) plotted against Z (logarithmic scales). Top of figure is hydrogenic value, $\alpha^2/24$. Squares are calculated, circles observed values for optical spectra, by number of electrons, N, in isoelectronic sequences. Triangles are calculated values and crosses are observed values of the L^{II}–L^{III} doublet interval due to the $(2p)^5$ configuration in X-ray spectra for which $N = Z - 1$.

Table 3 and Fig. 3 give a similar presentation of the results for ζ_{3d}. Here the ζ's are considerably smaller than for the p-orbitals because of their less penetrating character. Also the "observed" values cannot be directly inferred from the doublet intervals for the low values of Z in the sequences because some of these are actually inverted, due to the additional contribution to the doublet interval arising from higher-order perturbations such as were studied by Phillips (9). Even where the configuration-interaction effect is not large enough to invert the ^2D, its effect may still produce an appreciable effect on the doublet interval which is not considered in these comparisons. Here we see that there is quite close agreement of observed and calculated values in the $N = 3$ and 5 sequences, but less good agreement for the $N = 11$ sequence.

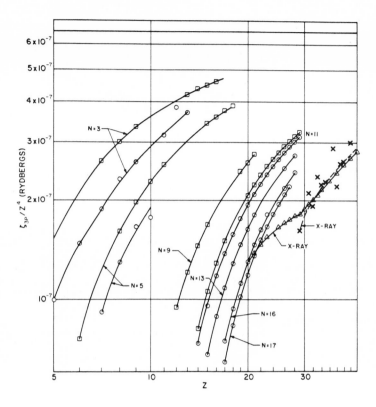

FIG. 2. ζ_{3p}/Z^4 (Rydbergs, plotted against Z (logarithmic scales). Top of figure is hydrogenic value, $\alpha^2/81$. Points designated as in Fig. 1 except that X-ray values refer to the $M_{II}-M_{III}$ doublet interval of the $(3p)^5$ configuration.

Table 4 and Fig. 4 provide a similar presentation of the results for ζ_{4p}. Here we made calculations for the $N = 11$ sequence, using Eqs. (4) and (15). We did not make any calculations for ζ_{4d}, but Fig. 5 gives a presentation of the observed values indicating that they show general trends similar to the other cases already considered.

Now we turn to a brief discussion of the corresponding doublet intervals in X-ray spectra as also shown in Figs. 1–5 and in Table 5 and Figs. 6 and 7. In X-ray spectra the doublet arises from an electron being removed from a normally closed shell in an atom from which one-electron has been removed, so that $N = (Z - 1)$. Thus the $(L_{II} - L_{III})$ interval arises from the open $(2p)^5$ shell in atoms in which the 2p shell is normally filled. Similarly the $(M_{II} - M_{III})$ interval arises from the open $(3p)^5$ shell in atoms in which the 3p shell is normally filled, and the $(M_{IV} - M_V)$ arises from the open $(3d)^9$ shell, in atoms in which the 3d shell is normally filled.

TABLE 2b

ζ_{3p} (in Rydbergs)

Z		Observed	Calculated	
			(4)	(15)
11	Na	0.0001044694	0.00011910	0.00011287
12	Mg	0.0005561761	0.00064770	0.00061754
13	Al	0.001412463	—	0.00158117
14	Si	0.0027963722	0.00323256	0.00310858
15	P	0.0048272808	0.00553160	0.00533591
16	S	0.0076728614	0.00870418	0.00841872
17	Cl	0.011481954	0.01292626	0.01253175
18	Ar	0.016512143	—	0.01786591
19	K	0.022878856	—	0.02462716
20	Ca	0.030867624	0.0338976	0.03304006
21	Sc	0.040642472	0.04440932	0.04334373
22	Ti	0.052610435	0.05709084	0.05579154
23	V	0.067312196	0.07222646	0.0706555
24	Cr	0.084565502	0.0900834	0.0882197
25	Mn	0.104491856	0.11099286	0.10878599
26	Fe	0.127395014	0.13524558	0.13267676
27	Co	0.15418624	0.16319978	0.16021989
28	Ni	0.184683282	0.19521012	0.19177413
29	Cu	0.219311398	0.23160832	0.22770043
30	Zn	—	—	0.26837353

The header spans: N = 11

The range of Z-values in the figures covers that in which the respective X-ray terms first make their appearance through filling of the shells. Here there is a considerable scatter in the X-ray observed values because the doublet intervals are quite small. The crosses show observed values and the triangles show the calculated values given by Herman and Skillman for even Z, supplemented by our calculations of the values for odd Z, by the same method. Making allowance for the scatter in the observed values, agreement of observation and calculation in all these cases is quite good.

Table 5 and Figs. 6 and 7 bring out a more detailed comparison of the transition between a particular doublet interval in optical spectra for the particular case of ζ_{2p}. The comparison is between the doublet interval due to $(2p)^5\ ^2P$ in the $N = 9$ optical spectra and the $L_{II} - L_{III}$ interval due to $(2p)^5\ ^2P$ in the $N = Z - 1$ X-ray spectra for $Z \geq 10$. In the $N = 9$ sequence the configuration remains as $1s^2 2s^2 2p^5$ with increasing Z. In the X-ray spectra for $Z = 10$ we have the same configuration, but for large values of Z we have an increasing number of outer electrons added to this configuration. These

TABLE 3a

ζ_{3d} (in Rydbergs)

$N=3$

Z		Observed	Calculated (4)	Calculated (15)
3	Li	0.0000001458	0.00000014	0.00000013
4	Be	—	0.00000218	0.00000214
5	B	0.000012393	—	0.00001086
6	C	0.000039002	—	0.00003430
7	N	0.0000874816	—	—
8	O	0.000186263	0.00017540	0.00017333
9	F	0.000328056	0.00032410	0.00032080
10	Ne	—	—	0.00054673
11	Na	0.0008164945	—	0.00087497
12	Mg	0.0017131804	—	0.00133251
13	Al	0.002041236	0.00196482	0.00194949
14	Si	0.003608614	0.00277946	0.00275922
15	P	0.004957288	0.00382370	0.00379816
16	S	—	0.00513838	0.00510595

$N=5$

Z		Observed	Calculated (15)
5	B	—	0.00000016
6	C	0.000005285	0.00000298
7	N	0.0000215059	0.00001525
8	O	0.0000608726	—
9	F	0.0001458026	0.00011266
10	Ne	—	0.00022793
11	Na	0.0004337627	0.00041289
12	Mg	0.0006196610	0.00069046
13	Al	0.0008748155	0.00108667
14	Si	0.0017131804	0.00163078
15	P	0.0024057428	0.00235507
16	S	—	0.00329537
17	Cl	—	0.00448996
18	Ar	—	0.00598100

$N=9$

Z		Calculated (15)
9	F	0.00000015
10	Ne	0.00000303
11	Na	0.00001737
12	Mg	0.00005797
13	Al	0.00014361
14	Si	0.00029601
15	P	0.00053973
16	S	0.00090223
17	Cl	0.00141383
18	Ar	0.00210805
19	K	0.00302145
20	Ca	0.00419378
21	Sc	0.00566826
22	Ti	0.00749033

TABLE 3b
ζ_{3d} (in Rydbergs)

Z		Observed	Calculated	
			(4)	(15)
11	Na	− 0.000000181	0.00000016	0.00000016
12	Mg	0.000003645	—	0.00000352
13	Al	− 0.000008311	0.00002548	0.00002207
14	Si	—	—	0.00007680
15	P	+ 0.000040825	0.00021686	0.00019266
16	S	0.000116642	0.00044114	0.00039622
17	Cl	0.0002660897	0.00078868	0.00071599
18	Ar	0.0005504048	0.00129314	0.00118294
19	K	0.0010643589	—	0.00183076
20	Ca	0.0015090568	—	0.00269633
21	Sc	0.00225994014	—	0.00381951
22	Ti	0.00324410767	0.00559484	0.00524336
23	V	0.0044834297	0.00746142	0.00701386
24	Cr	0.0062330608	0.00972088	0.00918058
25	Mn	0.0079826919	0.01246656	0.01179568
26	Fe	0.010351984	0.01570152	0.01491490
27	Co	0.013231585	0.01953884	0.01859687
28	Ni	0.016767298	0.02401522	0.02290380
29	Cu	0.0211413758	0.02916054	0.02700952
30	Zn	—	—	0.03365597

TABLE 4
ζ_{4p} (in Rydbergs)

			$N = 11$	
Z	Element	Observed	Calculated (4)	Calculated (15)
11	Na	0.0000342029	0.00003966	0.00003759
12	Mg	0.0001852908	0.00021982	0.00020958
13	Al	0.0004867984	—	0.00055007
14	Si	0.0009829525	0.00114856	0.00110441
15	P	0.0017253307	0.00199928	0.00192845
16	S	0.0027763243	—	0.00308599
17	Cl	0.0041796742	—	0.00464797
18	Ar	0.0060568825	—	0.00669253
19	K	0.0087542305	—	0.00930448
20	Ca	0.011573081	0.01290282	0.01257543
21	Sc	0.015370023	0.01701310	0.01660404
22	Ti	0.020290861	0.02199574	0.02149372
23	V	0.026548222	0.0279600	0.02735821
24	Cr	0.032623330	—	0.03431330
25	Mn	0.040946228	0.04335066	0.04248527
26	Fe	0.048965370	0.05301320	0.05200558
27	Co	0.0612737089	0.06419056	0.06301278
28	Ni	—	0.07701256	0.07565116
29	Cu	—	0.09162308	0.09007627
30	Zn	—	—	0.10643764

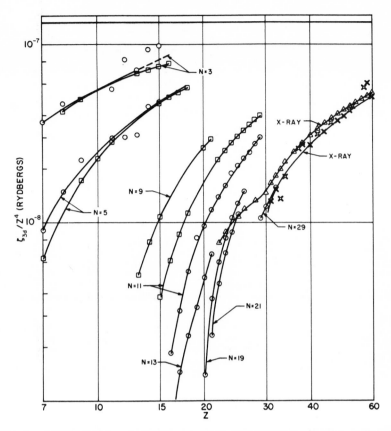

Fig. 3. ζ_{3d}/Z^4 (Rydbergs) plotted against Z (logarithmic scales). Top of figure is hydrogenic value, $\alpha^2/405$, Points are designated as in Fig. 1 except that X-ray values refer to the $M_{IV} - M_V$ doublet intervals.

are 3s, $3s^2$ for Na and Mg, then a gradual filling of the 3p shell from Al to Ar and the addition of 4s and $4s^2$ for $Z = 19$ and 20.

Hence the distinction between ζ_{2p} for a given Z is, for the X-ray case, the additional screening produced by these "outer" electrons to the small extent that they penetrate to radial values within the 2p-orbital, as compared with the $N = 9$ sequence for which no outer electrons are added to the $1s^2 2s^2 2p^5$ configuration. This effect means that ζ_{2p} should be smaller for the X-ray sequence than for the $N = 9$ sequence. The calculated values are shown in Table 5, as also a column of differences $[\zeta_{2p}(N=9) - \zeta_{2p}(N=Z-1)]$ in the column headed Δ.

In Fig. 6 the corresponding ζ_{2p} are shown, the squares referring to calculated values for the $N = 9$ sequence, and the triangles to the smaller

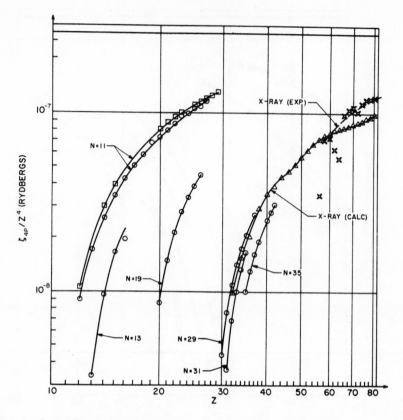

FIG. 4. ζ_{4p}/Z^4 (Rydbergs) plotted against Z. Top of figure is hydrogenic value, $\alpha^2/192$. Points are designated as in Fig. 1 except that X-ray values refer to the N_{II}–N_{III} doublet interval.

calculated values for the ζ_{2p} for the X-ray intervals, while the crosses show the ζ_{2p} inferred from the X-ray levels. These latter despite scatter tend to be systematically smaller than the calculated ζ_{2p}. Figure 7 shows a graph of the difference Δ against Z.

In conclusion it seems fair to say that the calculations show that the self-consistent fields are capable of giving quite good values of the spin-orbit parameters ζ_{nl} both with regard to absolute values and general trends with N and Z. Some discrepancies remain which can be reduced by the use of more elaborate approximations (10, 11), but this work shows that the spin-orbit parameters are quite adequately given for most purposes by calculations of the type considered here.

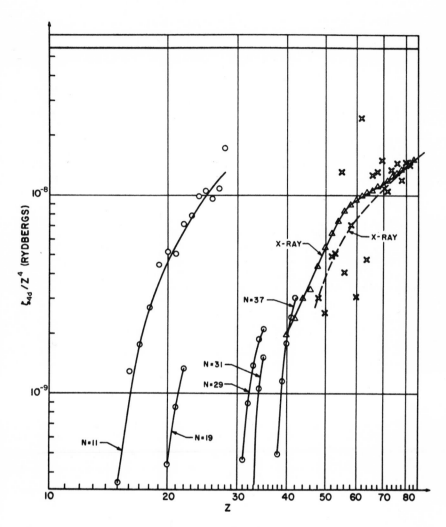

FIG. 5. Same as preceding figures, but for ζ_{4d}/Z^4. Top of figure is hydrogenic value, $\alpha^2/960$. Points refer to 4^2D intervals in optical spectra and $N_{IV}-N_V$ $(4d)^5$ intervals in X-ray spectra.

This research was supported in part by the Advanced Research Projects Agency (Project Defender), monitored by the U.S. Army Research Office, Durham, under Contract DA-31-124-ARO[D]-139 with the University of Colorado.

TABLE 5

ζ_{2p} (in Rydbergs)

		X-ray			$N = 9$	Δ
Z		Observed	(4)	(15)	(15)	(15)
10	Ne	0.00669868	0.00574064	0.0061954	0.0061954	0.00000000
11	Na	0.01004802	0.0098288	0.00945871	0.01046786	0.00100915
12	Mg	0.01339736	0.0156159	0.0150942	0.0166128	0.00151860
13	Al	0.01808644	0.0236047	0.022897	0.0251047	0.00220770
14	Si	0.02679472	0.0342703	0.0333372	0.0364729	0.00313570
15	P	0.04019208	0.0481425	0.0469410	0.0512990	0.0043580
16	S	0.06028812	0.065802	0.0642856	0.0702184	0.00593280
17	Cl	0.07368548	0.0879598	0.0859962	0.0939203	0.00792410
18	Ar	0.13397360	0.1150476	0.1127460	0.1231470	0.01041010
19	K	0.14737096	0.1481618	0.1453785	0.1586913	0.01331280
20	Ca	0.18086436	0.1880368	0.1847128	0.20140271	0.01668991

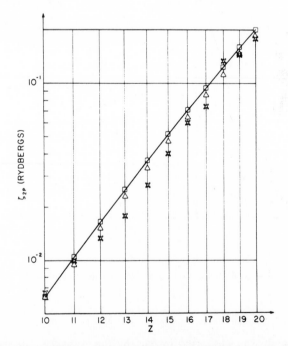

FIG. 6.   Effect of screening on doublet $2\,^2P$ interval as shown in value of ζ_{2p}. Squares are calculated values for the $1s^2 2s^2 2p^5$ ($N = 9$) ground states of the fluorine isoelectronic sequence. Triangles are calculated values for the $N = (Z - 1)$ $(2p)^5$ X-ray interval in elements $Z = 10$ to 20. Crosses are observed X-ray doublet intervals.

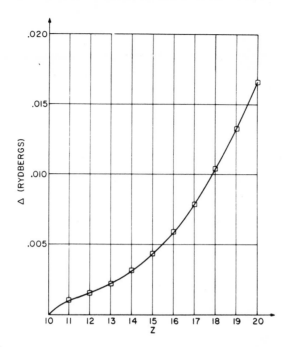

Fig. 7. Calculated difference between ζ_{2p} in $N = 9$ isoelectronic sequence and in calculated X-ray doublet interval due to $(2p)^5$ with $N = Z - 1$.

REFERENCES

1. C. Slater, "Quantum Theory of Atomic Structure", 2 Vols. McGraw-Hill, New York, 1960. Especially Chap. 17 for exposition of the method and the bibliography, p. 383, Vol. 2.
2. E. U. Condon and G. H. Shortley, "The Theory of Atomic Spectra" pp. 120–125, 144–147, 193–197. Cambridge Univ. Press, London and New York, 1935.
3. A. Landé, *Zeit. Physik*, **25**, 46 (1924).
4. B. Edlén, in "*Encyclopedia of Physics*", Vol. 27, p. 106. Springer-Verlag, Berlin, 1964.
5. F. Herman and S. Skillman, "Atomic Structure Calculations". Prentice-Hall, Englewood Cliffs, New Jersey, 1963.
6. R. Latter, *Phys. Rev.* **99**, 510 (1955).
7. C. E. Moore, "Atomic Energy Levels as Derived from Analysis of Optical Spectra," 3 Vols. National Bureau of Standards Circular 467.
8. A. E. Sandström, Experimental methods of X-ray spectroscopy: ordinary wavelengths, in "*Encyclopedia of Physics*", Vol. 30. Springer-Verlag, Berlin, 1957. See also "*American Institute of Physics Handbook*," 2nd ed., pp. 77–136–8. McGraw-Hill, New York, 1963.
9. M. Phillips, *Phys. Rev.* **44**, 644 (1933).
10. M. Blume and R. E. Watson, *Proc. Roy. Soc.* (*London*) A **270**, 1340 (1962).
11. M. Blume and R. E. Watson, *Proc. Roy. Soc.* (*London*) A**271**, 1347 (1963).

Collisions of Slow Positrons with Atoms

H. S. W. MASSEY, J. LAWSON, and D. G. THOMPSON

PHYSICS DEPARTMENT, UNIVERSITY COLLEGE, LONDON, ENGLAND

I. Introduction

In 1951 in the course of a discussion at the first post-war scientific confer-ence in West Berlin, Professor Carl Ramsauer remarked how interesting it would be if it were possible to repeat the experiments on the scattering of slow electrons by atoms with the electrons replaced by positrons. One's first reponse to this is apt to be that, because of its positive charge, a positron is repelled by the mean atomic field and such phenomena as the Ramsauer-Townsend effect which produces a minimum total cross section for collisions of electrons with argon, krypton, and xenon atoms at energies of the order of 0.5 eV, would not be expected to occur. Monotonous behavior of the positron-atom cross sections as a function of electron energy would be anticipated.

However, this is based on a misconception. It seems that the Ramsauer-Townsend effect for electron collisons arises principally because of the long-range polarization of the atom by the incoming slow electron. As long ago as 1929, Holtsmark found that the effect could be reproduced theoretically by calculating the scattering from the Hartree field of argon modified by addition of an empirical polarization potential having approximately the correct asymp-totic form. He found a similar result for krypton (Holtsmark, 1930). In the last few years, improved methods of calculation of the scattering of slow electrons by atoms have been developed and it is found that, if allowance is made for scattering by the undisturbed mean static field of the atom, by the nonlocal interaction due to electron exchange and by a dipole polarization field due to disturbance of the atom then good agreement with observation is found down to the lowest electron energies. Such calculations for argon, carried out by Thompson (1966), show that the Ramsauer-Townsend effect only appears when the polarization field is introduced in addition to the static and exchange interactions.

Turning now to the scattering of slow positrons we note that, while the mean static atomic field is now repulsive the polarization field should be essentially the same as for slow electrons. In view of the importance of the latter field for slow-electron scattering we must admit the possibility that it will be dominant also for the scattering of slow positrons. There may in fact exist effects similar to the Ramsauer-Townsend effect for some atoms. Before discussing this point further we must also point out that, although in the positron case there is no nonlocal interaction due to exchange, such an interaction is present through the possibility of virtual or real positronium production.

Calculations already carried out for the scattering of slow positrons by hydrogen atoms have confirmed the importance of polarization. Thus variational calculations using elaborate trial functions (Schwartz, 1961) have shown that the zero-energy scattering length for positrons is negative, corresponding to an attractive potential.

The possibility of carrying out experiments with slow positrons as mentioned by Ramsauer is now quite close. This is because of the growing availablity of intense positron sources generated from the high-current electron beams which have been accelerated in linear accelerators. It should not be long before both total and differential cross sections for elastic scattering of slow positrons of well-defined energy, will be observed. Apart from such direct observations indirect evidence about the cross sections may be obtained from observation of the annihilation spectra of positrons in gases.

A technique of this kind which has been especially fruitful is that of Garth Jones and his collaborators (Falk *et al.*, 1965; Jones *et al.*, 1965). They allow positrons diffusing in the gas to come to equilibrium in the presence of an electric field. The mean energy and energy distribution of the positrons is then determined by the field and by the momentum loss cross section for positron collisions with the gas atoms. For positrons of a given velocity v the annihilation cross section from gas atoms is given by

$$Q_a = \xi \pi r_0^2 c / v \tag{1}$$

where r_0 is the classical electron radius e^2/mc^2. ξ is an effective number of atomic electrons and is given by (Öre, 1949)

$$\xi = \int \rho(r) |F(\mathbf{r})|^2 \, d\mathbf{r} \tag{2}$$

where $\rho(r)$ is the number density of electrons in the atom at a distance r from the nucleus and $F(\mathbf{r})$ is the wave function of the motion of the positron referred to the nucleus as origin, which has the asymptotic form

$$F(\mathbf{r}) \sim e^{ikz} + r^{-1}e^{ikr}f(\theta). \tag{3}$$

k is the positron wave number $mv/\hbar$. It follows that the mean rate of annihilation of positrons in a gas in the presence of an electric field of strength E is given by

$$\bar{R} = (\pi e^2 N/mc) \int f(E, v)\xi(v) \, dv, \tag{4}$$

where N is the number of gas atoms per unit volume and $f(E, r)$ is the velocity distribution function for the positrons. The mean annihilation rate may be observed as a function of E. It depends both through $f(E, v)$ and ξ on the wave function describing the collision of a positron of given energy v with the atom. To take advantage of this it is best to make some assumptions about the effective positron interaction, determine the corresponding wave function F and thence f and ξ so that $\bar{R}$ may be obtained and compared with observation. This procedure may be used either to check an approximate theory or by a trial and error procedure to determine an empirical effective positron-atom interaction. Considerable progress in applying the latter technique has been made by Jones *et al.*, (1965) for argon and will be referred to again below.

Other even more indirect methods for investigating collision phenomena of slow positrons in gases are available. In view of all these sources of experimental information which are either already in operation or will shortly be so it is worthwhile to make some preliminary calculations for positron collisons with rare gas atoms to examine the kind of results to be expected when polarization is allowed for.

In carrying out the calculations which we now present, virtual positronium production is not allowed for. This means that the true effective attractive field is likely to be somewhat greater than we assume. It is, of course, possible to allow for this empirically by increasing the polarizability above the experimental value but in the absence of any control data from experiments there is no way of determining how much increase to allow for. Judging by the results of the atomic hydrogen calculations (Cody *et al.*, 1964) virtual positronium formation contributes considerably less to the effective attraction for slow positrons than does polarization.

II. Allowance for Polarization in the Theory of Scattering by Rare Gas Atoms

For argon and krypton we have used the semiempirical interactions which Holtsmark found were successful in yielding a good approximation for the scattering of slow electrons by atoms. This interaction took the form

$$V^-(r) = V_H(r) + V_p(r), \tag{5}$$

where V_H is the mean interaction with the Hartree charge distribution of the atom and V_p is a polarization potential with the asymptotic form

$$V_p \sim -\alpha e^2/r^4, \tag{6}$$

α being the atomic polarizability. We take for positrons

$$V^+(r) = -V_H(r) + V_p(r). \tag{7}$$

The differential cross section $I(\theta)\, d\omega$ for scattering through the angle θ into the solid angle $d\omega$ is then given by

$$I(\theta) = |f(\theta)|^2 \tag{8}$$

where

$$f(\theta) = \frac{1}{2ik} \cdot \sum_l (2l+1)(e^{2i\eta_l} - 1)P_l(\cos\theta) \tag{9}$$

and η_l is such that the solution of

$$\frac{d^2 g_l}{dr^2} + \left\{ k^2 - \frac{l(l+1)}{r^2} - \frac{2m}{\hbar^2} V^+ \right\} g_l = 0 \tag{10}$$

which vanishes at the origin has the asymptotic form

$$g_l \sim \sin(kr - \tfrac{1}{2}l\pi + \eta_l). \tag{11}$$

The total elastic and momentum loss cross section Q_t and Q_m respectively are then given by

$$Q_t = 2\pi \int_0^\pi I(\theta) \sin\theta \, d\theta, \qquad Q_m = 2\pi \int_0^\pi (1 - \cos\theta)I(\theta) \sin\theta \, d\theta. \tag{12}$$

The phases η_l were determined by electronic computation using the departmental computer in the Physics Department at University College, London.

For helium and neon a somewhat less empirical procedure was adopted based on the exchange adiabatic approximation of Temkin and Lamkin (1961). Following this method as formulated for electrons we find a similar interaction to (7) but with the Hartree-Fock instead of the Hartree approximation (the two are of course the same for helium) and a polarization potential which is determined as follows.

Consider for simplicity the case of helium. We write as an approximate wave function describing the system of two atomic electrons (coordinates $\mathbf{r}_1$, $\mathbf{r}_2$) and a free positron (coordinate $\mathbf{r}_3$) in the form

$$\Psi(\mathbf{r}_1, \mathbf{r}_2, \mathbf{r}_3) = [\psi_0(r_1, r_2) + \phi_0(\mathbf{r}_1, \mathbf{r}_2, \mathbf{r}_3)]F(\mathbf{r}_3), \tag{13}$$

where $\psi_0(r_1, r_2)$ is the ground state wave function of the helium atom and F is a proper function which has the asymptotic form

$$F(\mathbf{r}) \sim e^{ikz} + r^{-1}e^{ikr}f(\theta), \tag{14}$$

k being the wave number of the incident positron.

The function ϕ_0 represents the distortion of the atomic wave function through interaction with the incident positron. Following the same procedure as that of Temkin and Lamkin (1961) for dealing with slow-electron collisions we treat the perturbation due to the slow positron as adiabatic provided $r_3 > r_1, r_2$. We take the perturbing potential to be

$$v = v_{13} + v_{23},$$

where

$$v_{13} = (2r_1/r_3^2)\cos\theta_{13}, \qquad r_3 > r_1, \tag{15}$$

θ_{13} being the angle between $\mathbf{r}_1$ and $\mathbf{r}_3$. In this way we only include the dipole distortion of the atom. For $r_3 < r_1, r_2$, the perturbing potential is taken to be zero. This arbitrary assumption is probably less justified for positron than for electron collisions because of the absence of any symmetry relations between the incident and atomic particles.

Given v the change ϕ in the atomic wave function may be calculated as a function of $\mathbf{r}_1, \mathbf{r}_2$, and $\mathbf{r}_3$, using a method due to Sternheimer (1954).

Having determined ϕ in this way a differential equation is obtained for $F_0(\mathbf{r}_3)$ by requiring that

$$\int \psi_0(r_1, r_2)(\mathcal{H} - E)\Psi(\mathbf{r}_1, \mathbf{r}_2, \mathbf{r}_3)\, d\mathbf{r}_1\, d\mathbf{r}_2 = 0, \tag{16}$$

where $\mathcal{H}$ is the Hamiltonian for the three-particle system and E the total energy. This leads to the equation

$$\left[\nabla^2 + k^2 - \frac{2m}{\hbar^2}(V_{HF} + V_p)\right]F = 0 \tag{17}$$

where V_p is now given in terms of ψ_0 and ϕ_0. It has the asymptotic form

$$V_p \sim -\alpha e^2/r^4 \tag{18}$$

but α is now a calculated rather than the observed polarizability. It tends to zero for small r as r^2. As the most important effect of polarization arises from the long-range interaction which it introduces it is probable that the way in this interaction is cut off at small distances is not very important (cf., Lawson et al., 1966).

The Temkin-Lamkin procedure is consistent and convenient and gives very good results in electron-atom collisions. We must remember here, however, that in the latter cases it is also necessary to take into account electron exchange. The equivalent in the positron case, virtual positronium formation, has not been included in the present calculations.

Extension of the above procedure to neon presents no difficulties if one continues to work with the Hartree-Fock approximation (Mertz and Torrey, 1963) to the ground state wave function.

III. Results

Figures 1–3 illustrate the total elastic and momentum loss cross sections for positron collisions with helium, neon, argon and krypton calculated as described above. It must be realized that we cannot expect the results to represent reality too closely but they should expose the possibilities.

The cross section for helium is very small and with the approximations made exhibits a Ramsauer-Townsend effect at a positron energy of about 1.2 eV. For helium the value of the polarizability as calculated by the method outlined above is 1.56 a.u. which is a little greater than the observed value of

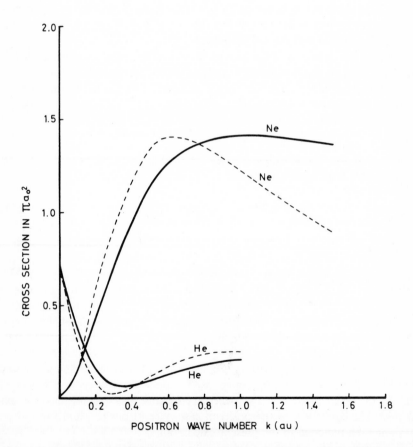

FIG. 1.   Calculated total and momentum-loss cross sections for collisions of slow positron with helium and with neon atoms: ———— total cross section; – – – – momentum-loss cross section.

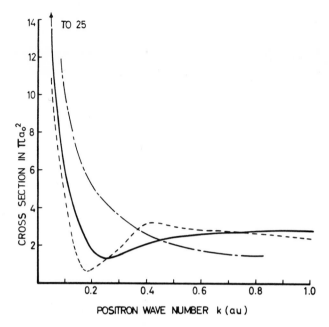

Fig. 2. Calculated total and momentum-loss cross sections for collisions of slow positrons with argon atoms: ———— total cross section; – – – – momentum-loss cross section; –·–·–·– total cross section derived by Jones *et al.* (1965).

1.38 a.u. (Herzfeld and Wolf, 1925) so that the calculation already allows a little for a further effective attraction such as that due to virtual positronium formation. Nevertheless it is likely that the full attraction is still a little underestimated. This means that the cross section minimum will be shifted to rather higher positron energies. Indirect evidence (Teutsch and Hughes, 1956) from the experiments of Marder *et. al.*, 1956) indicates a very low momentum-loss cross section for helium at a mean energy close to the positronium formation threshold, about 18 eV. Although this is qualitatively in agreement with expectation from our calculations it is still smaller than we would anticipate.

Neon also presents an interesting situation. Our calculated polarizability is 2.41 a.u. a little smaller than the observed 2.67 a.u. It is therefore likely that the true effective attractive interaction is underestimated by our method. In that case it looks likely that a Ramsauer-Townsend effect exists for collisions with neon of positrons with quite low energy; in our calculations which somewhat underestimate the attraction the minimum has not quite appeared even at zero energy. As for helium the momentum-loss cross section to be expected at a mean positron energy of 15 eV is much larger than suggested from the analysis (Teutsch and Hughes, 1956) of the experiment of Marder *et al.* (1956).

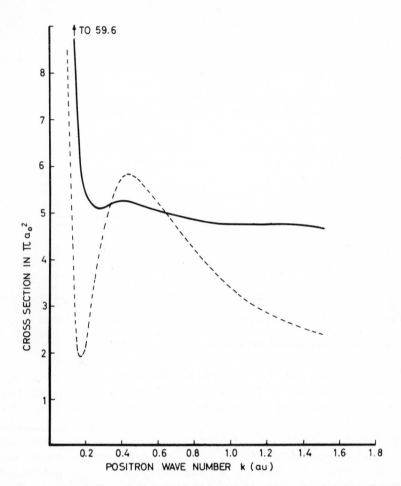

FIG. 3. Calculated total and momentum-loss cross sections for collisons of slow positrons with krypton atoms: ——— total cross section; – – – – momentum-loss cross section.

This gives about 0.12 πa_0^2 to be contrasted with about 1.0πa_0^2 for our calculations.

For argon our semiempirical interaction leads to a rather flat and shallow minimum in the total cross section at about 1.2 eV. In this case we may compare with the cross section derived from an effective interaction found by Falk *et al.* (1965) to give a good fit to their observations on the annihilation rate of positrons in argon as a function of time. Considering the simplicity of the theoretical approximation the agreement is not perhaps too unsatisfactory but it leaves unanswered the question as to whether a minimum cross section really exists for argon. The evidence is that conditions are not un-favorable for this though the minimum may be very shallow or smeared out completely. The momentum loss cross section which we obtain at 9 eV is $2.7\pi a_0^2$ which is closer to the value $2\pi a_0^2$ derived by Teutsch *et al.* (1956) than for helium and neon.

Finally, for krypton, the calculated results show a behavior rather similar to that for argon except that the momentum loss cross section differs very much more in shape from the total cross section. Thus Q_m has a very deep minimum at an energy below 0.5 eV which has almost disappeared from Q_t. This is clearly a sensitive case which it would be of considerable interest to investigate experimentally.

In Figs. 4–7 differential elastic cross sections are shown for a range of positron energies, scattered by each rare gas. These angular distributions are

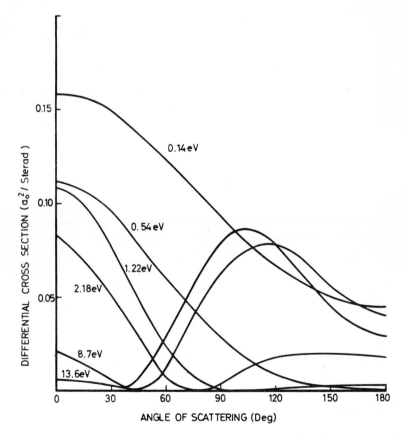

FIG. 4.   Differential cross sections for scattering of slow positrons by helium atoms.

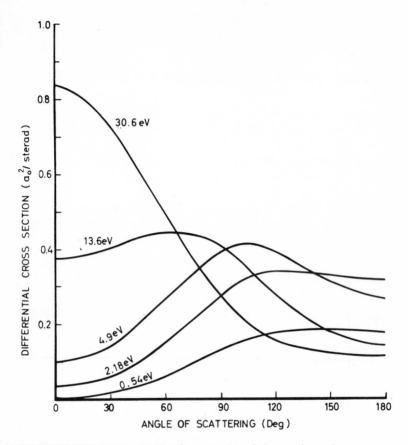

Fig. 5.   Differential cross sections for scattering of slow positrons by neon atoms.

highly variable and far from monotonic as would be the case if the mean effective interaction were a monotonic repulsion.

Finally in Table 1 we give the effective values of the number ξ of annihilation

TABLE 1

EFFECTIVE NUMBER ξ OF ANNIHILATION ELECTRONS PER ATOM FOR POSITRONS IN HELIUM, NEON, ARGON AND KRYPTON, CALCULATED FROM (2)

Positron wave number (au)	0.2	0.4	0.6	0.8	1.0
ξ helium	1.22	1.11	1.095	1.11	1.12
ξ neon	1.43	1.53	1.79	2.04	2.38
ξ argon	2.42	2.40	2.70	3.00	3.23
ξ krypton	5.08	4.77	2.18	2.33	2.36

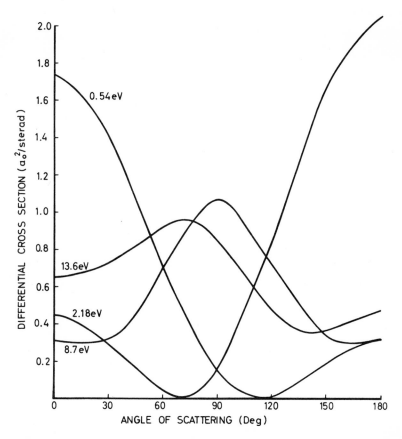

Fɪɢ. 6. Differential cross sections for scattering of slow positrons by argon atoms.

electrons per atom as a function of positron energy for each gas. These have been calculated from the formula (2) with $F(\mathbf{r})$ given from the solution of (17). No allowance has therefore been made for the distortion of the charge distribution in the atom during the collision with the positron. To include this effect requires a more accurate solution of the wave equation for the three-particle system than we have obtained. In particular we need to know more accurately how the function ϕ_0 in (13) behaves when r_3 is nearly equal to r_1 or r_2. It follows that the effective number of annihilation electrons, if it could be measured accurately as a function of positron energy at low energies, would be a more sensitive test of any theory of low energy positron collisions with atoms than the differential elastic cross sections. All we can say at this stage is that allowance for atomic distortion will tend to increase the values of ξ above those given in Table 1 because the electron density will be increased

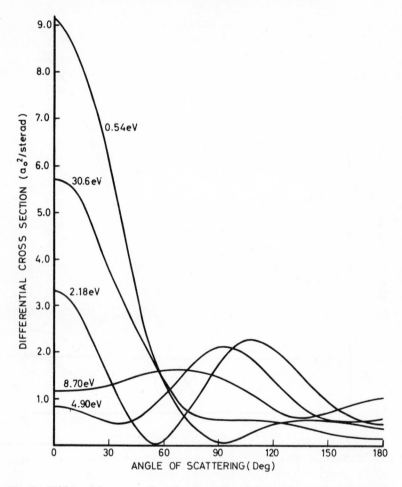

FIG. 7.   Differential cross sections for scattering of slow positrons by krypton atoms.

at large distances from the atom where the positron experiences an effective attraction.

From the values of ξ given in Table 1 together with the momentum-loss cross sections in Figs. 1–3 annihilation rates for positrons in the presence of electric fields may be derived and used as a basis for analyzing observed data on these rates.

IV. Summary

It is clear that, due to the destructive interference between the scattering from the mean repulsive atomic field and that due to the attraction arising from atom polarization, the elastic scattering of slow positrons by atoms is likely to show features at least as "unusual" as for the corresponding scattering of slow electrons. Accurate prediction of the behavior in any particular case is likely to present a considerable challenge to theorists because of the sensitivity arising from the destructive interference which is inherent.

ACKNOWLEDGMENT

We are grateful to Mr. W. Lawson for his assistance in the operation, for the purposes of this paper, of the computer in the Physics Department at University College, London which he designed and constructed.

REFERENCES

Cody, W. J., Lawson, J., Massey, H. S. W., and Smith, K. (1964). *Proc. Roy. Soc.* **A278**, 479.
Falk, W. R., Orth, P. H. R., and Jones, G. (1965). *Phys. Rev. Letters* **14**, 447.
Herzfeld, K. F., and Wolf, K. L. (1925). *Ann. Physik* **76**, 71, 567.
Holtsmark, J. (1929). *Z. Physik* **55**, 437.
Holtsmark, J. (1930). *Z. Physik* **66**, 49.
Jones, G., Falk, W. R., and Orth, P. H. R. (1965). Paper presented at the 4th International Conference on The Physics of Electronic and Atomic Collisions, Quebec.
Lawson, J., Massey, H. S. W., Wallace, J. B. G., and Wilkinson, D. (1966). *Proc. Roy. Soc. (London),* A., in press.
Marder, S., Hughes, V. W., Wu, C. S., and Bennett, W. (1956). *Phys. Rev.* **103**, 1258.
Mertz, A. L., and Torrey, M. D. (1963). *J. Chem. Phys.* **39**, 695.
Öre, A. (1949). Universitetet i Bergen Arbok, Naturvitenskapelig rekke No. 9
Schwartz, C. (1961). *Phys. Rev.* **124**, 1468.
Sternheimer, R. M. (1954). *Phys. Rev.* **96**, 951.
Temkin, A., and Lamkin, J.C. (1961). *Phys. Rev.* **121**, 788.
Teutsch, W. B., and Hughes, V. W. (1956). *Phys, Rev.* **103**, 1266.
Thompson, D, G. (1966). *Proc. Roy. Soc. (London)* A., in press.

Slater Screening Constants in Atomic and Molecular Orbitals*

J. O. HIRSCHFELDER and A. C. WAHL

THEORETICAL CHEMISTRY INSTITUTE, THE UNIVERSITY OF WISCONSIN
MADISON, WISCONSIN

I. Introduction

Slater screening constants and Slater orbitals (Slater, 1930) have enabled a whole generation of chemists and physicists to calculate approximate values of many of the physical properties of atoms. The use of screening constants implies that an atomic orbital corresponding to a given set of electronic quantum numbers is the same, except for a uniform scaling of the coordinates, quite irrespective of which atom or ion is under consideration. This concept of interchangeability of orbitals has greatly simplified our mental picture of atomic structure.

An adequate simple model of a molecular orbital certainly must be more complicated than a Slater atomic orbital. The molecular orbitals vary in size and shape as the internuclear separations are changed. Nevertheless, as chemists we feel confident that it must be possible to develop the concept of interchangeability of molecular orbitals on some sort of corresponding states basis. We are impressed with the simple regularities which characterize most molecules: the additivity of bond energies; the accurate reproducibility of bond lengths, bond angles, and bond force constants, etc.

As our theoretical treatments and mathematical experimentation give progressively closer analogs to natural phenomena, it is evident that two types of

* This research was supported by the following grant: National Aeronautics and Space Administration Grant NsG-275-62.

theories will emerge. First, due to the development of computers capable of remembering and manipulating very great detail, there will be the highly complex formulations representing numerical models of physical systems which can be assimilated only by the high-speed computing machines which generated them. And second, there will be the simplified semiempirical formulations which the human mind can comprehend and manipulate in a sophisticated conceptual or analytical manner. The computing machines will provide specific answers to specific questions in much the same manner as the results of laboratory experiments. However, there is a great need for the output of the computing machines describing these " numeric systems " to be in an accessible and usable form. These *simplified representations* will help the scientist to see the *important features* of the model and make it easier for him to develop a simple concept or *understanding* of the phenomena. The scientist will then make quantitative definitions of the important features and use the *numerical* output of the computing machines to interpolate and extrapolate the changes of these important features which occur when the " experimental " conditions are changed.

In seeking a simplified formulation of the behavior of a class of systems, we inevitably try to develop a corresponding states treatment in which all of the systems obey the same equations when each system is characterized by a set of parameters. Thus, the aerodynamical behavior of geometrically similar objects moving through different media can be characterized by Reynolds, Prandtl, and Schmidt numbers. The volumetric behavior of a gas or liquid can be characterized by the critical parameters: P_c, V_c, and T_c. In chemistry, a compound is characterized by its atomic composition and by its chemical bonds. In quantum chemistry, we further characterize a compound by its molecular orbitals. Underlying each of these uses of corresponding states is the inherent notion of the interchangeability of systems of a particular class. This interchangeability is certainly only an approximation, but it may be useful in helping us to comprehend and to predict the behavior of complex systems. In the present paper, let us consider on a simple basis, first, how Slater screening constants relate to the interchangeability of atomic orbitals and second, their role in molecular orbitals.

II. Atomic Orbitals

The notion of screening constants stems from a well-known theorem of classical electrostatics. Suppose that an atom is composed of a nucleus of charge $+Ze$ surrounded by a spherically symmetric cloud of electrons having a charge density $-e\rho(r)$. Then the electrostatic potential $V(r)$ at a distance r from the nucleus is

$$V(r) = +e(Z - S(r))/r = +eZ_{\text{eff}}(r)/r. \tag{1}$$

Here the screening constant $S(r) = 4\pi \int_0^r \rho r^{-2} \, dr'$ is the number of electrons lying within a sphere of radius r. The effective nuclear charge $Z_{eff}(r) = Z - S(r)$. It is a remarkable fact that $V(r)$ and $Z_{eff}(r)$ are unaffected by that part of the spherically symmetric electronic charge cloud which lies outside of the sphere of radius r. If the electrons were distributed in a set of spherical shells, then for electrons in the nth shell the electrostatic potential would be $V = e(Z - S_n)/r$ where S_n is the screening constant. If there are N_k electrons in the kth shell, then

$$S_n = \sum_{k=1}^{n-1} N_k + \tfrac{1}{2}(N_n - 1).$$ (2)

The reason why each of the other electrons in the nth shell is only half effective in its shielding of a particular electron is that (if the shell has finite thickness) it is equally probable that an arbitrary other electron has a radius greater than the radius of the particular electron under consideration.

In real atoms, the atomic orbitals are not highly localized in a spherical shell. Thus the concept of a screening constant for each type of orbital represents an approximation. And, indeed, for the expectation value of each different type of property, we should use a different value for the screening constant.

Historically, already in 1921 Schrödinger (1921) suggested that the orbits of the semiclassical Bohr quantum mechanics be divided into segments. In each of these segments, the ellipsoidal trajectories were approximated by assuming a coulomb potential with an effective nuclear charge characteristic of this segment. Schrödinger's concept of atomic structure was a crude beginning of the Hartree atom. In 1927, Pauling (1927; Pauling and Sherman, 1932) used Schrödinger's procedure to estimate (rather accurately) the molar refractivity, the diamagnetic susceptibility, and the sizes of various atoms.

In 1930, Slater (1930) made the use of screening constants simple and practical. It would have seemed logical to use hydrogenic orbitals (Naqvi, 1962, 1964; Naqvi and Victor, 1964). However, with hydrogen-like orbitals, many of the integrals required for the estimation of atomic properties are quite difficult to evaluate. Slater was impressed by Zener's (1930) work on analytical Hartree wave functions. Zener found that, as far as energy is concerned, the nodes in the orbitals are quite unimportant. Thus, Slater (1930) simplified the Zener wave functions to obtain the familiar Slater orbitals:

$$R(r) = r^{n-1} \exp(-(Z - S)r/n^*).$$ (3)

Here the screening constant S and the effective principal quantum number are embedded parameters which Slater determined so as to give good values for the X-ray energy levels of atoms, atomic and ionic radii, etc. Most of the Slater orbital integrals required for the determination of atomic properties are simple. For example, the mean value of the kth power of the radius of an electron is given by the relation

$$\langle r_i^k \rangle = \left[\frac{n_i^*}{2(Z - S_i)} \right]^k \prod_{j=1}^{k} (2n_i^* + j)\, a_0^k, \qquad k \geqq 1$$

$$\langle r_i^{-1} \rangle = [(Z - S_i)(n_i^*)^{-2}]\, a_0^{-1} \tag{4}$$

$$\langle r_i^{-2} \rangle = [2(Z - S_i)^2 (n_i^*)^{-3} (2n^* - 1)^{-1}]\, a_0^{-2}.$$

Much has been written elsewhere on the many different types of applications of Slater screening constants (Hirschfelder *et al.*, 1964). For some properties, such as the ionization potentials and the atomic radii, they give excellent values. For other properties, they give only fairly good approximations.

For really high accuracy it is necessary to have different screening constants for different properties. For example, consider the expectation value of a property which varies as r^k. If k is large, those portions of configuration space where r is large (and the screening by the other electrons is large) must be given the most weight. Thus, properties which vary as r^k require large screening constants if k is large and small screening constants if k is small. On this account, the energy screening constant (corresponding to $k = -1$) should be less than the diamagnetic susceptibility screening constants (corresponding to $k = 2$). With the use of perturbation theory and hypervirial theorems (Sanders and Hirschfelder, 1965; Robinson, 1965) we are now able to calculate good values of the screening constants appropriate to a particular property. In the perturbation theory calculations, the screening constant is adjusted so as to make the first-order correction to the expectation value vanish. Table 1 shows a comparison between the Slater screening constant values, the perturbation theory values (calculated with hydrogenic orbitals), and the exact expectation values for a number of one electron operators.

TABLE 1

EXPECTATION VALUES OF ONE-ELECTRON OPERATORS FOR THE HELIUM
GROUND STATE.[a] ALL VALUES ARE GIVEN IN ATOMIC UNITS

Operator	Slater orbital with $S = 0.30$	Perturbation theory	Exact
r_1	0.882	0.923 ($S = 0.375$)	0.929
r_1^2	1.038	1.170 ($S = 0.398$)	1.192
r_1^4	2.694	3.745 ($S = 0.434$)	3.944
r_1^6	13.05	23.63 ($S = 0.460$)	
r_1^{-2}	5.78	5.977 ($S = 0.271$)	6.017
$\delta(\mathbf{r}_1)$	4.913	5.616 ($S = 0.223$)	5.688

[a] Sanders and Hirschfelder (1965).

III. Molecular Orbitals

Slater-type orbitals (STO's) have formed the building blocks for a vast number of calculations on molecules (Allen and Karo, 1960). These have ranged from very exact treatments on H_2 to semiempirical π-electron calculations. The simpler of these approaches uses at most one Slater orbital on each atom of the molecule to represent each molecular orbital. The more arduous and sometimes more refined treatments express molecular orbitals as a linear combination of many STO's on all centers of the molecular system. The MO's obtained by the former treatments may be conveniently called *minimal* basis set MO's and by the latter *extended* basis set MO's.

Due to their feasibility and often their qualitative success *minimal* basis set calculations have been and are extensively pursued, particularly for large systems (more than two centers). It is thus useful now that *extended* STO basis set MO's very near the Hartree-Fock solutions are available for many diatomic molecules (Nesbet, 1962; Kahalas and Nesbet, 1963; McLean, 1963; Wahl, 1964; Huo, 1965; Wahl *et al.*, 1966; Cade *et al.*, 1966) to present some comparisons between the minimal STO basis set MO's and the extended STO basis set MO's.

In Table 2 we have compared total energy, binding energy, ionization potentials, and (where relevant) dipole moments. Extensive comparisons of this sort, which also involve quadrupole moments and field gradients, are given in the papers cited.

Several points have become clear. One is that the *minimal* basis set provides a poor and unreliable *quantitative* representation of *the* molecular orbital (see, for example, dipole moment behavior). Second, the Hartree-Fock values of one-electron properties are quite good and definite while small basis set properties can oscillate widely with change in basis set composition. Third, we obviously must go beyond the Hartree-Fock model to describe chemical binding in a nonempirical manner (Nesbet, 1965). Perhaps the most compelling reason for pursuing the exhaustive and expensive calculations necessary to obtain HF solutions is that they provide us with good one-electron properties and a solid and consistent platform from which we can build the improvements necessary to adequately describe molecules (Das and Wahl, 1966; Gilbert, 1965). Last, it is encouraging that the molecular Hartree-Fock wave function seems to be attainable with an extended but manageable basis set of STO's, derived from atomic SCF calculations.

Although not sufficient as an accurate description of charge distributions and not suitable when crudely used for predicting molecular properties, the Slater screening constants and the single Slater atomic orbitals seem to provide a rough measure for the size of many molecular orbitals. Although, of course, there are other molecular orbitals which are so distorted that they bear little relation to the atomic orbitals.

TABLE 2

COMPARISON OF SLATER LCAO-MO SCF WAVE FUNCTIONS WITH RECENT EXTENDED BASIS SET SCF WAVE FUNCTIONS FOR Li_2, N_2, F_2, CO, BF, LiF, HF, AND LiH

Molecule	Total energy (hartrees)			Dissociation energy (eV)			Ionization[j] potential (eV)		
	Minimal[a] STO set	Extended STO set	Exptl.	Minimal[a] STO set	Extended STO set	Exptl.	Minimal[a] STO set	Extended STO set	Exptl.
LiH	−7.9667	−7.9860[b]	−8.0703	1.39	1.44[b]	2.52	8.24		
Li_2	−14.84075	−14.8715[c]	−14.9944	0.15	0.17[c]	1.05	4.86	4.93[c]	4.96
N_2	−108.57362	−108.8928[d]	−109.586	1.19	5.31[d]	9.90	14.82	17.36[d]	15.77
F_2	−197.85686	−198.7683[e]	−199.670	−.30	−1.37[e]	1.68	11.75	18.04[e]	15.7
HF	−99.4785	−99.9911[f]	−100.527	1.21	4.44[f]	6.08	12.65	18.16[f]	15.77
LiF	−106.3652	−106.9885[g]	−107.502	0.37	4.03[g]	5.99	9.26	13.02[g]	
CO	−112.34357	−112.7860[h]	−113.377	5.38	7.84[h]	11.24	13.08	14.978[h]	14.01
BF	−123.61550	−124.1659[h]	−124.777	5.24	6.18[h]	8.58	9.61	10.999[h]	10.969

Dipole moments

Molecule	Minimal STO set[a]	Extended STO set	Exptl.
CO	0.730 C⁻O⁺	0.274[h] C⁺O⁻	0.118 C⁻O⁺[i]
BF	2.16 B⁻F⁺	0.945[h] B⁻F⁺	

Dipole moments

Molecule	Minimal STO set[a]	Extended STO set	Exptl.
LiF	2.94 Li⁺F⁻	6.297[g] Li⁺F⁻	6.284 Li⁺F⁻
HF	0.878 H⁺F⁻	1.827[f] H⁺F⁻	1.818 H⁺F⁻
LiH	6.41 Li⁺H⁻	5.888[b] Li⁺H⁻	5.882 Li⁺H⁻

[a] Ransil (1960).
[b] Kahalas and Nesbet (1963).
[c] Wahl et al. (1966).
[d] Cade et al. (1966).
[e] Wahl (1964).
[f] Nesbet (1962).
[g] McLean (1963).
[h] Huo (1965).
[i] There is some indication that the experimental assignment of sign as C⁻O⁺ is doubtful (Nesbet, 1965).
[j] These ionization potentials were calculated using Koopman's theorem. Ionization potentials calculated *directly* as the difference between the SCF energy of the ion and the neutral system show better agreement (see Wahl et al., 1966).

A following Chapter by Wahl in this book presents the electron density of very nearly the Hartree-Fock molecular orbitals of the homonuclear diatomic molecules in the first row of the periodic table. As a step in parameterization of these orbitals (since we now have them we should try to put them in a simpler form), it is interesting to see how accurately we can estimate some general features of these molecular Hartree-Fock orbitals with a very unsophisticated use of Slater screening constants. First of all, we can consider the distance from the nucleus at which a 2s or 2p atomic orbital has a maximum charge density. According to Slater orbitals this should occur at $r_{max} = (Z - S)^{-1} a_0$. If the molecular orbitals were the same as the atomic orbitals in the separated atoms, and if neglect of overlap is justifiable, then the values of r_{max} measured toward the *outside* of the molecule for the $2\sigma_g$, $2\sigma_u$, $1\pi_u$, $3\sigma_g$, and $1\pi_g$ Hartree-Fock orbitals should all be comparable to the $(Z - S)^{-1} a_0$ for the separated atoms. Table 3 shows this comparison. Whereas

TABLE 3

COMPARISON OF r_{max} FOR HARTREE-FOCK MOLECULAR ORBITALS WITH r_{max} FOR SLATER ATOMIC ORBITALS[a]

		$r_{max}(a_0)$				
	Minimal STO atom $(Z\text{-}S)^{-1}$	Extended basis MO's				
		$2\sigma_g$	$2\sigma_u$	$1\pi_u$	$3\sigma_g$	$1\pi_g$
Li_2	1.54	2.3				
B_2	0.77	1.7	0.90	0.80		
C_2	0.65	1.0	0.75	0.65		
N_2	0.51	0.80	0.65	0.50	0.50	
O_2	0.44	0.75	0.60	0.45	0.45	0.40
F_2	0.38	0.70	0.57	0.35	0.35	0.35

[a] Here r_{max} is the distance from the nucleus to the maximum electron density in the outer loop of the orbital. The Hartree-Fock molecular orbitals are given in the preceding paper.

our simple Slater screening constant prediction of the r_{max} is excellent for the $1\pi_u$, $3\sigma_g$, and $1\pi_g$, it is very poor for the $2\sigma_g$ and the $2\sigma_u$.

The next question which we can ask is how well do the Slater screening constants with Slater orbitals predict the position of the outermost electron density contour as shown in the preceding paper. This contour corresponds to an electron density in the orbital of $6.1 \times 10^{-5} ea_0^{-3}$. Table 3 shows this comparison. The agreement is excellent for the $1\sigma_g$ and $1\sigma_u$ orbitals which, except for H_2, really " look like " atomic cores.

For the other orbitals the outer perimeter predicted by nonoverlapping

TABLE 4

THE $r_c(a_0)$ OUTER PERIMETER[a]

	Minimal STO atom 1s	Extended basis MO's		Minimal STO atom 2s, 2p	Extended basis MO's				
		$1\sigma_g$	$1\sigma_u$		$2\sigma_g$	$2\sigma_u$	$1\pi_u$	$3\sigma_g$	$1\pi_g$
H_2	4.5	(3.8) 4.5							
Li_2	2.30	(2.3) 2.3	(2.3) 2.3	7.1	(6.2) 7.7				
B_2	1.50	(1.5) 1.5	(1.5) 1.5	4.55	(3.9) 4.5	(5.5) 4.5	5.3		
C_2	1.25	(1.25) 1.35	(1.25) 1.25	3.87	(3.25) 3.9	(4.7) 4.0	5.0		
N_2	1.10	(1.15) 1.2	(1.22) 1.12	3.39	(2.8) 3.5	(4.1) 3.5	4.5	(4.3)	
O_2	0.99	(1.0) 1.0	(1.0) 1.0	3.02	(2.8) 3.2	(3.5) 3.1	4.1	(3.9)	3.8
F_2	0.90	(0.9) 0.9	(0.9) 0.9	2.75	(2.7) 3.0	(3.1) 3.0	3.8	(3.5)	3.7

[a] Comparison of the outer perimeter of the Hartree-Fock molecular orbitals with the outer perimeter of the Slater atomic orbitals. The outer perimeter of the orbitals is taken to be the radius at which the electron density is $6.1 \times 10^{-5} ea_0^{-3}$. This corresponds to the outermost contour shown in the pictures of molecular orbitals in the preceding paper. Two sets of numbers are given for the molecular orbitals: the values in parentheses are measured from the nucleus outward along the internuclear axis, the other values are measured from the nucleus perpendicular to the internuclear axis.

single STO's with atomic screening constants is quite poor. The $2\sigma_g$ Hartree-Fock MO perimeter shows a " pulling in " along the molecular axis relative to the simple Slater atomic orbital while the $2\sigma_u$ Hartree-Fock perimeter has moved out relative to the Slater atomic orbital. The $1\pi_u$, $3\sigma_g$, and $1\pi_g$ orbitals all have a much larger perimeter than the corresponding Slater atomic orbital. However, the charge along this perimeter is extremely small, and it is only as they reflect more significant shifts in charge that these observations are important. The differences displayed in Tables 3 and 4 arise from: (1) neglect of overlap, (2) the HF MO's form an orthonormal set while the Slater AO's are only normalized, (3) the inadequacies of a single STO in representing any orbital, atomic or molecular, (4) the Slater AO has been " frozen " in the molecule and not allowed to distort through the variational procedure. Since these are just the four consequences of the usual assumptions made in the most simple use of single STO's in molecules, these comparisons may be instructive.

IV. Conclusion

Certainly these are crude observations and a detailed analysis of these MO's is needed, but we feel that some Slater-type parameterization of these accurate MO's can provide us with molecular building blocks and molecular screening parameters useful for proceeding to larger systems and estimating molecular properties just as Slater screening constants have enabled us to think about and represent atoms adequately for many purposes.

REFERENCES

Allen, L. C., and Karo, A. M. (1960). *Rev. Mod. Phys.* **32**, 275.
Cade, P. E., Sales, K. D., and Wahl, A. C. (1966). *J. Chem. Phys.* **44**, 1973.
Das, G., and Wahl, A. C. (1966). *J. Chem. Phys.* **44**, 487.
Gilbert, T. L. (1965). *J. Chem. Phys.* **43**, S248.
Hirschfelder, J. O., Curtiss, C. F., and Bird, R. B. (1964). "Molecular Theory of Gases and Liquids" 2nd Printing, p. 953. Wiley, New York.
Huo, W. (1965). *J. Chem. Phys.* **43**, 624.
Kahalas, S. L., and Nesbet, R. K. (1963). *J. Chem. Phys.* **39**, 529.
McLean, A. D. (1963). *J. Chem. Phys.* **39**, 2653.
Naqvi, A. M. (1962). The screened hydrogenic wave functions, Geophysical Corporation of America Tech. Rept. 62-14-A.
Naqvi, A. M., and Victor, G. A. (1964). Calculation of wave functions and transition probabilities, Geophysical Corporation of America Tech. Rept. RTD TDR-63-3118.
Naqvi, A. M. (1964). *J. Quant. Spectr. Radiative Transfer* **4**, 597.
Nesbet, R. K. (1962). *J. Chem. Phys.* **36**, 1518.
Nesbet, R. K. (1965). *J. Chem. Phys.* **43**, S30.
Pauling, L. (1927). *Proc. Roy. Soc. (London)* **A114**, 181.

226 J. O. HIRSCHFELDER AND A. C. WAHL

Pauling, L., and Sherman, J. (1932). *Z. Kristallog.* **81**, 1.
Ransil, B. J. (1960). *Rev. Mod. Phys.* **32**, 245.
Robinson, P. D. (1965). *Proc. Roy. Soc. (London)* **A283**; 229.
Sanders, W. A., and Hirschfelder, J. O. (1965). *J. Chem. Phys.* **42**, 2904; **43**, S204.
Schrödinger, v. Erwin (1921). *Z. Physik* **4**, 347.
Slater, J. C. (1930). *Phys. Rev.* **36**, 57.
Wahl, A. C. (1964). *J. Chem. Phys.* **41**, 2600.
Wahl, A. C., Sales, K. D., and Cade, P. E. (1966). To be submitted to *J. Chem. Phys.*
Zener, C. (1930). *Phys. Rev.* **36**, 51.
Zener, C., and Guillemin, V. (1930). *Z. Physik* **61**, 199.

Accurate Gaussian Wave Functions: HF Again*

J. W. MOSKOWITZ and D. NEUMANN

CHEMISTRY DEPARTMENT, NEW YORK UNIVERSITY
WASHINGTON SQUARE COLLEGE, NEW YORK, NEW YORK

and

M. C. HARRISON

THE COURANT INSTITUTE OF MATHEMATICAL SCIENCES
NEW YORK UNIVERSITY, NEW YORK, NEW YORK

I. Introduction

The development during the last decade of large digital computers has stimulated the quest for accurate Hartree-Fock self-consistent-field wave functions for small polyatomic molecules. The solution of the Hartree-Fock equations by expanding the molecular orbitals as a linear combination of atomic orbitals has been elegantly formulated by Roothaan (1951). The problem is thus reduced to that of choosing an adequate set of basis functions. This is complicated by the need to evaluate the many multicenter molecular integrals that arise in the course of the computation.

The use of Gaussian-type functions was proposed about fifteen years ago by Boys (1950) and some early molecular calculations were performed by Meckler (1953) and Nesbet (1960). The disadvantage of the Gaussian functions in contrast to the Slater orbitals lies in the slow convergence of the expansion due to their poor behavior both at the nucleus and in the tail. The main advantage is that formulae for all multicenter integrals are available and readily adapted to high-speed computation. The essence of the Gaussian approximation is thus the transformation of the integral evaluation problem

* This research was supported in part by the Air Force Cambridge Research Laboratories, Office of Aerospace Research, under contract No. AF 19 (628)-4040.

to one of data processing. In order to surmount this difficulty a set of programs was developed at M.I.T. principally by Harrison (1963) in collaboration with Sutcliffe, Csizmadia, and Moskowitz to perform nonempirical calculations for small molecules in a Gaussian basis.

The structure of the programs differs somewhat from the one usually adopted. First, the programs were designed to be as open ended as possible and so were written as a set of independent Fortran chain links. Second, generality was preferred to efficiency. That is, where there was a choice between a general-purpose program and a special-purpose one, the former was chosen. Third, simplicity was preferred to efficiency, so that all except the most basic programs were written in Fortran and these were heavily subroutinized to preserve readability. These principles were adopted not because of indifference to the economics of such calculations but because the authors felt that much work in this field has been duplicated because of unduly specialized programs and excessive pride in writing programs which no one else can understand.

Previous papers in this series have reported Hartree-Fock wave functions for numerous molecular systems including HF (Harrison, 1964), ethylene (Moskowitz and Harrison, 1965a), water (Moskowitz and Harrison, 1965b), formyl fluoride (Csizmadia et al., 1966), acetylene (Moskowitz, 1965), and benzene (Schulman and Moskowitz, 1965) to name a few. Extensive calculations in a Gaussian basis have also recently been performed by Allen and Whitten (1965), Burnelle (1965), Huzinaga (1965), Krauss (1963, 1965), and Reeves (1963).

Since our original work on HF, Roothaan and Cade (1965) at Chicago have computed extremely accurate self-consistent-field functions for diatomic molecules in a Slater basis. They have also suggested the desirability of approaching the self-consistent-field limit in order to assure convergence of one-electron properties computed from the molecular wave function. Under the stimulus of the Chicago effort we have reexamined the HF molecule in order to answer the following questions: (1) How accurate a result can one obtain in a Gaussian basis, (2) What are the effects of polarization functions; i.e., d-orbitals on fluorine and p-orbitals on the hydrogen, (3) How well does the Gaussian basis handle one-electron molecular properties?

The calculated values of total energy, dipole moment (μ), field gradient at the nucleus (q), the molecular quadrupole moment (Q), and $\langle r^2 \rangle$ for several Slater and Gaussian bases are presented in Table 1. The notation (95/32) stand for nine s-like, five p-like Gaussians on fluorine and three s-like, two p-like on hydrogen. In the same manner (952/32) indicates the addition of two d-like functions for both sigma and pi symmetry on the fluorine, etc. The exponents used included those obtained by Huzinaga (1965) for the fluorine atom, and by Reeves (1963) for the hydrogen atom. The exponents for the

TABLE 1

ENERGY, DIPOLE MOMENT (μ), FIELD GRADIENT AT THE NUCLEUS (q), MOLECULAR
QUADRUPOLE MOMENT (Q), AND $\langle r^2 \rangle$ OF HF ($R = 1.7328$ au) FOR SEVERAL SLATER
AND GAUSSIAN BASES[a]

Basis	Energy	μ	q_{zz}^H	q_{zz}^F	Q_{zz}^F	$\langle r^2 \rangle^F$
Clementi[b]	−100.0580	0.78	0.597	3.501	—	—
Nesbet[b]	−100.0571	0.79	0.582	2.778	—	—
(95/32)	−100.0319	0.923	0.586	3.131	1.876	13.524
(952/3)	−100.0411	0.757	0.579	2.990	1.945	13.539
(952/32)	−100.0489	0.751	0.570	2.896	1.853	13.566
(1062/42)	−100.0622	0.756	0.565	2.897	1.888	13.718
Chicago	−100.0703	0.762	0.540	2.869	1.884	—
Exptl	−100.1325	0.68	0.513	—	—	—

[a] All properties in atomic units.
[b] Recomputed by P. E. Cade, private communication.

polarization functions were estimated from previous work with Slater functions.*

II. Results

The results show that the energy of the largest Gaussian basis (1062/42) is lower than the Slater calculations of Nesbet (1962) and Clementi (1962), and only about a 0.01 of an atomic unit from the Hartree-Fock limit as estimated from the Chicago computation. It should be remembered that the Slater basis results represent an extensive optimization of the nonlinear parameters. In the Gaussian case no reoptimization of the orbital exponents taken from atomic calculations has been attempted. Part of the discrepancy in the total energy is undoubtedly due to this constraint on the wave function. The remainder of the error probably arises both from the inherently poor representation of the wave function in the vicinity of the nuclei and the lack of f-orbitals as polarization functions.

The one-electron properties in the Gaussian basis have evidently converged to the Hartree-Fock limit. Further, the effect of changing from the (952/32) basis to the (1062/42) basis has a neglible effect on the one-electron properties, though lowering the energy noticeably. The results also suggest that to a first approximation the d-functions on the fluorine have a greater effect than the hydrogen p-orbitals on one-electron properties. This is quite encouraging for future work on larger polyatomic systems.

* The Gaussian exponents on fluorine were: d_σ, 2.5, 0.5; d_Π, 1.5, 0.3. The exponents on hydrogen were: both P_σ and P_Π, 1.5, 0.3.

In summary we conclude that the Gaussian basis is acceptable for the representation of accurate Hartree-Fock wave functions. Indeed, further experience should lead to the choice of basis sets which, although giving energies inferior to the Hartree-Fock values, will give adequate values of the important one-electron properties.

ACKNOWLEDGMENTS

Two of the authors (J. W. Moskowitz and M. C. Harrison) would like to thank Professor J. C. Slater for the encouragement and warm hospitality he extended to them during their stay at M.I.T.

REFERENCES

Allen, L. C., and Whitten, J. L. (1965). Unpublished results.
Boys, S. F. (1950). *Proc. Roy. Soc. (London)* **A200**, 542.
Burnelle, L. (1965). *J. Chem. Phys.*, **43**, 3540.
Clementi, E. (1962). *J. Chem. Phys.* **36**, 33.
Csizmadia, I. G., Harrison, M. C., and Sutcliffe, B. T. (1966). *Tetrahedron*, in press.
Harrison, M. C. (1963). Technical Note No. 36, Cooperative Computing Laboratory, MIT (unpublished).
Harrison, M. C. (1964). *J. Chem. Phys.* **41**, 499.
Huzinaga, S. (1965). *J. Chem. Phys.* **42**, 1293.
Krauss, M. (1963). *J. Chem. Phys.* **38**, 564.
Krauss, M. (1965). Unpublished results.
Meckler, A. (1953). *J. Chem. Phys.* **21**, 1750.
Moskowitz, J. W. (1965). *J. Chem. Phys.* **43**, 60.
Moskowitz, J. W., and Harrison, M. C. (1965a). *J. Chem. Phys.* **41**, 495.
Moskowitz, J. W., and Harrison, M. C. (1965b). *J. Chem. Phys.* **43**, 3550.
Nesbet, R. K. (1960). *J. Chem. Phys.* **32**, 1114.
Nesbet, R. K. (1962). *J. Chem. Phys.* **36**, 1518.
Reeves, C. M. (1963). *J. Chem. Phys.* **39**, 1.
Roothaan, C. C. J. (1951). *Rev. Mod. Phys.* **23**, 69.
Roothaan, C. C. J., and Cade, P. E. (1965). Unpublished data from the Laboratory of Molecular Structure and Spectra, University of Chicago.
Schulman, J. M., and Moskowitz, J. W. (1965). *J. Chem. Phys.*, **43**, 3287.

The Bonding Characteristics of Diatomic MO's*

ROBERT S. MULLIKEN

LABORATORY OF MOLECULAR STRUCTURE AND SPECTRA, DEPARTMENT OF PHYSICS
UNIVERSITY OF CHICAGO,
AND
INSTITUTE OF MOLECULAR BIOPHYSICS
FLORIDA STATE UNIVERSITY, TALLAHASEE, FLORIDA†

I. Introduction

In attempting to understand the energetics and geometry of molecular formation, it is usual to deal with orbital approximations to molecular wave functions. The most prominent orbital methods, because of their conceptual simplicity, are the approximations based on the assignment of electrons either to molecular orbitals (MO's), or to atomic orbitals (AO's) of the atoms which have been combined to form the molecule. The AO method includes the Heitler-London and valence bond methods for dealing with interatomically paired electrons, but also includes ion-pair bonding and other situations using AO's. The MO method can be presented in various forms; the most typical is that which uses completely delocalized MO's conforming to representations of the symmetry group of the whole molecule. These MO's can be called *spectroscopic MO's*, because it is they which are most directly needed in dealing with spectroscopic excitation and with ionization. On the other hand, localized MO's, in particular bond MO's, are very useful in understanding various characteristics of chemical bonds; they, together with lone pair AO's, can be called *chemical orbitals*.

* This work was assisted by the Office of Naval Research, Physics Branch under Contract Nonr-2121(01), with the University of Chicago, and by a contract between the Division of Biology and Medicine, U.S. Atomic Energy Commission and the Florida State University.
† In winter.

Although orbitals have no substantial existence, and one can argue that they are merely mathematical conveniences, they have been and still are useful as conceptual units whose characteristics are worth examining. The present paper is limited mainly to a survey of the bonding properties of spectroscopic molecular orbitals in diatomic molecules.

The term "bond strength" is commonly used very loosely. Usually it seems to mean "bond energy", i.e., energy of formation of a bond (Pauling, 1960). However, Mulliken (1931, 1932) has distinguished the "energy bonding power" and the "distance bonding power" of molecular orbitals. The total bond energy, or the equilibrium value of the intermolecular distance R, respectively, are then regarded as determined by a summation of effects from electrons in individual MO's. For diatomic valence-shell MO's, as first emphasized by Lennard-Jones (1929), expressions of LCAO form generally furnish good approximations. For diatomic hydrides, however, UAO (united-atom AO) forms are perhaps usually better than LCAO forms even for valence-shell MO's.

II. Empirical Criteria for MO Bonding Powers

The usual criteria (Mulliken, 1928, as modified by inclusion of the category of antibonding electrons: Herzberg, 1929, 1931; also Mulliken, 1931, 1932) for a bonding, antibonding, or nonbonding MO for a neutral molecule in its normal state N can be stated in terms of what happens (1) to the dissociation energy D or (2) to R_e and/or the related quantity ω_e (or to the corresponding force constant k), when an electron is removed from the MO under consideration. If (1) the change ΔD is negative or if (2) ΔR_e is positive and/or $\Delta \omega_e$ is negative when an electron is removed from it, the MO is adjudged bonding; if the opposite changes occur, it is considered antibonding; if little or no changes occur, it is nonbonding. Simple examples are the $1\sigma_g$ MO of H_2 (strongly bonding by either criterion), and the $1\sigma_u$ MO of He_2 (strongly antibonding by either criterion: although He_2 is not stable, removal of one $1\sigma_u$ electron gives stable He_2^+). Criteria (1) and (2) can be called the *thermochemical* and the *equilibrium* MO bonding criteria respectively.

Additive and subtractive valence-shell LCAO MO's ($\chi_a \pm \chi_b$ for homopolar or $\alpha\chi_a + \beta\chi_b$ and $\beta\chi_a - \alpha\chi_b$, with $\alpha > \beta$, for heteropolar molecules), which have ξ (the "reduced internuclear distance") near 1 at R_e, are in general expected from simple LCAO theory to be respectively bonding or antibonding by both the thermochemical and the equilibrium criterion. [The quantity ξ is defined as the ratio of the internuclear distance R to twice the radius of maximum radial density for the relevant AO, which may be the AO used in the LCAO expression, or, for small ξ, may be a UAO (Mulliken, 1932, p. 40).]

Actually, however, factors to be discussed below sometimes play havoc with the applicability of the thermochemical criterion even for state N. The main such factor is the noncrossing rule, according to which the $U(R)$ curve of any molecular state as $R \to \infty$ may have to make a short cut to the lowest available atom-pair state of the proper group-theoretical species, even if (as happens not infrequently) this does not correspond to the valence structure of the molecular state. For *excited* states, even those of valence-shell type, such dissociation short-cuts are very prevalent; some examples will be discussed in a later section. Inner-shell MO's, which are of LCAO type with $\xi \gg 1$ when R is near R_e, are expected to be essentially nonbonding by both criteria. For Rydberg MO's, which at R_e are of UAO type with $\xi < 1$, thermochemical criteria are irrelevant, but by the equilibrium criterion they are nonbonding or nearly so.

Instead of ΔD, a very direct criterion for bond energy is simply the magnitude of D itself, but in general this is a measure of the total effect of all the electrons and cannot easily be used as a criterion for individual MO's. However, this D criterion can be used in simple cases. In state N of H_2^+, it coincides with the ΔD criterion, since D for H_2^{++} is zero. In state N of H_2 with two $1\sigma_g$ electrons, D is nearly twice as large at R_e as for H_2^+ with one $1\sigma_g$ electron at its R_e, as seems reasonable. The D criterion makes sense also for the $1\sigma_u$ state of H_2^+ $(D = 0)$, the $1\sigma_g^2 1\sigma_u^2$ state of He_2 $(D = 0)$, and the $1\sigma_g^2 1\sigma_u$ $(D > 0)$ and $1\sigma_g 1\sigma_u^2$ $(D = 0)$ states of He_2^+, if $1\sigma_u$ is antibonding and more strongly so than $1\sigma_g$ is bonding (a relation which is rather well understood).

The larger D for state N of M_2^+ than for that of M_2, when M is any alkali metal, is less easy to explain (Barrow *et al.*, 1960; Robertson and Barrow, 1961; Lee and Mahan, 1965). Here the ΔD criterion ($\Delta D < 0$) contradicts the evidence of the ΔR_e and $\Delta \omega_e$ criteria ($\Delta R_e > 0$, $\Delta \omega_e < 0$), and of D itself, which all support the expectation from its additive form that the valence-shell MO is bonding. However, this case is very exceptional.

For state N of first-row molecules built from atoms with 2p electrons, as Herzberg (1929, 1931) first pointed out, D runs parallel to the excess of the number of bonding over that of antibonding electrons if one attributes D just to those MO's which can be constructed as LCAO's from the 2p electrons, and the net effect of $2s^2$ closed shells on bonding is considered nil. However, as SCF MO calculations have shown especially clearly in recent years, matters are really less simple in that the 2s as well as the 2p atomic shells actually are involved to an important extent in bonding and antibonding, and even the 1s shells make an appreciable (antibonding) contribution.

While the empirical D is a good practical measure of bond energy, in general, a theoretically more significant D, the *intrinsic* D, can be obtained if the dissociation energy is measured from an asymptote in which the atoms are in suitable valence states (see Hinze and Jaffe, 1962 and references given by them).*† For example in N_2, the two N atoms should be in their V_3 (trivalent) states, which for each atom are about 1.1 eV above the $1s^2 2s^2 2p^3$, ^4S normal state; thus the intrinsic D is 12.0 eV, 2.2 eV larger than the ordinary or net D of 9.76 eV. In the N_2 example, promotion to the $s^2 p^3$ trivalent valence state is intraconfigurational. In other cases, for example CH_4 and most other carbon compounds, pluvalent *configurational promotion* (from $s^2 p^2$, V_2 to sp^3, V_4) is essential to obtain an intrinsic D.

Another complication is that of hybridization during bond formation; this could be deemed to call for the use of a valence state with *partial* configurational promotion (partial because the hybridization is only partial), which would increase the intrinsic D further. For example in N_2, there is very appreciable isovalent hybridization which would call for partial (about 25%) isovalent configurational promotion to a $1s^2 2s2p^4$, V_3 valence state (Fraga and Mulliken, 1960, and references given by them). However, the construction of the energy of a partially promoted valence state to take care of hybridization is generally fraught with uncertainty, and in view also of the fact that s, p "hybridization" is only one of several forms of modification which atomic valence shell AO's have to undergo during bond formation, it is in the writer's present opinion just as well to omit any allowance for hybridization in obtaining an intrinsic D. [Whether viewed in the context of AO theory or of MO theory, the orbitals in the actual molecule really involve MAO's (modified AO's) instead of free-atom AO's: MAO's directly in AO theory, LCMAO's in MO theory. These modifications include scaling, symmetrical distortion, and polarization (including hybridization in the usual sense, but also the mixing in of higher-shell, higher-l orbital forms). It can be shown that *all* of these are equivalent to using various configurationally promoted states, some with higher n only, others with higher l, but all of course with equal λ (Mulliken, 1962, 1965).] Thus in the present discussion the only promotion which will be admitted in assessing intrinsic D's, other than any necessary pluvalent promotion to pluvalent valence states, is intraconfigurational promotion to valence states.

The preceding discussion regarding intrinsic D's must be qualified in one respect. Namely, at large R values near dissociation, every molecular state wave function approximates to a single LCAPAS based on state N AS's of the two atoms. [Here "LCAPAS" refers to a function which is (in general) a *linear combination* (LC) of over-all *antisymmetrized products* $A\psi_a\psi_b$ (AP's)

---

* Different authors give slightly different values for atomic valence state energies, because of intrinsic difficulties (due to configuration interaction) in defining them exactly.

† The term valence "state" is somewhat misleading, as Longuet-Higgins has pointed out in conversation, since a valence state wave function cannot be written as a linear combination of individual state functions. (The difficulty is that no definite *signs*—or phase relations at all—can be assigned to the terms in such linear combinations.) It is only the valence state *energy* which is a definite linear combination of individual state energies.

of atomic substate (AS) strong-field (i.e., characterized by definite M_L and M_S values) wave functions ψ_a and ψ_b of the two atoms (Mulliken, 1966). This large-R LCAPAS could very properly be called an "atoms-in-molecule" function. Although the atoms-in-molecule method was developed intensively by Moffitt (1951)—see also Ellison (1965) and references given there— atomic-state bonding, in contrast to electron-pair Heitler-London bonding, was earlier extensively discussed by Nordheim-Pöschl (1936).] Only at rather small R values does mixing with other LCAPAS's, both of the same two-atom AO configuration and of promoted (including ionic) configurations, come importantly into play, under the action of valence forces. However, these other LCAPAS's never mix in, even at R_e, in quite as large proportions as would correspond to an ideal valence state. In other words, lower-energy AO state-pairs always have larger, and higher-energy ones smaller, weights as compared with ideal valence-state proportions. For example in the normal state of N_2, the $(^4S, \, ^4S)$, $^1\Sigma_g^+$ LCAPAS must contribute somewhat disproportionately relative to the several $^1\Sigma_g^+$ LCAPAS's from the pairs $(^2D, \, ^2D)$, $(^2D, \, ^2P)$, and $(^2P, \, ^2P)$ of the same s^2p^3, s^2p^3 configuration. For similar reasons the C atom, whose normal state configuration is capable only of bivalence, cannot be quite fully quadrivalent in typical compounds like CH_4, CO_2, C_2H_2, and so on (Van Vleck and Sherman, 1935; Voge, 1936; Kotani and Siga, 1937).

All in all, it appears that even intrinsic D values (and certainly not ordinary net D values when they differ much from intrinsic D values) have in general no very simple theoretical meaning. In terms of SCF-MO theory they usually do not, because the SCF-MO wave function in the absence of configuration mixing ceases for most neutral molecules to be a good approximation as R increases during dissociation. In terms of valence-bond theory, defined as that part of AO theory which for neutral molecules connects molecular states with atom-pair valence states, intrinsic D values do have some meaning. This significance is, however, usually only roughly approximate because promotion of the atoms is not quite in the ideal proportions required for true valence states and, especially, a rather large amount of additional promotion not contemplated in valence bond theory, to excited atom-pair and to ion-pair states, is present (see the discussion above about the necessity of MAO's). The foregoing treatment, although stated primarily in terms of neutral homopolar molecules, can also be extended to heteropolar and to charged molecules.

Having concluded that neither ordinary net nor intrinsic D values are in general useful criteria for the bonding characteristics of individual MO's, we next consider the ΔD criterion. First we note that for homopolar molecules

$$AD \equiv D^+ - D \equiv [U^+(\infty) - U^+(R_e^+)] - [U(\infty) - U(R_e)]$$

$$= [U^+(\infty) - U(\infty)] - [U^+(R_e^+) - U(R_e)] \tag{1}$$

$$= I_\infty - I_e = I_{\text{atom}} - I_{\text{molecule}} \equiv {}_e\Delta_\infty I$$

where D^+, U^+, R_e^+ refer to the positive ion and D, U, R_e to the neutral mole-cule. It is seen that ΔD is exactly equal to the difference between I of one of the atoms into which the molecule dissociates and I of the molecule.

For MO's of LCMAO form $(\alpha x_a + \beta x_b$, or $x_a \pm x_b$ for homopolar molecules), it was noted empirically some time ago that when valence-state I's are used, the quantity ${}_e\Delta_\infty I$ (and so ΔD) is positive for valence-shell MO's of additive LCAO form and negative for those of subtractive LCAO form, with magnitudes in the neighborhood of 2 or 3 eV if suitable valence-state values I^0 and I^* are used for the AO's (Mulliken, 1934, 1935). Here the positive or negative sign respectively of ${}_e\Delta_\infty I$ (or equally of ΔD) is found to be indicative of bonding or antibonding. For heteropolar molecules, I_∞ in Eq. (1) is a (perhaps weighted) mean of the appropriate I's of the two atoms.

However, it should be noted that the ${}_e\Delta_\infty I$ criterion has no real theoretical basis, but involves a comparison which corresponds to an MO *pseudo-correlation*. That is, in Eq. (1), although I_e corresponds to ionization of the molecule in the region of R values where the MO approximation is good, and represents a good approximation for an MO term value, $I_\infty = I_{atom}$ is a free-atom value corresponding to the use of the AO approximation, which is now accurate whereas an SCF-MO function at $R = \infty$, which would be required (and can in fact easily be constructed) for a true MO correlation, would have much too high an energy. [See Mulliken (1966) for a discussion of MO correlation diagrams, in which it is pointed out that for those valence-shell electrons which are usually considered to be bonding electrons the usual MO correlations are only pseudo-correlations as $R \to \infty$.] Nevertheless ${}_e\Delta_\infty I$ proves *empirically* to be a rather satisfactory thermochemical criterion in the case of valence-shell MO's. At the same time, it appears from the preceding discussion that there are no general *theoretically* well-based thermochemical criteria for the bonding powers of individual MO's.

There now remains to be considered the equilibrium (ΔR_e or $\Delta \omega_e$) criterion of MO bonding power. As is well known, there exists for different states of any one diatomic molecule the qualitatively almost invariant empirical relation that a state with larger R_e has smaller ω_e* (see Herzberg, 1950). Hence the ΔR_e and $\Delta \omega_e$ criteria are very nearly equivalent. The ΔR_e and $\Delta \omega_e$ criteria as applied to molecular states where both the molecule and its ion are stable seem to be very satisfactory criteria of MO bonding characteristics in actual molecules. Because the operation of these criteria is confined to moderate R values near an R_e, or else one of the states involved is unstable ($D = 0$) as in the examples of He_2 and H_2^+ cited at the beginning of this paper, usually no

---

* The exceptions are rare and quantitatively trivial. They occur only for pairs of states of nearly equal R_e; in such cases the ω_e's are also always nearly equal, but occasionally a slightly larger ω_e may accompany a slightly larger R_e contrary to the usual rule.

difficulty about failure of the SCF-MO approximation to be a good approximation, such as normally occurs with D and ΔD criteria, arises here. And unlike the latter criteria which fail most conspicuously for some of the Rydberg states of molecules, the ΔR_e and $\Delta \omega_e$ criteria indicate, as would be expected theoretically, that Ryberg MO's are nearly nonbonding.

Comparisons among the R_e and ω_e data on the CH and CH$^+$ states listed in the following Table 1 are instructive. The normal-state MO configuration of

TABLE 1

Low-Energy States of CH and CH$^+$

| State | Molecular constants | | | Dissociation | |
	Excitation energy(eV)	R_e (Å)	ω_e (cm^{-1})	Energy D(ev)	Products[b]
$\sigma\pi$, $^1\Pi$	13.56	1.234	1865	0.7	^2P
σ^2, $^1\Sigma^+$	10.64	1.131	(2867)	3.6	^2P
$\sigma\pi^2$, $^2\Sigma^+$	3.94	1.113	2824	0.79	^1D
$\sigma\pi^2$, $^2\Sigma^-$	3.19	1.186	2543	0.28	^3P
$\sigma\pi^2$, $^2\Delta$	2.87	1.102	2921	1.86	^1D
$\sigma\pi^2$, $^4\Sigma^-$	[0.6][a]	[1.09][a]	[2970][a]	[2.9][a]	^3P
$\sigma^2\pi$, $^2\Pi$	0	1.120	2862	3.47	^3P

[a] Estimated.
[b] One product is 1s$_H$, the other is the carbon ion or atom state listed, of configuration 1s^{2}2s^{2}2p or 1s^{2}2s^{2}2p^2.

CH is $1\sigma^2\ 2\sigma^2\ 3\sigma^2\ 1\pi$, the state being $^2\Pi$, while for the first excited MO configuration $1\sigma^2\ 2\sigma^2\ 3\sigma\ 1\pi^2$ there are several states $^4\Sigma^-$, $^2\Delta$, $^2\Sigma^-$, and $^2\Sigma^+$. All of the $\sigma\pi^2$ states except the $^4\Sigma^-$ are well known experimentally. The ΔR_e and $\Delta \omega_e$ comparisons of the CH and CH$^+$ normal states indicate that the 3σ MO is nearly nonbonding. A comparison of R_e and ω_e values between the normal and excited states of CH then indicates that the 1π MO (as would be expected from its form) is also nearly nonbonding. Such ΔR_e, $\Delta \omega_e$ intercomparisons between different states of a neutral molecule are valuable in showing the relative bonding powers of different MO's.

[The CH molecule supplies also one of the rare examples where the ΔR_e and $\Delta \omega_e$ rules fail. Namely, in a comparison of the R_e and ω_e data for the excited $^1\Pi$ state of CH$^+$ with those for the normal state of CH (cf. Table 1), ΔR_e and $\Delta \omega_e$ would now indicate that 3σ is a bonding MO. Or comparing the $^1\Pi$ data with the R_e, $\Delta \omega_e$ data for the excited states of CH, ΔR_e and $\Delta \omega_e$ would indicate that 1π also is a bonding MO. These conclusions contradict the more reasonable conclusions (since 1π surely must be nearly nonbonding) reached above. They serve as a warning that it is an oversimplification to assume that the ΔR_e, $\Delta \omega_e$ rule is infallible. Reasons for the contradiction may perhaps be sought in a less nearly united-atom character for the $^1\Pi$ state than for the other states; a detailed analysis would be rather lengthy.]

The fact that ΔR_e and $\Delta \omega_e$ are both small when a nonbonding electron is removed can be expressed in a concise and slightly generalized form by saying that *the potential curve near R_e for an electronic state containing a nearly nonbonding electron runs almost parallel to that of the state of the positive ion which results when this electron is removed.* However, these curves may be expected to diverge increasingly at R values increasingly far from R_e. Rydberg states are typical examples of states with a nonbonding MO, here the Rydberg MO, and it is characteristic for them that the shapes of their potential curves near R_e are nearly the same as those of the corresponding positive ion. Beyond R_e, out to $R = \infty$, a rough parallelism of potential curves in some cases continues, while in others a sharp divergence occurs (Mulliken, 1966).

III. Effects of Dissociation Products on R_e and ω_e

Returning to a consideration of Table 1, it is of interest to note that the potential curves of different states of the $\sigma\pi^2$ configuration of CH must differ strongly at large R values because of differences in the relations of their energies at R_e to those of their allowable dissociation products. It is notable that in spite of the corresponding large differences in their D values (see Table 1), all these states have nearly the same R_e and ω_e. However, R_e is somewhat larger and ω_e smaller depending on how small the dissociation energy D is. This effect can reasonably be ascribed to incipient small differences in (kind and) amount of minor CM (configuration mixing) near R_e (more CM when D is smaller) related to differences in LCAPAS correlation as $R \rightarrow \infty$.

Table 2 for N_2 shows indications of similar effects. In particular, the $^3\Sigma_u^+$ state of the $\pi_u^3 \sigma_g^2 \pi_g$ configuration, whose D is considerably smaller than for the other states, shows definitely smaller ω_e and a little larger R_e than for the others. However, the $^1\Delta_u$ state, in spite of a somewhat smaller D than for the $^1\Sigma_u^-$ state, shows a slightly larger ω_e and smaller R_e than the latter. Again, the $^1\Pi_g$ state of configuration $\pi_u^4 \sigma_g \pi_g$, in spite of a distinctly larger D, shows a slightly smaller ω_e and larger R_e than the $^3\Pi_g$ state of the same configuration. But in the N_2 states cited the relative values of D differ far less than in Table 1 for CH. The tentative conclusion seems justified that ω_e and R_e values tend to be nearly the same for different states of any one configuration, but ω_e tends to be smaller and R_e larger for states with exceptionally small D.

However, this is not quite the whole story. The so-called V states of diatomic molecules have exceptionally large R_e and small ω_e coupled with fairly large D, features which are attributable to their predominantly ion-pair character in AO theory approximation (Mulliken, 1936, 1939). On the other hand, the corresponding T (triplet) states of the same configuration are repulsion states. The T and V states of H_2, well describable at small R values

TABLE 2

SOME LOW-ENERGY STATES OF N_2

State	Molecular constants[a]			Dissociation	
	Excitation energy(eV)	R_e (Å)	ω_e (cm^{-1})	Energy D(eV)	Products[b]
$\pi_u^3 \sigma_g^2 \pi_g$, $^1\Sigma_u^+$	12.85(?)[c]	1.44(?)[c]	752(?)[c]		
$\pi_u^3 \sigma_g^2 \pi_g$, $^1\Delta_u$	8.89	1.26	1548	5.57	$^2D + {}^2D$
$\pi_u^3 \sigma_g^2 \pi_g$, $^1\Sigma_u^-$	8.40	1.27	1530	6.06	$^2D + {}^2D$
$\pi_u^3 \sigma_g^2 \pi_g$, $^3\Sigma_u^-$	8.16	1.28	1518	5.12	$^4S + {}^2P$
$\pi_u^3 \sigma_g^2 \pi_g$, $^3\Delta_u$	[7.17][d]	[1.28][d]	[1510][d]	[4.94][c]	$^4S + {}^2D$
$\pi_u^3 \sigma_g^2 \pi_g$, $^3\Sigma_u^+$	6.17	1.29	1460	3.59	$^4S + {}^4S$
$\pi_u^4 \sigma_g \pi_g$, $^1\Pi_g$	8.55	1.22	1694	5.91	$^2D + {}^2D$
$\pi_u^4 \sigma_g \pi_g$, $^3\Pi_g$	7.35	1.21	1734	4.76	$^4S + {}^2D$
$\pi_u^4 \sigma_g^2$, $^1\Sigma_g^+$	0.00	1.09	2358	9.76	$^4S + {}^4S$

[a] See Wilkinson, P. G., and Mulliken, R. S. (1959). *J. Chem. Phys.* **31**, 674; and Wilkinson, P. G. (1960). *J. Chem. Phys.* **32**, 1061, for recent data on the $^1\Delta_u$, $^1\Sigma_u^-$, and $^3\Sigma_u^-$ states.

[b] All from the normal two-atom configuration $1s_a^2 2s_a^2 2p_a^3 1s_b^2 2s_b^2 2p_b^3$.

[c] It is not certain that the observed $^1\Sigma_u^+$ state (called b') with these molecular constants is the predicted $\pi_u^3 \sigma_g^2 \pi_g$, $^1\Sigma_u^+$ state (see text).

[d] Estimated.

as $1\sigma_g\, 1\sigma_u$ (or $1\sigma_g\, 2p\sigma$), $^3\Sigma_u^+$ and $^1\Sigma_u^+$, represent a familiar example. This is an extreme case where the difference in dissociation energies and products exercises a dominant influence on R_e and ω_e.

More typical is the situation illustrated by the CH states in Table 1, and most of the N_2 states in Table 2, where a common MO electron configuration tends strongly to establish definite R_e and ω_e values. However, it should be noted that in the examples cited, the electron configurations of the separate atoms ($1s + 1s^2 2s^2 2p^2$ for CH and $1s^2 2s^2 2p^3 + 1s^2 2s^2 2p^3$ for N_2) are the same for all dissociation products for a given MO configuration even when the D values vary because of different states of the separate atoms. In the case of T and V states of an MO configuration, this condition is not fulfilled, and just in that case the R_e, ω_e near-constancy breaks down. In the case of N_2, it is probable that a similar break-down occurs for the $^1\Sigma_u^+$ state of the

$\pi_u^3 \sigma_g^2 \pi_g$ configuration, as compared with the other states. Unfortunately the empirical identification of this state is not certain, but trustworthy theoretical calculations predict that it differs strongly from all the other states of the same configuration in being much higher in energy and in being much more ionic in LCAPAS character than all the others. This last characteristic strongly suggests that it should behave like a V state, with small ω_e and large R_e, as is true of the tentatively identified observed state whose molecular contents are listed in Table 2. The questions touched on above, pertaining to the factors which determine R_e and ω_e values, deserve further exploration.

IV. Theoretical Criteria for MO Bonding Powers

Theoretically computed MO overlap populations per electron, n_i/N_i, calculated for molecules at R values in the MO region, seem to be rather good as roughly quantitative indicators of the bonding properties of individual MO's in the case of valence-shell and inner-shell MO's (Mulliken, 1955). (Here n_i means the overlap population in the ith MO when occupied by N_i electrons.) Among other things, computed n_i/N_i values correlate rather well with values of $(\Delta R_e)_i$ for removal of an electron. The quantity n_i/N_i can be calculated for any MO *in situ* in a molecule, using information from SCF-MO calculations. [A slightly better quantity should be Δn_i, the change in n_i when an electron is removed from the ith MO, with R constant.]

The validity of overlap populations as indicators of bonding is of course restricted to regions of R where MO's can be reasonably well approximated by LCMAO expressions based on separate-atom AO's; as is well known, the extent of positive or negative overlap of these is well correlated with bonding or antibonding repectively. However, the validity of the overlap population criterion has no rigorous theoretical foundation, and it is fallible in special or extreme situations. A very different kind of measure of the bonding effects associated with electrons in individual MO's seems to be afforded by an application of the Hellman-Feynmann theorem, in terms of forces exerted on the nuclei by the electrons in various MO's (Bader and Henneker, 1965). However, while the method seems to have interesting possibilities, until now there seems to be extremely poor correlation between the computed force exerted by an electron in an MO and its bonding power as judged by the thermochemical or equilibrium criterion.

ACKNOWLEDGMENT

Although no specific references have been made in this paper to J. C. Slater, his work has been fundamental in the development of much that is discussed here.

REFERENCES

Bader, R. F. W., and Henneker, W. H. (1965). *J. Am. Chem. Soc.* **87**, 3063, and earlier references given there to Bader *et al.*

Barrow, R. F., Travis, N., and Wright, C. V. (1960). *Nature* **187**, 141.

Ellison, F. O. (1965). *J. Chem. Phys.* **43**, 3654.

Fraga, S., and Mulliken, R. S. (1960). *Rev. Mod. Phys.* **32**, 254–265.

Herzberg, G. (1929). *Z. Physik* **57**, 616.

Herzberg, G. (1931). "Leipziger Vortrage," p. 167. Hirzel, Leipzig.

Herzberg, G. (1950). "Molecular Spectra and Molecular Structure I. Spectra of Diatomic Molecules," 2nd Ed. Van Nostrand, Princeton, New Jersey.

Hinze, J., and Jaffe, H. H. (1962). *J. Am. Chem. Soc.* **84**, 540.

Kotani, M., and Siga, K. (1937). *Proc. Phys. Math. Soc. Japan*, **19**, 471.

Lee, Y-T., and Mahan, B. H. (1965). *J. Chem. Phys.* **42**, 2893.

Lennard-Jones, J. E. (1929). *Trans. Faraday Soc.* **25**, 668.

Moffitt, W. (1951). *Proc. Roy. Soc.* **A210**, 245.

Mulliken, R. S. (1928). *Phys. Rev.* **32**, 186.

Mulliken, R. S. (1931). *Chem. Rev.* **9**, 347.

Mulliken, R. S. (1932). *Rev. Mod. Phys.* **4**, 1–3, 40.

Mulliken, R. S. (1934). *Phys. Rev.* **46**, 549.

Mulliken, R. S. (1935). *J. Chem. Phys.* **3**, 514.

Mulliken, R. S. (1936). *Phys. Rev.* **50**, 1017, 1028.

Mulliken, R. S. (1939). *J. Chem. Phys.* **7**, 20.

Mulliken, R. S. (1955). *J. Chem. Phys.* **23**, 1841, 2343.

Mulliken, R. S. (1962). *J. Chem. Phys.* **36**, 3428 –3439, Section II, 1–3.

Mulliken, R. S. (1965). *J. Chem. Phys.* **43**, S39.

Mulliken, R. S. (1966). *J. Am. Chem. Soc.* **88**, 1849.

Nordheim-Pöschl, G. (1936). *Ann. Physik* **26**, (5), 258.

Pauling, L. (1960). "The Nature of the Chemical Bond," 3rd ed., pp. 113–121. Cornell Univ. Press, Ithaca, New York.

Robertson, E. W., and Barrow, R. F. (1961). *Proc. Chem. Soc.* **329**.

Van Vleck, J. H., and Sherman, A. (1935). *Rev. Mod. Phys.* **7**, 167–228.

Voge, H. H. (1936). *J. Chem. Phys.* **4**, 581.

Pictures of Molecular Orbitals*

A. C. WAHL

THE UNIVERSITY OF WISCONSIN THEORETICAL CHEMISTRY INSTITUTE
MADISON, WISCONSON
AND
ARGONNE NATIONAL LABORATORY
ARGONNE, ILLINOIS

I. Introduction

Motivated by a desire to bridge and if possible to stem the widening gap between the "computors" and the "non-computors" in molecular quantum mechanics as so disturbingly defined by Coulson (1960), this paper and others to follow presents directly and on a consistent basis pictorial representations of certain quantum-mechanical concepts. Here accurate charge density pictures of molecular orbitals (MO's) very close to the Hartree-Fock MO's (Wahl, 1966) are given.

Recently much has been written elsewhere about the development and present state of the molecular-orbital method (Löwdin and Pullman, 1964; Slater, 1965; Nesbet, 1965), therefore we shall confine ourselves to a brief statement of crucial steps in its history.

The molecular orbital method as introduced by Mulliken (1928, 1929, 1932) and Hund (1928) was used extensively in the semiempirical interpretation of band spectra. However, mathematically and computationally the concept matured rather slowly. Its early development (and the search for the

* This research was supported by the following grant: National Aeronautics and Space Administration NsG-275-62 and based in part on work performed under the auspices of the USAEC

"best" MO's) may be traced from the recognition by Lennard-Jones (1929) of its relationship to Hartree's (1928) self-consistent field work on atoms followed by the introduction of the determinantal form for the wave function (Slater 1930a, 1932) with the application of the variational principle (Fock, 1930; Slater, 1929, 1930b) to yield the now familiar pseudo-eigenvalue equations of the form

$$F\varphi_i = \varepsilon_i \varphi_i \tag{1}$$

known as the Hartree-Fock equations, which provide a rigorous mathematical definition of best orbitals. Lennard-Jones (1929) presented the equations for an arbitrary system; Coulson (1938) foreshadowed their solution by the expansion method; and Roothaan (1951, 1960) developed and perfected the extensively used matrix formulation of the expansion method. Important also are the proofs by Delbrück (1930), Löwdin (1962), and Roothaan (1960) that the Hartree-Fock functions are always self-consistent, symmetry-adapted, and correspond to a specific minimum of the total energy. Extremely relevant to the potency and appeal of Hartree-Fock wave functions was the work of Brillouin (1933, 1934), Møller and Plesset (1934) on corrections to the Hartree-Fock approximation. They showed that one-electron properties computed from Hartree-Fock wave functions have first-order corrections in perturbation theory which vanish provided that degeneracy is not present. Koopman (1933) developed similar theorems for ionization potentials.

II. Hartree-Fock Molecular Orbitals as Linear Combinations of Expansion Functions

Having clearly defined the Hartree-Fock model of a molecular system it still remained a formidable practical problem to obtain the MO's φ_i. In 1951, Roothaan had cast the Hartree-Fock equations into a solid computational framework remarkably suitable for the then-embryonic digital computers. In what is now referred to as the Roothaan (1951, 1960) method the orbital φ_i is expanded in terms of some suitable truncated basis set χ_p

$$\varphi_i = \sum_p C_{ip}\chi_p. \tag{2}$$

The expansion coefficients C_{ip} are optimized through the iterative self-consistent field process (Roothaan and Bagus, 1964). In the full numerology of the process the best truncated set of basis functions χ_p is also hunted down, usually by brute force methods. In practice a very close approximation to the Hartree-Fock molecular orbitals can be obtained in this way. Calculations of this type utilizing analysis and computer programs developed recently (Wahl, 1964; Wahl *et al.*, 1964) have resulted in the determination of the molecular orbitals for a large number of diatomic molecules in the form of Eq. (2). These functions, in which the basis set χ_p consists of many Slater-type orbitals (STO's), are very close to the Hartree-Fock result. They were used in the pictorial calculations presented in this work.*

III. Densities and Contours

At this point, in order to clarify the diagrams of the shell model, it is convenient to introduce two new indices λ and α which indicate respectively the symmetry species and subspecies of the molecular orbitals φ_i. The electronic density $\rho_{i\lambda}$ associated with the *i*λth molecular *shell* at a point **r** in space is defined by

$$\rho_{i\lambda}(\mathbf{r}) = e^- N_{i\lambda} d_\lambda^{-1} \sum_\alpha \varphi_{i\lambda\alpha}(\mathbf{r})\varphi_{i\lambda\alpha}^*(\mathbf{r}) \tag{3}$$

where we have now grouped the molecular orbitals $\varphi_{i\lambda\alpha}$ according to their symmetry species λ and their subspecies α and have defined the density of shell *i*λ which contains $N_{i\lambda}$ electrons in terms of the sum over the modulus squared of the d_λ degenerate molecular orbitals making up the shell. Here e^- is the charge on the electron (negative number). The total electron density $\rho(\mathbf{r})$ of the molecule is then given by

$$\rho(\mathbf{r}) = \sum_\lambda \sum_i \rho_{i\lambda}(\mathbf{r}) \tag{4}$$

and is thus the sum of the densitites of all shells making up the molecule.

The density associated with one of the d_λ degenerate molecular orbitals $\varphi_{i\lambda\alpha}$ making up shell *i*λ is

$$\rho_{i\lambda\alpha}(\mathbf{r}) = \rho_{i\lambda}(\mathbf{r})/d_\lambda \tag{5}$$

which is just the shell density divided by the number of degenerate molecular orbitals making up the shell. In the diagrams presented in this paper it is the total density [Eq. (4)] and the orbital density [Eq. (5)] which have been plotted.

---

* Wave functions: The molecular orbital SCF wave function used F_2 (Wahl, 1964); O_2 (Malli, and Cade, 1966); N_2 (Cade *et al.*, 1966); C_2 and B_2 (Greenshields, 1966); Li_2 (Sales *et al.*, 1966); H_2 (Das and Wahl, 1966). All wave functions are comparable in sophistication to the published F_2 and N_2 functions. The basis sets have been extensively optimized and explored. All these MO wave functions can be obtained on request from the author.

TABLE 1

ELECTRON CONFIGURATION OF MOLECULES

Total molecular density	Molecular shells								Spectroscopic designation
H_2	$1\sigma_g^2$								$^1\Sigma_g^+$
He_2	$1\sigma_g^2$	$1\sigma_u^2$							$^1\Sigma_g^+$
Li_2	$1\sigma_g^2$	$1\sigma_u^2$	$2\sigma_g^2$						$^1\Sigma_g^+$
Be_2	$1\sigma_g^2$	$1\sigma_u^2$	$2\sigma_g^2$	$2\sigma_u^2$					$^1\Sigma_g^+$
B_2	$1\sigma_g^2$	$1\sigma_u^2$	$2\sigma_g^2$	$2\sigma_u^2$	$1\pi_u^2$				$^3\Sigma_g^-$
C_2	$1\sigma_g^2$	$1\sigma_u^2$	$2\sigma_g^2$	$2\sigma_u^2$	$1\pi_u^4$				$^1\Sigma_g^+$
N_2	$1\sigma_g^2$	$1\sigma_u^2$	$2\sigma_g^2$	$2\sigma_u^2$	$1\pi_u^4$	$3\sigma_g^2$			$^1\Sigma_g^+$
O_2	$1\sigma_g^2$	$1\sigma_u^2$	$2\sigma_g^2$	$2\sigma_u^2$	$1\pi_u^4$	$3\sigma_g^2$	$1\pi_g^2$		$^3\Sigma_g^-$
F_2	$1\sigma_g^2$	$1\sigma_u^2$	$2\sigma_g^2$	$2\sigma_u^2$	$1\pi_u^4$	$3\sigma_g^2$	$1\pi_g^4$		$^1\Sigma_g^+$
Ne_2	$1\sigma_g^2$	$1\sigma_u^2$	$2\sigma_g^2$	$2\sigma_u^2$	$1\pi_u^4$	$3\sigma_g^2$	$1\pi_g^4$	$3\sigma_u^2$	$^1\Sigma_g^+$

NOTE: Superscript of 2 or 4 indicates number of electrons $N_{i\lambda}$ occupying molecular shell $i\lambda$. For the π shells, which consist of 2 degenerate molecular orbitals, it is a molecular orbital, containing $\frac{1}{2}$ of the electrons in the π *shell*, that has been plotted.

(For σ *symmetry* $d_\lambda = 1$ and thus the *orbital* density equals the *shell* density. For π symmetry in diatomic molecules, $d_\lambda = 2$ and the orbital density equals $\frac{1}{2}$ of the shell density. The molecular shells and their occupation $N_{i\lambda}$ are given in Table 1 for the molecules studied. The only molecular symmetries occurring in this work are σ_g, σ_μ, π_μ, and π_g.)

In what follows in this section the symmetry indexes λ and α of the orbital density $\rho_{i\lambda\alpha}(\mathbf{r})$ will be suppressed since they are unnecessary for the description of the contour drawing process.

An orbital contour line indicating a density C in the xz-plane (ρ and ρ_i for diatomic molecules are cylindrically symmetric about the z-axis and plots in any plane containing this axis convey complete density information) may be defined by the equation,

$$\rho_i(x, z) = C,$$

and its path by the relation,

$$\frac{\partial \rho_i}{\partial x} \Delta x + \frac{\partial \rho_i}{\partial z} \Delta z = 0,$$

which gives the direction of the tangent to the contour at any point on it to be

$$\frac{\Delta x}{\Delta z} = -\frac{\partial \rho_i / \partial z}{\partial \rho_i / \partial x}. \tag{6}$$

A step $\Delta s = (\Delta x^2 + \Delta z^2)^{1/2}$ is taken along this tangent and a density found such that

$$\rho_i'(x + \Delta x, z + \Delta z) = C + \Delta\rho_i, \tag{7}$$

then a correction is applied perpendicular to the initial tangent along the new line

$$\frac{\Delta x'}{\Delta z'} = +\frac{\partial\rho_i/\partial x}{\partial\rho_i/\partial z}$$

a distance

$$\Delta z' = \frac{\Delta\rho_i}{\dfrac{\partial\rho_i'}{\partial z'} + \dfrac{\partial\rho_i'}{\partial x'}\dfrac{\partial\rho_i/\partial x}{\partial\rho_i/\partial z}}. \tag{8}$$

This correction [Eq. (8)] is continued until $\Delta\rho_i$ falls within a small preset threshold. This hunt process [Eqs. (6–8)] is continued until the entire contour is traced out. Analogous equations result for the total molecular density or for any linear combination of molecular orbital densities.

The input to the computer program consists of the symmetry basis functions $\chi_{p\lambda\alpha}$, the orbital coefficients C_{ip}, the internuclear distance, a series of the contour values desired with the associated thresholds, and finally the physical scale in which diagrams are to be plotted. The output consisted of 35 mm negatives of the diagrams presented in this work. The process has been more completely documented elsewhere (Wahl, 1966).

IV. Results and Implications

In Fig. 2 the contours of density associated with the homonuclear diatomic molecules constructed from first row atoms are given on a consistent basis as defined in the key (Fig. 1). Both the total molecular densities and the orbital densities are displayed. [These diagrams are available in a larger scale (Wahl, 1966).] It is hoped that in addition to their obvious tutorial value these contour diagrams of the molecular-orbital model for these simple homonuclear diatomic molecules, H_2, Li_2, B_2, C_2, N_2, O_2, and F_2, will prove to be useful symbols which will stimulate thought about chemical binding, steric hindrance bonding and antibonding orbitals, in addition to providing a correct and more complete picture of molecular orbitals were only a rudimentary one, based primarily on hydrogen atom wave functions and single STO's, existed before.

Using these computational techniques, concepts and changes which are best presented visually may be so presented. Such visual presentations have been quite limited in the past due to the prohibitive labor involved (Huo, 1965; Peyerimhoff, 1965). Studies of interatomic forces and the formation of

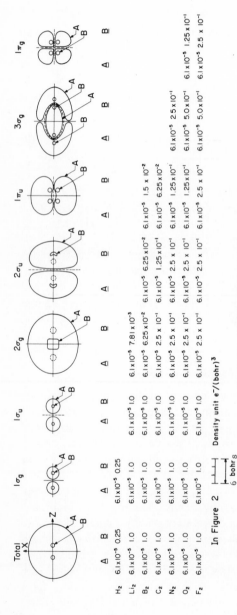

	Total		$1\sigma_g$		$1\sigma_u$		$2\sigma_g$		$2\sigma_u$		$1\pi_u$		$3\sigma_g$		$1\pi_g$	
	A	B	A	B	A	B	A	B	A	B	A	B	A	B	A	B
H_2	6.1×10^{-5}	0.25	6.1×10^{-5}	0.25												
Li_2	6.1×10^{-5}	1.0	6.1×10^{-5}	1.0	6.1×10^{-5}	1.0	6.1×10^{-5}	7.81×10^{-3}								
B_2	6.1×10^{-5}	1.0	6.1×10^{-5}	1.0	6.1×10^{-5}	1.0	6.1×10^{-5}	6.25×10^{-2}	6.1×10^{-5}	6.25×10^{-2}	6.1×10^{-5}	1.5×10^{-2}				
C_2	6.1×10^{-5}	1.0	6.1×10^{-5}	1.0	6.1×10^{-5}	1.0	6.1×10^{-5}	2.5×10^{-1}	6.1×10^{-5}	1.25×10^{-1}	6.1×10^{-5}	6.25×10^{-2}				
N_2	6.1×10^{-5}	1.0	6.1×10^{-5}	1.0	6.1×10^{-5}	1.0	6.1×10^{-5}	2.5×10^{-1}	6.1×10^{-5}	2.5×10^{-1}	6.1×10^{-5}	1.25×10^{-1}	6.1×10^{-5}	2.5×10^{-1}		
O_2	6.1×10^{-5}	1.0	6.1×10^{-5}	1.0	6.1×10^{-5}	1.0	6.1×10^{-5}	2.5×10^{-1}	6.1×10^{-5}	2.5×10^{-1}	6.1×10^{-5}	1.25×10^{-1}	6.1×10^{-5}	5.0×10^{-1}	6.1×10^{-5}	1.25×10^{-1}
F_2	6.1×10^{-5}	1.0	6.1×10^{-5}	1.0	6.1×10^{-5}	1.0	6.1×10^{-5}	2.5×10^{-1}	6.1×10^{-5}	2.5×10^{-1}	6.1×10^{-5}	2.5×10^{-1}	6.1×10^{-5}	5.0×10^{-1}	6.1×10^{-5}	2.5×10^{-1}

In Figure 2   Density unit $e^-/(bohr)^3$

6 bohrs

The SHELL MODEL of MOLECULES

In Figure 2 **are** contour diagrams of the electron densities characteristic of the shell model of the molecules H_2, Li_2, B_2, C_2, N_2, O_2, and F_2. Both the total molecular density and the constituent shell densities are displayed at the experimental internuclear distance of each molecule. (He_2, Be_2, and Ne_2 which are members of this homonuclear series are not bound in their ground state and therefore not displayed.)

VALUE of CONTOURS

The above diagrams indicate the general structure of each plot. A labels the lowest contour value plotted and B the highest contour value plotted in each molecule (except for the contours which rise to a value of 1.0 $e^-/(bohr)^3$ inside the $2\sigma_g$ node). Adjacent contour lines differ by a factor of 2. Thus all contours plotted are members of the geometric progression 2^{-N} $e^-/(bohr)^3$ where N runs from 0 to 14. All plots are in a plane passing through the two nuclei. Dotted lines indicate nodal surface.

FIG. 1.   Key to density contours.

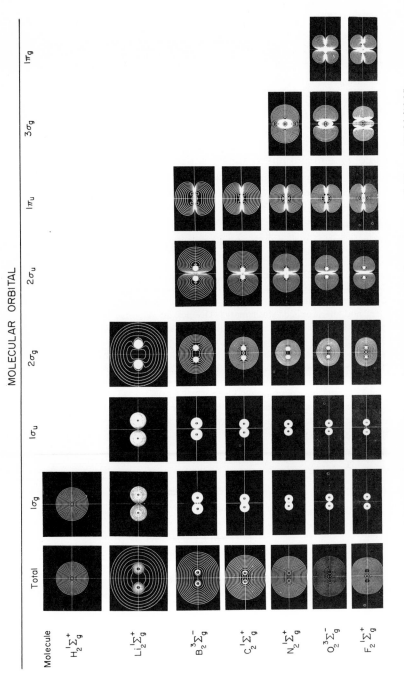

FIG. 2. Comparison of density of molecular orbitals. Larger scale diagrams are available, see Wahl (1966).

the chemical bond using extended Hartree-Fock wave functions (Das and Wahl, 1966) are underway in which these programs are being used to display the changes occurring in electronic charge density as a molecule forms. In a study of molecular ionization these automatic contour programs are being used to illustrate directly changes in the molecular charge distribution with electron removal. In other theoretical work a pictorial display of configuration mixing provides a physical picture of wave-function improvements and electron correlation as produced by added optimal configurations. This work contains the development of a new tool; namely, the synthesis of high-speed digital computers and linked analog devices into a medium capable of efficiently communicating certain types of new information. Since many of us involved in large scale computational efforts are often swamped by our own computer output and are able to competently analyze only a small fraction of the potentially useful information we have generated, this problem of communication is well worth consideration (Coulson, 1960)

ACKNOWLEDGMENTS

The author is particularly grateful to the Computation Center Staff of the CDC 3600 computer and the Applied Mathematics Division at Argonne National Laboratory for their painstaking efforts in processing these calculations, maintaining the DD 80 plotter, and providing library programs, all of which greatly facilitated the work presented in this paper. Thanks are also due to the Laboratory of Molecular Structure and Spectra for providing wave functions for C_2 and B_2 prior to their publication.

It is indeed a pleasure to contribute this work to a volume honoring Professor J. C. Slater. In the long analytic and computational path which finally lead to these pictures, his concepts have been always at hand, namely: the Slater-type orbitals which formed the basis sets; the Slater determinantal form of the wave function; and in addition, his early contributions to Hartree-Fock theory itself, as well as his many and substantial educational contributions (Slater, 1963).

REFERENCES

Brillouin, L. (1933). *Actualities Sci. Ind.* **71**.
Brillouin, L. (1934). *Actualities Sci. Ind.* **159**.
Cade, P. E., Sales, K. D., Wahl, A. C. (1966) *J. Chem. Phys.* **44**, 1973
Coulson, C. A. (1938). *Proc. Cambridge Phil. Soc.* **34**, 204.
Coulson, C. A. (1960). *Rev. Mod. Phys.* **32**, 170.
Das, G., and Wahl, A. C. (1966). *J. Chem. Phys.*, **44**, 87.
Delbrück, M. (1930). *Proc. Roy. Soc. (London) Ser.* **A129**, 686.
Fock, V. (1930). *Z. Physik* **61**, 126.
Greenshields, J. (1966). To be published.
Hartree, D. R. (1928). *Proc. Cambridge Phil. Soc.* **24**, 89.
Hund, F. (1928). *Z. Physik* **51**, 759.
Huo, W. (1965). *J. Chem. Phys.* **43**, 624.
Koopman, T. (1933). *Physica* **1**, 104.

Lennard-Jones, J. E. (1929). *Trans. Faraday Soc.* **25**, 668.

Löwdin, P.-O. (1962). *J. Appl. Phys. Suppl.* **33**, 270.

Löwdin, P.-O., and Pullman, B. (1964). "Molecular Orbitals in Chemistry, Physics, and Biology." Academic Press, New York.

Malli, G. L., and Cade, P. E., (1966). To be published.

Møller, C., and Plesset, M. S. (1934). *Phys. Rev.* **46**, 618.

Mulliken, R. S. (1928). *Phys. Rev.* **32**, 186, 388, 761.

Mulliken, R. S. (1929). *Phys. Rev.* **33**, 730.

Mulliken, R. S. (1932). *Phys. Rev.* **40**, 55; **41**, 49, 751.

Nesbet, R. K. (1965). *J. Chem. Phys.* **43**, 530.

Peyerimhoff, S. (1965). *J. Chem. Phys.* **43**, 998.

Roothaan, C. C. J. (1951). *Rev. Mod. Phys.* **23**, 69.

Roothaan, C. C. J. (1960). *Rev. Mod. Phys.* **32**, 179.

Roothaan, C. C. J., and Bagus, P. (1963). *In* "Methods in Computational Physics" (B. Alder, S. Fernbach, and M. Rotenberg, eds.), Vol. 2, p. 47. Academic Press, New York.

Sales, K. D., Cade, P. E., Wahl, A. C. (1966). To be published.

Slater, J. C. (1929). *Phys. Rev.* **34**, 1929.

Slater, J. C. (1930a). *Phys. Rev.* **35**, 509.

Slater, J. C. (1930b) *Phys. Rev.* **35**, 210.

Slater, J. C. (1932). *Phys. Rev.* **41**, 255.

Slater, J. C. (1963). "Quantum Theory of Molecules and Solids. Electronic Structure of Molecules," Vol. 1. McGraw-Hill, New York.

Slater, J. C. (1965). *J. Chem. Phys.* **43**, S11.

Wahl, A. C. (1964). *J. Chem. Phys.* **41**, 2600.

Wahl, A. C., Cade, P. E., Roothaan, C. C. J. (1964). *J. Chem. Phys.* **41**, 2578.

Wahl, A. C. (1966). *Argonne National Laboratory Report No. 7076*, also *Science.* **151**, 961.

Localized Orbitals and Localized Adjustment Functions

S. F. BOYS

THEORETICAL CHEMISTRY DEPARTMENT
UNIVERSITY OF CAMBRIDGE, CAMBRIDGE, ENGLAND

Soon after the acceptance of Slater determinants as the most useful anti-symmetric functions for electronic quantum calculations it was realized that these were left invariant by any unitary transformation of the orbitals, and that the new orbitals could be chosen to be the most suitable for the investigation of a particular physical problem [see Pauling (1931) and Slater (1931)]. The most interesting case is when a transformation is made to orbitals which are localized as much as possible.

The early investigations of such transformations were mostly for particular approximations such as that where atomic orbitals are hybridized to give functions more appropriate for use in approximate molecular calculations. Later treatments have approached nearer to the general molecular problem. The well-known equivalent orbitals investigated by Hall and Lennard-Jones (1950) provided a general method for molecules with certain symmetry.

The first practical method of construction of localized orbitals for a general molecule was given by Foster and Boys (1960) by their definition of exclusive orbitals. These were defined in terms of the matrix elements of the dipole moment operator between all the orbitals of the molecule and they were calculated by a fairly simple iteration procedure using these $3n^2$ matrix elements. Later Edmiston and Rudenberg (1963) performed a calculation with the criterion of the minimization of electrostatic exchange energy, which was an alternative definition discussed by Lennard-Jones and Pople (1950). This was a rather heavy iterative calculation dependent on the n^4 matrix elements of the two-electron electrostatic integrals.

A completely new addition to the localized orbitals was introduced by Foster and Boys in an attempt to define some localized functions suitable for use in the additional Slater determinants which have to be combined with the first, or SCF, determinant to allow for electronic correlation. These new localized functions were described as oscillator orbitals. Unfortunately the original definition had a deficiency which makes it satisfactory only for the lowest range of members. This is remedied in the formulation given below. The new definition satisfies the same aims as originally described. In the calculation for the formaldehyde molecule by these authors only the lowest oscillator orbitals were used and these are unaffected by the change in the definition.

Such a general scheme of localization is of considerable interest because it provides the only method yet proposed for a localized analysis of induced phenomena and other properties of molecules and crystals. Any such property of the whole system can be expressed as a sum of contributions each of which can be ascribed to a particular localized electron pair, or to an interaction between two of these. In the latter case the contribution to the property can have half of its magnitude ascribed to each pair. This appears to provide a complete quantum analogue to the way in which it was once hoped with classical mechanics to attribute all phenomena to contributions from individual electrons or the interactions between pairs of these. All this can be set out formally once a system of localized orbitals and expansion functions has been defined by some procedure such as the exclusive oscillator system of functions proposed by Foster and Boys. The detailed definitions which seem most satisfactory at the present will now be set out.

The exclusive orbitals will be defined first, since the oscillator orbitals are later defined in terms of these. The definition proposed here is a minor modification of that given by Foster and Boys (1960). The reason for the change and the relation between the two forms will be shown later. It will also be shown that there are several equivalent forms of the present statement and that although the one given now is the most compact, a later one is the simplest for computation. The present condition is that the sum of the quadratic repulsions of the orbitals with themselves shall be minimized. This can be written as the minimization of

$$I = \sum_{a}^{n} \langle \varphi_a \varphi_a | r_{12}^2 | \varphi_a \varphi_a \rangle \tag{1}$$

subject to the condition that the φ_a are orthonormal linear combinations of the space factors of the $2n$ occupied electronic orbitals. The whole of the present analysis is restricted to the circumstances when the Slater determinant contains each spatial orbital both with α and β spin functions. The above expression is written in the usual quantum matrix element notation and, in a product of functions at either side, it is implied that the first function depends on r_1, the second function on r_2, and so forth. Thus in a single electron integral we shall write $\langle \varphi_a | r_1^2 | \varphi_a \rangle$ to mean that all the quantities are dependent on x_1, y_1, z_1. It will be shown later that the above definition is equivalent to the maximization of the sum of the squares of the distances of the orbitals from each other and so is similar to the original definition.

When these orbitals have been calculated for a molecule under consideration the oscillator orbitals are to be derived from a system of primary functions.

$$\bar{\varphi}_{apqs} = x_a^p y_a^q z_a^s \varphi_a \qquad (2)$$

Here the coordinates x_a, y_a, z_a are defined to be measured from the centroid of the orbital density $\varphi_a^* \varphi_a$ and with respect to axes taken parallel to the principal axes of the moment of inertia tensor of the distribution $\varphi_a^* \varphi_a$. The longest axis is to be ascribed to x and the shortest to z.

In this notation the functions with $p = q = s = 0$ are just the original exclusive orbitals, which can be regarded as the early members of the whole sequence. The final functions which will be obtained after a special orthonormalization process will be denoted by φ_{apqs}. The orthonormalization method can be regarded as a Schmidt procedure between classes of different degree, which is defined to be $p + q + s$, and a Löwdin-type orthonormalization within each class of specified degree. Hence within a class of given degree the order of the functions does not affect the result and any symmetry among the $\bar{\varphi}_{apqs}$ also occurs among the φ_{apqs}. There is always a one-to-one correspondence between the original and the derived set and if the former were orthonormal then the orthonormalization procedure would cause no change.

The quantity $p + q + s$ will be called the degree of a particular function $\bar{\varphi}_{apqs}$ and the whole system will be considered as arranged in sets of the same degree with the sets in order of increasing degree. Let some arbitrary choice be specified for the order within these sets and let $\bar{\eta}_u^k$ denote the uth member of the kth set of the $\bar{\varphi}_{apqs}$ so arranged. Let η_u^k be the φ_{apqs} which is derived from this $\bar{\eta}_u^k$.

The most compact definition of the orthonormal η_u^k is given by describing the procedure for η_u^k when all the η_v^l of lower degree have already been calculated. For the first stage it is postulated that

$$\varphi_{a000} = \bar{\varphi}_{a000} \qquad \text{or} \qquad \eta_u^0 = \bar{\eta}_u^0. \qquad (3)$$

For the functions of any degree k there are defined a set of intermediate functions

$$\bar{\bar{\eta}}_u^k = \left[\bar{\eta}_u^k - \sum_{lv}^{k-1} \eta_v^l \langle \eta_v^l | \bar{\eta}_u^k \rangle \right] \left[\langle \bar{\eta}_u^k | \bar{\eta}_u^k \rangle - \sum_{lv}^{k-1} \langle \bar{\eta}_u^k | \eta_v^l \rangle \langle \eta_v^l | \bar{\eta}_u^k \rangle \right]^{-1/2} \qquad (4)$$

This is just the relation of the Schmidt method of orthonormalization to make each η_u^k orthogonal to all the functions of lower degree, though not to the functions with the same k value. The next stage is to make these orthonormal to each other by a procedure which is closely related to the Löwdin procedure of making orthonormal linear combinations. The η_u^k are defined to be those linear combinations

$$\eta_u^k = \sum_v X_v^k \bar{\bar{\eta}}_v^k \qquad (5)$$

of the $\bar{\bar{\eta}}_v^k$ which maximize

$$I = \text{Re} \sum_u \langle \bar{\eta}_u^k | \eta_u^k \rangle \tag{6}$$

subject to the condition that they are orthonormal, that is

$$\langle \eta_u^k | \eta_v^k \rangle = \delta_{uv}. \tag{7}$$

Since the sum of the overlaps with the original functions is being maximized the η_u^k may be said to be the best approximations to the original $\bar{\eta}_u^k$ which are also orthogonal to the lower sets and which are orthonormal to each other.

When the orthonormal η_u^k have been obtained it is possible to revert to the original type of notation and to denote these by φ_{apqs} where the values of a, p, q, and s are the same as in the original $\varphi_a x_a^p y_a^q z_a^s$ from which this was derived. However for physical theoretical work it is most convenient to replace the last three suffixes by a single suffix m. Let $m = 0, 1, 2, \ldots$, stand for all the combinations of p, q, s arranged in order of increasing value of the degree, and in descending order of p within a set of the same degree, and in decreasing order of q within a set of constant p and constant degree. In principle any other choice which gave an unambiguous labeling of all the functions derived from a given exclusive orbital φ_a or φ_{a0} would be satisfactory. It can, however, be noted that with this choice, when φ_{a0} corresponds to a chemical bond, the first oscillator orbital φ_{a1} is an approximation to the antibonding orbital of approximate theories, while φ_{a2} and φ_{a3} could be said to correspond to transverse polarizations of the bond.

It will be assumed that the oscillator orbitals (including the exclusive orbitals as first members) will be a complete system of functions. They will be complete if the original nonorthogonal system $\varphi_a x_a^p y_a^q z_a^s$ is complete, and although we cannot prove this, it is very likely to be true for this type of function. In fact by its general nature a partial set of the type $(1s)x^p y^q z^s$, arising from an inner shell, is likely to be complete. In any case it is not likely in the foreseeable future that more than ten oscillator orbitals per exclusive orbital will be used in a practical calculation and these early functions appear very suitable to be good expansion functions for most purposes.

The most direct application of the oscillator orbitals is to express in a compact form the more accurate wave function approximations which consist of linear combinations of many Slater determinants. Such forms allow for the effects of electronic correlation and are frequently described as including configurational interaction. All the Slater determinants except the first depend on other single electron functions as well as the occupied orbitals and it was suggested by Foster and Boys (1960) that the oscillator orbitals would be very effective for these. In principle if any complete system of single-electron functions were used in the Slater determinants the result would converge to the correct answer and if the above definition of oscillator orbitals is satisfactory this should be true for them. In this case any wave function can be approximated to sufficient accuracy if sufficient Slater determinants are used but it is also to be expected that the Slater determinants will only occur with coefficients which fall off rapidly as higher substitutions of the exclusive orbitals by oscillator orbitals are made, or if exclusive orbitals are replaced by oscillator orbitals from more distant sets. In various practical calculations the first Slater determinant, Φ_1, which consists only of the exclusive orbitals each associated with an α and β spin, has been found to have coefficients in the range 0.97 to 0.99. The other Slater determinants are conveniently denoted by means of substitution operators $P(x, y, \ldots /x', y', \ldots)$ which denote the operation of replacing x' by x, y' by y, etc.

In this notation the most important terms after the first may be written as $P(\varphi_{a1}\alpha\varphi_{a1}\beta/\varphi_{a0}\alpha_{a0}\beta)\Phi_1$, which shows that the particular exclusive orbital φ_a has been replaced by its first oscillator orbital in both the α and β functions. With the above conventions this first oscillator orbital has been chosen to be a function which approximates to the ordinary antibonding orbital. In this case, a Slater determinant with the above structure is usually found to have a coefficient in the range from -0.07 to -0.09. Such terms increase the probability of finding the electrons at the opposite ends of a bond. It is convenient to let $P(\varphi_{a1}\varphi_{b1}/\varphi_{a0}\varphi_{b0})\Phi_1$ denote all the relevant spin combinations when one of the exclusive orbitals φ_{a0} is replaced by its first oscillator φ_{a1} and another φ_{b0} is replaced by its first oscillator orbital. Slater determinants of this type have been found generally to occur with coefficients whose magnitudes are in the range from 0.02 to 0.03. They correspond to the longitudinal correlation between the electrons in different bonds. Not many such calculations have yet been performed and in these it has not been possible to include functions of as high a degree as is desirable. But the available evidence does suggest that the coefficients fall off rapidly and systematically as more distant replacements or replacements of higher degree are made.

The value of this analysis is not only that the largest terms are obtained at the beginning, it lies also in the fact that each of these terms corresponds in some definite way to the bonds in a particular locality so that we might expect similar terms with the same size of coefficients in a similar locality for a calculation on another molecule. Of course, the neighboring bonds would have to be the same for a close correspondence, but then we might expect considerable similarity. The term corresponding to the correlation within a single bond would probably agree within 10% or so, and also terms such as the above, corresponding to the correlation between neighboring bonds of some specified chemical types, would be expected to be approximately invariant.

Consider other effects of chemical interest such as the change at a few bonds distant when a C atom is replaced by a N^+ ion. In such a case it would be interesting not to recalculate the new wave function from the beginning but to find the changes in the orbitals in terms of the exclusive and oscillator orbitals of the original molecule. This can be done by a calculation of the perturbation type. We should expect similar changes in similar molecules and that the same changes could be predicted for other similar molecules without further calculation. It would be expected that the changes in any exclusive orbital, when expanded in terms of all oscillator orbitals, would only have appreciable coefficients for the oscillator orbitals corresponding to this exclusive orbital itself and to its nearest neighbors. Such a calculation would be quite straightforward for the single Slater-determinant approximation but it would require sophisticated analysis for a general case which included configurational interaction.

Consider a perturbation of the whole system by some field V. Such calculations are most frequently performed in terms of the Hamiltonian eigenfunctions, but, at the expense of introducing reciprocals of nondiagonal matrixes, it is possible to perform them in terms of any system of expansion functions, and this can be done in terms of the oscillator orbitals. In this case the first-order perturbed value $D^{\cdot}$ of an observable with operator D is found to be linearly dependent on the matrix elements of D and the coefficients of these to be linearly dependent on the matrix elements of V, so that the total observed effect can be written

$$D^1 = \sum_{abcd} \sum_{klpq} C(a, b, c, d, k, l, p, q)\langle\varphi_{ak}|D|\varphi_{bl}\rangle\langle\varphi_{cp}|V|\varphi_{dq}\rangle \tag{8}$$

where the $C(a, b, c, d, k, l, p, q)$ are the appropriate coefficients to be evaluated in the calculation on any particular molecule. It is now possible to define a quantity which measures the effect arising in the vicinity of φ_a due to the perturbing effect acting in the vicinity of φ_d. Let D_{ad} be defined to be

$$D_{ad} = \text{Re} \sum_{bc} \sum_{klpq} C(a, b, c, d, k, l, p, q)\langle\varphi_{ak}|D|\varphi_{bl}\rangle\langle\varphi_{cp}|V|\varphi_{dq}\rangle. \tag{9}$$

Since the original D^1 is real, the Re, denoting the real part operation, can be omitted before it and it follows that $D^1 = \sum_{ad} D_{ad}$. It can be seen that normally the largest contributions to D_{ad} will come from the terms in which $b = a$ and $c = d$ and that the contributions will be very small if φ_b is at all distant from φ_a etc. This is the main justification for taking this expression to be the effect caused at φ_a by the field at φ_d. It can be seen that if the φ_a were nearly separate from each other, as would be the case in a system of a few separate He atoms then D_{ad} would measure the physical effect caused in one atom by the field acting at another atom. The symmetric terms D_{aa} would normally be expected to be the largest terms since they represent the effect at one orbital due to the field acting on the same orbital.

The above definition is a mathematical way of representing quantities which the chemist would intuitively describe as the effect transmitted from one bond to another. However the setting out of the details of the mathematical analysis for particular properties will be quite complicated and the construction of a systematic method of computation will be still more complicated. G. W. Smith and the writer have made an exploratory calculation of this type for ethylene. This calculation has been found to be difficult even though programs were available for general molecular integrals, and the calculation has only been performed to the refinement of using one oscillator orbital per exclusive orbital. However the subsequent development after a first beginning is frequently much more rapid than appears feasible at such a time. Also once the formulation of the general representation becomes familiar it is quite possible that alternative methods of calculation may become apparent.

It is interesting to see that the definition of exclusive orbitals which was given above is equivalent to several other simple definitions. It should be noted that for the use of the second criterion given below it is only necessary to know the dipole moment matrix to calculate the exclusive orbitals. Let $\mathbf{R}_a$ be defined by

$$\mathbf{R}_a = \langle \varphi_a | \mathbf{r}_1 | \varphi_a \rangle \tag{10}$$

so that this is the centroid of the orbital φ_a. Let $\mathbf{r}_{1a} = \mathbf{r}_1 - \mathbf{R}_a$ so that the criterion which was minimized for the exclusive orbitals may be written

$$I = \sum_a \langle \varphi_a \varphi_a | r_{12}^2 | \varphi_a \varphi_a \rangle = \sum_a \langle \varphi_a \varphi_a | (\mathbf{r}_{1a} - \mathbf{r}_{2a})^2 | \varphi_a \varphi_a \rangle$$

$$= \sum_a \langle \varphi_a \varphi_a | r_{1a}^2 + r_{2a}^2 - 2\mathbf{r}_{1a} \cdot \mathbf{r}_{2a} | \varphi_a \varphi_a \rangle$$

$$= 2 \sum_a \langle \varphi_a | r_{1a}^2 | \varphi_a \rangle - 2 \sum_a \langle \varphi_a | \mathbf{r}_1 - \mathbf{R}_a | \varphi_a \rangle \cdot \langle \varphi_a | \mathbf{r}_1 - \mathbf{R}_a | \varphi_a \rangle$$

$$= 2 \sum_a \langle \varphi_a | r_{1a}^2 | \varphi_a \rangle. \tag{11}$$

The definition of $\mathbf{R}_a$ justifies the omission of the term shown in the last equality. This last expression is just the sum of the spherical quadratic moments of each exclusive orbital about its centroid and it shows that the minimization process is equivalent to making each exclusive orbital contract as close to its own centroid as can be done while retaining the condition that these are orthonormal linear combinations of the original orbitals of the given Slater determinant.

The next criterion follows by writing with another small alteration of form.

$$I = \sum_a \langle \varphi_a \varphi_a | (\mathbf{r}_1 - \mathbf{r}_2)^2 | \varphi_a \varphi_a \rangle$$

$$= 2 \sum_a \langle \varphi_a | r_1^2 | \varphi_a \rangle - 2 \sum_a \langle \varphi_a | \mathbf{r}_1 | \varphi_a \rangle \cdot \langle \varphi_a | \mathbf{r}_1 | \varphi_a \rangle$$

$$= -2 \sum_a R_a^2 + 2 \sum_a \langle \varphi_a | r_1^2 | \varphi_a \rangle. \tag{12}$$

If this is taken for the practical form to be minimized it is apparent that the second term does not enter into the minimization because it is invariant for all unitary transformations. Hence only the first term $-\sum_a R_a^2$ need be minimized and this depends only on the matrix elements of the dipole moments matrixes. This maximization of $\sum_a R_a^2$ is used in our current programs.

It can also be shown that the maximization of J the sum of the squares of the distances between the centroids of the orbitals is equivalent to the minimization of the last form of I. This can be written

$$
\begin{aligned}
J &= \sum_{ab}^{n} [\langle \varphi_a | \mathbf{r}_1 | \varphi_a \rangle - \langle \varphi_b | \mathbf{r}_1 | \varphi_b \rangle]^2 \\
&= 2n \sum_a \langle \varphi_a | \mathbf{r}_1 | \varphi_a \rangle^2 - 2 \sum_a \sum_b \langle \varphi_a | \mathbf{r}_1 | \varphi_a \rangle \cdot \langle \varphi_b | \mathbf{r}_1 | \varphi_b \rangle \\
&= 2n \sum_a R_a^2 - 2[\sum_a \langle \varphi_a | \mathbf{r}_1 | \varphi_a \rangle]^2.
\end{aligned}
\tag{13}
$$

The second term is invariant for unitary transformations of the orbitals so that the maximization of J is equivalent to the minimization of I which was equivalent to the other definitions of the exclusive orbitals.

It may be noted that if R_{ab} denotes the distance between the centroids of φ_a and φ_b then the above exclusive orbitals are given by the maximization of $\sum_{a>b} R_{ab}^2$ while the original condition suggested by Foster and Boys was $\prod_{a>b} R_{ab}^2$. The writer does not regard this change as having a very great effect. He is in favor of the sum form because one system involving an activated complex was found for which the product criterion did not converge in a reasonable physical way while the sum definition gave no difficulty. The fact that the sum criterion has these equivalent definitions with simple physical interpretations also appears to be in its favor.

It is apparent from the above analysis that the difference between the present exclusive orbitals and the localized orbitals of Edmiston and Rudenberg can be expressed by saying that the former use an r_{12}^2 repulsion field where the latter use the r_{12}^{-1} Coulomb field. It might be claimed that the latter is more natural to physical systems but the necessary calculation in this case involves iterations with an n^4 matrix while the r_{12}^2 field only uses the n^2 dipole matrix. It is the opinion of the writer that the exclusive orbitals are more convenient for ordinary and easy use. For the further stage of localized adjustment functions there are at the present no alternatives to the oscillator orbitals. It is probably these which will have the more far reaching consequences for the interpretation of physical phenomena as due to localized contributions arising from the electron pairs in chemical bonds, lone pairs, and inner shells. The definition of these could be appended to the orbitals calculated by the method of Edmiston and Rudenberg but it is probably more uniform to use them with the exclusive orbitals, since both of them depend on relatively simple transformations of the single-electron moment integrals.

There is nothing in the mathematics to prevent the application of these methods to crystals such as metals, or to molecules with large systems of conjugated Π-orbitals, but in these cases the localized orbitals would not be localized to the degree which is to be expected in systems whose bonds are all of the covalent type. For the former systems the best localized orbitals would penetrate each other to an extent which would make any analysis into properties of individual localized bonds and interactions between these only a formal mathematical process. In a covalent bond system it is to be expected, and has been found in several cases, that the penetrations and interactions do fall off quite rapidly as the combinations which are more removed from nearest neighbors are considered. This is, of course, to be expected from the general chemical evidence on how little bonds which are somewhat removed from nearest neighbors do influence each other. From the purely theoretical point of view the analysis can be applied to any system but if the results of this show that the orbitals do penetrate each other much more than for other covalent systems, and the interactions do not fall off sufficiently rapidly as orbitals a few removes from each other are considered, then the application to such a system had better be abandoned. It is not to be expected that this will be found in molecules or crystals which would normally be represented as having a structure of covalent bonds.

It is not feasible here to set out the details of the corresponding analysis for a wave function which is expressed as a linear combination of a number of Slater determinants. But if these are expressed in terms of a scheme of exclusive and oscillator orbitals it is possible to assign all the contributions to any simple property, or phenomenon, to the individual exclusive orbitals. If a contribution is dependent on oscillator orbitals of one exclusive orbital then this is counted in the total contribution of that exclusive orbital. If a contribution is dependent on two oscillator orbitals from different exclusive orbitals then it is assigned half to one and half to the other. Such a scheme is artificial but it does provide a definite meaning to the contributions of particular bonds, or lone pairs, etc., to any particular phenomenon. This is very close to the general intuitive picture which would be used in the analysis of empirical data on properties of molecules or crystals.

The construction of such a scheme is possible whenever the orbitals of a Slater determinant are first transformed to localized orbitals and then a system of expansion functions suitable for a general perturbation calculation is constructed so that these are localized as closely as possible to the first localized orbitals.

REFERENCES

Edmiston, C., and Rudenberg, K. (1963). *Rev. Mod. Phys.* **35**, 457.
Foster, J. M., and Boys, S. F. (1960). *Rev. Mod. Phys.* **32**, 300.
Hall, G. G , and Lennard-Jones, J. E. (1950). *Proc. Roy. Soc.* **202**, 155.
Lennard-Jones, J. E., and Pople, J. A. (1950). *Proc. Roy. Soc.* **202**, 166.
Pauling, L. (1931). *J. Am. Chem. Soc.* **53**, 1367.
Slater, J. C. (1931). *Phys. Rev.* **37**, 481.

Localized Atomic and Molecular Orbitals. III*†

C. EDMISTON‡ and K. RUEDENBERG§

DEPARTMENT OF CHEMISTRY
THE JOHNS HOPKINS UNIVERSITY
BALTIMORE, MARYLAND
AND
INSTITUTE FOR ATOMIC RESEARCH, DEPARTMENT OF CHEMISTRY
AND DEPARTMENT OF PHYSICS, IOWA STATE UNIVERSITY, AMES, IOWA

I. Introduction

The investigation into the nature of localized atomic and molecular orbitals which was begun in two earlier articles (*1,2*) is further pursued in the present note by examining more complex systems. Two subjects are examined (a) For several polyatomic molecules the localized molecular orbitals are determined and discussed and, in particular, the correlation between this theoretical approach and empirical chemical intuition is examined. (b) For several non-trivial systems, the relationship between localized orbitals and equivalent

* Work supported by the Ames Laboratory of the U.S. Atomic Energy Commission (Contribution No. 1868) and by the National Science Foundation under NSF Grant GP 129 to Johns Hopkins University.
  † Part of a thesis submitted by C. Edmiston to Iowa State University in partial fulfillment of the requirements for the Ph.D. degree.
  ‡ *Present address:* C. Edmiston, Department of Chemistry, University of Wyoming, Laramie, Wyoming.
  § *Present address:* K. Ruedenberg, Department of Chemistry and Department of Physics, Iowa State University, Ames, Iowa.

orbitals is analyzed and it is found that the latter do not always exhibit maximum localization.

Since the basic premises used are the same as those in the previous papers (1,2), the introductory remarks made there apply also to the present investigation. Localized molecular orbitals are denoted as LMO's.

II. Localized Molecular Orbitals in Simple Polyatomic Molecules

In the following, localized molecular orbitals are discussed for the molecules H_2O, NH_3, CH_4, C_2H_6. In all cases, they are obtained from minimal-basis-set LCAO-SCF wave functions based on Slater orbitals.* For water, the molecular orbitals of Ellis (3) were localized, for ammonia those of Duncan (4) were localized, and for methane a wave function of Pitzer (5) was chosen. For ethane, the LMO's were taken which Pitzer had calculated (6) by applying the authors'. method to a wave function which he had obtained earlier with Lipscomb (7).

The localized molecular orbitals of H_2O, and NH_3 are given in Tables 1 and 2, respectively. The data in these tables are arranged exactly in the same manner as those in the tables of reference (2): The first matrix contains the exchange integrals for the canonical MO's, the second contains those for the localized MO's, the third matrix represents the transformation connecting the canonical and the localized MO's, the fourth matrix contains the LCAO expansions of the localized MO's in terms of the orthogonalized Slater AO's. The localized molecular orbitals of ethane and methane are given in Table 3. In Table 4, there are given the normalized atomic components of the localized molecular orbitals on various atoms in several molecules in a way which permits comparison of related atomic hybrids in different molecules.

A. H_2O (TABLE 1)

The LMO's of water are seen to consist of an inner shell, two equivalent oxygen lone pair orbitals, and two equivalent bond orbitals extending about equally over the O and H atoms of the bond. The normalized atomic component to the inner shell, given in Table 4, is quite similar to that of the oxygen atom in CO, and also that of the free O atom, which were found in (2).

A question of interest is the angle between the two equivalent atomic s-p hybrids, which the oxygen atom contributes to the equivalent bonding LMO's. It is found to be about 90°, not too close to the bond angle (104.5°), but not unreasonable. Nevertheless, the normalized hybrids contain considerable s-character (about one-half as much as an sp^3 hybrid). Consequently,

---

* That is, Slater-type orbitals (STAO's) with Slater's exponent values.

TABLE 1

LOCALIZED MOLECULAR ORBITALS IN H₂O

H₂O(SAO)

	$1a_1$	$2a_1$	$3a_1$	$1b_2$	$1b_1$
$1a_1$	4.78160	0.06579	0.03086	0.01065	0.02756
$2a_1$	0.06579	0.73500	0.12288	0.13050	0.14983
$3a_1$	0.03086	0.12289	0.77682	0.04372	0.05505
$1b_2$	0.01065	0.13050	0.04372	0.59236	0.02834
$1b_1$	0.02756	0.14983	0.05505	0.02834	0.89045

	iO	$l1O$	$l2O$	bOH''	bOH'
iO	4.90951	0.01798	0.01798	0.00929	0.00929
$l1O$	0.01798	1.01823	0.06107	0.04623	0.04623
$l2O$	0.01798	0.06107	1.01826	0.04623	0.04623
bOH''	0.00929	0.04623	0.04623	0.74658	0.03325
bOH'	0.00929	0.04623	0.04623	0.03325	0.74644

	$1a_1$	$2a_1$	$3a_1$	$1b_2$	$1b_1$
iO	−0.98994	−0.12677	−0.06286	−0.00004	−0.00000
$l1O$	0.08980	−0.42419	−0.55867	0.00004	−0.70702
$l2O$	−0.08979	0.42433	0.55835	0.00014	−0.70719
bOH''	0.04418	−0.55881	0.43165	−0.70672	−0.00025
bOH'	0.04408	−0.55827	0.43110	0.70749	−0.00006

	O1s	O2s	O2pz	O2py	O2px	H″1s	H′1s
iO	−0.99218	0.12017	−0.03475	−0.00002	0.00000	0.00391	0.00396
$l1O$	0.09459	0.65308	−0.37605	0.00003	−0.70702	−0.10191	−0.10196
$l2O$	−0.09457	−0.65302	0.37578	0.00008	−0.70719	0.10189	0.10175
bOH''	0.01400	0.22611	0.41371	−0.41179	−0.00025	−0.16025	0.56575
bOH'	0.01394	0.22597	0.41321	0.41223	−0.00006	0.56591	−0.16087

they are nonorthogonal, with an overlap integral of 0.134 (equivalent orthogonal s-p hybrids, enclosing a 90° angle would be pure p orbitals).

On the other hand, if equivalent MO's are constructed in such a way that the lone pair LMO's contain no contributions from the H atoms, then the oxygen bond-hybrids form an angle of 74.9° between them. Finally, an angle of 73.6° is found between the two bonding hybrids on oxygen, if they are obtained by an equivalent orbital transformation between the two MO's [(3 a_1) and (1 b_2)] which have the highest energies among those being symmetric in the plane of the molecule. Thus, the LMO's obtained by the present method yield the most reasonable hybrids.

Returning to the LMO's, we find the angle between the oxygen components of the lone pair LMO's to be 124°. They are directed above and below the plane of the molecule. The overlap between the normalized oxygen component to one of the lone pair LMO's and the normalized oxygen component to one of the bonding LMO is -0.010. The mutual overlap between the two normalized oxygen lone pair components is 0.071. Thus, the long held assumption that atomic hybrid orbitals are very nearly orthogonal, is approximately, but not quantitatively correct.

B. NH_3 (TABLE 2)

The LMO's for NH_3 consist of an inner shell, a lone pair on the N atom, and three equivalent bond orbitals. The bond orbitals found in NH_3 are slightly less equivalent than the equivalent LMO's found in the other molecules. This is probably due to a small error in the input integrals which could not be located.*

According to Table 4, the N component to the lone pair contains much less s-character than the lone pair in N_2 which was given in Table 15 of ref. (2). This appears to be the only great deviation thus far found for the forms of two chemically similar LMO's.

The inner shell of NH_3 has a larger than usual contribution from the Slater 1s orbital. This also occurs in NH and C_2H_6 (see below), but not in H_2O or HF.

The angle between the equivalent nitrogen hybrids which form the N contributions to the bond LMO's is 104.5° (the HNH bond angle is close to 107°). Correspondingly, the angle between one of the bonding hybrids and the lone pair hybrid is 114°; the corresponding overlap is -0.028. The mutual overlap of two of the bonding hybrids is 0.004.

Using the same wave function, Duncan (4) constructed localized MO's assuming that the H orbitals do not contribute to the lone pair. This leads to

---

* The deviations from complete equivalence in the other molecules merely reflects the fact that 8-figure accuracy in the self-energy allows only about 4-figure accuracy in the LMO's.

TABLE 2

LOCALIZED MOLECULAR ORBITALS IN NH₃

NH₃(SAO)ᵃ

	Φ_1	Φ_2	Φ_3	Φ_5	Φ_7
Φ_1	0.58367	0.09214	0.04395	0.11755	0.11648
Φ_2	0.09214	0.78023	0.02718	0.02950	0.02915
Φ_3	0.04395	0.02718	4.16101	0.01139	0.01139
Φ_5	0.11755	0.02950	0.01139	0.56915	0.02880
Φ_7	0.11648	0.02915	0.01139	0.02880	0.57123

	iN	lN	bNH''	bNH'	bNH
iN	4.24396	0.01525	0.00893	0.00893	0.00894
lN	0.01525	0.86677	0.03785	0.03785	0.03785
bNH''	0.00893	0.03785	0.70809	0.02198	0.02238
bNH'	0.00893	0.03785	0.02198	0.70808	0.02238
bNH	0.00894	0.03785	0.02238	0.02238	0.70875

	Φ_1	Φ_2	Φ_3	Φ_5	Φ_7
iN	0.10785	-0.05307	-0.99275	0.00000	0.00000
lN	-0.28038	0.95641	-0.08159	-0.00206	-0.00001
bNH''	0.54928	0.16448	0.05088	-0.41070	-0.70709
bNH'	0.54925	0.16448	0.05088	-0.41068	0.70712
bNH	0.55350	0.16838	0.05113	0.81404	-0.00001

	H1s	H'1s	H"1s	N1s	N2s	N2px	N2py	N2pz
iN	0.01638	0.01638	0.01638	-0.99752	0.07460	0.00000	0.00000	-0.03518
lN	0.04667	0.04820	0.04821	-0.08495	-0.60142	-0.00001	-0.00131	0.82396
bNH''	-0.08749	-0.08566	0.52164	0.02060	0.28229	-0.44791	-0.26016	0.22813
bNH'	-0.08748	0.52165	-0.08568	0.02060	0.28227	0.44793	-0.26014	0.22813
bNH	0.52099	-0.08450	-0.08450	0.02057	0.28330	0.00000	0.51565	0.23227

ᵃ Φ_1, Φ_2, Φ_3, Φ_5, and Φ_7 are Duncan's notation for the canonical SCF MO's.

the less reasonable angle of 93.7° between two of the equivalent bond hybrids. If one applies the equivalent orbital transformation directly to the three canonical bonding MO's (Φ_1, Φ_5, Φ_7 in Duncan's paper), one obtains the even more unlikely angle of 165° between two equivalent bond hybrids.

C. C_2H_6 AND CH_4 (TABLE 3)

The three types of equivalent LMO's for C_2H_6 are given in Table 3 in terms of orthogonalized Slater orbitals (Pitzer gives them in terms of a non-orthogonal 2s). H_1, H_2, and H_3 are bonded to the C atom, and H_7, H_8, and H_9 to the C'. The staggered configuration of C_2H_6 is considered here, and H_7 lies trans to H_1. The carbon 2pz orbitals are along the C—C' bond axis pointed toward each other. The carbon 2px orbitals lie in the H_1—C—C'—H_7 plane. As one would anticipate, the LMO's turn out to be six equivalent CH bond orbitals, a CC' bond orbital, and an inner shell on each of the C atoms.

For CH_4 the exact LMO's were not obtained. However, since it is certain that the valence shell LMO's are four equivalent CH bond orbitals, and since the inner shell can be expected to be quite similar to those in C_2H_6, we were able to write down a good approximation for the LMO-CMO transformation matrix. They are listed in Table 3 in terms of a basis analogous to that in C_2H_6, for comparison purposes. The C2pz is directed toward H_2, which is taken to occupy a position analogous to that of the C' atom in C_2H_6. The C2px lies in the H_2—C—H_1 plane, with its positive lobe close to H_1. The inner shell LMO, (iC), is a linear combination of the ($1a_1$) and ($2a_1$) CMO's, *taken to be such that the normalized component on the C atom is essentially identical to the corresponding ones in C_2H_6*. Thereby a new ($2'a_1$) MO (a linear combination of the orginal $1a_1$ and $2a_1$) is determined which is orthogonal to the inner shell LMO. This is then hybridized tetrahedrally with the $1t_x$, $1t_y$, and $1t_z$ CMO's, to give the bonding LMO's bCH_1, bCH_2, bCH_3, and bCH_4. The latter two are not listed, because they furnish no new information or comparisons.

The inner shell LMO's of CH_4 and C_2H_6 are seen to have quite similar contributions from the hydrogens, which implies that the procedure used for estimating the CH_4-(iC)-LMO is probably quite reliable. In any case, the forms of the valence shell LMO's are not greatly sensitive to the (iC) LMO (even though, the exchange effects between the shells are very sensitive), and these are what we are primarily interested in comparing.

A comparison of the bCH_1 bond orbitals in the two molecules is very interesting. First, the ratio of the coefficients of the 2pz and 2px orbitals is slightly larger in C_2H_6 than it is in CH_4. This indicates that in C_2H_6 the bCH_1 orbital is not directed exactly along the CH_1 bond axis, but the pyramid formed by the three (bCH_k) bond LMO's lies slightly inside the pyramid formed by the three CH_k bonds. The angle between two of the C atomic

TABLE 3

LOCALIZED MOLECULAR ORBITALS IN CH_4 AND C_2H_6

C_2H_6

	H_11s	H_21s	H_31s	$C1s$	$C2s$	$C2pz$	$C2px$
iC	− 0.02084	− 0.02084	− 0.02084	1.00138	− 0.04453	0.00171	0.00000
bCC'	− 0.07351	− 0.07351	− 0.07351	0.02964	0.34188	0.47499	0.00000
bCH_1	0.53875	− 0.09382	− 0.09382	0.02579	0.32882	− 0.17095	0.47148

	H_71s	H_81s	H_91s	$C'1s$	$C'2s$	$C'2pz$	$C'2px$
iC'	0.00578	0.00578	0.00578	0.00004	− 0.01030	− 0.02230	0.00000
bCC'	− 0.07351	− 0.07351	− 0.07351	0.02964	0.34188	0.47499	0.00000
bCH_1	0.05861	− 0.03341	− 0.03341	− 0.00757	− 0.05318	− 0.05070	− 0.00825

CH_4

	H_11s	H_21s	H_31s	H_41s	$C1s$	$C2s$	$C2pz$	$C2px$
iC	− 0.01984	− 0.01984	− 0.01984	− 0.01984	1.00185	− 0.04451	0.00000	0.00000
bCH_2	− 0.08899	0.52129	− 0.08899	− 0.08899	0.02704	0.34088	0.50992	0.00000
bCH_1	0.52129	− 0.08899	− 0.08899	− 0.08899	0.02704	0.34088	− 0.16994	0.48077

TABLE 4

PRINCIPAL ATOMIC CONTRIBUTIONS TO LONE-PAIR AND ATOMIC CONTRIBUTIONS TO BONDING LOCALIZED MOLECULAR ORBITALS

Atom	Molecule	LMO	Normalized atomic contributions to localized molecular orbitals					Coefficient in LMO
			1s	2s	2pz	2px or 2py	2p (total)	
			Principal atomic contributions to inner shell LMO's					
C	C_2H_6	(iC)	0.9990	−0.0444	0.0016			1.0024
C	CH_4	(iC)	0.9990	−0.0443	0.0000			1.0028
N	NH_3	(iN)	0.9966	−0.0745	0.0352			1.0009
O	H_2O	(iO)	0.9925	−0.1184	0.0298			1.0001
			Principal atomic contributions to lone pair LMO's					
N	NH_3	(σlN)	0.0833	0.5905	−0.8027			1.0234
O	H_2O	(lO)	0.0912	0.6293	−0.3622	0.6814	0.7718	1.0377
			Normalized σ-projections of principal atomic contributions to lone pair LMO's					
O	H_2O	(σlO)	0.1191	0.8330	−0.5403			1.0520
			Atomic contributions to bonding LMO's					
C	C_2H_6	(bCC′)	0.0506	0.5834	0.8106			0.5860
C	C_2H_6	(bCH₁)	0.0430	0.5478	−0.2848	0.7855	0.8355	0.6003
C	CH_4	(bCH₁)	0.0440	0.5552	−0.2768	0.7830	0.8305	0.6140
N	NH_3	(bNH)	0.0325	0.4476	0.3670	0.8147	0.8890	0.6329
O	H_2O	(bOH)	0.0223	0.3610	0.6600	0.6585	0.9323	0.6260
			Normalized σ-projections of atomic contributions to bonding LMO's					
C	CH_4	(bCH₂)	0.0440	0.5552	0.8305			0.6122
N	NH_3	(σbNH)	0.0557	0.7690	0.6369			0.3648
O	H_2O	(σbOH)	0.0426	0.5243	0.8504			0.5115

hybrids contained in the (bCH) bond LMO's is $109.0°$ in C_2H_4, whereas it is of course $109.5°$ in CH_4.

Secondly, one finds that the (bCH$_1$) bond LMO gives a larger contribution to the net atomic population (8) of the C atom than to that of the H atom, which is in agreement with the general feeling that the carbon atom is more electronegative than the hydrogen atom. The net atomic contributions are 0.543 for H and 0.754 for C in CH_4, and 0.581 for H and 0.721 for C in C_2H_6.

The largest coefficient of the (H1s) orbitals in the bond LMO's of C_2H_6 differs only by about 3% from that in the CH_4 bond orbitals. This is not surprising, since it is generally assumed that the CH bond orbitals are virtually identical in all saturated hydrocarbons, and this assumption is the basis of many semiempirical theories. One would have guessed that the hydrogens are slightly more positive in ethane than in methane because, in the former, there are fewer hydrogen atoms available to donate charge to the more electronegative carbon atom. The present results would indicate, however, a weak effect in the opposite direction, i.e. the hydrogens in CH_4 are slightly more positive than those in C_2H_6. This can also be seen from a simple population analysis using Mulliken's definition of net atomic populations (8). One finds hydrogen populations of 0.628 and 0.592 in C_2H_6 and CH_4, respectively. These atomic populations contain of course contributions from all LMO's.

Since the same type of basis functions are used in both molecules (Slater orbitals, i.e. Slater-type orbitals with Slater exponent values), it seems unlikely that the decrease of the hydrogen positivity in going from CH_4 to C_2H_6 should be a peculiarity of the approximation and absent in the exact SCF solution. Nevertheless, it would seem to be of interest to know whether the effect remains true for the exact SCF wave function.

III. Localized Orbitals and Equivalent Orbitals

Historically, Hund (9), Coulson (10), and Lennard-Jones (11), both alone and with Hall (12) first discussed the idea of equivalent orbitals to establish correspondence to chemical intuition. Equivalent orbitals are defined by the property that any symmetry operation of the molecular symmetry group merely *permutes* the equivalent orbitals. Later Lennard-Jones and Pople (13), realizing that this concept was of little help within one symmetry species, proposed the self-energy criterion for localization within one species. Since then it seems to have been frequently assumed that equivalent orbitals always satisfy this criterion (14). The following examples will show that there are conditions under which this assumption is not justified.

A. NONEQUIVALENT LOCALIZED ORBITALS IN THE CASE OF S-P HYBRIDIZATION

It is generally imagined that the two digonal hybrids

$$h_+ = (s + p)/\sqrt{2}, \quad h_- = (s - p)/\sqrt{2}$$

are more localized than the original orbitals, s, p. However, such is the case only if there exists a sufficiently large *local* overlap between the s-orbital and the p-orbital because, then, hybridization can be effective in decreasing the local overlap. If on the contrary, the s-orbital and the p-orbital have very small local overlap, then hybridization would tend to increase it (by making the orbitals comparable in size) and thereby decrease the localization. Thus it is to be expected that the s-orbital and the p-orbital themselves represent the LMO's in the case that one is very much more contracted than the other.*

For a quantitative investigation, we fall back on Eqs. (15)ff of our first communication (*1*). Choosing $\varphi_1 = s$ and $\varphi_2 = p$ in those equations, we find that transformation from (s, p) to (h_+, h_-) changes the localization sum by

$$\Delta D = D(h_+, h_-) - D(s, p) = 2[sp|sp] - \tfrac{1}{2}[s^2 - p^2|s^2 - p^2].$$

The LMO's are identical with (h_+, h_-) if $\Delta D > 0$, and with (s, p) if $\Delta D < 0$. In the following, two cases are being considered: $\{s = 1s, p = 2p\}$ and $\{s = 2s \text{ (-Slater)}, p = 2p\}$. Let ζ_s and ζ_p be the orbital exponents of the two functions, and

$$\zeta = \tfrac{1}{2}(\zeta_s + \zeta_p),$$

$$\tau = (\zeta_s - \zeta_p)/(\zeta_s + \zeta_p) = [1 - (\zeta_p/\zeta_s)]/[1 + (\zeta_p/\zeta_s)].$$

Then one obtains

$$2[sp|sp] = \zeta X(\tau), \qquad \tfrac{1}{2}[s^2 - p^2|s^2 - p^2] = \zeta C(\tau)$$

where, for s = 1s, p = 2p;

$$16\, X(\tau) = \frac{7}{3}(1 + \tau)^3(1 - \tau)^5,$$

$$16\, C(\tau) = 5(1 + \tau) - \frac{1}{2}(1 - \tau^2)(14 - 7\tau - \tau^2 + 3\tau^3 - \tau^4) + \frac{501}{160}(1 - \tau);$$

and, for s = 2s, p = 2p

$$128\, X(\tau) = \frac{185}{9}(1 - \tau^2)^5,$$

$$128\, C(\tau) = \frac{93}{4}(1 + \tau) - \frac{1}{2}(1 - \tau^2)(93 - 47\tau^2 + 23\tau^4 - 5\tau^6) + \frac{501}{20}(1 - \tau).$$

---

* This section was stimulated by A. C. Hurley's remark that, according to unpublished observations in C. A. Coulson's laboratory, s-p hybridization decreases localization, when the 2s functions are exceedingly contracted.

Figure 1 gives $\Delta D/\zeta$ as a function of τ for the two cases and shows that the LMO's are digonal hybrids $h_\pm$ if and only if

$-0.601 < \tau < 0.108$, i.e. $0.249 < \zeta(1s)/\zeta(2p) < 1.24$ in the 1s-2p case,

$-0.352 < \tau < 0.367$, i.e. $0.479 < \zeta(2s)/\zeta(2p) < 2.16$ in the 2s-2p case.

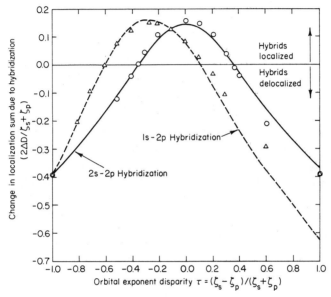

FIG. 1.   Localization sum changes (lines) and approximation by a linear function of the local overlap (points). Full line and circular points: 2s-2p hybridization. Dashed line and triangular points: 1s-2p hybridization. (Energy in atomic units).

The relation to local overlap can be formulated quantitatively by comparing the localization sum changes $(\Delta D/\zeta)$ with the overlap integrals between the s-orbitals and the absolute value of the p-orbital, i.e.,

$$S(1s, |2p|) = \int dV(1s)\,|2p|,$$

$$S(2s, |2p|) = \int dV(2s)\,|2p|.$$

One finds that, in atomic units, one has approximately

$$(\Delta D/\zeta) \approx 0.6211 S - 0.3914,$$

for the 1s case as well as for the 2s case. The close correspondence is exhibited in Fig. 1 by inserting selected values of $(0.6211\ S - 0.3914)$ as circular points for S (2s,|2p|) and as triangular points for S (1s,|2p|). In all cases, the digonal hybrids represent the localized orbitals whenever, approximately, $S \gtrsim 0.63$.

Since it is unlikely that $\zeta(2s)$ and $\zeta(2p)$ differ by as much as a factor 2, it can be expected that digonal hybrids usually represent localized orbitals in the valence shell. In contrast, there is probably no case where $\zeta(1s)$ is as small as twice $\zeta(2p)$, and hence localization never leads to 1s-2p digonal hybrids. This latter circumstance can be considered as fortunate because it presumably has the consequence that the inner shell LMO of an atom within a molecule will remain relatively unaffected by directional variations of the bonding LMO's i.e. the inner shell will be pretty much the same in different molecules, even though 2s-2p hybridization may change. This fact is indeed found to be the case for the systems investigated in this and a previous paper (2).

B. NONEQUIVALENT LOCALIZED ORBITALS IN C_2 (TABLE 5)

In the case of the $1\sigma_g^2 1\sigma_u^2 2\sigma_g^2 2\sigma_u^2 \pi_u^2 \bar{\pi}_u^2$, $^1\Sigma_g$ ground state of the C_2 molecule, it is difficult to guess what type of equivalent orbitals should exhibit maximum localization. It was therefore considered of interest to analyze the C_2 calculation of Ransil (15) from this point of view. Application of the localization technique to Ransil's calculation yields the results given in Table 5, which is arranged in the same manner as Tables 1 and 2. It is readily seen that the LMO's of C_2 are not equivalent orbitals of any type.

The localization sum D is found to be 9.5188 ± 0.0001 H for the LMO's. Except for the inner shell orbitals, it was not possible to determine the LCAO expansions of the LMO's to more than about two figures. When the starting orbitals were changed, the localization procedure resulted in somewhat different orbitals, indicating that, here, one can have variations of the mentioned magnitude in the orbitals without changing D by more than 10^{-8} H, the limit in sensitivity of the program used. For each of the sets of localized orbitals found, D was found to have the same value.

In order to establish whether any set of *equivalent* orbitals would be as localized as the LMO's, we examined D for various possible types of equivalent orbitals. In all these cases the valence orbitals alone were treated and the inner shells taken to be those given by the localization procedure for the LMO's mentioned above. The localization of the inner shells alone results in the configuration $(iC)^2 (iC')^2 (2\bar{\sigma}_g)^2 (2\bar{\sigma}_u)^2 (\pi_u)^2 (\bar{\pi}_u)^2$, where the bars on $2\bar{\sigma}_g$ and $2\bar{\sigma}_u$ indicate that these orbitals have been changed somewhat by the localization of the inner shells. The localization of the inner shells changes D from 6.0315 H, for the canonical SCF MO's, to 9.3092 H for the LMO's.

One possible set of equivalent orbitals can now be obtained by left-right combination of $(2\bar{\sigma}_g)$ and $(2\bar{\sigma}_u)$. The electronic configuration can then be written as $(iC)^2(iC')^2 \sigma_+^2 \sigma_-^2 \pi_u^2 \bar{\pi}_u^2$, where

$$\sigma_+ = (2\bar{\sigma}_g + 2\bar{\sigma}_u)/\sqrt{2}, \quad \sigma_- = (2\bar{\sigma}_g - 2\bar{\sigma}_u)/\sqrt{2}.$$

LOCALIZED MOLECULAR ORBITALS IN C₂

C₂(BMO)

	$1\sigma_g$	$2\sigma_g$	$1\sigma_u$	$2\sigma_u$	π_u	$\bar\pi_u$
$1\sigma_g$	1.97658	0.02876	1.55084	0.02795	0.00762	0.00762
$2\sigma_g$	0.02876	0.61070	0.02856	0.06295	0.09116	0.09116
$1\sigma_u$	1.55084	0.02856	1.97745	0.02818	0.00715	0.00715
$2\sigma_u$	0.02795	0.06295	0.02818	0.47459	0.04356	0.04356
π_u	0.00762	0.09116	0.00715	0.04356	0.49608	0.02068
$\bar\pi_u$	0.00762	0.09116	0.00715	0.04356	0.02068	0.49608

	iC	iC'	$v1CC'$	$v2CC'$	$v3CC'$	$v4CC'$
iC	3.61346	0.00010	0.00585	0.00429	0.00625	0.00686
iC'	0.00010	3.61346	0.00538	0.00723	0.00610	0.00453
$v1CC'$	0.00585	0.00538	0.61193	0.03893	0.05100	0.03338
$v2CC'$	0.00429	0.00723	0.03893	0.58322	0.04139	0.04671
$v3CC'$	0.00625	0.00610	0.05100	0.04139	0.50006	0.04521
$v4CC'$	0.00686	0.00453	0.03338	0.04671	0.04521	0.59671

	$1\sigma_g$	$2\sigma_g$	$1\sigma_u$	$2\sigma_u$	π_u	$\bar\pi_u$
iC	0.70105	-0.09237	-0.70148	0.08905	0.00065	-0.00011
iC'	-0.70106	0.09229	-0.70146	0.08914	0.00088	0.00041
$v1CC'$	0.08059	0.61404	-0.00753	-0.05844	0.07947	-0.77889
$v2CC'$	-0.06999	-0.52921	-0.05476	-0.42567	-0.57269	-0.45041
$v3CC'$	0.00182	0.01325	-0.10582	-0.83780	0.52004	0.12758
$v4CC'$	0.07519	0.57067	-0.04031	-0.31241	-0.62870	0.41735

	C1s	C2s	C2pz	C2px	C2py	C'1s	C'2s	C'2pz	C'2px	C'py
iC	0.99462	-0.10590	0.00419	-0.00040	-0.00007	0.00601	0.02215	-0.03699	0.00040	-0.00007
iC'	-0.00603	-0.02227	0.03699	0.00054	-0.00025	-0.99461	0.10594	-0.00422	0.00054	0.00025
$v1CC'$	0.03028	0.36315	0.10277	0.04886	-0.47891	0.01625	0.26581	0.12566	0.04886	-0.47891
$v2CC'$	0.03060	0.08351	-0.18182	-0.35212	-0.27694	-0.07145	-0.62559	-0.01505	-0.35212	-0.27694
$v3CC'$	0.09960	0.70458	-0.16167	0.31975	0.07844	-0.09848	-0.69100	0.16660	0.31975	0.07844
$v4CC'$	0.05936	0.55249	0.04495	-0.38657	0.25661	-0.01571	0.03205	0.16735	-0.38657	0.25661

Note: The symbols $v1CC'$, $v2CC'$, $v3CC'$, $v4CC'$ denote the four localized valence molecular orbitals.

The localization sum D is found to increase to 9.3397 H.

Another possible set of equivalent orbitals is obtained by trigonal hybridization between the π-MO's and a σ-MO

$$\sigma_\alpha = \cos \alpha (2\bar{\sigma}_g) + \sin \alpha (2\bar{\sigma}_u)$$

where the angle α remains to be determined. The electronic configuration can be written $(iC)^2(iC')^2 t_1^2 t_2^2 t_3^2 (\sigma'_\alpha)^2$, where

$$\sigma'_\alpha = -\sin \alpha (2\bar{\sigma}_g) + \cos \alpha (2\bar{\sigma}_u)$$

is orthogonal to σ_α and

$$t_k = (\sigma_\alpha + \sqrt{2}\,\pi_k)/\sqrt{3}$$

are polarized banana bond orbitals with

$$\pi_1 = \pi_u, \ \pi_2 = \tfrac{1}{2}(-\pi_u + \sqrt{3}\bar{\pi}_u), \ \pi_3 = \tfrac{1}{2}(-\pi_u - \sqrt{3}\bar{\pi}_u).$$

The localization sum

$$D = 3[t_1 t_1 | t_1 t_1] + [\sigma'_\alpha \sigma'_\alpha | \sigma'_\alpha \sigma'_\alpha] + 2[iCiC|iCiC]$$

becomes

$$D = A \cos 4\alpha + B \sin 4\alpha + C \cos 2\alpha + F \sin 2\alpha + G$$

with

$$A = \tfrac{1}{6}[gg - uu|gg - uu] - \tfrac{2}{3}[gu|gu]$$

$$B = \tfrac{2}{3}[gg - uu|gu]$$

$$C = \tfrac{1}{3}[gg - uu|gg + uu - 2\pi\pi] + \tfrac{4}{3}[g\pi|g\pi] - \tfrac{4}{3}[u\pi|u\pi]$$

$$F = \frac{-2}{3}[gu|gg + uu - 2\pi\pi] + \tfrac{8}{3}[g\pi|u\pi]$$

$$G = \tfrac{1}{2}[gg - uu|gg - uu] + \tfrac{2}{3}\{2[gg|uu] + [gg|\pi\pi] + [uu|\pi\pi] + [gu|gu]$$

$$+ 2[g\pi|g\pi] + 2[u\pi|u\pi] + 2[\pi\pi|\pi\pi]\} + 2[iCiC|iCiC]$$

where g, u, π denote $(2\bar{\sigma}_g)$, $(2\bar{\sigma}_u)$, π_u, respectively. By virtue of the $g - u$ symmetry, one finds $B = F = 0$, and further substitution of the numerical values

$[gg|gg] = 0.61377$	$[gg|uu] = 0.44816$	$[gu|gu] = 0.06372$
$[uu|uu] = 0.47636$	$[gg|\pi\pi] = 0.51835$	$[g\pi|g\pi] = 0.09328$
$[\pi\pi|\pi\pi] = 0.49608$	$[uu|\pi\pi] = 0.43980$	$[u\pi|u\pi] = 0.04525$
$[iCiC'|iCiC'] = 3.61346$		

yields

$$D = -0.01018 \cos 4\alpha + 0.07060 \cos 2\alpha + 9.44876.$$

The $\cos 2\alpha$ term dominates the variation with α and maximal localization occurs for $\alpha = 0$. The localized configuration is therefore $(iC)^2(iC')^2 t_1^2 t_2^2 t_3^2 (2\bar{\sigma}_u)^2$ where t_k are *unpolarized* banana bonds, the value of D being 9.5092 H. It is of interest that the *minimum* value within trigonal hybridization is 9.3680 H and, thus, still higher than that for the (σ_+, σ_-) hybridization discussed earlier. It occurs for $\alpha = \frac{1}{2}\pi$, i.e. for the configuration $(iC)^2(iC')^2(t_1')^2(t_2')^2$ $(t_3')^2(2\bar{\sigma}_g)^2$, the t_k' being π-$(2\bar{\sigma}_u)$ hybrids.

Thus, the localization of the orbitals in the $(iC)^2(iC')^2 t_1^2 t_2^2 t_3^2 (2\bar{\sigma}_u)^2$ configuration is almost as strong as that of the true LMO's (i.e. 9.5188 H), but they are definitely not identical with the LMO's. One can imagine other possible hybridizations to equivalent orbitals, such as that of the $2\bar{\sigma}_g$ orbital with only one of the π_u orbitals, but these are surely less localized. For the purposes of semiempirical or pair theories, there might be an advantage to work with a set of equivalent orbitals; where localization is important, however, one would want to choose that set of equivalent orbitals which is most localized.

C. Nonequivalent Localized Orbitals in Benzene

In the ground state of benzene, the six pi-electrons occupy the delocalized canonical MO's

$$(a) = N_a\{\chi_1 + \chi_2 + \chi_3 + \chi_4 + \chi_5 + \chi_6\},$$
$$(ex) = N_x\{\chi_1 \quad - \chi_3 - \chi_4 \quad + \chi_6\},$$
$$(ey) = N_y\{\chi_1 + 2\chi_2 + \chi_3 - \chi_4 - 2\chi_5 - \chi_6\},$$

where $\chi_1 \cdots \chi_6$ are the atomic p-orbitals and N_k normalization constants. Within the molecular symmetry group D_{6h}, the orbital (a) transforms according to the representation A_{2u}, and the orbital pair (ex), (ey) according to E_{1g}.

Hall and Lennard-Jones *(16)* pointed out that it is possible to construct three equivalent orbitals k_1, k_2, k_3 which can be formulated as follows

$$k_1 = (\tfrac{1}{3})^{1/2}(a) + (\tfrac{2}{3})^{1/2}(ex)$$
$$k_2 = C_3 k_1, \quad k_3 = C_3^{-1} k_1,$$

where the operator C_3 represents a rotation by 120°. These orbitals correspond to the classical Kekulé structures in as much as k_1 contains strong and identical contributions from the two adjacent atoms 1 and 6, and lesser contributions from the other atoms.

Later Allen and Shull *(17)* remarked that another set of equivalent orbitals, l_1, l_2, l_3, can be formulated, which we can express as

$$l_1 = (\tfrac{1}{3})^{1/2}(a) + (\tfrac{2}{3})^{1/2}(ey),$$

$$l_2 = C_3 l_1, \quad l_3 = C_3^{-1} l_1.$$

Here, the orbital l_1 has a major contribution on the one atom 2, somewhat smaller identical contributions from atoms 1 and 3, and lesser contributions from the remaining atoms. The question arises whether this set is less or more localized than that proposed by Hall.

In trying to apply the localization procedure, we noted that these two sets are actually equally localized. In the following, we shall show that, in fact, they represent only two special cases of an *infinity of sets of equally localized equivalent orbitals* (18).

The most general set of equivalent orbitals, which can be formed here, is

$$\varphi_1 = (\tfrac{1}{3})^{1/2}(a) + (\tfrac{2}{3})^{1/2}[\cos \alpha(ex) + \sin \alpha(ey)]$$

$$\varphi_2 = C_3 \varphi_1, \quad \varphi_3 = C_3^{-1} \varphi_1$$

where α is an arbitrary angle, $0 \le \alpha \le \tfrac{1}{2}\pi$. It is readily verified that these three orbitals are mutually orthogonal. They are equivalent orbitals in the group C_6 but, if $\alpha \ne 0$, $\tfrac{1}{2}\pi$, they are not equivalent orbitals in the group C_{6v}. It can now be proved that the localization sum

$$D(\varphi) = 3[\varphi_1^2 | \varphi_1^2]$$

is independent of α, which means that all possible sets of this type are, in fact, equally localized.

The proof rests on the following transformation properties of orbital products in the group D_{6h}:

$$p_0 = (a)^2 \qquad\qquad \text{transforms according to } A_{1g},$$

$$p_1 = [(ex)^2 + (ey)^2] \qquad \text{transforms according to } A_{1g},$$

$$\left.\begin{aligned} p_2 x &= (a)(ex) \\ p_2 y &= (a)(ey) \end{aligned}\right\} \quad \text{transform according to } E_{1u},$$

$$\left.\begin{aligned} p_3 x &= (ex)^2 - (ey)^2 \\ p_3 y &= 2(ex)(ey) \end{aligned}\right\} \quad \text{transform according to } E_{2g}.$$

Consequently the following identities hold between electron interaction integrals

$$\left.\begin{aligned} [p_0|p_k\xi] = [p_1|p_k\xi] = 0 \\ [p_i\xi|p_k\eta] = \delta_{ik}\delta_{\xi\eta}[p_i x|p_i x] \end{aligned}\right\} \text{ for } \left\{\begin{aligned} i &= 2, 3; \quad k = 2, 3; \\ \xi &= x, y; \quad \eta = x, y; \end{aligned}\right.$$

Using these identities and others resulting by combination, for example,

$$[ex^2|ex^2] - [ex^2|ey^2] - 2[ex\ ey|ex\ ey] = 0,$$

one obtains

$$3D = [a^2|a^2] + 4(\cos^4\alpha + \sin^4\alpha)[(ex)^2|(ex)^2] + 8\cos^2\alpha\sin^2\alpha[(ex)^2|(ey)^2]$$
$$+ 16\cos^2\alpha\sin^2\alpha[(ex)(ey)|(ex)(ey)] + 8(\cos^2\alpha + \sin^2\alpha)[a(ex)|a(ex)]$$
$$+ 4(\cos^2\alpha + \sin^2\alpha)[a^2|(ex)^2],$$

$$3D = [a^2|a^2] + 4(\cos^2\alpha + \sin^2\alpha)^2[(ex)^2|(ex)^2]$$
$$+ 8\cos^2\alpha\sin^2\alpha\{-[(ex)^2|(ex)^2] + [(ex)^2|(ey)^2] + 2[(ex)(ey)|(ex)(ey)]\}$$
$$+ 8[a(ex)|a(ex)] + 4[a^2|(ex)^2],$$

$$3D = [a^2|a^2] + 4[(ex)^2|(ex)^2] + 8[a(ex)|a(ex)] + 4[a^2|(ex)^2],$$

which is indeed independent of α.

It may be noted that the lone pairs of the F_2 molecule, mentioned in a previous paper (2), represent another example of equivalent sets of equivalent orbitals.

ACKNOWLEDGMENTS

The authors wish to express their appreciation to Dr. D. E. Ellis, Dr. A. B. F. Duncan, Dr. R. M. Pitzer, and Dr. B. J. Ransil for making available the integral values on which their calculations were based, and to Lydia S. Salmon for the hand calculations in the second part of this investigation.

REFERENCES

1. C. Edmiston and K. Ruedenberg, *Rev. Mod. Phys.* **34**, 457 (1963).

2. C. Edmiston and K. Ruedenberg, *J. Chem. Phys.* **43**, S97 (1965).

3. D. E. Ellis, private communication. A preliminary report of this calculation was given in the *Quart. Progr. Rep., Solid State Molecular Theory Group No.* 50, Massachusetts Institute of Technology, October 15, 1963. Subsequently these results had to be corrected when an error in the transformation of the one-electron integrals was discovered. We are grateful to D. E. Ellis for sending us the corrected wave functions and the integrals. This calculation differs from that of F. Ellison and H. Shull [*J. Chem. Phys.* **23**, 2348 (1955)] only, in that all three-center integrals were calculated correctly.

4. A. B. F. Duncan, *J. Chem. Phys.* **27**, 423 (1957).

5. R. M. Pitzer, private communication. The results of a similar calculation by J. J. Sinai [*J. Chem. Phys.* **39**, 1575 (1963)] are numerically incorrect.

6. R. M. Pitzer, *J. Chem. Phys.* **41**, 2216 (1964).

7. R. M. Pitzer and W. N. Lipscomb, *J. Chem. Phys.* **39**, 1995 (1963).

8. R. S. Mulliken, *J. Chem. Phys.* **23**, 1833, 1841, 2338, 2343, (1955).

9. F. Hund, *Z. Physik* **73**, 1 (1931); **73**, 565 (1962).

10. C. A. Coulson, *Trans. Faraday Soc.* **38**, 433 (1942).

11. J. E. Lennard-Jones, *Proc. Roy. Soc.* (*London*) **A198**, 1, 14 (1949).

12. G. G. Hall and J. E. Lennard-Jones, *Proc. Roy. Soc.* (*London*) **A202**, 155 (1950).

13. J. E. Lennard-Jones and J. A. Pople, *Proc. Roy. Soc.* (*London*) **A202**, 166 (1950).

14. G. G. Hall, *Rept. Progr. Phys.* **23**, 1 (1959).
15. B. J. Ransil, *Rev. Mod. Phys.* **32**, 239 (1960).
16. G. G. Hall and J. E. Lennard-Jones, *Proc. Roy. Soc.* (*London*) **A205**, 357 (1951).
17. T. L. Allen and H. Shull, *J. Chem. Phys.* **35**, 1644 (1961).
18. This observation was also made independently by D. D. Ebbing and R. C. Henderson, *J. Chem. Phys.* **42**, 2225 (1965).

Ein neuer Ansatz für die Energiehyperflächen drei- und mehrzentriger Systeme

H. PREUSS

MAX-PLANCK-INSTITUT FÜR PHYSIK UND ASTROPHYSIK
MUNICH, GERMANY

Abstract. This work presents an interpolation method for obtaining potential surfaces of multicenter systems using information on the united atoms, separated atoms, and atomic associations limits. The interpolation formula given by Eq. (13) is a rational function of the nuclear coordinates. Its main advantages are that it leads to a set of *linear* equations for the determination of the surface's parameters. The computational work involved is fairly simple. Its usefulness will depend on the future requirements of the theories of molecular spectroscopy and molecular reactions.

Es wird ein neuer Ansatz für die Energiehyperflächen von mehratomigen Systemen angegeben und diskutiert, der im Prinzip für beliebige Anzahlen von Atomen verwendet werden kann und alle über eine Energiehyperfläche bekannten Informationen zu berücksichtigen gestattet.

Das Verfahren wird an dem Systeme und den Molekülen H_2, He, H, H und H_3^+ erläutert und es wird gezeigt, daß schon mit sehr einfachen Ansätzen die Energiefunktionen von He, H, H und H_3^+ in guter Näherung erhalten werden. Mit einem verbesserten Ansatz kann die Potentialkurve für H_2 in einer bisher noch nicht vorliegenden Genauigkeit berechnet werden.

I. Einleitung

Kaum ein anderer Begriff ist in der theoretischen Molekülspektroskopie so fundamental wie der der Energiehyperfläche oder Energiekurve. Er basiert in seiner Begründung auf dem Näherungsstandpunkt, daß die Atombewegungen wesentlich langsamer verlaufen als die Bewegungen der Elektronen (Born-Oppenheimer-Näherung (*1*)). Aus diesem Grunde kann in sehr guter Näherung für jeden Elektronenzustand (k) eine Gesamtmolekülenergie $\mathscr{E}_k$ als Funktion der Kernlagen $\mathscr{R} = \{R_1, \ldots, R_F\}$ im Raum eingeführt werden. R steht hier für die Gesamtheit aller F unabhängigen Kernparameter. Dabei ist allgemein $F = 3N - 6$, wenn N die Anzahl der betrachteten Atome ist. Diese Zahl verringert sich bei eingeschränkten Bewegungen der Zentren und beträgt zum Beispiel $F = N - 1$, wenn alle Atome auf einer Geraden liegen sollen. Allgemein gibt es $\binom{N}{2}$ Kernabstände $R_{\lambda\mu}$ zwischen dem λ-ten und μ-ten Atom ($\lambda, \mu = 1, \ldots, N$). Von denen sind aber nur F unabhängig. $N - F$ Kernabstände lassen sich also durch die übrigen F ausdrücken! Man bezeichnet $\mathscr{E}_k(\mathscr{R})$ als Energiehyperfläche. Nur für $F = 1$ bzw. 2 liegt eine Kurve bzw. Fläche vor. Für $F > 2$ sprechen wir von Hyperfläche, weil sich diese Funktion in einem $F + 1$-dimensionalen Raum als solche interpretieren läßt. Die Gesamtheit aller Vektoren zu den Zentren wollen wir mit $\mathscr{R}' = \{\mathscr{R}_\lambda\}$, ($\lambda = 1, \ldots, N$) bezeichnen.

Die $\mathscr{E}_k$ ergeben sich als Energieeigenwerte der Schrödingergleichung (Wellengleichung)

$$\mathscr{H}\psi_k = \mathscr{E}'_k(\mathscr{R}')\psi_k, \tag{1}$$

wenn $\mathscr{H}$ der Hamiltonoperator des Elektronensystems bedeutet, wobei die Atomkerne als festgehalten gedacht werden (Kernkoordinaten als Parameter). In $\mathscr{E}'$ kann im Prinzip zu den $\mathscr{R}$ übergegangen werden, so daß

$$\mathscr{E}'(\mathscr{R}') \equiv \mathscr{E}(\mathscr{R}). \tag{1a}$$

Im Rahmen der oben angegebenen Näherung ergeben sich die Kernbewegungen (Rotation und Schwingungen) aus der Wellengleichung

$$\{\underline{K} + \mathscr{E}'_k(\mathscr{R}')\}\chi_{kj}(\mathscr{R}') = \bar{\mathscr{E}}_{kj}\chi_{kj}(\mathscr{R}'), \tag{2}$$

wenn $\underline{K}$ der Operator der kinetischen Energie der Kerne bedeutet. $\mathscr{E}'_k$ spielt in (2) die Rolle des Potentials, in welchem sich die N Kerne bewegen. $\bar{\mathscr{E}}_{kj}$ sind damit die Energieeigenzustände des Kerngerüstes, wobei sich der Einfluß der Elektronen auf die Bindungen zwischen den Atomen (Wechselwirkungen zwischen den Atomen) in $\mathscr{E}'_k$ zeigt. Auch die Wellenfunktionen χ_{kj} der Atomkerne können in $\mathscr{R}$ umgeschrieben werden, genauso wie $\mathscr{E}'$ in (1a). Die Wellenfunktion der Elektronen ψ_k hängt neben den Elektronenkoordinaten r auch von $\mathscr{R}$ bzw. $\mathscr{R}'$ ab, die in (1) als Parameter auftreten!

Die Born-Oppenheimer-Näherung ermöglicht an Stelle der zeitabhängigen Schrödingergleichung die beiden zeitunabhängigen Gleichungen (1) und (2) zu verwenden, wenn stationäre Zustände des Systems vorausgesetzt werden.

Es läßt sich zeigen, daß exakt gilt

$$\mathscr{E}'(\mathscr{R}') = E(\mathscr{R}) + W \tag{3}$$

wobei

$$W = \sum_{\lambda=1}^{N-1} \sum_{\mu=\lambda+1}^{N} \frac{Z_\lambda Z_\mu}{R_{\lambda\mu}} \tag{3a}$$

und Z_λ und Z_μ die jeweiligen Kernladungszahlen bedeuten. E stellt die sogenannte reine Elektronenenergie (ohne Kernabstoßungsenergie W) dar. Sie ist, im Gegensatz zu $\mathscr{E}$ (bzw. $\mathscr{E}'$) im ganzen $\mathscr{R}$-Raum ($\mathscr{R}'$-Raum) endlich [beschränkte Funktion $\mathscr{E}(\mathscr{R})$].

II. Das Problem

Um die Zustände des Kernsystems auszurechnen, müßte $\mathscr{E}'_k$ aus (1) bestimmt werden. Danach wäre dann $\mathscr{E}'_k$ in (2) einzusetzen und Gleichung (2) zu behandeln. Die Berechnung von $\mathscr{E}'_k$ aus der Wellengleichung des Elektronensystems stößt auf große Schwierigkeiten, da die Gleichung wegen der großen Anzahl von Elektronen hochdimensional ist. Man kann diese Schwierigkeit näherungsweise umgehen, wenn man für $\mathscr{E}_k$ eine Approximation $\tilde{\mathscr{E}}_k$ ansetzt

$$\tilde{\mathscr{E}} \approx \mathscr{E}, \tag{4}$$

die vorerst noch freie Parameter α_j enthält, welche durch Forderungen an $\tilde{\mathscr{E}}$ bestimmt werden können

$$\tilde{\mathscr{E}} = \tilde{\mathscr{E}}(R_1, \ldots, R_F ; \alpha_j). \tag{4a}$$

Zur Zeit sind nur sehr wenige Potentialkurven von zweiatomigen Molekülen bekannt und diese auch nur näherungsweise. Man erhält diese entweder aus spektroskopischen Daten (2) unter Verwendung der Rydberg-Klein-Rees Methode (3) oder aus *ab-initio*-Rechnungen, dann aber bisher nur in der Umgebung des Energieminimums. Neuere *ab-initio*-Verfahren (4) erlauben dagegen eine Reihe von $\mathscr{E}$-Werten mit befriedigender Genauigkeit auch bei Systemen mit mehr als zwei Atomen und außerhalb der stabilen Konstellation der Kerne zu berechnen. Da aber bisher kein analytischer Ansatz $\tilde{\mathscr{E}}$ für $N > 2$ vorlag, war es nicht möglich, Aufschlüsse über höherzentrige Energiehyperflächen zu erhalten, die nicht nur für spektroskopische Fragen, sondern besonders zur Diskussion von Reaktionsvorgängen notwendig sind.

Die bisher bekannten Ansätze $\tilde{\mathscr{E}}$, wenn $F = 1$ ($N = 2$), reichen für viele Ansprüche der Spektroskopie aus, sie nutzen aber nicht alle Kenntnisse aus, die wir in diesem Falle über $\tilde{\mathscr{E}}$ besitzen, besonders dann, wenn Rechnungen außerhalb der Gleichgewichtslage vorliegen. Aus diesem Grunde ist der

Verlauf dieser Energiekurven nicht in allen R-Bereichen zufriedenstellend. Dies bedeutet wiederum, daß bestimmte chemische und physikalische Vorgänge, die sich gerade in diesen R-Bereichen abspielen, ungenügend erfaßt werden und daß ein eventueller Aufbau von Energiehyperflächen (siehe Abschnitt III) aus niederzentrigen $\mathscr{E}$-Funktionen nicht möglich ist. Die Aufgabe besteht also darin, einen Ansatz $\tilde{\mathscr{E}}$ nach (4) zu finden, der in allen R-Bereichen eine gute Approximation ermöglicht und alle Forderungen zu erfüllen gestattet, die sich jeweils an $\tilde{\mathscr{E}}$ stellen lassen, um die freien Parameter α_j zu fixieren. Im Gegensatz zu den bisherigen Ansätzen (5) $\tilde{\mathscr{E}}$ für $N = 2$ ($F = 1$), die auf Grund ihrer analytischen Formen nicht alle Forderungen erfüllen können, muß somit ein $\tilde{\mathscr{E}}$ gefunden werden, was nicht nur alle zu stellenden Forderungen erfüllt, sondern sich auch auf die Fälle $N > 2$ erweitern läßt.

Im Falle zweier Zentren ($N = 2, F = 1$) lassen sich folgende Forderungen an $\tilde{\mathscr{E}}$ stellen, die von $\mathscr{E}$ erfüllt sind, wobei $R = R_0$ den Bindungsabstand bedeutet:

$$\left. \frac{d\tilde{\mathscr{E}}}{dR} \right|_{R_0} = 0, \tag{5a}$$

$$\left. \frac{d^j\tilde{\mathscr{E}}}{dR^j} \right|_{R_0} = k^{(j)}, \tag{5b}$$

$$\tilde{\mathscr{E}}(R_0) = B + \mathscr{E}(a\,|\,b), \tag{5c}$$

$$\tilde{E} = E(ab) + \sum_{j=1}^{\infty} E_j R^j \qquad (R \ll 1), \tag{5d}$$

$$\tilde{\mathscr{E}} = \mathscr{E}(a\,|\,b) + \sum_{j=1}^{\infty} \frac{e_j}{R^j} \qquad (R \gg 1). \tag{5e}$$

Daneben tritt noch die Forderung, daß $\tilde{\mathscr{E}}$ die Form nach (3), (3a) haben soll. $k^{(j)}$ bedeutet die "Kraftkonstante" ("höhere Kraftkonstanten" für $j > 2$). Im einzelnen bedeuten noch

$$\lim_{R \to 0} E(R) = E(ab) \tag{6a}$$

und

$$\lim_{R \to \infty} \mathscr{E}(R) = \mathscr{E}(a\,|\,b) \equiv E(a\,|\,b). \tag{6b}$$

Die beiden Energien $E(a\,|\,b)$ and $E(ab)$ sind diejenigen der getrennten und vereinigten Atome (Modell des "separated" und "united atoms"). B ist die Bindungsenergie. Die Koeffizienten E_j und e_j können näherungsweise aus Störungsrechnungen bestimmt werden (6,7).

Es werden also für $N = 2$ die Größen $k^{(j)}$, B, R_0, $E(ab)$, E_1, E_2, ... und $E(a\,|\,b)$, e_1, e_2, ... zur Bestimmung der α_j in (4a) herangezogen.

Für $N > 2$ ($F > 1$) sind die entsprechenden Forderungen an $\tilde{\mathscr{E}}$, die von $\mathscr{E}$ schon erfüllt werden, komplexer. Wir erhalten zuerst einmal

$$\frac{\partial \tilde{\mathscr{E}}}{\partial R_i}\bigg|_{\mathscr{R}^{(0)}} = 0 \tag{7a}$$

$$\frac{\partial^j \tilde{\mathscr{E}}}{\partial R_i^j}\bigg|_{\mathscr{R}^{(0)}} = k_i^{(j)} \tag{7b}$$

und

$$\tilde{\mathscr{E}}(\mathscr{R}^{(0)}) = B + \mathscr{E}(a\,|\,b\,|\,c\,|\,\cdots\,|\,N), \tag{7c}$$

wobei $\mathscr{R}^{(0)}$ für die Gesamtheit aller R_j ($j = 1, \ldots, F$) steht, die in der stabilen Konstellation der Kerne eingenommen werden

$$\mathscr{R}^{(0)} = \{R_1^{(0)}, \ldots, R_F^{(0)}\}. \tag{8}$$

Das System nimmt dann die tiefste Energie ein, die um B tiefer liegt als die der getrennten Atome, die mit $\mathscr{E}(a\,|\,b\,|\,c\,|\,\cdots\,|\,N)$ bezeichnet wurde. Die Kraftkonstanten sind im Hinblick auf die Koordinate R_i definiert. In beiden Gleichungen (7a) und (7b) gilt $i = 1, 2, \ldots, F$, so daß schon $F(1 + G) + 1$ Forderungen an $\tilde{\mathscr{E}}$ vorliegen, wenn j in (7b) bis G läuft.

Bezüglich der Erweiterungen der Gleichungen (5d), (5e) bzw. (6a) und (6b) hilft die Vorstellung der Atomassoziationen weiter (8). Danach kann für (6a) und (6b) geschrieben werden

$$\lim_{[K]} E(\mathscr{R}) = E(K), \tag{9}$$

wenn $E(K)$ die Elektronenenergie der Assoziation $[K]$ bedeutet. Die Anzahl der Atomassoziationen steigt rasch an; so existieren für $N = 2$ noch zwei [nach (6a) (6b)], für $N = 3$ sind es fünf:

$$E(a\,|\,b\,|\,c) \qquad E(c\,|\,ab)$$

$$E(a\,|\,bc) \qquad E(abc). \tag{10}$$

$$E(b\,|\,ac)$$

Liegen vier Atome vor, so können schon 15 Assoziationen aufgeschrieben werden

$E(a\,|\,b\,|\,c\,|\,d)$	$E(b\,|\,ac\,|\,d)$	$E(d\,|\,abc)$
$E(a\,|\,cd\,|\,b)$	$E(a\,|\,bc\,|\,d)$	$E(c\,|\,abd)$
$E(a\,|\,bd\,|\,c)$	$E(ad\,|\,bc)$	$E(b\,|\,acd)$
$E(b\,|\,ad\,|\,c)$	$E(ac\,|\,bd)$	$E(a\,|\,bcd)$
$E(c\,|\,ba\,|\,d)$	$E(ab\,|\,cd)$	$E(abcd)$.

(11)

Darin werden die Atome mit a, b, c und d bezeichnet und $E(a\,|\,bc\,|\,d)$ bedeutet die Elektronenenergie eines Systems, in welchem sich die Atome b und c zu einem neuen Atom bc (Teilvereinigung) mit der Kernladung $Z_b + Z_c = Z_{bc}$ vereinigt haben, wobei die drei Atome a, bc und d unendlich weit voneinander entfernt sind. Die Gleichung (9) stellt den Übergang zu einer Assoziationsenergie dar.

Diese Überlegungen führen zu dem oben angedeuteten "Baukastenprinzip"! Wird nun zu den sogenannten unvollständigen Atomassoziationen [K'] übergegangen

$$\lim_{[K']} E(\mathscr{R}) = E(K'),\tag{12}$$

indem nur die zu jedem Übergang $\lim_{[K']}$ [vergl. (9)] gehörenden Übergänge $R_{\lambda\mu} \to 0$ durchgeführt werden, aber das so erhaltene Atomsystem seine neuen und alten (ursprünglichen) Atome in endlichen Abständen läßt, so folgen daraus aus dem anfänglichen $\tilde{\mathscr{E}}$ neue Energiehyperflächen, die von geringerer Zentrigkeit sind. Man kann also Rechnungen an kleineren Systemen verwenden, um größere damit in der $\mathscr{E}$-Darstellung zu erfassen!

Was die Gleichungen (5d) und (5e) anbetrifft, so sind ihre Erweiterungen auf $N > 2$ darin zu sehen, daß gegebenenfalls beim Übergang zu einer Assoziation, wenn einige $R_{\lambda\mu}$ sehr klein und andere sehr groß werden, entsprechende Darstellungen wie in (5d) und (5e) für die jeweils sehr nahen oder entfernten Atome aufgeschrieben werden. Auch im Rahmen der unvollständigen Assoziationen lassen sich solche Beziehungen aufstellen.

Das Problem besteht nun darin, einen Ansatz von dieser Flexibilität zu finden!

III. Die Lösung

Ein Ansatz $\tilde{\mathscr{E}}$ nach (4a), der *alle* Forderungen erfüllen kann, ist der folgende (9):

$$\tilde{E} = \frac{\displaystyle\sum_{f_1,f_2,\dots f_F=0}^{M_1,M_2,\dots,M_F} \alpha_{f_1,f_2,\dots,f_F} R_1^{f_1} R_2^{f_2} \cdots R_F^{f_F}}{\displaystyle\sum_{f_1,f_2,\dots f_F=0}^{M_1,M_2,\dots,M_F} \alpha'_{f_1,f_2,\dots,f_F} R_1^{f_1} R_2^{f_2} \cdots R_F^{f_F}}\tag{13}$$

wobei $\tilde{\mathscr{E}}$ nach (3) und (3a) gegeben ist

$$\tilde{\mathscr{E}} = \tilde{E} + W.\tag{13a}$$

Die Summierungsgrenzen $M_1, M_2, \dots, M_F$ sind, wie die α und α' noch frei und können jeweils vorgegeben werden, im Hinblick darauf wie genau die Approximation bei ausreichend vorhandenen Forderungen sein soll und wie groß der Rechenaufwand zulässig und berechtigt ist.

Bemerkenswert an dem Ansatz (13), (13a) ist die Tatsache, was hier nicht näher ausgeführt werden soll, daß *alle hier diskutierten Forderungen zu linearen Gleichungen in* α *und* α' *führen!* Für $F = 1$ ($N = 2$) geht (13) über in (*10*)

$$\tilde{E} = \frac{\sum\limits_{j=0}^{M} \alpha_j R^j}{\sum\limits_{j=0}^{M} \alpha'_j R^j},\qquad (14a)$$

und W ist dann gegeben durch

$$W = \frac{Z_a Z_b}{R}.\qquad (14b)$$

Liegen drei Zentren vor, so hat der Ansatz die folgende Form ($F = 3$):

$$\tilde{E} = \frac{\sum\limits_{k=0}^{M_1}\sum\limits_{l=0}^{M_2}\sum\limits_{m=0}^{M_3} \alpha_{klm} R_1^k R_2^l R_3^m}{\sum\limits_{k=0}^{M_1}\sum\limits_{l=0}^{M_2}\sum\limits_{m=0}^{M_3} \alpha'_{klm} R_1^k R_2^l R_3^m}\qquad (15a)$$

wobei

$$W = \frac{Z_a Z_b}{R_1} + \frac{Z_a Z_c}{R_2} + \frac{Z_b Z_c}{R_3}.\qquad (15b)$$

Dabei haben wir angenommen, daß die Kernabstände wie folgt zwischen den drei Atomen a, b und c definiert sind

ABB. 1

Die Kenntnis dieser Fläche erlaubt die Reaktion

$$a + bc \rightleftharpoons ab + c\qquad (16)$$

zu diskutieren. Im Rahmen der unvollständigen Assoziationen sind bei der Berechnung von (15a), (15b) die Energiekurven von $ab\text{-}c$, $ac\text{-}b$ und $bc\text{-}a$ erforderlich. Geht ein Atom nach unendlich, so bleiben noch die Energiekurven von $a\text{-}c$, $a\text{-}b$ und $b\text{-}c$ übrig.

IV. Beispiele

A. DAS H_2-MOLEKÜL (10)

Mit $M = 6$ in (14a) wurden 13 Forderungen erfüllt. Dazu waren die Größen (in at.E.)

$$
\begin{array}{llll}
E(ab) = -2,9037 & k = 0,277 & e_2 = 0 & e_6 = -11,0 \\
E_1 = 0 & R_0 = 1,40 & e_3 = 0 \\
E_2 = 3,792 & B = -0,1744 & e_4 = 0 \\
E(a|b) = -1,0000 & e_1 = 0 & e_5 = 0
\end{array}
\tag{17}
$$

erforderlich, die hier in atomaren Einheiten angegeben werden. Für e_6 wurde anstelle des richtigen Wertes $-6,4999$, repräsentativ für die folgenden e_j-Werte, die negativ (oder Null) sind der Wert nach (17) verwendet. Man erhielt dann aus den linearen Gleichungen für α_j und α_j' die Werte

$$
\begin{array}{ll}
\alpha_0 = -2,9037 & \alpha_0' = +1,000 \\
\alpha_1 = -1,804 & \alpha_1' = +0,622 \\
\alpha_2 = +0,355 & \alpha_2' = +1,183 \\
\alpha_3 = -0,043 & \alpha_3' = -1,539 \\
\alpha_4 = -0,901 & \alpha_4' = +1,582 \\
\alpha_5 = +0,566 & \alpha_5' = -0,681 \\
\alpha_6 = -0,117 & \alpha_6' = +0,117,
\end{array}
\tag{18}
$$

mit denen eine ausgezeichnete Übereinstimmung mit der wirklichen Energiekurve erzielt wurde, wie ein Vergleich mit sehr genauen ab-initio-Rechnungen (11) zeigt (Tab. 1).

TAB. 1

R	$\tilde{\mathscr{E}}$	$\mathscr{E}$
0,5	−0,520	—
1,0	−1,124	−1,124
1,5	−1,173	−1,173
2,0	−1,138	−1,138
2,5	−1,092	−1,094
3,0	−1,049	−1,051
4,0	−1,010	−1,013

B. DAS SYSTEM He, H, H

Hier soll vorerst nur eine sehr grobe Näherung für $\mathscr{E}$ gegeben werden. Es soll vielmehr der Gang der Berechnung gezeigt werden. Aus diesem Grunde setzen wir in (13a) $M_1 = M_2 = M_3 = 1$ und (15b) hat hier die Form

$$W = \frac{2}{R_1} + \frac{2}{R_2} + \frac{1}{R_3} \tag{19}$$

wenn

ABB. 2

Aus Symmetriegründen muß in diesem Falle die Energie invariant gegenüber der Vertauschung der zwei H-Atome sein, wir haben also

$$\alpha_{klm} \equiv \alpha_{lkm}; \qquad \alpha'_{klm} \equiv \alpha'_{klm} \tag{20}$$

und $\tilde{E}$ nimmt die Form an

$$\tilde{E} = \frac{\alpha_{000} + \alpha_{100}(R_1 + R_2) + \alpha_{001}R_3 + \alpha_{110}R_1R_2 + \alpha_{101}R_3(R_1 + R_2) + \alpha_{111}R_1R_2R_3}{1 + \alpha'_{100}(R_1 + R_2) + \alpha'_{001}R_3 + \alpha'_{110}R_1R_2 + \alpha'_{101}R_3(R_1 + R_2) = \alpha'_{111}R_1R_2R_3} \tag{21}$$

weil

$$\alpha_{100} \equiv \alpha_{010}, \qquad \alpha_{101} \equiv \alpha_{011}; \qquad \alpha'_{100} \equiv \alpha'_{010}, \qquad \alpha'_{101} \equiv \alpha_{011}. \tag{21a}$$

Geht das He-Atom gegen unendlich ($R_1, R_2 \to \infty$), so geht (21) mit (19) über in

$$\mathscr{E} = \frac{\alpha_{100} + \alpha_{111}R_3}{\alpha'_{110} + \alpha'_{111}R_3} + \frac{1}{R_3}; \qquad H_2 \cdots He \tag{22}$$

andererseits resultiert .

$$\mathscr{E} = \frac{\alpha_{101} + \alpha_{111}R_2}{\alpha'_{101} + \alpha'_{111}R_2} + \frac{2}{R_2}; \qquad H \cdots He \cdots H \tag{23}$$

wenn ein H-Atom entfernt wird ($R_1, R_3 \to \infty$). Die Entfernung des anderen führt, wegen (21a) zum gleichen Ergebnis.

Die Vereinigung von He und H liefert in (21)

$$\tilde{E} = \frac{\alpha_{000} + \alpha_{100}R + \alpha_{101}R^2}{1 + \alpha'_{100}R + \alpha'_{101}R^2}, \tag{24}$$

weil $R_1 \to 0$ und $R_2 = R_3 = R$. In (24) liegt dann, wenn das entsprechende W addiert wird,

$$\tilde{\mathscr{E}} = \frac{\alpha_{000} + \alpha_{100}R + \alpha_{101}R^2}{1 + \alpha'_{100}R + \alpha'_{101}R^2} + \frac{3}{R} \tag{24a}$$

die Approximation für die Energiekurve des LiH-Moleküls vor.

Entsprechend erhält man die Näherung für He $\cdots$ He, wenn $R_3 \to 0$ und $R_1 = R_2 = R$ gezeigt wird:

$$\tilde{\mathscr{E}} = \frac{\alpha_{000} + 2\alpha_{100}R + \alpha_{110}R^2}{1 + 2\alpha'_{100}R + \alpha'_{110}R^2} + \frac{4}{R}. \tag{25}$$

Aus den Gleichungen (22) bis (25) lassen sich dann die α_{klm} und α'_{klm} bestimmen. Man erhält schließlich

$$\tilde{E} = \frac{\begin{aligned}-14{,}670 - 7{,}5(R_1 + R_2) - 10{,}754R_3 - 5{,}807R_1R_2 \\ - 5{,}904R_3(R_1 + R_2) - 3{,}123R_1R_2R_3\end{aligned}}{1 + R_1 + R_2 + 1{,}507R_3 + R_1R_2 + R_3(R_1 + R_2) + 0{,}8R_1R_2R_3}, \tag{26}$$

was sicher, mit (19), eine sehr grobe Näherung ist. Verbesserungen werden dann durch Erhöhung der M_j-Werte erreicht und durch Berücksichtigung weiterer Informationen, besonders durch bessere Näherungen der zweizentrigen Systeme. Leider liegt zur Zeit die He-H-Kurve noch nicht ausreichend genau vor.

Werden die drei Atome auf eine Gerade gelegt, wobei das He-Atom außen liegt, so ergibt sich qualitativ folgende Energiefläche ($R_2 = R_1 + R_3$)

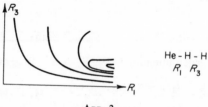

ABB. 3

Bei der linearen Anordnung mit mittlerem He-Atom resultiert (ebenfalls qualitativ), (wobei $R_3 = R_1 + R_2$):

ABB. 4

Man wird in Anbetracht der groben Näherung das schwache Minimum nicht allzu ernst nehmen dürfen.

C. Das H_3^+-Molekül

Hier ist

$$W = \frac{1}{R_1} + \frac{1}{R_2} + \frac{1}{R_3} \tag{27}$$

und der Ansatz für $\tilde{E}$ wurde ebenfalls wieder mit $M_1 = M_2 = M_3 = 1$ vorgenommen. Die Bedingungen an α und α' lauten hier

$$\begin{aligned}
\alpha_{klm} &\equiv \alpha_{lkm} \equiv \alpha_{kml} \equiv \alpha_{mlk} \\
\alpha'_{klm} &\equiv \alpha'_{lkm} \equiv \alpha'_{kml} \equiv \alpha'_{mlk}
\end{aligned} \tag{28}$$

so daß sich der Ansatz für H_3^+ in der folgenden Form ergibt

$$\tilde{E} = \frac{\alpha_{000} + \alpha_{100}(R_1 + R_2 + R_3) + \alpha_{110}(R_1 R_2 + R_1 R_3 + R_2 R_3) + \alpha_{111} R_1 R_2 R_3}{1 + \alpha'_{100}(R_1 + R_2 + R_3) + \alpha'_{110}(R_1 R_2 + R_1 R_3 + R_2 R_3) + \alpha'_m R_1 R_2 R_3} \tag{29}$$

weil

$$\begin{aligned}
\alpha_{100} &\equiv \alpha_{010} \equiv \alpha_{001}; & \alpha_{110} &\equiv \alpha_{101} \equiv \alpha_{011} \\
\alpha'_{100} &\equiv \alpha'_{010} \equiv \alpha'_{001}; & \alpha'_{110} &\equiv \alpha'_{101} \equiv \alpha'_{011}
\end{aligned} \tag{29a}$$

Die Energiefläche des H_3^+ ist seit einiger Zeit an vielen Stellen bekannt. Besonders das Minimum der Gesamtenergie bei linearer und dreieckiger Konstellation der drei Protonen. Die geringe Anzahl der freien Parameter erlaubt nicht, alle bekannten Informationen zu verwenden. Neben einem ähnlichen Vorgehen wie in (22) bis (25) wurde noch die Bindungsenergie $\hat{B}$ der dreieckigen Raumlage berücksichtigt, sowie der Gleichgewichtsabstand $\overset{\wedge}{R_0}$ dieses gleichseitigen Dreiecks. Im linearen Fall wurde nur die Bindungsenergie $\bar{B}$ im Gleichgewicht gefordert.

Das Endresultat für H_3^+ lautet:

$$\tilde{E} = \frac{-22,648 - 3,619(R_1 + R_2 + R_3) - 5,528(R_1 R_2 + R_1 R_3 + R_2 R_3) - 2,925 R_1 R_2 R_3}{1 + 1,817(R_1 + R_2 + R_3) + R_1 R_2 + R_1 R_3 + R_2 R_3 + 2,925 R_1 R_2 R_3}. \tag{30}$$

Der Vergleich mit den bisher berechneten $\mathscr{E}$-Werten nach Variationsverfahren *(12)* $\tilde{\mathscr{E}}$, wobei in einigen Fällen aus den Rechnungen durch Interpolation die entsprechenden $\tilde{\mathscr{E}}$-Werte erhalten wurden, und den Werten, die sich nach (30)

und (27) ergeben, ist im Falle einer gleichseitigen Dreieckskonstellation
(Abstand $\overset{\Delta}{R}$) in der folgenden Tabelle angegeben worden (Tab. 2).

TAB. 2

$\overset{\Delta}{R}$	$\tilde{\mathscr{E}}$	$\tilde{\tilde{\mathscr{E}}}$
1,0	−1,284	−1,17
1,5	−1,338	−1,33
2,0	−1,335	−1,33
3,0	−1,298	−1,23
4,0	−1,261	−1,13

Liegen die drei Atome auf einer Geraden, wobei das mittlere Atom den Abstand der beiden anderen halbiert, so ergibt sich folgender Vergleich (Tab. 3):

TAB. 3

$\overline{R}$	$\tilde{\mathscr{E}}$	$\tilde{\tilde{\mathscr{E}}}$
1,0	−1,194	−1.17
1,5	−1,278	−1,28
2,0	−1,288	−1,26
3,0	−1,261	−1,18
4,0	−1,227	−1,10

Der Abstand benachbarter H-Atome ist mit $\overline{R}$ bezeichnet. Die Näherung ist in Anbetracht ihrer Einfachheit und der Tatsache, daß nicht alle Informationen verwendet wurden, befriedigend. Die Abweichungen betragen im Mittel nur wenige Prozent. Eine Verbesserung ist wiederum durch Erhöhung von M_j und durch Verwendung weiterer Informationen, sowie durch bessere Näherungen in den geringerzentrigen Systemen zu erreichen.

Frau I. Funke danke ich herzlich für die hier durchgeführten Rechnungen und für die Hilfe bei der Herstellung der Programme.
Dem Verband der Chemischen Industrie sei für die Verfügungstellung von Forschungsmitteln gedankt.

BIBLIOGRAPHIE

1. M. Born und R. Oppenheimer *Ann. Physik* **84**, 457 (1927).
2. J. L. Dunham, *Phys. Rev.* **41**, 713 (1932).

3. Vergl. z.B. G. Herzberg, "Molecular Spectra and Molecular Structure," S.102 u.f. Van Nostrand, Princeton, New Jersey, 1963.

4. H. Preuß, *Mol. Phys.* **8**, 157 (1964); *Z. Naturforsch,* **19a**, 1335 (1964); **20a**, (17) 1965; **30a,** 21 (1965).

5. Y. P. Varshni und R. C. Shukla, *Rev. Mod. Phys.* **35**, 130 (1963).

6. W. A. Bingel, *J. Chem. Phys.* **30**, 1250, 1254 (1959); *Z. Naturforsch.* **16a**, 688 (1961).

7. z.B. C. A. Coulson, *Proc. Roy. Soc.* **61**, 20 (1943); A. Margenau, *Phys. Rev.* **38**, 747 (1931); L. Pauling und J. Y. Beach, *Phys. Rev.* **47**, 686 (1935). Zusammenfassung: L. Pauling and E. B. Wilson, "Introduction to Quantum Mechanics," S.383f. McGraw-Hill, New York, 1955.

8. H. Preuss, *Z. Naturforsch.* **12a**, 599 (1957); **13a**, 364 (1958); *Naturwissenschaften* **47**, 241 (1960); *Z. Naturforsch.* **18a**, 489 (1963); *Rev. Mod. Phys.* **35**, 646 (1963); *Theoret. Chim. Acta* **1**, 42 (1962); **2**, 344 (1964); **2**, 370 (1964).

9. H. Preuß, *Theoret. Chim. Acta* **2**, 370 (1964).

10. H. Preuß, *Theoret. Chim. Acta* **2**, 102 (1964).

11. W. Kolos und C. C. J. Roothaan, *Rev. Mod. Phys.* **32**, 219 (1960).

12. H. Conroy, *J. Chem. Phys.* **40**, 603 (1964).

Molecular Diagrams and Photochemistry

R. DAUDEL

SORBONNE AND CENTRE DE MÉCANIQUE ONDULATOIRE APPLIQUÉE, PARIS, FRANCE

I. Introduction

It is well known [see, for example, Daudel (1966)] that following the transition-state theory [see, for example, Glasstone *et al.* (1941)] the rate constant k of a chemical reaction,

$$A + B + \cdots \rightleftarrows M^{\ddagger} \rightarrow C + D + \cdots,$$

taking place in a certain solvent, is given by the equation:

$$k = \eta(1+t)\frac{\chi T}{h}\frac{f_{M\ddagger}}{f_A f_B \cdots} \exp\left[-\frac{\Delta\mathscr{E}_v^{\ddagger} + \Delta\mathscr{E}_l^{\ddagger} + \Delta\mathscr{E}_d^{\ddagger} + \Delta\mathscr{E}_{nb}^{\ddagger} + \Delta\mathscr{E}_s^{\ddagger}(T)}{\chi T} \right]. \tag{1}$$

In this equation χ is the Boltzmann constant; η, the transmission coefficient; t, the tunnel-effect factor; f_A, f_B, $f_{M\ddagger}$ are the various partition functions and $\Delta\mathscr{E}_v^{\ddagger}$, $\Delta\mathscr{E}_l^{\ddagger}$, $\Delta\mathscr{E}_d^{\ddagger}$, $\Delta\mathscr{E}_{nb}^{\ddagger}$, $\Delta\mathscr{E}_s^{\ddagger}(T)$ denote respectively the contributions to the *potential barrier* of the vibrational energy, the localized bonds, the delocalized bonds, the interaction between nonbonded atoms, and the solvation energy.

The effective application of this theory for conjugated organic molecules began in 1942 when Wheland proposed a convenient way to calculate $\Delta\mathscr{E}_d^{\ddagger}$ (Wheland, 1942) which is very often the most important term of Eq. (1). This term $\Delta\mathscr{E}_d^{\ddagger}$ is often called *localization energy* in the case of substitution reactions and *para or ortholocalization* energy in the case of addition reactions.

Localization energies are examples of *dynamic indexes* and their use based on Eq. (1) represents the *dynamic method* of studying the chemical reactivity. There is another approach to the same problem which is based on the consideration of various properties associated with the reagents as: (a) the *bond order* introduced by Pauling in the valence-bond method (Pauling, 1932) and by Coulson (1939) in the molecular-orbital theory; (b) and the *free valence* number introduced by Daudel and Pullman (1945a)* in the valence bond theory following an idea of Swartholm (1941) and by Coulson in the molecular-orbital theory (Coulson, 1946).

Bond orders, free valence numbers, atomic charges, etc., are often called *static indexes* as they do not depend on the transition state. Their use for the interpretation of chemical reactions which is mainly based on chemical intuition (see for example Daudel and Pullman, 1945b) or perturbation theory (Coulson and Longuet-Higgins, 1947) corresponds to the *static method* which is also called the molecular diagram method as Daudel and Pullman (1946) proposed the name "molecular diagram" to design a graph representing the distribution of the static indexes in a given molecule.

In the author's opinion the theoretical background of the static method is less satisfactory than the basis of the dynamic method, and the first convenient explanation of the success of the static method was given when it was possible to establish *relationships between static and dynamic indexes, at least for the ground states of organic molecules.*

Daudel *et al.* (1950) observed such a relation between the free valence numbers and the localization energies in the case of alternant hydrocarbons by using the valence-bond method. This relation has been extended by Roux (1950) in the framework of the molecular-orbital method. This last work has been confirmed by Burkitt *et al.* (1951).

But when both the static and the dynamic methods are used to study the same reaction between nonexcited molecules *the second one appears to be usually better* from the practical point of view (Sung *et al.*, 1960) as it is from the theoretical one.

II. Examples of Application of the Molecular Diagram Method to Photochemistry

A. PHOTOCYCLIZATION OF BUTADIENE

It seems that the first proposal to use the static indexes in studying a photochemical problem is due to Pullman and Daudel (1946). They calculated the bond orders and the free valence numbers for the ground state and the first excited state of butadiene using the valence bond method in which,

* See also Daudel *et al.* (1946).

as is well known, the wave function is expanded on *Slater determinants*. The molecular diagrams of Fig. 1 symbolize their results.

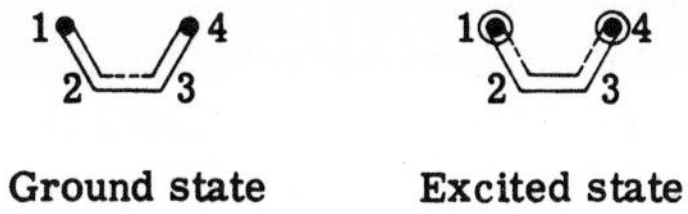

FIG. 1.

Ground state   Excited state

In the ground state the two bonds 1—2 and 3—4 have the highest bond orders. The free valence numbers in 1 and 4 are yet important but they become very large in the first excited state in which the central bond 2—3 becomes similar to a double bond, the bond orders in 1—2 and 3—4 becoming on the contrary very small.

We can describe these results in other words. In the valence-bond method the wave function describing a state of butadiene is written as

$$\Psi = a\Psi_I + b\Psi_{II}$$

if Ψ_I represents the Kekule formula (I) and Ψ_{II} the Dewar formula (II).

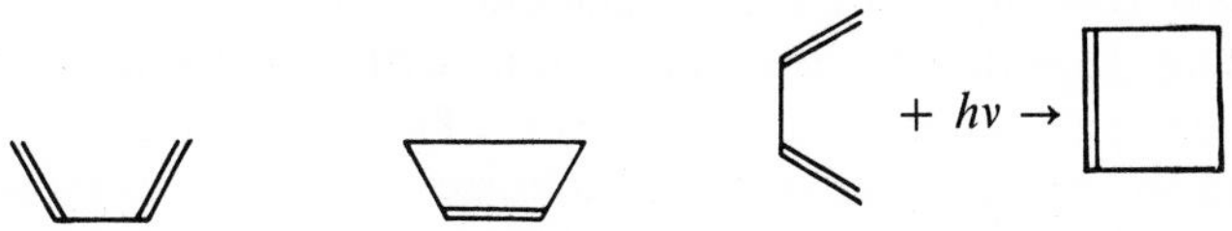

(I)   (II)   (III)

In the ground state a is large and b small. The ground state is represented conveniently by the Kekule formula. In the excited state a is small and b large. The excited state is conveniently represented by the Dewar formula. It could be anticipated that under the effect of light the butadiene could be transformed into cyclobutene. In 1946, there was no experimental evidence for such a phenomenon. But recently Srinivasan (1963) has found that when butadiene is irradiated in dilute ether solution, cyclobutene (III) is formed.

B. PHOTOHYDROLYZE OF NITROPHENYL ETHERS

The distribution of the electronic charges for various electronic states of nitrobenzene was calculated by Fernandez-Alonso (1951) during his stay in our laboratory.

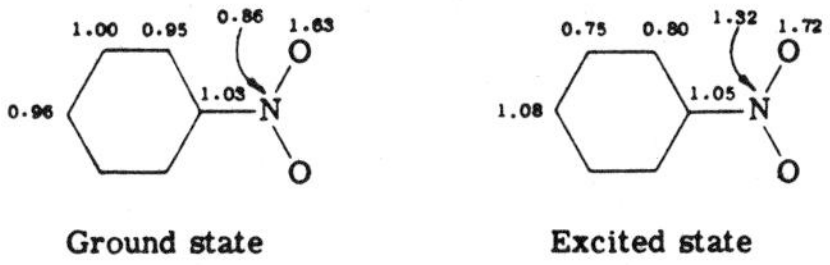

FIG. 2.

Ground state   Excited state

Figure 2 makes it possible to compare these distributions for the ground state and for one of the first excited states which, as stated by the author, could be reached under usual photochemical conditions. A striking difference appears between the two states. On the ground state the nitro group withdraws electrons from the ortho and para positions and does not alter the electronic charge of the meta position.

In the excited state, on the contrary, the nitro group withdraws electrons mainly from the meta position, the para position being not significantly perturbated.

Five years later, Havinga et al. (1956) studied the photochemical hydrolysis of the isomeric nitrophenyl dihydrogen phosphate and also the bisulfate esters. They observed that the process is most efficient for the meta isomers as if on the excited state of these molecules the nitro group were able to withdraw electrons from the phenolic-phosphate oxygen atom, thus facilitating heterolytic fission.

More recently Zimmerman (1963) studied the photochemical behavior of the trityl ethers of m-nitrophenol and p-nitrophenol in aqueous dioxane. They observed that in the absence of light, in the dark at 25°, the meta compound is stable, the para compound is slowly hydrolyzed. Under the effect of light, on the contrary, the quantum efficiency is much greater for the meta compound (0.062) than for the para derivative (0.006). Again an interpretation is given if we admit, as suggested by the Fernandez-Alonso calculation, that on some excited states of these molecules the nitro group withdraws electrons from the meta position.

Zimmerman and Somasekhara (1963) have calculated the distribution of the electronic charges for the ground states and the first excited states of the considered trityl ethers.

Table 1 contains the electronic charges obtained for the oxygen of the $OC\emptyset_3$ group.

TABLE 1

	Ground state	Excited state
Meta derivative	1.764	1.279
Para derivative	1.703	1.307

It is clear that, as for the reactivity, the order of the electronic charges on the ground state is the reverse of the corresponding order for the ground state.

C. Phototransformation of a Base in an Acid

Coulson and Jacobs (1949) had studied, theoretically, charge migration in aniline under the effect of irradiation. They observed that the electronic charge of nitrogen is smaller on the first singlet excited state than on the ground state, that is to say, it should be less basic. Forster (1949a) has effectively observed that if a base, such as 3-aminopyrene (which must have a similar behavior), is irradiated by normal light, the excited molecules have acidic properties. More precisely, Forster studied absorption and fluorescence spectra as a function of the pH of the solution containing the amino compound. Obviously, the absorption spectrum gives information about the ground state of the molecule. The fluorescence spectrum is related with the electronic-excited states. Up to pH 2 the absorption spectra are essentially those of the $ArNH_3^+$ ions, whereas the fluorescence spectra correspond to $ArNH_2$. This shows that the molecules in their excited states have less tendency to add a proton than the ground-state molecules. Furthermore, near pH 12 some new bands appear in the fluorescence spectra which can be assigned to the $ArNH^-$ ions. These ions are probably the result of a reaction such as the following:

$$ArNH_2 \rightleftharpoons ArNH^- + H^+,$$

where the amino compound acts as an acid. No such bands appear in the absorption spectra.

To interpret this result, Sandorfy (1951) has calculated the distribution of the electronic charges in an aromatic amine by the molecular-orbital method taking account of both the π and the σ orbitals. He found that the nitrogen which is negative in the ground state becomes positive in the first electronic excited state which will explain why the molecule becomes an acid.

Other cases have been described which follow the same procedure. For example, Jaffe *et al.* (1964) have observed that the pK of some excited states of azobenzene follows the charge of the nitrogen atom and that in the case of azoxybenzene there is a satisfactory relation between the charge of the oxygen atom and the pK.

D. OTHER EXAMPLES

Crawford and Coulson (1948) studied the photodimerization of acenaphtylene following a similar method. Later it was observed (Sandorfy, 1950; Buu-Hoï *et al.*, 1951) that all the free valence numbers of molecules like anthracene, naphtacene on their first electronic excited states are greater than those of the corresponding ground states: the greatest free valences remaining those of the meso carbon atoms. This increase of the free valence numbers could play a role during the photodimerization and during the photooxadition of the considered molecule. On the contrary, the bond order of the central bond of stilbene on its first excited state is smaller than those of the ground state (Buu-Hoï *et al.*, 1951). This phenomenon could be an explanation of the trans → cis photoisomerization of stilbene. In following the same procedure Masse (1954) and Bloch-Chaudé and Masse (1955) try to explain the photochromic properties of some derivatives of pyranospirane. We must also point out the work of Mantione and Pullman (1964) on the photodimerization of thymine.

Finally, a new kind of static index has been recently introduced. Woodward and Hoffmann (1965) have studied some reactions resulting in the formation of a single bond between the terminals of a linear system containing π-electrons. The authors suggested that the steric course of the reaction is determined by the symmetry of the highest occupied molecular orbital of the open-chain partner and should therefore differ for different electronic states. Longuet-Higgins and Abrahamson (1965) have discussed along these lines the conversion of cyclobutene to butadiene.

III. Discussion

Now a question arises: Is the explanation of the brilliant success of the molecular diagram method in interpreting or even predicting photochemical reactivity the same as for molecules in their ground state?

To answer this question we must consider separately the case of the pK because Forster (1949b) has shown that the new acid-base equilibrium in the excited state is often established during the lifetime of that state.

Therefore we are often in presence of a real equilibrium, and the success of the molecular diagram method lies probably in the existence of a relation between the charges and the term $\Delta \mathscr{E}_d$ representing the difference between the energy of the delocalized bond of the ion and that of the initial molecule. This point needs further investigation. It is, however, interesting to recall that the rate of proton transfer from a solvent such as water to an acid is nearly constant (Eigen *et al.*, 1964). The pK gives, in a sense, a measure of the rate of proton transfer from the acid to the solvent.

In conclusion, the case of the pK seems to be rather clear, and Table 2 shows the variation of some pK with the electronic state of the molecule (Jackson and Porter, 1961).

TABLE 2

	pK (ground state)	pK (first singlet excited state)	pK (first triplet state)
β-naphtol	9.46	2.8	8.1
β-naphthylamine	4.1	-2	3.3
Acridine	5.5	10.6	5.6

Obviously the pK of the triplet state is very similar to the pK of the ground state, but the pK of the first singlet excited state is much smaller than the latter. Murrell (1964) has given an explanation of this phenomenon observing that the orbitals which are responsible for the charge transfer lie much more above the triplet state energy than above the first excited singlet. Linnett (1964) has offered another explanation based on the consideration of electron correlation.

The case of the other reactions is completely different as we do not know if it is possible to use the transition-state theory, which is open to criticism from the theoretical point of view (Laidler, 1955). Furthermore, usually no temperature coefficients are found, and when both the static method and the dynamic one are compared with experimental results (Havinga, 1966) the static method appears to be the best regardless of what happens in the case of molecules in their ground state.

In the case of excited molecules the success of the molecular diagram method lies perhaps in the fact that the static indexes remain in relation to the shape of the potential surface. This certainly plays an important role in the determination of the reaction rates even if the transition-state theory does not apply. This statement certainly needs further investigations.

REFERENCES

Bloch-Chaudé, O., and Masse, J. L. (1955). *Bull. Soc. Chim. France* 625.
Burkitt, F. H., Coulson, C. A., and Longuet-Higgins, H. C. (1951). *Trans. Faraday Soc.* 47, 553.
Buu-Hoï, N. P., Daudel, P., Daudel, R., Jacquigon, P., Morin, G., Muxart, R., and Sandorfy, C. (1951). *Bull. Soc. Chim. France* 18, 132.
Coulson, C. A. (1939). *Proc. Roy. Soc.* A169, 413.
Coulson, C. A. (1946). *Trans. Faraday Soc.* 42, 106, 265.
Coulson, C. A., and Jacobs, J. (1949). *J. Chem. Soc.* 1983.
Coulson, C. A., and Longuet-Higgins, H. C. (1947). *Proc. Roy. Soc.* A191, 39; A192. 16.
Crawford, V. A., and Coulson, C. A. (1948). *J. Chem. Soc.* 1990.
Daudel, P., Daudel, R., Jacques, R., and Jean, M. (1946). *Rev. Scientifique* 84, 489.
Daudel, R. (1966). *Advan. Quant. Chem.* (in press).
Daudel, R., and Pullman, A. (1945a). *Compt. Rend.* 220, 888.
Daudel, R., and Pullman, A. (1945b). *Compt. Rend.* 221, 201.
Daudel, R., and Pullman, A. (1946). *J. Phys. (Paris)* 105.
Daudel, R., Sandorfy, C., Vroelant, C., Yvan, D., and Chalvet, O. (1950). *Bull. Soc. Chim. France* 17, 66.
Eigen, M., Kruse, W., Maasse, G., and de Maeyer, L. (1964). "Progress in Reaction Kinetics," Vol. II, p. 287. Oxford Univ. Press, London and New York.
Fernandez-Alonso, J. I. (1951). *Compt. Rend.* 233, 2403.
Forster, Th. (1949a). *Z. Elektrochem.* 54, 42, 531.
Forster, Th. (1949b). *Naturwissenschaften* 36, 186.
Glasstone, S., Laidler, K. J., and Eyring, H. (1941). "The Theory of Rate Processes." McGraw-Hill, New York.
Havinga, E. (1966). "Rapport au 13ème Conseil Solvay" (in press).

Havinga, E., de Jongh, R. O., and Dorst, W. (1956). *Rec. Trav. Chim.* **75**, 378.

Jackson, G., and Porter, G. (1961). *Proc. Roy. Soc.* **A260**. 13.

Jaffe, H. H., Beveridge, D. L., and Jones, H. L. (1964). *J. Am. Chem. Soc.* **86**, 2932.

Laidler, K. J. (1955). "The Chemical Kinetics of Excited States," p. 41. Oxford Univ. Press, London and New York.

Linnett, J. W. (1964). "Electronic Structure of Molecules," Methuen, London.

Longuet-Higgins, H. C., and Abrahamson, E. W. (1965). *J. Am. Chem. Soc.* **87**, 2045.

Mantione, M. J., and Pullman, B. (1964). *Biochim. Biophys. Acta* **91**, 387.

Masse, J. L. (1954). *Compt. Rend.* **238**, 1320.

Murrell, J. N. (1964). The Theory of Electronic Spectra of Organic Molecules." Methuen, London.

Pauling, L. (1932). *Proc. Natl. Acad. Sci. U.S.* **18**, 293.

Pullman, A., and Daudel, R. (1946). *Compt. Rend.* **222**, 288.

Roux, M. (1950). *Bull. Soc. Chim. France* **17**, 861.

Sandorfy, C. (1950). *Compt. Rend.* **230**, 961.

Sandorfy, C. (1951). *Compt. Rend.* **232**, 841.

Srinivasan, R. (1963). *J. Am. Chem. Soc.* **85**, 4045.

Sung, S., Chalvet, O., and Daudel, R. (1960). *J. Chim. Phys.* **57**, 31.

Swartholm, N. V. (1941). *Arkiv. Kemi* **15A** (13).

Wheland, G. W. (1942). *J. Am. Chem. Soc.* **64**, 900.

Woodward, R. B., and Hoffmann, R. (1965). *J. Am. Chem. Soc.* **87**, 395.

Zimmerman, H. E. (1963). *Tetrahedron*, **19**, Suppl. 2, 397.

Zimmerman, H. E., and Somasekhara, S. (1963). *J. Am. Chem. Soc.* **85**, 922.

Electron Transfer and Atomic Magnetic Moments in the Ordered Intermetallic Compound AlFe₃

LINUS PAULING

CENTER FOR THE STUDY OF DEMOCRATIC INSTITUTIONS,
SANTA BARBARA, CALIFORNIA

During the past four decades a vigorous effort has been made by many investigators, of whom one of the foremost has been Professor John C. Slater, to develop a satisfactory and comprehensive quantum mechanical theory of the electronic structure of metals and alloys. There is general agreement that the Schrödinger equation provides a correct basis for such a theory, but the mathematical difficulties in its application to crystals are so great that even now, forty years after the discovery of quantum mechanics, the theory remains incomplete.

Throughout this period I have striven to formulate a semiempirical theory of metals and alloys, based upon a set of postulates suggested by quantum mechanical arguments and supported by observed properties, especially magnetic properties (1) and interatomic distances (2). This theory, the resonating-valence-bond theory ($3,4$), permits the discussion in a moderately satisfactory way of some properties of metals and alloys that have not yet been incorporated into the rigorous quantum mechanical theory. As an example there is given in the following paragraphs a discussion of the observed interatomic distances and atomic magnetic moments in the ordered intermetallic compound AlFe₃.

The compound AlFe₃ has the $L12$ structure, which is closely related to the body-centered cubic structure of alpha iron (5). The atomic coordinates are 8 Fe^A at 000, 0½½, ½0½, ½½0, ½½½, ½00, 0½0, 00½; 4 Al at ¼¼¼, ¼¾¾, ¾¼¾, ¾¾¼; and 4 Fe^B at ¾¾¾, ¾¼¼, ¼¾¼, ¼¼¾. The lattice constant has the value $a_0 = 5.794$ Å. The structure can be described as having Fe^A atoms at the corners of small cubes (edge one-half that of the unit cube), with Al atoms and Fe^B atoms alternating in their centers. Each Al atom is in contact with 8 Fe^A, at the distance 2.509 Å, each Fe^A with 4 Al and 4Fe^B, and each Fe^B with 8 Fe^A. There are also six neighbors about each atom at the distance 2.897 Å ($a_0/2$).

303

The observed bond length for alpha iron is 2.482 Å, and that for aluminum, changed from ligancy 12 to the body-centered structure,* is 2.792 Å. The weighted average of these, 2.560 Å, is expected for $AlFe_3$ from Vegard's rule of additivity, which has been found to agree with observation for many alloys. The considerable deviation of this value from the observed value, 2.509 Å, requires explanation.

Moreover, neutron-diffraction studies (6) have led to the assignment of the magnetic moment value 1.50 Bohr magnetons to the Fe^A atoms and 2.18 to the Fe^B atoms (the observed value for alpha iron being 2.22); these values also need a theoretical explanation.

The explanation is given by the theory of electron transfer in alloys (7; 4, p. 431), which is a part of the resonating-valence-bond theory. Metal atoms are divided into three classes: hypoelectronic atoms, such Na, Mg, Al, K, Ca, etc. (elements at the left of the periodic table); buffer atoms, such as the atoms of the iron group and other transition groups; and hyperelectronic atoms, such as Cu, Zn, etc. The valence of a hypoelectronic atom is limited by the number of electrons in its valence shell; it has an excess of orbitals. A hypoelectronic atom can increase its valence by accepting electrons from other atoms; thus the aluminum atom, which usually has valence 3, can achieve valence 4 by accepting one electron. Hyperelectronic atoms, which have an excess of electrons over orbitals in the valence shell, can increase their metallic valence by donating electrons. Buffer atoms can donate or accept electrons without change in valence. We expect accordingly that alloys containing hypoelectronic atoms and either hyperelectronic atoms or buffer atoms would tend to undergo electron transfer from the hyperelectronic or buffer atoms to the hypoelectronic atoms, thus increasing the number of valence bonds per atom and causing increased stability of the alloy. In accordance with this argument, it might be expected that the aluminum atom would accept one electron from the iron atoms in $AlFe_3$, increasing its valence to 4. Aluminum and iron have nearly the same electronegativity [1.5 and 1.8, respectively (4, p. 93)], so that little transfer of electric charge as a consequence of partial ionic character of bonds is expected; hence the charge of an aluminum atom to which an electron has been transferred is close to -1, a limit of the range (-1 to $+1$) allowed by the electroneutrality principle (8; 4, p. 172).

Stabilization by Coulomb interaction requires that the positive charges balancing the negative charge of the aluminum atom be at the minimum distance; hence we locate these charges on the Fe^A atoms (at distance 2.509 Å), and conclude that half an electron has been removed from each Fe^A atom, by transfer to Al.

* The change is made with use of the equation $D(n) = D(1) - 0.600 \log n$, where $D(n)$ is bond distance for bond number n (Ref. 2; Ref. 4, p. 400), with consideration of the eight nearest and six next-nearest neighbors in the body-centered structure.

Electron transfer to or from an atom is expected to change its metallic radius. It is difficult to make a reliable estimate of the change in metallic radius resulting from electron transfer; however, it is found that as a rough approximation the value of the metallic radius may be taken as that of the atom with atomic number equal to the electron number of the atom involved in electron transfer. Thus the metallic radius of aluminum with an added electron may be taken to be that of the next element in the periodic table, silicon, which for the body-centered structure* corresponds to the bond length 2.578 Å. The effective diameter of an atom Fe^A that has lost half an electron is found by interpolating between the values for manganese (valence 6, body-centered structure) and iron; it is 2.486 Å. Accordingly, the average bond length expected for $AlFe_3$, with electron transfer as described above, is 2.508 Å, in excellent agreement with the observed value.

Electron transfer from iron to aluminum in this alloy also decreases the strain that would otherwise result from the insertion of the large aluminum atoms, 13% larger than the iron atoms, into the iron lattice. After electron transfer the aluminum atoms are only 3.7% larger than the iron atoms.

The observed saturation magnetic moment per iron atom in alpha iron is 2.22 Bohr magnetons. This is, according to the Zener theory of induced magnetic polarization of conduction electrons (9), to be divided into the part 2.00 attributed to the atomic electrons of the iron atom and the part 0.22 attributed to the induced moment of the conduction electrons (10). The atoms Fe^B in $AlFe_3$ would be expected to have the same atomic moment, 2.00, and the atoms Fe^A, which have lost half an electron, would be expected to have a value 0.5 less, 1.5 Bohr magnetons, in each case increased by the induced moment of the conduction electrons, which is about 0.14 (the value for alpha iron multiplied by the ratio of the average atomic moments for $AlFe_3$ and alpha iron). Accordingly, the conclusion is reached that the magnetic moments should be about 2.14 for Fe^B, 1.64 for Fe^A, and 0.14 for Al (or probably slightly larger for Fe^B and smaller for Al), in agreement with the observed values, 2.18 for Fe^B, 1.50 for Fe^A, and zero for Al, all ± 0.10.

We can in the same way predict values for the magnetic moments of atoms in other alloys. For example, in the ordered alloy $AlCo_3$, with the same structure as $AlFe_3$, we predict for Co^B the value 1.72 (the same as for the element) and for Co^A the larger value 2.25 Bohr magnetons. The resonating valence bond theory of metals and alloys leads clearly to the prediction that a cobalt atom on losing half an electron would undergo an increase in its magnetic moment, rather than a decrease, as found for the iron atom.

A neutron diffraction study has been reported (11,12) for the magnetic

---

* The observed value of $D(1)$ for the Si—Si bond is 2.353 Å. Change to the value for the body-centered structure is made as described in Footnote on p. 304.

form factors of the iron atoms in $AlFe_3$. A difference has been found between Fe^A and Fe^B. In the theoretical discussion of this difference, it would, I think, be wise to take into consideration the transfer of electrons from the Fe^A atoms to aluminum atoms, as discussed above.

REFERENCES

1. L. Pauling, *Phys. Rev.* **54**, 899 (1938).
2. L. Pauling, *J. Am. Chem. Soc.* **69**, 542 (1947).
3. L. Pauling, *Proc. Roy Soc. (London)* **A196**, 343 (1949).
4. L. Pauling, "The Nature of the Chemical Bond," 3rd ed., Chap. 11. Cornell Univ. Press, Ithaca, New York. 1960.
5. A. J. Bradley and A. H. Jay, *Proc. Roy. Soc. (London)* **A136**, 201 (1932).
6. R. Nathans, M. T. Pigott, and C. G. Shull, *Proc. Conf. Magnetism Magnetic Mat., Boston, 1956* p. 242. Am. Inst. Electrical Engineers, New York, 1957.
7. L. Pauling, *Proc. Natl. Acad. Sci. U.S.* **36**, 533 (1950).
8. L. Pauling, *J. Chem. Soc.(London)* **1948**, 1461.
9. C. Zener, *Phys. Rev.* **81**, 440 (1951).
10. L. Pauling, *Proc. Natl. Acad. Sci. U.S.* **39**, 551 (1953).
11. S. J. Pickart and R. Nathans, *Phys. Rev.* **123**, 1163 (1961).
12. C. G. Shull, *In* "Electronic Structure and Alloy Chemistry of the Transition Elements," p. 69. Wiley (Interscience), New York, 1963.

The One-Electron Approximation
Epistemological, Spectroscopic, and Chemical Comments

CHR. KLIXBÜLL JØRGENSEN

CYANAMID EUROPEAN RESEARCH INSTITUTE, COLOGNY (GENEVA), SWITZERLAND

I. The Point of View of Atomic Spectroscopy

Slater (*1*) wrote the paper on many-electron systems on which the treatise by Condon and Shortley (*2*) is based. Slater proposed that parameters of interelectronic repulsion express the main effects of separation into different S,L-multiplet terms of configurations containing at least one partly filled shell. It had previously been realized (*3*) how J and parity are the exact quantum numbers of energy levels in spherical symmetry, and that S and L are also fairly good quantum numbers if Russell and Saunders' coupling scheme is a good approximation. However, in the minds of many physicists the origins of the energy differences were some rather mysterious spin-spin and orbit-orbit coupling forces. Slater's theory suggested that the only two-electron operator of practical importance is the Coulombic repulsion e^2/r_{12} and that, to a first approximation, the different energy levels of a given configuration have the same electronic density in our three-dimensional space, but different values of the average reciprocal interelectronic distance $\langle 1/r_{12} \rangle$. The ground term of a given configuration (usually, according to Hund's rule, the maximum L compatible with the maximum S) has the lowest value of this expression.

Charlotte Moore-Sitterly's "Atomic Energy Levels" clearly demonstrate a great success in the application of these ideas to the classification of the first ten or first hundred energy levels of a given gaseous atom or monatomic ion. Frequently, all the levels expected of complicated configurations have been identified, and there is hardly any case known where "superfluous" low-lying energy levels resist this classification.

At the time when numerous atomic spectroscopists lived (and one may deplore that artificial radioactivity and nuclear transmutation depopulated

307

this class nearly entirely) it was the general feeling that intermixing of configurations is only important when two configurations of the same parity overlap or at least are separated by a distance smaller than the width of the individual configurations, the nondiagonal elements of the interelectronic repulsion normally being smaller than the energy differences produced by differences of the diagonal elements in a given configuration. A typical case of coinciding configurations is [Ar]$3d^q4s^2$ and [Ar]$3d^{q+1}4s$ in neutral atoms of the first transition group (and the analogous configurations in the 4d and 5d groups) whereas the ions M^{++} or M^{3+} have [Ar]$3d^q$ well below [Ar]$3d^{q-1}$ 4s. In such cases, it was previously assumed that the well-separated configurations do not interact appreciably.

In a certain sense, this was an unduly optimistic attitude. The ground state ^1S of the helium atom has a wave function (4) which, in the squared amplitudes, consists of 99.19% of the conventional configuration $1s^2$. The two next-largest contributions, 0.38%$(\infty s)^2$ and 0.40%$(\infty p)^2$ come from orbitals essentially belonging to the continuum. Though their diagonal energy above the ground state is some one to three times the ionization energy, and hence proportional to Z_*^2, Z_* being some effective charge of the type $(Z - 0.31)$, the nondiagonal elements are proportional to Z_*, and the second-order perturbation energy hence essentially invariant as function of Z_*. Thus, one can at most hope for wave functions of many-electron systems having the conventional configuration $C = a_1^2 a_2^2 a_3^2 \cdots a_n^2$ (containing $2n$ electrons) to exhibit the approximate form

$$\Psi = (1 - \sum_k \sum_r N_{kr}^2 - \cdots)^{1/2}\Psi(C) + \sum_{k=1}^n \sum_r N_{kr}\Psi(Ca_k^{-2}a_r^2) + \cdots \quad (1)$$

where two-electron substitutions $a_k^2 \rightarrow a_r^2$ have been considered only. The effects of one-electron substitutions are known nearly to vanish for self-consistent orbitals ϕ_k. The groundstate ^1S of the beryllium atom (5) agrees qualitatively with Eq. (1), the important substitutions of $1s^22s^2$ being $1s^22p^2$, $(\infty s)^22s^2$ and $(\infty p)^22s^2$. The first of these substituted configurations involve orbitals with negative energy known from discrete, excited states, and the second-order perturbation argument suggests a stabilization of the ground state proportional to Z_* rather than being invariant in an isoelectronic series. This situation is called near-degeneracy of orbitals.

The theory of many-electron atoms was refined by Racah for d-shells (6) and f-shells (7) using sophisticated group theoretical techniques (8) and in a more modest way analyzing the known energy expressions (9,10). Thus, one can show that the baricenter of all states having a definite value of S belonging to a given configuration containing one partly filled shell l^q has the interelectronic repulsion energy

$$\frac{q(q-1)}{2}A_1 + \left[\frac{3}{4}q\left(1 - \frac{q-1}{4l+1}\right) - S(S+1)\right]D \quad (2)$$

the average value A_1 and the spin-pairing energy parameter D having the expressions in terms of Slater's and Racah's parameters:

$$A_1 \qquad\qquad\qquad D$$

$$p: \quad F^0 - \frac{2}{25}F^2 \qquad\qquad\qquad \frac{3}{20}F^2$$

$$d: \quad F^0 - \frac{2}{63}F^2 - \frac{2}{63}F^4 = A - \frac{14}{9}B + \frac{7}{9}C \qquad \frac{5}{84}F^2 + \frac{5}{84}F^4 = \frac{7}{6}\left(\frac{5}{2}B + C\right)$$

$$f: \quad F^0 - \frac{4}{195}F^2 - \frac{1}{143}F^4 - \frac{100}{5577}F^6 \qquad \frac{7}{180}F^2 + \frac{33}{1256}F^4 + \frac{175}{5148}F^6 \tag{3}$$

$$= E^0 + \frac{9}{13}E^1 \qquad\qquad\qquad = \frac{9}{8}E^1$$

There does not exist a general parameter dependent on L, but it is striking (9) how frequently the multiplet terms have energies being linear functions of $L(L + 1)$.

The deviations of the observed levels from the predictions (considering the F^k integrals as parameters to be determined from experience) can frequently be ascribed to effects of near-degeneracy. Racah and Trees introduced l correction terms besides the $(l + 1)$ different F^k integrals; a closer analysis (11) shows that effectively, the energies of the $(2l + 1)$ multiplet terms of $l^2(^1S, ^3P, ^1D, ^3F, ...)$ are the intrinsic variables of such a description which is an application of fractional parentage building l^q wave functions from those of l^2. Quite unexpectedly, even the configurations $[Ne]3s^2 3p^4 3d^{q+2}$ have a perceptible influence of the near-degeneracy type on the conventional configuration $[Ne]3s^2 3p^6 3d^q$ of first transition-group ions (12). It would be possible (10) to extend the concept of seniority number v to the idea of uncoupling of l-values. Terms with $v < q$ have wave functions which could be constructed by adding spherically symmetric contributions ^1S to a lower number of electrons with positive l. Hence, the terms with decreased v allow the mixing of $l^{q-2}s^2$ and l^q. The similar condition of admixture of $l^{q-2}p^2$ and l^q would be the separability of ^1S, ^3P or ^1D components for two of the electrons, furnishing a mechanism of slight stabilization of these three terms but not ^3F and ^1G of d^2, one of the goals of the Racah-Trees corrections. On the other hand, the uncoupling of l^q to $l^{q-2}(l')^2$ with $l' \geq l$ disturbs all term distances, but we do not yet know whether there would be a systematic dependence on S and L. Racah (13) seems to prefer "model interactions" of mutual dipolar polarization etc. of the orbitals, producing perturbation energies proportional to the Racah-Trees corrections.

Watson (14,15) calculated analytical Hartree-Fock functions for 3d group ions and Freeman and Watson (16) for 4f group ions. The deviations of the integrals of interelectronic repulsion F^k calculated for the 3d group ions with ionic charge z relative to the empirical values of these parameters show a number of striking regularities (9): to the first approximation, they are all too large by a factor $(z + 3)/(z + 2)$. Such a behavior of an isoelectronic series indicates predominant effects of continuum orbitals because the F^k integrals themselves are roughly proportional to $(z + 2)$, i.e., all term distances are decreased in a way not much dependent of z in an isoelectronic series. However, these decreases are dependent on S and L (corresponding to the Racah-Trees corrections) and ^2P of $3d^3$ has lower energy than ^2H though the two terms are degenerate in Slater's theory.

Another interesting result is that term distances such as $^3F \rightarrow {}^3P$ or $^4F \rightarrow {}^4P$ between terms having the maximum value of S are decreased to the same extent as the other energy differences. Some authors thought that electrons with parallel spin would produce much weaker correlation effects than electrons with opposite sign because the antisymmetrization conditions posed on Ψ prevent very large values of $1/r_{12}$ in the former case. However, this argument is doubtful because of the long-range nature of the Coulomb interactions (10) and has been refuted quantitatively for the helium atom where the correlation effects have a spatial extent comparable to the average diameter of the electronic cloud (17).

We must admit at present that we have no certain idea about the actual form of Eq. (1) for transition-group ions though configurations such as $3d^{q-2}(\infty f)^2$ and $3d^{q-2}(\infty g)^2$ must be responsible for a large part of the difference between Hartree-Fock and empirical F^k parameters. A conservative estimate would make Eq. (1) divergent for at least one-hundred electrons because four- and six-electron substitutions then are more important than two-electron substitutions. However, this divergence may very well occur at a much lower number of electrons. On the other hand, the classification of energy levels according to electron configurations is not less successful for radium and actinium than for lighter atoms.

It may be quite legitimate to ask whether the conventional Ψ is an entirely satisfactory description of many-electron systems. A theorem first shown by Dirac has recently been discussed by Löwdin (4): if only two-electron interactions occur, the second-order density matrix with two spin and six spatial variables is sufficient for obtaining all observable quantities. There is much evidence that the Hartree-Fock Ψ gives very good agreement with the first-order density matrix in our three-dimensional space. After all, the concord with experimental data is the supreme criterion for quantum mechanics, and the results of x-ray diffraction by electronic density or neutron diffraction by uncompensated spin density are compatible with the calculations though, unfortunately, the experimental precision which can be obtained is not very high. On the other hand, the second-order density matrix of the Hartree-

Fock Ψ exaggerates the average value $\langle 1/r_{12} \rangle$. In other words, there is an "internal polarization" in the second-order density matrix without great effect on the first-order electronic density. This is the physical significance of the two-electron substitutions with continuum orbitals having a radial extension comparable to the filled orbitals. In molecular calculations, Julg (*18*) and other authors have proposed, for empirical reasons, to decrease all parameters of interelectronic repulsion roughly to the same extent as observed in isolated atoms. This is also the basis for Moffitt's ideas (*19*) about "atoms in molecules." If the Z_*-dependent effects of near-degeneracy of orbitals are neglected, it seems to be a surprisingly good approximation (*20*) to assume that the inter-n-shell interelectronic repulsion $F^k(nl, n'l')$ is not affected, that $F^0(nl, nl)$ (or perhaps rather A_1 of Eq. (1)) and $F^0(nl, nl')$ are decreased from their Hartree-Fock value as if the effective charge Z_* were 0.0747 unit lower, whereas the parameters separating the terms of a given configuration are decreased as if Z_* was a whole unit smaller. This corresponds to two different "effective dielectric constants" for the internal polarization but has not yet found any solid theoretical justification. However, the regularities observed suggest that a correlated second-order density matrix is a more appropriate description than configuration interaction.

II. MO Theory of Molecules and Inorganic Chromophores

Slater (*21*) wrote a highly fascinating technical report which has only been published in part (*22,23*; Chapter 4). In particular, the analysis of H_2 at varying internuclear distance shows that V. B. treatments meet intrinsic difficulties of rather unexpected nature. If the participating atomic orbitals are properly orthogonalized, no chemical bonding can be predicted by the diagonal element of one structure only. On the other hand, it had been known since Vol. 1 of *The Journal of Chemical Physics* in 1933 that the MO configuration σ_g^2 is an appropriate description of the ground state $^1\Sigma_g^+$ of the hydrogen molecule only if the internuclear distance is not considerably longer than at the minimum of the potential curve. The exact Ψ at this minimum can be expanded (*24*) in configurations of natural spin orbitals, the squares of the amplitude being closely similar to the three most important contributions to the He ground state, viz. 98.22% σ_g^2, 0.99% σ_u^2, 0.42% π_u^2 and 0.30% of a second σ_g^2. It is instructive to compare with the behavior of two isolated hydrogen atoms, i.e., a hydrogen molecule stretched to a very large internuclear distance, whose Ψ is an exact mixture of 50% σ_g^2 and 50% σ_u^2. The diagonal elements of energy of the two latter configurations are considerably higher than for two isolated H atoms. In other words, H_2 is a typical example of how MO theory, using qualitative arguments related to well-defined configurations, is applicable only in situations of relevant symmetry (25). The symmetry group of the nuclei in a molecule is not necessarily the best to use in MO theory; the nondiagonal elements of the two-electron operator are frequently much larger than the one-electron energy differences, if the orbitals are adapted to irrelevant symmetry components. This point clarifies many problems recently discussed in literature, and removes the most serious criticism one can make of molecular orbital and energy band theory.

Ligand field theory (26–28) is essentially an application of MO theory to the relevant symmetry of inorganic chromophores (29) MX_N where the central atom M connected to N ligand atoms X contains a partly filled d or f shell. The influence of the ligand atoms cannot be represented by an external electrostatic field (except the group-theoretical properties (30)) but is represented in the angular overlap model (31–33) in a way somewhat comparable to the Hückel model for organic molecules, but utilizing the properties of the hydrogenic angular l-functions of the central atom. The diagonal elements of these highly heteronuclear molecules are more difficult to evaluate; it is imperative to take Madelung-energy into account (10,34).

For our purpose, the important point of view is that the absorption spectra frequently allow the determination of the preponderant configuration (35) in the sense of classifying the low-lying energy levels of the chromophore. Thus, there is no doubt that the complicated distribution of absorption bands of numerous V(II), Cr(III), Mn(IV), Mo(III), Tc(IV), Re(IV), and Ir(VI) complexes (36) containing octahedral chromophores MX_6 indicate the preponderant configuration d^3. It is actually the main reason why we can assign oxidation states written with Roman numerals, vanadium(II), chromium(III), etc. because the fractional charge on the central atom is certainly not as high as $+2$, $+3$, etc. There exist ligands, such as NO and certain macrocyclic molecules, which do not allow a preponderant configuration with an integral number of electrons in the partly filled shell to be defined (37). However, most common ligands are "innocent," i.e., they allow the preponderant configuration to be detected.

Lanthanide compounds are in a completely extreme category. The energy levels fall in narrow groups each corresponding to a definite J-level of $4f^q$ in spherical symmetry (8,10,38,39). The interelectronic repulsion parameters which are some 30% smaller for the gaseous ions than calculated from the Hartree-Fock functions (16) are some 1–5% smaller in compounds than in gaseous ions (40–42) (the evidence for this statement was somewhat indirect until Sugar (43) recently found twelve of the thirteen J-levels of $[Xe]4f^2$ in gaseous Pr^{3+}). In metallic alloys or in semiconductors with low energy gap, the magnetic moments (44) and other physical properties indicate that the number of electrons in the partly filled 4f shell normally is an integer. The metallicity seems frequently to be connected with a calculated lower energy (45) of the lowest term of $4f^{q-1}5d$ than of $4f^q$. Professor K. A. Jensen,

Copenhagen, has proposed to put oxidation states determined in this way from preponderant configurations in brackets, $4f^7$ for instance corresponding to Eu[II], Gd[III], or Tb[IV], in order to distinguish this concept from the normal oxidation numbers. The physical origin of the integral values of q normally found may reside in the coefficient $q(q - 1)/2$ to A_1 in Eq. (2). The partly filled 4f shell has an unusually small average radius, and hence A_1 is larger than in the four other transition groups, also contributing to the nearly invariant oxidation state M(III) of the 4f group in contrast to the 5f group (*39*). If the 4f electrons were highly delocalized, the classical coefficient $q^2/2$ would obtain to A_1. The difference, $-qA_1/2$, explains the tendency towards localization of a definite number of electrons in partly filled shells with large A_1.

Bloch's theory of energy bands is the logical extension of MO theory to infinite crystals. However, it has to be looked upon with great circumspection because of the disastrous effects of nondiagonal elements of the two-electron operator strongly mixing configurations adapted to irrelevant symmetry components (*25*) as we saw above in the case of two hydrogen atoms at large distance. The partly filled energy bands of normal lanthanide compounds, such as $PrCl_3$ or Nd_2O_3, certainly do not produce metallic properties. The excuse in the energy-band jargon is " hardly any curvature of the energy bands and vanishing mobility." One may not be convinced that this statement indicates the profound reasons for nonmetallicity. The central atoms have a much lower electron affinity than ionization energy, differing approximately to the extent of A_1 about 18 eV, and consequently, it requires a great deal of energy to transport an electron by the "hopping process" in such a lattice (*46*). Many 3d group compounds, such as NiO, are in the same situation. For group-theoretical reasons, the paramagnetic form of this compound, which has cubic symmetry, ought to have a half-filled energy band though it is nonmetallic in the same way as the lanthanide salts previously discussed were. It is also impossible that the antiferromagnetic form that exists below the Curie temperature has the upper energy bands of opposite spin separated sufficiently to explain its behavior on a one-electron basis. Thus, the absorption spectra of NiO and the isomorphous diluted crystals $Ni_xMg_{1-x}O$ are all essentially similar (*47*) corresponding to the octahedral chromophore $Ni(II)O_6$ and the x-ray absorption corresponding to $2p^63d^8 \rightarrow 2p^53d^9$ in NiO shows only the fine-structure expected from the two- and one-electron parameters present in Slater's theory for the isolated central atom Ni(II) (*48*).

It has frequently been suggested (*44,49*) that metallic bonding occurs only for internuclear distances below a sharply defined threshold. In certain cases, such as $Nd_xSm_{1-x}Se$, the limit as function of composition x seems very narrow (*50*). It must not be ignored that the periodicity of ideal lattices is a mathematically convenient assumption in the energy-band theory rather than an absolute condition for metallicity. After all, liquid metals do exist. In the nonmetallic systems, chromophores can be recognized with remarkable frequency. Thus, the absorption spectra of glasses (51) and molten salts (52) containing transition-group ions are very similar to analogous solutions and crystalline solids.

In the sense of determining preponderant configurations, there is no doubt about the frequent, though not universal, individuality of chromophores MX_N. The possibility of an individuality for atoms M and X in compounds is a much more intricate question. Slater (53) discussed Bragg's old idea that atoms approximately have a constant radius independent of the nature of the chemical bonding. It is indeed true that the observable distance M–X frequently is divided with 0.7 Å larger radius of M and 0.7 Å smaller radius of X assuming "covalent radii" than assuming "ionic radii." As Slater himself admits, the main difficulty is that typically ionic compounds such as CsF has a shorter Cs–Cs distance than in metallic Cs, but shows no physical consequences of intermetallic bonding. There is an absolute sense in which atoms of metallic elements contract when forming fairly electrovalent compounds. It is not a sufficient argument for VO being an interstitial compound that the V–V distance is roughly the same as in vanadium metal.

X-ray diffraction results agree that the inner shells of atoms in compounds fill only a tiny proportion of the total volume and have radial distributions compatible with Hartree-Fock calculations. The low electronic density in the space between the atomic cores is the main subject for chemical discussions. At the present, the most prominent evidence for the expansion and delocalization of the partly filled shells in transition-group compounds is the nephelauxetic effect (54,55) that the parameters of interelectronic repulsion are decreased in compounds relative to the corresponding gaseous ions M^{+z}. This evidence would be somewhat ambiguous, because of the discrepancy between Hartree-Fock and empirical F^k integrals, if it were not for the extremely regular variation in the d groups as a function of the central atom and of the ligands. In general, oxidizing central atoms (such as Fe(III), Co(III), and all M(IV)) and reducing ligands (such as Br^-, I^- and S^{--}) show a much more pronounced nephelauxetic effect than the opposite extreme represented by MnF_2 and $KMnF_3$ (both containing the chromophore $Mn(II)F_6$) and $Mn(H_2O)_6^{++}$. This agrees with the qualitative expectation of MO theory; that is, the delocalization of the (antibonding) central atom orbitals is largest when the difference between the diagonal elements of energy H_M and H_X is smallest.

III. The Unexplained Success of One-Particle Classifications

Perhaps nowhere is the astonishing expedience of one-particle models as spectacular as in the nuclear-shell quantum numbers. It is absolutely unacceptable to use Hartree and Fock's arguments in nuclei, and yet, the classification of the lowest energy levels works.

The next-most-surprising case is the inorganic chromophores MX_N. Here, the configurations of molecular orbitals are adapted to the relevant symmetry classifying the lower energy levels in a striking way. It is worth emphasizing the evidence for the excitation or ionization of inner shells which produce apparently discrete (though auto-ionizing) levels at far higher energy than the first ionization energy. Thus, the absorption spectra in the far ultraviolet region of gaseous Cs atoms show excitations of the 5p shell (56); the 3d shell of Kr (57) and 4d shell of Xe (57,58); and the 3s shell of Ar and 4s shell of Kr (59). There is no longer a sharp experimental distinction between the far ultraviolet and the soft x-ray regions. In crystalline substances, such excitations can also be observed, e.g. of 2p and 2s of fluorine and 1s of lithium in LiF (60).

A valuable new technique for the accurate measure of the energy of electrons ejected by monochromatic far ultraviolet radiation (photoelectron spectroscopy) has allowed the ionization energies of the penultimate orbitals of many molecules to be determined (61,62). The agreement with Mulliken's MO classification is very good. The ionization energies of inner shells can be shown (Chap. 12, (10)) to vary for a given element roughly to the same extent as the energy of the loosest bound electrons. This result was confirmed by Watson's calculations for different ionic charges (14) and by recent, very accurate, measurements (63) on compounds of light elements.

Actually, the definition of one-electron energies is by no means a trivial task (10,64). If one desires to include large amounts of two-electron quantities in the otherwise far-too-negative values, one really has the choice among three sensible possibilities: to take all interelectronic repulsion between non-core electrons explicitly into account; to consider differences between baricenters of configurations (where the one-electron energies no longer are exactly additive); or to correct for effects on shells with low average radii having particularly large A_1 parameters (39).

It is instructive to remark that atomic spectroscopists in the period from 1925 to 1930 classified the J-levels observed into configurations with little appeal to quantum mechanics for approval. In the author's opinion, molecules and inorganic chromophores were in a similar situation from 1955 to 1965. The MO classifications, adapted to the relevant symmetry, work, whether or not they ought to. The field of quantum mechanics is in an unpleasant position at two interesting points: the manifest existence of quasi-discrete states in the continuum, apparently belonging to inner-shell excitations; and the fact that because the correlation energy of all neutral atoms heavier than neon is larger than the first ionization energy, the backbone is taken out of the variation principle.

It is not known how the field of quantum mechanics will look in five years, or in 500 years. It is the author's belief that atomic spectroscopists classifying energy levels, or chemists inducing them from experimental facts, should not worry more about the probable revolutions in physics to come than pilots of airplanes or users of vacuum cleaners normally consider relativistic or quantum deviations from Newton's mechanics. The successful classification is here to stay. Finally, it may be worth mentioning that the approximate transferability of Koopmans' type of one-electron quantities from one configuration to another is perhaps the most profound property of the one-electron approximation. We should not concentrate on the description of a single state, but also consider all the low-lying energy levels under the same angle in a sort of super-Hilbert-space. The meaning of the " preponderant configuration " of a state may be slightly more general than $\Psi(C)$ in Eq. (1); actually, its coefficient may be nearly as small in many-electron systems as it is in nuclei. It might be preferable to apply B. Russell's theory of types (cf. a short discussion in a recent paper on a classification of categorical propositions (65)) and say that the collection of preponderant configurations is a higher type property of the manifold of all the low-lying energy levels of a given system.

REFERENCES

1. J. C. Slater, *Phys. Rev.* **34**, 1293 (1929).
2. E. U. Condon and G. H. Shortley, "Theory of Atomic Spectra," 2nd ed. University Press, Cambridge, 1953.
3. F. Hund, "Linienspektren und Periodisches System der Elemente." Springer, Berlin, 1927.
4. P. O. Löwdin, *Advan. Chem. Phys.* **2**, 207 (1959).
5. R. E. Watson, *Phys. Rev.* **119**, 170 (1960).
6. G. Racah, *Phys. Rev.* **62**, 438 (1942); **63**, 367 (1942).
7. G. Racah, *Phys. Rev.* **76**, 1352 (1949).
8. B. R. Judd, "Operator Techniques in Atomic Spectroscopy." McGraw-Hill, New York, 1963.
9. C. K. Jørgensen, *Solid State Phys.* **13**, 375 (1962).
10. C. K. Jørgensen, "Orbitals in Atoms and Molecules." Academic Press, New York, 1962.
11. R. E. Trees, *J. Res. Natl. Bur. Stand.* **53**, 35 (1954).
12. R. E. Trees and C. K. Jørgensen, *Phys. Rev.* **123**, 1278 (1961).
13. G. Racah, "Proceedings of the Rydberg Centennial Conference on Atomic Spectroscopy." Lund, 1955.
14. R. E. Watson, "Iron-Series Hartree-Fock Calculations." Technical Report No. 12 from Solid-State and Molecular Theory Group, M.I.T., 1959.
15. R. E. Watson, *Phys. Rev.* **118**, 1036 (1960); **119**, 1934 (1960).
16. A. J. Freeman and R. E. Watson, *Phys. Rev.* **127**, 2058 (1962).
17. B. M. Gimarc, W. A. Cooney, and R. G. Parr, *J. Chem. Phys.* **42**, 21 (1965).
18. A. Julg, *J. Chim. Phys.* **57**, 19 (1960).
19. W. Moffitt, *Proc. Roy. Soc.* (London) **A210**, 224, 245 (1951).

20. C. K. Jørgensen, *Mol. Phys.* **8**, 191 (1964).
21. J. C. Slater, "Electronic Structure of Atoms and Molecules." Technical Report No. 3 from Solid-State and Molecular Theory Group, M.I.T., 1953.
22. J. C. Slater, *J. Chem. Phys.* **19**, 220 (1951).
23. J. C. Slater, "Quantum Theory of Molecules and Solids." Vol. 1, "Electronic Structure of Molecules," McGraw-Hill, New York, 1963.
24. S. Hagstrom and H. Shull, *Rev. Mod. Phys.* **35**, 624 (1963).
25. C. K. Jørgensen, *Phys. Stat. Solidi* **2**, 1146 (1962).
26. L. E. Orgel, "An Introduction to Transition-Metal Chemistry." Methuen, London, 1960 (U.S. distributor: Wiley).
27. C. K. Jørgensen, "Absorption Spectra and Chemical Bonding in Complexes." Pergamon Press, Oxford, 1962 (U.S. distributor: Addison-Wesley).
28. C. K. Jørgensen, *Advan. Chem. Phys.* **5**, 33 (1963); **8**, 47 (1965).
29. C. K. Jørgensen, "Inorganic Complexes." Academic Press, New York, 1963.
30. J. S. Griffith, "The Theory of Transition-Metal Ions." University Press, Cambridge, 1961.
31. C. K. Jørgensen, R. Pappalardo, and H.-H. Schmidtke, *J. Chem. Phys.* **39**, 1422 (1963).
32. H.-H. Schmidtke, *Z. Naturforsch.* **19a**, 1502 (1964).
33. C. E. Schäffer and C. K. Jørgensen, *Mol. Phys.* **9** (1965) 401; *Mat. fys. Medd. Dan. Vid. Selsk.* **34** (13), (1965).
34. C. K. Jørgensen, S. M. Horner, W. E. Hatfield, and S. Y. Tyree, *Int. J. Quantum Chem.* in press.
35. C. K. Jørgensen, *J. Physique* **26**, 825 (1965).
36. C. K. Jørgensen and K. Schwochau, *Z. Naturforsch.* **20a**, 65 (1965).
37. C. K. Jørgensen, *Z. Naturw.-Mediz. Grundlagenforsch.* **2**, 248 (1965).
38. B. G. Wybourne, "Spectroscopic Properties of Rare Earths." Interscience (Wiley), New York, 1965.
39. C. K. Jørgensen, "Lanthanides and 5f Elements." Academic Press, New York, 1967.
40. C. K. Jørgensen, *Mat. fys. Medd. Dan. Vid. Selsk.* **30** (22), (1956).
41. C. K. Jørgensen, R. Pappalardo, and E. Rittershaus, *Z. Naturforsch.* **19a**, 424 (1964); **20a**, 54 (1965).
42. C. K. Jørgensen, R. Pappalardo, and J. Flahaut, *J. Chim. Phys.* **62**, 444 (1965).
43. J. Sugar, *Phys. Rev. Letters* **14**, 731 (1965); *J. Opt. Soc. Am.* **55**, 1058 (1965).
44. J. B. Goodenough, "Magnetism and the Chemical Bond." Interscience (Wiley), New York, 1963.
45. C. K. Jørgensen, *Mol. Phys.* **7**, 417 (1964).
46. H. Krebs and W. Schottky, *Halbleiterprob.* **1**, 25 (1954).
47. D. Reinen, *Ber. Bunsenges.* **69**, 82 (1965).
48. C. Bonnelle and C. K. Jørgensen, *J. Chim. Phys.* **61**, 826 (1964).
49. N. F. Mott, *Phil. Mag.* **6**, 287 (1961).
50. F. J. Reid, L. K. Matson, J. F. Miller, and R. C. Himes, *J. Chem. Phys. Solids* **25**, 969 (1964).
51. W. A. Weyl, "Coloured Glasses." Dawson, London, 1959.
52. D. M. Gruen and R. L. McBeth. *Pure Appl. Chem.* **6**, 23 (1963).
53. J. C. Slater, *J. Chem. Phys.* **41**, 3199 (1964).
54. C. E. Schäffer and C. K. Jørgensen, *J. Inorg. Nucl. Chem.* **8**, 143 (1958).
55. C. K. Jørgensen, *Progr. Inorg. Chem.* **4**, 73 (1962); *Helv. Chim. Acta* (Proc. 9.I.C.C.C.) in press.
56. H. Beutler and K. Guggenheimer, *Z. Physik* **88**, 25 (1934).

57. K. Codling and R. P. Madden, *Phys. Rev. Letters* **12**, 106 (1964).
58. N. Damany-Astoin, *Compt. Rend.* **259**, 1493 (1964).
59. J. A. R. Samson, *Phys. Rev.* **132**, 2122 (1963).
60. A. Milgram and M. P. Givens, *Phys. Rev.* **125**, 1506 (1962).
61. M. I. Al-Joboury and D. W. Turner, *J. Chem. Soc.* **1963**, 5141; **1964**, 4434.
62. M. I. Al-Joboury, D. P. May, and D. W. Turner, *J. Chem. Soc.* **1965**, 616, 6350.
63. A. Fahlman, K. Hamrin, R. Nordberg, C. Nordling, and K. Siegbahn, *Phys. Rev. Letters* **14**, 127 (1965).
64. J. C. Slater, *Phys. Rev.* **98**, 1039 (1955).
65. C. K. Jørgensen, *Logique et Analyse (Louvain)* **7**, 233 (1964).

Linear Diamagnetic and Paramagnetic Response*

H. PRIMAS and J. RIESS

LABORATORY OF PHYSICAL CHEMISTRY
SWISS FEDERAL INSTITUTE OF TECHNOLOGY, ZURICH, SWITZERLAND

I. Introduction

The aim of this paper is twofold. First, we present a general, compact and fairly rigorous theory of the linear magnetic response of a quantum mechanical system, using the formalism of the thermodynamic free energy functional. Secondly, we propose a new, unequivocal and gauge invariant definition of the diamagnetic part of the linear magnetic response.

For illustration consider an atom (without relativistic and spin effects) in a homogeneous magnetic field $\mathbf{B} = (0, 0, B_z)$. If we fix the origin of the coordinate system, say to the center of the atom, we still have many different possibilities of gauging the vector potential $\mathbf{A}$, defined by $\mathbf{B} = \operatorname{curl} \mathbf{A}$. If we choose the vector potential as

$$A_x = -B_z y/2, \qquad A_y = B_z x/2, \qquad A_z = 0$$

* This work has been supported by the Swiss National Foundation for the Advancement of Science.

we get the usual result for the susceptibility χ

$$\chi = -(e^2/4mc^2)\langle 0|\sum_k (x_k^2 + y_k^2)|0\rangle. \tag{1}$$

Taking the Landau gauge

$$A_x = A_z = 0, \qquad A_y = B_z x,$$

straightforward perturbation theory gives

$$\chi = -(e^2/mc^2)\langle 0|\sum_k x_k^2|0\rangle$$

$$+ (2e^2/m^2c^2)\sum_{s\neq 0} (E_s - E_0)^{-1}|\langle 0|\sum_k x_k p_{ky}|s\rangle|^2, \tag{2}$$

where in the second term the summation is over all excited states, including the continuum. Both expressions are identical of course [the explicit verification can be found in the lucid paper of Bloch (1961), from which this example is taken], but it is disturbing to find a simple gauge transform converting a plain problem in a complicated one. In this example as well as in many others the appearance of excited states is a mere mathematical artifact. In the case of an atom a symmetry argument shows that the second choice of the gauge is not adapted to the problem. In a molecule without symmetry, however, a good choice of the gauge is not at all evident. As in Eq. (2), the usual expression for the susceptibility of a general molecule consists of an inherently negative term, involving the ground state wave function only, and of an inherently positive term, involving all excited states, including the continuum.

In theoretical discussions of the susceptibility of molecules (Van Vleck, 1932, p. 275ff.) and of the magnetic shielding of nuclei in molecules (for a review compare, e.g., Abragam, 1961, p. 175ff.) it has become usual to call the ground state term the "diamagnetic" part and the term involving the excited states the "paramagnetic" part. This partition is not gauge invariant and makes therefore no sense unless the gauge chosen is clearly specified. As our example shows, a specification of the origin of the coordinate system is not sufficient. In Section IV we give a unique procedure to determine an optimal gauge, in the sense that the difficult term involving the excited states will be as small as possible. Then the response kernel can be separated in a gauge invariant manner into two kernels giving this optimal partition, and we propose to call these kernels "diamagnetic" and "paramagnetic."

We intend to present a careful analysis of the magnetic response of molecules, making no pretence of strict mathematical rigor. The recent investigations on Dirac's δ-function as a linear functional (for a review compare, e.g. Gel'fand and Schilow, 1960, 1964; Gel'fand and Vilenkin, 1964) and on the validity of the expansion postulate of quantum mechanics (compare Jauch and Misra, 1965; Hellwig, 1964; Marlow, 1965) show that with a great deal of effort the Dirac formalism can be given a meaningful mathematical interpretation. For our purpose full rigor is hardly worth the trouble, and we use the Dirac formalism without further apology. In order to have a compact notation we often do not distinguish between discreet and continuous variables, summation and integration, Kronecker δ and Dirac δ. The perturbation of the spectrum of the Hamiltonian by an external field leads to delicate questions; the mathematical problems involved are far from trivial (compare, e.g., Friedrichs, 1965). We circumvent these difficulties by the physically sound assumption of the existence of a linear continuous response functional; *no assumption about the nature of the spectrum of the perturbed Hamiltonian will be needed.*

NOTATION

Vectors are printed in Roman boldface. We use a rectangular coordinate system and the summation convention, Greek indices running from 1 to 3. Space coordinates are designated by $\mathbf{r} = (r_1, r_2, r_3)$; for integrations we use the notation $d^3r = dr_1\, dr_2\, dr_3$, all integrals extend over the whole three dimensional space. Quantum mechanical operators are printed in capital German, superoperators in lowercase German.

II. Model Assumptions

A. THE THERMODYNAMIC APPROACH

The theory of the response of a system to an external disturbance* is often based on the adiabatic perturbation theory which, from the mathematical point of view, is exposed to severe criticism. In the case of an equilibrium system with a time independent Hamiltonian, however, the thermodynamic perturbation theory (reviewed by Nakajima, 1955) is both physically and mathematically more satisfactory. Most investigations of the magnetic properties of free molecules refer to a pure state and are hampered by the difficulties a rigorous discussion of nodes of the wave function and possible degeneracies involves (compare, e.g., the discussion by McLachlan and Baker, 1961). The concept of a " pure state " is an idealization never actually realized. Using the canonical ensemble may be more realistic and even simpler; the ground state properties are then given by the limit of zero temperature. The troubles caused by the singular nature of pure states are avoided by working out the theory for $T \neq 0$, postponing the zero temperature limit to the final result. Our main mathematical tool will be a temperature-dependent scalar

---

* There is an extensive literature on response theories. Besides the fundamental paper of Martin and Schwinger (1959) we should like to select for quotation the paper of Konstantinov and Perel' (1960) and the recent summary by Kubo (1965).

product for operators, discussed in the appendix. This scalar product becomes singular for $T = 0$ (i.e., for $T = 0$ the relation $\langle \mathfrak{A} \,|\, \mathfrak{A} \rangle = 0$ may hold even for $\mathfrak{A} \neq 0$); therefore this limit has to be discussed carefully.

We restrict our discussion to *finite systems* and use a statistical ensemble containing a fixed number of molecules. Most of the arguments can be extended to include condensed phases, but our main interest lies in the magnetic properties of *free molecules*.

B. THE OPERATOR OF THE CURRENT DENSITY

A molecular Lagrangian depends on external fields *linearly* only, even if relativistic corrections and spin interactions are included. Therefore the Lagrangian $\mathfrak{L}[A]$ of a system under the influence of an external, time independent magnetic field $\mathbf{B}(\mathbf{r}) = \mathrm{curl}\, \mathbf{A}(\mathbf{r})$ is given by

$$\mathfrak{L}[A] = \mathfrak{L}_0 + (1/c) \int d^3r\, \mathfrak{J}_\nu(\mathbf{r}) A_\nu(\mathbf{r}), \tag{3}$$

where $\mathfrak{J}_\nu(\mathbf{r})$ is the current density operator of the system. The Lagrangian $\mathfrak{L}\,(q, \dot{q}, A)$ is related to the Hamiltonian $\mathfrak{H}(q, p, A)$ by a Legendre transformation, hence

$$\left(\frac{\delta \mathfrak{L}}{\delta \mathbf{A}} \right)_{q=\mathrm{const},\ \dot{q}\,=\mathrm{const}} = - \left(\frac{\delta \mathfrak{H}}{\delta \mathbf{A}} \right)_{q=\mathrm{const},\ p=\mathrm{const}}$$

In spite of the fact that the Hamiltonian may have a complicated dependence on the external field, the correct current density operator can be obtained by a variational derivative of the Hamiltonian,

$$\mathfrak{J}_\nu(\mathbf{r}) = -c\, \delta \mathfrak{H}[A]/\delta A_\nu(\mathbf{r}), \tag{4}$$

where partial derivatives here and in the following always are in respect to the canonical variables (i.e., $q = \mathrm{const}$ and $p = \mathrm{const}$). In the canonical representation, the current density operator may contain the external field in high orders; for the linear response the first order only is needed,

$$\mathfrak{J}_\nu(\mathbf{r}) = \mathfrak{J}_{0\nu}(\mathbf{r}) + \int d^3r'\, \mathfrak{J}_{1\nu\mu}(\mathbf{rr}') A_\mu(\mathbf{r}') + \cdots, \tag{5}$$

where

$$\begin{aligned}
\mathfrak{J}_{0\nu}(\mathbf{r}) &= \{ \mathfrak{J}_\nu(\mathbf{r}) \}_{A=0}, \\
\mathfrak{J}_{1\nu\mu}(\mathbf{rr}') &= \{ \delta \mathfrak{J}_\nu(\mathbf{r})/\delta A_\mu(\mathbf{r}') \}_{A=0}.
\end{aligned} \tag{6}$$

Hence the Hamiltonian may be written in the following form:

$$\begin{aligned}
\mathfrak{H} = \mathfrak{H}_0 - (1/c) \int d^3r\, \mathfrak{J}_{0\nu}(\mathbf{r}) A_\nu(\mathbf{r}) \\
- (1/2c) \int d^3r \int d^3r'\, \mathfrak{J}_{1\nu\mu}(\mathbf{rr}') A_\nu(\mathbf{r}) A_\mu(\mathbf{r}') + \cdots.
\end{aligned} \tag{7}$$

C. Specification of a Born-Oppenheimer Hamiltonian

The discussion in Section IV uses an operator scalar product which is positive definite only if the Hamiltonian $\mathfrak{H}_0$ has a *complete* set of eigenfunctions; therefore $\mathfrak{H}_0$ should be self-adjoint. To the best of our knowledge this problem is not solved for a general molecule. As a result of the pioneering work of Kato (Kato, 1951; Ikebe and Kato, 1962; Žislin, 1960) it is known that a Born-Oppenheimer Hamiltonian (fixed nuclei) of N electrons with Coulomb interactions only is essentially self-adjoint, and has an infinite number of bound states with energies below the dissociation energy. If we choose as unperturbed Hamiltonian $\mathfrak{H}_0 = \mathfrak{H}[A = 0]$ the Born-Oppenheimer Hamiltonian without spin interactions and without relativistic terms, i.e., the operator

$$\mathfrak{H}_0 = \sum_{n=1}^{N} \frac{\mathbf{p}_n^2}{2m} - \sum_{n=1}^{N} \sum_{K} e_0^2 Z_K |\mathbf{R}_K - \mathfrak{q}_n|^{-1} + \sum_{\substack{n < m \\ 1}}^{N} e_0^2 |\mathfrak{q}_n - \mathfrak{q}_m|^{-1}, \tag{8}$$

we are therefore on safe ground. From the corresponding Hamiltonian in the presence of an external magnetic field $\mathbf{B} = \text{curl } \mathbf{A}$, the current density operator can be deduced according to Eq. (4) to (7). The well-known result is

$$\mathfrak{J}_0(\mathbf{r}) = -(e_0/2m) \sum_{n=1}^{N} \{\mathbf{p}_n \delta(\mathbf{r} - \mathfrak{q}_n) + \delta(\mathbf{r} - \mathfrak{q}_n)\mathbf{p}_n\}$$

$$+ c \sum_{n=1}^{N} \text{curl } \gamma \mathfrak{S}_n \delta(\mathbf{r} - \mathfrak{q}_n), \tag{9}$$

$$\mathfrak{J}_{1\nu\mu}(\mathbf{r}\mathbf{r}') = -(e_0^2/mc)\delta_{\nu\mu}\delta(\mathbf{r} - \mathbf{r}')\mathfrak{N}(\mathbf{r}), \tag{10}$$

with the number density operator $\mathfrak{N}$

$$\mathfrak{N}(\mathbf{r}) = \sum_{n=1}^{N} \delta(\mathbf{r} - \mathfrak{q}_n). \tag{11}$$

The vector $\mathbf{r}$ is an arbitrary parameter vector; $\mathfrak{q}_n$, $\mathbf{p}_n$, and $\mathfrak{S}_n$ are the position operator, the momentum operator, and the spin operator of the nth electron. e_0 represents the elementary charge, $e_0 > 0$; the charge of the electron is $-e_0$ and γ its gyromagnetic ratio.

III. Linear Magnetic Response

A. The Induced Current Density

We consider a specimen of substance in thermal equilibrium under the action of a magnetic field $\mathbf{B}(\mathbf{r})$,* which we assume to be time independent,

---

* Today there is no question that E and B are the basic field vectors, the fields D and H describing the influence of matter (compare, e.g., Born and Wolf, 1959, p. 1). Consequently (but in contrast to the historical tradition) we refer to E and B (and not to E and H) as to the electric and magnetic field vectors.

defined throughout all space, quadratic integrable in the sense of Lebesgue, and vanishing at infinity at least as a magnetic dipole, $|\mathbf{B(r)}| = O(r^{-3})$.* Under the action of the magnetic field $\mathbf{B(r)}$ a field of magnetization $\mathbf{M(r)}$ is established. The magnetization $\mathbf{M(r)}$ is an *experimentally measurable* quantity (e.g., by magnetic resonance experiments) and is given by the fundamental relation (compare, e.g., Phillips, 1962, p. 27)

$$\mathbf{M(r)} = - \frac{\delta F}{\delta \mathbf{B(r)}}. \tag{12}$$

It is convenient to replace the solenoidal vectors $\mathbf{B}$ and $\mathbf{M}$ by the vector potential $\mathbf{A}$ and the current density $\mathbf{J}$, respectively. The relations

$$\mathbf{B(r)} = \operatorname{curl} \mathbf{A(r)}, \tag{13}$$

$$\mathbf{A(r)} = \mathbf{A}^T(\mathbf{r}) + \operatorname{grad} \chi(\mathbf{r}), \qquad \operatorname{div} \mathbf{A}^T = 0, \tag{14}$$

$$\mathbf{J(r)} = c \operatorname{curl} \mathbf{M(r)}, \qquad \operatorname{div} \mathbf{J} = 0, \tag{15}$$

define $\mathbf{J(r)}$ and the transversal vector potential $\mathbf{A}^T$ uniquely, but the longitudinal part grad χ is arbitrary. In the following, however, grad χ is assumed to be single valued, time independent, and square integrable in the sense of Lebesgue; the function χ is then called a *gauge function*.

In consequence of Eqs. (12) and (15) the induced current density is given rigorously by a variational derivative of the free energy,

$$\mathbf{J(r)} = -c \frac{\delta F}{\delta \mathbf{A(r)}}. \tag{16}$$

According to Bloch's theorem (compare, e.g., the discussion by Schafroth, 1960, p. 405) and due to the time inversal invariance, the current density of any system in thermal equilibrium and not subject to external magnetic fields (internal fields are permitted, however) vanishes everywhere, i.e.,

$$\{\mathbf{J(r)}\}_{\mathbf{A}=0} = 0. \tag{17}$$

Excluding phase transitions, it is physically evident that the induced current density as an experimentally measurable quantity has to be a *continuous* functional of the external field. Therefore the linear part $\mathbf{J}^L$ of the response $\mathbf{J}$ is a continuous linear functional of the vector potential $\mathbf{A}$, warranting by the Riesz representation theorem (compare, e.g., Neumark, 1959) the existence

---

* Differentiability is not necessary, the vector operations grad, div, and curl are used in the sense of Weyl (1940) or Müller (1957). The usual assumption of a magnetic field homogeneous over all space is unphysical, leads to severe mathematical difficulties, and should therefore not be used.

of an integrable kernel $F_{\nu\mu}(\mathbf{rr}')$. The linear response $\mathbf{J}^L$ is therefore given by

$$J_\nu^L(\mathbf{r}) = -c \int d^3r' \, F_{\nu\mu}(\mathbf{rr}')A_\mu(\mathbf{r}'), \tag{18}$$

where

$$F_{\nu\mu}(\mathbf{rr}') = \left\{ \frac{\delta^2 F[\mathbf{A}]}{\delta A_\nu(\mathbf{r})\delta A_\mu(\mathbf{r}')} \right\}_{\mathbf{A}=0} \tag{19}$$

The kernel $F_{\nu\mu}(\mathbf{rr}')$ is real and symmetric,

$$F_{\nu\mu}(\mathbf{rr}') = \{F_{\nu\mu}(\mathbf{rr}')\}^*, \qquad F_{\nu\mu}(\mathbf{rr}') = F_{\mu\nu}(\mathbf{r}'\mathbf{r}). \tag{20}$$

It goes without saying that the free energy is gauge-invariant, i.e., the relation

$$F[\mathbf{A} + \text{grad } \chi] = F[\mathbf{A}] \tag{21}$$

holds for any gauge function χ. Taking the variational derivatives in respect to the function χ, we get the important relations

$$\text{div } \mathbf{J}^L = 0 \tag{22}$$

$$\partial F_{\nu\mu}(\mathbf{rr}')/\partial r_\nu = \partial F_{\nu\mu}(\mathbf{rr}')/\partial r_\mu' = 0 \tag{23}$$

B. THE KERNEL OF THE LINEAR MAGNETIC RESPONSE

If $\mathfrak{A}$ is some observable, the quantum-statistical expectation value $\langle \mathfrak{A} \rangle$ of $\mathfrak{A}$ with respect to the canonical ensemble of a system with the temperature T ($\beta = 1/kT$) is given by

$$\langle \mathfrak{A} \rangle = (1/Z) \, \text{Tr}\{\mathfrak{A} \exp(-\beta \mathfrak{H})\}, \tag{24}$$

$$Z = \text{Tr}\{\exp(-\beta \mathfrak{H})\}, \tag{25}$$

where the trace runs over a complete set of states with appropriate permutation symmetry. From a knowledge† of the partition functional or, equivalently, the functional of the free energy F,

$$-\beta F = \ln Z, \tag{26}$$

all expectation values or response kernels can be evaluated. Since no current flows in thermal equilibrium in the absence of a magnetic field [Eq. (17)], the response kernel $F_{\nu\mu}(\mathbf{rr}')$ [Eq. (19)] can be reduced to a second derivative of the partition functional Z,

$$-\beta F_{\nu\mu}(\mathbf{rr}') = \frac{1}{Z}\left\{ \frac{\delta^2 Z}{\delta A_\nu(\mathbf{r})\delta A_\mu(\mathbf{r}')} \right\}_{\mathbf{A}=0}. \tag{27}$$

† The partition function and related quantities are most conveniently and systematically evaluated in the formalism of the temperature dependent 1-particle Green function (compare the excellent introductions by Bonch-Bruevich and Tyablikov, 1962; Kadanoff and Baym, 1962; Abrikosov *et al.*, 1963).

Using the fact that the trace of a product of operators is invariant under cyclic permutations, the second functional derivative of the partition functional can be written as*

$$\frac{\delta^2 Z}{\delta A_\nu(\mathbf{r})\delta A_\mu(\mathbf{r}')} = -\beta \, \mathrm{Tr}\left\{ e^{-\beta\mathfrak{H}} \, \frac{\delta^2 \mathfrak{H}}{\delta A_\nu(\mathbf{r})\delta A_\mu(\mathbf{r}')} \right\}$$

$$-\beta \, \mathrm{Tr}\left\{ \frac{\delta\mathfrak{H}}{\delta A_\mu(\mathbf{r}')} \, \frac{\delta}{\delta A_\nu(\mathbf{r})} \, e^{-\beta\mathfrak{H}} \right\}. \tag{28}$$

The second term in Eq. (28) is best evaluated with the aid of the following operator identity:

$$\frac{\delta}{\delta\Phi} \exp(-\beta\mathfrak{H}[\Phi]) = -\exp(-\beta\mathfrak{H}[\Phi])\mathfrak{k}\left\{ \frac{\delta\mathfrak{H}[\Phi]}{\delta\Phi} \right\}, \tag{29}$$

where $\mathfrak{k}$ is the superoperator† of the Kubo transform, defined by

$$\mathfrak{k}\{\mathfrak{X}\} = \int_0^\beta d\lambda \, \exp(\lambda\mathfrak{H}) \, \mathfrak{X} \, \exp(-\lambda\mathfrak{H}) \qquad \text{for any operator } \mathfrak{X}. \tag{30}$$

With this relation and using Eqs. (4) and (24), Eq. (28) can be written in the form

$$\frac{1}{Z}\frac{\delta^2 Z}{\delta A_\nu(\mathbf{r})\delta A_\mu(\mathbf{r}')} = (\beta/c)\langle \delta\mathfrak{J}_\nu(\mathbf{r})/\delta A_\mu(\mathbf{r}')\rangle$$

$$+ (\beta/c^2)\langle \mathfrak{k}\{\mathfrak{J}_\nu(\mathbf{r})\}\mathfrak{J}_\mu(\mathbf{r}')\rangle. \tag{31}$$

The kernel Eq. (27) is the limit $\mathbf{A} = 0$ of this expression; using Eq. (6) the kernel of the linear magnetic response is therefore given by

$$F_{\nu\mu}(\mathbf{rr}') = -(1/c)\langle\mathfrak{J}_{1\nu\mu}(\mathbf{rr}')\rangle_0$$

$$-(1/c^2)\langle\mathfrak{k}_0\{\mathfrak{J}_{0\nu}(\mathbf{r})\}\mathfrak{J}_{0\mu}(\mathbf{r}')\rangle_0 \tag{32}$$

whereby all quantities are in respect to the unperturbed system. The following abbreviations are used

$$\langle\mathfrak{X}\rangle_0 = \mathrm{Tr}\{\mathfrak{X} \exp(-\beta\mathfrak{H}_0)\}/\mathrm{Tr}\{\exp(-\beta\mathfrak{H}_0)\}, \tag{33}$$

$$\mathfrak{k}_0\{\mathfrak{X}\} = \int_0^\beta d\lambda \, \exp(\lambda\mathfrak{H}_0) \, \mathfrak{X} \, \exp(-\lambda\mathfrak{H}_0). \tag{34}$$

---

* In this step we also assumed the functional derivative to be interchangeable with the trace, but we are not aware of a rigorous proof (the situation improved by the recent work by Langerholc, 1965). Experimentally measurable quantities are rigorously related to Eq. (27); if this relation should not be equivalent to Eq. (32), then the current density $\mathbf{J}$ defined by Eq. (18) would not be given by the quantum statistical expectation value of the current density operator.

† A superoperator is an operator which transforms an operator on the Hilbert space of quantum mechanical state vectors into a new operator on this Hilbert space.

In the appendix it is shown that the expression

$$\langle \mathfrak{k}_0 \{ \mathfrak{X}^+ \} \mathfrak{Y} \rangle_0 = \langle \mathfrak{X} | \mathfrak{Y} \rangle_0 \qquad (35)$$

has all properties of a scalar product. The final result for the linear magnetic response may therefore be written in the form

$$
\begin{aligned}
cJ_\nu^L(\mathbf{r}) &= \int d^3 r'\, K_{\nu\mu}(\mathbf{rr}') A_\mu(\mathbf{r}') \\
K_{\nu\mu}(\mathbf{rr}') &= K_{\nu\mu}^{(1)}(\mathbf{rr}') + K_{\nu\mu}^{(2)}(\mathbf{rr}') \\
K_{\nu\mu}^{(1)}(\mathbf{rr}') &= c \langle \mathfrak{J}_{1\nu\mu}(\mathbf{rr}') \rangle_0 \\
K_{\nu\mu}^{(2)}(\mathbf{rr}') &= \langle \mathfrak{J}_{0\nu}(\mathbf{r}) | \mathfrak{J}_{0\mu}(\mathbf{r}') \rangle_0
\end{aligned}
\qquad (36)
$$

The kernel $K^{(1)}$ is just an expectation value of a simple operator in respect to the unperturbed ensemble, and therefore relatively easy to evaluate. In the metric chosen the kernel $K^{(2)}$ is the current-current autocorrelation tensor; the positive definite character of the scalar product [Eq. (35)] implies

$$\int d^3 r \int d^3 r'\, V_\nu(\mathbf{r}) K_{\nu\mu}^{(2)}(\mathbf{rr}') V_\mu(r') > 0$$

for any admissible vector $\mathbf{V} \neq 0$, therefore $K^{(2)}$ is positive definite, $K^{(2)} > 0$. The complete evaluation of $K^{(2)}$ is much more complicated than that of $K^{(1)}$, but these two kernels are not independent. The gauge relation (23) gives the interrelation

$$\partial K_{\nu\mu}^{(2)}(\mathbf{rr}')/\partial r_\nu = -\partial K_{\nu\mu}^{(1)}(\mathbf{rr}')/\partial r_\nu, \qquad (37)$$

$$\partial K_{\nu\mu}^{(2)}(\mathbf{rr}')/\partial r_\mu' = -\partial K_{\nu\mu}^{(1)}(\mathbf{rr}')/\partial r_\mu'. \qquad (38)$$

IV. The Diamagnetism vs Paramagnetism

A. THE OPTIMAL GAUGE FOR A FREE MOLECULE

In this section we restrict our considerations to free molecules. Therefore we are supposed to have a system of noninteracting molecules in thermal equilibrium at a fixed temperature $T \neq 0$. The Hamiltonian of the whole system separates then into a sum of molecular Hamiltonians; in the following the terms "free energy," "partition function," and "Hamiltonian" refer to a single molecule. As molecular Hamiltonian we choose the simple Born-Oppenheimer operator Eqs. (7) to (11).

The free energy per molecule, according to Section III, is given by

$$F = F_0 - (1/c^2)\{F^{(1)} + F^{(2)}\} + O(A^3), \qquad (39)$$

where F_0 is the free energy of the molecule without an external field and

$$F^{(i)} = \int d^3r \int d^3r' \, A_\nu(\mathbf{r}) K^{(i)}_{\nu\mu}(\mathbf{r}\mathbf{r}') A_\mu(\mathbf{r}') \qquad (i = 1, 2). \tag{40}$$

Neither $F^{(1)}$ nor $F^{(2)}$ is gauge-invariant but their sum depends on the transversal vector potential only. According to Eqs. (10) and (36), $F^{(1)}$ is given by

$$F^{(1)} = -(e_0^2/m) \int d^3r \, \rho_0(\mathbf{r}) A^2(\mathbf{r}), \tag{41}$$

where $\rho_0(\mathbf{r})$ is the expectation value of the number density in respect to the unperturbed ensemble,

$$\rho_0(\mathbf{r}) = \langle \mathfrak{N}(\mathbf{r}) \rangle_0. \tag{42}$$

Hence $F^{(1)}$ is negative, while the positive definite correlation kernel $K^{(2)}$ implies a positive $F^{(2)}$,

$$F^{(1)} < 0, \qquad F^{(2)} > 0. \tag{43}$$

Because of the difficulties involved in the practical evaluation of the kernel $K^{(2)}$ it is useful to choose a gauge minimizing $F^{(2)}$. Maximizing the functional $F^{(1)}$ in respect to the gauge function χ for a given $\mathbf{A}^T$ yields the necessary condition

$$\boxed{\operatorname{div}\{\rho_0(\mathbf{r}) \operatorname{grad} \chi(\mathbf{r})\} + A^T(\mathbf{r}) \operatorname{grad} \rho_0(\mathbf{r}) = 0} \tag{44}$$

This elliptic differential equation has to be solved for χ (compare Section IV,B). There is a unique solution that we call the *optimal gauge function** for the transversal vector potential $\mathbf{A}^T$. In this gauge $F^{(1)}$ is maximal and given by

$$F^{(1)}_{\mathrm{opt}} = -(e_0^2/m) \int d^3r \, \rho_0(\mathbf{r})\{[\mathbf{A}^T(\mathbf{r})]^2 - [\operatorname{grad} \chi_{\mathrm{opt}}(\mathbf{r})]^2\}. \tag{45}$$

B. A GAUGE INVARIANT PARTITION OF THE MAGNETIC RESPONSE

It is useful to state the result of the preceding section in a gauge invariant manner. Equation (44) has to be solved in an infinite region for the optimal gauge function $\chi = \chi_{\mathrm{opt}}$. To this end we consider the corresponding eigenvalue problem,

$$\operatorname{div}\{\rho_0(\mathbf{r}) \operatorname{grad} \phi_n(\mathbf{r})\} + \alpha_n \phi_n(\mathbf{r}) = 0. \tag{46}$$

According to the theory of generalized eigenfunctions (Gel'fand and Schilow, 1964, p. 170) and to a theorem of L. Schwartz (compare, e.g., Bers and

---

* Similar-looking equations and the problem of an optimal gauge have been discussed by Stephen (1957), Rebane (1960), McLachlan and Baker (1961), Guy et al. (1961), and others. Their equations were not elliptic and the existence of solutions could not be proved, probably they do not have regular solutions.

Schechter, 1964, p. 139) an elliptic operator over an infinite region has a complete set of square integrable eigenfunctions, provided $\rho_0(\mathbf{r})$ is infinitely differentiable. Furthermore all eigenvalues α_n are positive what can be proved as follows. From Eqs. (10), (36), and (38) the following kernel representation of the operator $\mathrm{div}\,\rho_0\,\mathrm{grad}$ is obtained

$$\int d^3r'\, D(\mathbf{rr'})f(\mathbf{r'}) = -(e_0^2/m)\,\mathrm{div}\{\rho_0(\mathbf{r})\,\mathrm{grad}\,f(\mathbf{r})\}, \tag{47}$$

with

$$D(\mathbf{rr'}) = \frac{\partial}{\partial r_\nu}\frac{\partial}{\partial r'_\mu}\,K^{(2)}_{\nu\mu}(\mathbf{rr'}), \tag{48}$$

or with Eq. (37),

$$D(\mathbf{rr'}) = \langle \mathrm{div}\,\mathfrak{J}_0(\mathbf{r})\,|\,\mathrm{div}\,\mathfrak{J}_0(\mathbf{r'})\rangle_0 . \tag{49}$$

In the appendix it is shown that $\langle \mathfrak{X}\,|\,\mathfrak{X}\rangle_0 > 0$ for $\mathfrak{X} \neq 0$, hence the kernel $D(\mathbf{rr'})$ (in the space of quadratically integrable functions) is positive definite and all eigenvalues of D are positive.

Therefore an optimal gauge function χ_{opt} exists, is uniquely determined, and given by

$$\chi_{\mathrm{opt}}(\mathbf{r}) = \sum_n (1/\alpha_n)\phi_n(\mathbf{r})\int d^3r'\,\phi_n(\mathbf{r'})\mathbf{A}^T(\mathbf{r'})\,\mathrm{grad}\,\rho_0(\mathbf{r'}), \tag{50}$$

where the eigenfunctions are taken orthonormalized,

$$\int d^3r\,\phi_n(\mathbf{r})\phi_m(\mathbf{r}) = \delta_{nm} . \tag{51}$$

In an arbitrary gauge χ the contribution of the kernel $K^{(1)}$ to the current density is given by

$$cJ^{(1)}_\nu(\mathbf{r}) = \int d^3r'\,K^{(1)}_{\nu\mu}(\mathbf{rr'})\{A^T_\mu(\mathbf{r'}) + \partial\chi/\partial r'_\mu\}. \tag{52}$$

In the optimal gauge $\chi = \chi_{\mathrm{opt}}$, $\mathbf{J}^{(1)} = \mathbf{J}^{\mathrm{opt}}$, Eq. (52) can be written as

$$cJ^{\mathrm{opt}}_\nu(\mathbf{r}) = \int d^3r'\,K^D_{\nu\mu}(\mathbf{rr'})A^T_\mu(\mathbf{r'}), \tag{53}$$

where, according to Eq. (50), the new kernel K^D is given by

$$\boxed{\begin{aligned}
K^D_{\nu\mu}(\mathbf{rr'}) &= -(e_0^2/m)\rho_0(\mathbf{r})\delta_{\nu\mu}\delta(\mathbf{r}-\mathbf{r'}) \\
&\quad + (e_0^2/m)\rho_0(\mathbf{r})\rho_0(\mathbf{r'})\sum_n \frac{1}{\alpha_n}\frac{\partial\phi_n(\mathbf{r})}{\partial r_\nu}\frac{\partial\phi_n(\mathbf{r'})}{\partial r'_\mu}
\end{aligned}} \tag{54}$$

In general $\mathbf{J}^{(1)}$ defined by Eq. (52) is not solenoidal. It is therefore remarkable that $\mathbf{J}^{\mathrm{opt}}$ is a true current, i.e.,

$$\mathrm{div}\,\mathbf{J}^{\mathrm{opt}} = 0 \tag{55}$$

as a simple calculation using Eq. (46) and the completeness relation for the functions ϕ_n shows. Equation (55) is identical with the relations

$$\partial K_{\nu\mu}^D(\mathbf{rr}')/\partial r_\nu = \partial K_{\nu\mu}^D(\mathbf{rr}')/\partial r_\mu' = 0 \qquad (56)$$

the second following from the symmetry of the kernel K^D. The validity of the gauge relations Eq. (56) permits a calculation of the current $\mathbf{J}^{\mathrm{opt}}$ in a gauge invariant manner, i.e., the current density $\mathbf{J}^D$ defined by

$$c J_\nu^D(\mathbf{r}) = \int d^3r' \, K_{\nu\mu}^D(\mathbf{rr}') A_\mu(\mathbf{r}') \qquad (57)$$

may be calculated in any gauge of the vector potential and is equal to $\mathbf{J}^{\mathrm{opt}}$.

C. CONCLUSIONS

The conventional splitting of the response kernel K according to Eq. (36) into the two kernels $K^{(1)}$ and $K^{(2)}$ is not gauge invariant and the quantities,

$$\int d^3r' \, K_{\nu\mu}^{(i)}(\mathbf{rr}') A_\mu(\mathbf{r}') \qquad (i = 1, 2),$$

are in general not solenoidal and therefore cannot be interpreted as partial currents.

Imposing physically reasonable restrictions (the external magnetic field approaches zero at large distances like r^{-3}; nonzero temperature), we have given an optimal and gauge invariant partition of the response kernel,

$$K = K^D + K^P, \qquad (58)$$

where K^D is defined by Eq. (54). The gauge invariance is reflected by the relations

$$\begin{aligned} \partial K_{\nu\mu}^D(\mathbf{rr}')/\partial r_\nu &= \partial K_{\nu\mu}^D(\mathbf{rr}')/\partial r_\mu' = 0, \\ \partial K_{\nu\mu}^P(\mathbf{rr}')/\partial r_\nu &= \partial K_{\nu\mu}^P(\mathbf{rr}')/\partial r_\mu' = 0, \end{aligned} \qquad (59)$$

implying that the linear response $\mathbf{J}^L$ consists of two solenoidal and gauge invariant currents $\mathbf{J}^D$ and $\mathbf{J}^P$,

$$\begin{aligned} \mathbf{J}^L(\mathbf{r}) &= \mathbf{J}^D(\mathbf{r}) + \mathbf{J}^P(\mathbf{r}), \\ \mathrm{div}\, \mathbf{J}^D &= \mathrm{div}\, \mathbf{J}^P = 0, \end{aligned} \qquad (60)$$

which can be calculated from the relations

$$c J_\nu^D(\mathbf{r}) = \int d^3r' \, K_{\nu\mu}^D(\mathbf{rr}') A_\mu(\mathbf{r}'),$$

$$c J_\nu^P(\mathbf{r}) = \int d^3r' \, K_{\nu\mu}^P(\mathbf{rr}') A_\mu(\mathbf{r}') \qquad (61)$$

in any gauge of the vector potential. This partition is optimal in the sense that both K^D and K^P are maximal negative, i.e.,*

$$K^D \leqq K^{(1)} < 0, \qquad 0 < K^P \leqq K^{(2)}. \tag{62}$$

This relation holds for $T > 0$; for $T = 0$ there may be exceptional situations (e.g., for atoms at $T = 0$ the contribution of K^P may vanish). The kernel K^D [Eq. (54)] may be calculated by a knowledge of the charge density $-e_0 \rho_0(\mathbf{r})$ of the unperturbed system only. For a given external field the direct solution of Eq. (44) may be more practical, the current $\mathbf{J}^D$ is then given by

$$\mathbf{J}^D(\mathbf{r}) = -(e_0^2/mc)\rho_0(\mathbf{r})\{\mathbf{A}^T(\mathbf{r}) + \mathrm{grad}\, \chi_{\mathrm{opt}}(\mathbf{r})\}. \tag{63}$$

The kernel K^P is given by $K - K^D$ and is the true current-current autocorrelation tensor.

Because of these unique properties we propose to call $\mathbf{J}^D$ and $\mathbf{J}^P$ *diamagnetic and paramagnetic current density* respectively; K^D the diamagnetic part and K^P the paramagnetic part of the response kernel K. All linear magnetic properties of a molecule are determined by the response kernel, therefore the concepts of a diamagnetic and paramagnetic part say of the susceptibility tensor $\chi_{\nu\mu}(\mathbf{rr}')$ or the chemical shift tensor $\sigma_{\nu\mu}(\mathbf{rr}')$ are uniquely and optimally defined, e.g.,

$$\chi^D \leqq \chi^{(1)} < 0, \qquad 0 < \chi^P \leqq \chi^{(2)}, \tag{64}$$

$$\sigma^D \leqq \sigma^{(1)} < 0, \qquad 0 < \sigma^P \leqq \sigma^{(2)}. \tag{65}$$

Appendix. A Temperature Dependent Scalar Product for Operators

It is convenient to introduce a metric into the algebra of the operators on the Hilbert space of quantum mechanical state vectors. In this operator algebra, a scalar product is a scalar valued function of two operators $\mathfrak{X}$ and $\mathfrak{Y}$, written $\langle \mathfrak{X} | \mathfrak{Y} \rangle$, such that

(a) $\langle \mathfrak{X} | \mathfrak{Y} \rangle = \langle \mathfrak{Y} | \mathfrak{X} \rangle^*$

(b) $\langle \mathfrak{X} | \alpha_1 \mathfrak{Y}_1 + \alpha_2 \mathfrak{Y}_2 \rangle = \alpha_1 \langle \mathfrak{X} | \mathfrak{Y}_1 \rangle + \alpha_2 \langle \mathfrak{X} | \mathfrak{Y}_2 \rangle$ $(\alpha_i = \mathrm{scalar})$

(c) $\langle \mathfrak{X} | \mathfrak{X} \rangle > 0$ for $\mathfrak{X} \neq \mathfrak{O}$ $(\mathfrak{O} = \text{zero operator})$

For a response theory in respect to an unperturbed canonical ensemble with

---

* $K > 0$ means a positive definite kernel, $\int d^3r \int d^3r' V_\nu(\mathbf{r})K_{\nu\mu}(\mathbf{rr}')V_\mu(\mathbf{r}')$ for all admissible vectors V. $K > L$ means that $K - L$ is positive definite.

the Hamiltonian $\mathfrak{H}$ the following definition of a proper scalar product is appropriate:[†]

$$\langle \mathfrak{X} | \mathfrak{Y} \rangle = \langle \mathfrak{k}\{\mathfrak{X}^+\} \mathfrak{Y} \rangle$$

$$= \int_0^\beta d\lambda \, \mathrm{Tr}\{e^{-\beta\mathfrak{H}} \, e^{\lambda\mathfrak{H}} \mathfrak{X}^+ e^{-\lambda\mathfrak{H}} \mathfrak{Y}\} / \mathrm{Tr}\{e^{-\beta\mathfrak{H}}\},$$

where k is the superoperator of the Kubo transform [Eq. (30)]. The verification of the conditions (a) and (b) is trivial, just as that of the additional relation

$$\langle \mathfrak{X} | \mathfrak{Y} \rangle = \langle \mathfrak{Y}^+ | \mathfrak{X}^+ \rangle.$$

This scalar product is tailored to a problem with the Hamiltonian $\mathfrak{H}$. The derivation superoperator $\mathfrak{h}$ of the Hamiltonian $\mathfrak{H}$, defined by

$$\mathfrak{h}(\mathfrak{X}) = [\mathfrak{H}, \mathfrak{X}] \qquad \text{(for all operators } \mathfrak{X}\text{)}$$

is hermitean in respect to this metric, i.e.,

$$\langle \mathfrak{X} | \mathfrak{h}(\mathfrak{Y}) \rangle = \langle \mathfrak{h}(\mathfrak{X}) | \mathfrak{X} \rangle.$$

The positive definite character of this scalar product depends essentially on the Hamiltonian used, the property (c) holds if and only if the Hamiltonian has a *complete* set of eigenfunctions. Let $\{\psi_n\}$ be a complete, orthonormalized system of eigenfunctions of the Hamiltonian,

$$\mathfrak{H}\psi_n = E_n\psi_n, \qquad (\psi_n, \psi_m) = \delta_{nm},$$

$$X_{nm} = (\psi_n | \mathfrak{X} | \psi_m).$$

In this representation, the norm of $\mathfrak{X}$ is given by

$$\langle \mathfrak{X} | \mathfrak{X} \rangle = (1/Z) \sum_n \sum_m \int_0^\beta d\lambda \, \exp(-\beta E_n + \lambda E_n - \lambda E_m) \, X_{nm}^* X_{mn}$$

$$= (1/Z) \sum_n \sum_m |X_{nm}|^2 \frac{\exp(-\beta E_m) - \exp(-\beta E_n)}{E_n - E_m}$$
$$\scriptstyle (E_n \neq E_m)$$

$$+ (1/z)\beta \sum_n \sum_m |X_{nm}|^2 \exp(-\beta E_n).$$
$$\scriptstyle (E_n = E_m)$$

If $\mathfrak{X}$ is not the zero operator, there exists at least one X_{nm} different from zero, whence $\langle \mathfrak{X} | \mathfrak{X} \rangle > 0$ for $0 < \beta \, \infty$. For $\beta = 0$ or $T = 0$, the scalar product becomes semidefinite.

[†] This scalar product was used by Nakano (1960, 1963) and by Mori (1965), but its important property of positive definiteness was neither used nor proved.

REFERENCES

Abragam, A. (1961). "The Principles of Nuclear Magnetism." Oxford Univ. Press (Clarendon), London and New York.

Abrikosov, A. A., Gorkov, L. P., and Dzyaloshinski, I. E. (1963). "Methods of Quantum Field Theory in Statistical Physics." Prentice-Hall, Englewood Cliffs, New Jersey.

Bers, L., and Schechter, M. (1964). *In* "Lectures in Applied Mathematics, Vol. III, Partial Differential Equations." Wiley (Interscience), New York.

Bloch, F. (1961). *In* "Werner Heisenberg und die Physik unserer Zeit" (F. Bopp, ed.), pp. 93–102. Vieweg, Braunschweig.

Bonch-Bruevich, V. L., and Tyablikov, S. V. (1962). "The Green Function Method in Statistical Mechanics." North-Holland Publ., Amsterdam.

Born, M., and Wolf, E. (1959). "Principles of Optics." Pergamon Press, Oxford.

Friedrichs, K. O. (1965). "Perturbation of Spectra in Hilbert Space." Am. Math. Soc., Providence, Rhode Island.

Gel'fand, I. M., and Schilow, G. E. (1960)."Verallgemeinerte Funktionen," Vol. I. VEB Deutscher Verlag der Wissenschaften, Berlin.

Gel'fand, I. M., and Schilow, G. E. (1964). "Verallgemeinerte Funktionen," Vol. 3. VEB Deutscher Verlag der Wissenschaften, Berlin.

Gel'fand, I. M., and Vilenkin, N. Ya. (1964). "Generalized Functions," Vol. 4. Academic Press, New York.

Guy, J., Cabaret, F., and Didry, J. (1961). *Compt. Rend.* **252**, 1296.

Hellwig, G. (1964). "Differentialoperatoren der Mathematischen Physik." Springer, Berlin.

Ikebe, T., and Kato, T. (1962). *Arch. Rat. Mech. Anal.* **9**, 77.

Jauch, J. M., and Misra, B. (1965). *Helv. Phys. Acta* **38**, 30.

Kadanoff, L. P., and Baym, G. (1962). "Quantum Statistical Mechanics." Benjamin, New York.

Kato, T. (1951). *Trans. Am. Math. Soc.* **70**, 195.

Konstantinov, O. V., and Perel', V. I. (1960). *Soviet Phys. JETP (English Transl.)* **10**, 560.

Kubo, R. (1965). *In* "Statistical Mechanics of Equilibrium and Nonequilibrium" (J. Meixner, ed.), pp. 81–99. North-Holland Publ., Amsterdam.

Langerholc, J. (1965). *J. Math. Phys.* **6**, 1210.

Marlow, A. R. (1965). *J. Math. Phys.* **6**, 919.

Martin, P. C., and Schwinger, J. (1959). *Phys. Rev.* **115**, 1342.

McLachlan, A. D., and Baker, M. R. (1961). *Mol. Phys.* **4**, 255.

Mori, H. (1965). *Progr. Theoret. Phys. (Kyoto)* **33**, 423.

Müller, C. (1957). "Grundprobleme der Mathematischen Theorie Elektromagnetischer Schwingungen." Springer, Berlin.

Nakajima, S. (1955). *Advan. Phys.* **4**, 363.

Nakano, H. (1960). *Progr. Theoret. Phys. (Kyoto)* **23**, 526.

Nakano, H. (1963). *Proc. Phys. Soc. (London)* **82**, 757.

Neumark, M. A. (1959). "Normierte Algebren." VEB Deutscher Verlag der Wissenschaften, Berlin.

Phillips, M. (1962). *In* "Encyclopedia of Physics" (S. Flüegge, ed.), Vol. IV. Springer, Berlin.

Rebane, T. K. (1960). *Soviet Phys. JETP (English Transl.)* **11**, 694.

Schafroth, M. R. (1960). *Solid State Phys.* **10**, 293–498.

Stephen, M. J. (1957). *Proc. Roy. Soc. (London)* **A243**, 264.

Van Vleck, J. H. (1932). "The Theory of Electric and Magnetic Susceptibilities." Oxford Univ. Press, London and New York.

Weyl, H. (1940). *Duke Math. J.* **7**, 411.

Žislin, G. M. (1960). *Tr. Mosk. Mat. Obše.* **9**, 82.

Molecular Fragment Models of Parts of Conjugated Heterocyclics*¶ I

R. B. HERMANN,† P. G. LYKOS, J. D. SHARP-RITTER,‡
and R. MOCCIA§

ILLINOIS INSTITUTE OF TECHNOLOGY, CHICAGO, ILLINOIS

I. Introduction

Pi-electron theory has proven to be a useful theory in explaining molecular electronic and magnetic spectra, ionization potentials, and relative reactivity where this can be interpreted in terms of electron-density distribution. The theory developed rather intuitively via Hückel theory and was given a more quantitative foundation by Goeppert-Mayer and Sklar. Essential simplifications introduced by Pariser, Parr, and Pople led to a very tractable and successful parameterized theory. Finally, the pi-electron approximation was given a general theoretical formulation by Lykos and Parr (Lykos, 1964). Now that this adequate theoretical framework has been developed, the next step is to test it by first making *ab initio* calculations on selected systems, and then analyzing these within the theoretical framework of pi-electron theory.

There exists a substantial gap between accurate *ab initio* calculations for small molecules such as Cl_2^- (Wahl and Gilbert, 1966) and semiempirical

* A preliminary account of this work was given by P. G. Lykos, R. B. Hermann, J. D. Sharp-Ritter, and R. Moccia, *Bull. Am. Phys. Soc.* 9, 145 (1964).

† Present address: Analytical Research Department, Eli Lilly and Company, Indianapolis Indiana.

‡ Present address: Roosevelt University, Chicago, Illinois.

§ Present address: University of Pisa, Pisa, Italy.

¶ A continuation of this work and an extension to heterocyclics is given in: Molecular Fragments of Heterocyclic Aromatic Compounds, J. D. Sharp-Ritter, Ph.D. Thesis, Illinois Inst. Tech. (1965).

calculations on larger molecules such as purine. While the formalism of the *ab initio* approaches has now come to be more and more widely used as a basis for improved semiempirical theories, ultimately a representation for the molecular orbitals involved needs to be specified and the corresponding one- and two-electron integrals somehow evaluated if numbers relating to physical observables are to be produced. There have been two separate levels of approximation used here.

The first level has been concerned with the identity and the size of the basis set to be used for representing the molecular orbitals for the system. It has been common for various workers to use a single Slater orbital, or Slater-type orbital at each nucleus per electron or per electron pair brought to the molecule by the corresponding atom. More recently Hartree-Fock orbitals found for the corresponding free atom have been used in constructing molecular orbitals for the molecular system. In the case where single Slater-type orbitals have been used there have been some attempts to "condition" the atomic orbital to its molecular environment by adjusting the scale of the orbital empirically. However, all of these procedures prove to be inadequate when tested within the framework of a simple system where higher accuracy can be achieved. The most promising new development for *ab initio* work appears to be that where Hartree-Fock orbitals for the corresponding free atoms are used as building blocks and appropriate additional Slater-type orbitals introduced to allow for changes in the outermost atomic orbitals which are most affected by the process of bond formation (Das and Wahl, 1966). In semiempirical work the problem of selection of a basis has been circumvented to a large extent by considering that the molecule is made up of atomlike parts where such atomlike parts can be identified with free atoms or smaller molecules existing in appropriate valence states. Then experimentally determined quantities are used to " evaluate " those molecular integrals relating to the atomlike parts (Cusachs and Reynolds, 1965). However, no satisfactory technique has been evolved which assesses the interaction between such atomlike parts without necessitating actual evaluation of integrals over explicit atomlike wave functions.

The second level of approximation has been in the evaluation of the one- and two-electron integrals that arise once the basis for the representation has been fixed. Here it has been customary to use the Mulliken or Sklar or even rougher approximations in order to reduce all integrals to combinations of one-center integrals and two-center Coulomb-type and overlap integrals (Fischer-Hjalmars, 1965). Furthermore, in dealing with conjugated systems, only some of the electrons are handled explicitly and the effect of the remaining electrons is assessed in some average way, usually empirically. It has been at this level where the most striking breakthroughs have been made in the recent past in semiempirical pi-electron theory. In fact, in the more successful pi-electron theories such as the Pariser-Parr and Pople theories, no atomic orbital is ever explicitly specified (Parr, 1963). More recently, however, it has become clear that, even in dealing with semiempirical approaches, the overlap integrals between wave functions representing different atom- or molecular fragment-like parts need to be calculated as these quantities cannot be inferred from experiment (Adams and Miller, 1966).

The present state of development of electronic digital computers and the corresponding coordinated molecular wave function computer programs is such that fairly accurate Hartree-Fock and Extended Hartree-Fock wave functions can be determined for small molecules such as hydrides and diatomic molecules made up from first and second row elements. Accordingly, even though *ab initio* accurate calculations on large molecules may not be feasible at this time, it is possible to define models for portions of larger molecules for which fairly accurate Hartree-Fock or Extended Hartree-Fock solutions can be found. The present work constitutes a case in point.

In this paper we report and analyze the results of large-scale computations on the simplest molecules involving pi electrons, namely, the planar molecules CH_3^+, CH_3, and CH_3^-. The methyl positive ion is included as part of the homologous series even though it has no pi electrons while the radical and the negative ion have one and two pi electrons, respectively. One advantage of treating these simplest systems is that the analysis is not complicated by any of the ancillary approximations usually appended to the basic pi-electron approximation. In addition the sensitivity of the "core" to change in pi-electron density may be assessed in going from no pi electrons, to one pi electron, to two pi electrons.

II. Description of Calculation

The theoretical framework within which the work was done was the Hartree-Fock-Roothaan method (Roothaan, 1960). A one-center representation centered on the carbon nucleus was used (Moccia, 1964). Five basis functions were used for the pi orbital and twenty-two basis functions used to represent the core electrons. These basis functions were real Slater-type orbitals (STO's) and the scale factors, treated as variational parameters, were selected optimally to within ± 0.1.

More specifically, an f_0 function was added variationally to the four p_0 orbital basis for the pi orbital in order that oblateness of the charge distribution would be permitted should this prove to be energetically favorable within this procedural framework. For the core, several basis functions of s, p, d, and f-type symmetry were employed in order to represent the inner-shell charge density about the carbon nucleus, the charge density between the several nuclei, and the charge density about the protons. There was no attempt to use very large powers of r in the STO's to improve the charge distribution about the protons (Joy and Handler, 1965).

The size of the basis for the peel as well as the core was adjusted in order to determine the sensitivity of the size and shape of the pi orbital to the basis for the representation. As was expected, refinement of the core description, especially in the vicinity of the protons, did not alter the pi orbital significantly.

A one-center and a two-center STO representation for a Hartree-Fock-Roothaan treatment of NH were compared recently by Lounsbury (1965) and he found that the nitrogen inner-shell orbitals and the NH pi orbitals obtained with the two representations compared very well.

The best wave functions obtained for the three fragments CH_3^+, CH_3 and CH_3^- are given in Tables 1, 2, and 3. In addition, the best wave function for CH_3 where only p_0 orbitals were used to represent the pi orbital is given in Table 4.

TABLE 1

CH_3 POSITIVE ION[a]

N	L	M	Orb Exp.	Eigenvectors			
1	0	0	5.3820	0.923458	−0.247883	0.	0.
1	0	0	9.1520	0.083020	0.015562	0.	0.
3	0	0	3.0370	0.012900	−0.080459	0.	0.
2	0	0	1.6840	−0.010936	1.010937	0.	0.
2	1	1	0.9740	−0.	−0.	0.018656	0.
2	1	1	1.6840	−0.	−0.	0.497836	0.
2	1	1	3.5540	−0.	−0.	0.100648	0.
2	1	−1	0.9740	−0.	−0.	0.	0.018656
2	1	−1	1.6840	−0.	−0.	0.	0.497835
2	1	−1	3.5540	−0.	−0.	0.	0.100648
3	2	0	1.8000	−0.000289	−0.239525	0.	0.
3	2	0	2.3000	−0.000749	0.104640	0.	0.
3	2	2	1.8000	−0.	−0.	0.	−0.384982
3	2	2	2.3000	−0.	−0.	0.	0.184554
3	2	−2	1.8000	−0.	−0.	−0.384982	0.
3	2	−2	2.3000	−0.	−0.	0.184554	0.
7	3	1	3.3000	−0.	−0.	−0.083356	0.
7	3	−1	3.3000	−0.	−0.	0.	−0.083356
7	3	−3	3.3000	−0.000409	−0.120242	0.	0.
4	0	0	2.0000	0.004110	0.089028	0.	0.
4	1	1	2.0000	−0.	−0.	0.435169	0.
4	1	−1	2.0000	−0.	−0.	0.	0.435170
			Eigenvalues[b]	−11.631391	−1.262828	−0.917259	−0.917259

Electronic energy[b]   = −48.82312632
Nuclear repulsion energy =   9.80425858
Total energy   = −39.01886749

[a] The nuclear configuration is planar with all protons 2.0126 bohrs from the carbon atom and defining an equilateral triangle.
[b] All energies are expressed in hartrees.

TABLE 2

CH$_3$ RADICAL[a]

N	L	M	Orb. exp.	Eigenvectors				
2	1	0	0.9550	0.	0.	0.	0.	0.434626
2	1	0	1.4209	0.	0.	0.	0.	0.438395
2	1	0	2.5880	0.	0.	0.	0.	0.193138
2	1	0	6.3400	0.	0.	0.	0.	0.011716
7	3	0	2.9000	0.	0.	0.	0.	−0.028428
1	0	0	5.3820	0.923116	−0.224453	0.	0.	0.
1	0	0	9.1520	0.083105	0.009811	0.	0.	0.
3	0	0	3.0370	0.012616	−0.018086	0.	0.	0.
2	0	0	1.6840	−0.009322	0.848610	0.	0.	0.
2	1	1	0.9740	0.	0.	0.121023	0.	0.
2	1	1	1.6840	0.	0.	0.419144	0.	0.
2	1	1	3.5540	0.	0.	0.087917	0.	0.
2	1	−1	0.9740	0.	0.	0.	0.121024	0.
2	1	−1	1.6840	0.	0.	0.	0.419143	0.
2	1	−1	3.5540	0.	0.	0.	0.087917	0.
3	2	0	1.8000	0.000027	−0.281292	0.	0.	0.
3	2	0	2.2000	−0.000627	0.146625	0.	0.	0.
3	2	2	1.8000	0.	0.	0.	−0.484756	0.
3	2	2	2.2000	0.	0.	0.	0.271046	0.
3	2	−2	1.8000	0.	0.	−0.484755	0.	0.
3	2	−2	2.2000	0.	0.	0.271046	0.	0.
7	3	1	3.2000	0.	0.	−0.092244	0.	0.
7	3	−1	3.2000	0.	0.	0.	−0.092244	0.
7	3	−3	3.2000	−0.000383	−0.126107	0.	0.	0.
4	0	0	1.9000	0.003330	0.205516	0.	0.	0.
4	1	1	1.9000	0.	0.	0.426057	0.	0.
4	1	−1	1.9000	0.	0.	0.	0.426057	0.
Eigenvalues				−11.188883	−0.887634	−0.536939	−0.536939	−0.362691

Electronic energy = −49.14288664
Nuclear repulsion energy = 9.80425858
Total energy = −39.33862782

[a] The nuclear configuration is planar with all protons 2.0126 bohrs from the carbon atom and defining an equilateral triangle.

TABLE 3

CH₃ Negative Ion[a]

N	L	M	Orb. exp.	Eigenvectors				
2	1	0	0.6370	0.	−0.	0.	0.	0.590621
2	1	0	1.3380	0.	−0.	0.	0.	0.371632
2	1	0	2.5820	0.	−0.	0.	0.	0.173049
7	3	0	2.9000	0.	−0.	0.	0.	−0.041928
2	1	0	6.3000	0.	−0.	0.	0.	0.007288
1	0	0	5.3820	0.923091	−0.200160	0.	0.	−0.
1	0	0	9.1520	0.093176	0.000449	0.	0.	−0.
3	0	0	3.0370	0.012454	0.120689	0.	0.	−0.
2	0	0	1.6840	−0.009324	0.607702	0.	0.	−0.
2	1	1	0.9740	0.	−0.	0.268957	0.	−0.
2	1	1	1.6840	0.	−0.	0.345042	0.	−0.
2	1	1	3.5540	0.	−0.	0.086262	0.	−0.
2	1	−1	0.9740	0.	−0.	0.	0.268956	−0.
2	1	−1	1.6840	0.	−0.	0.	0.345043	−0.
2	1	−1	3.5540	0.	−0.	0.	0.086262	−0.
3	2	0	1.8000	0.000445	−0.280525	0.	0.	−0.
3	2	0	2.2000	−0.000900	0.146692	0.	0.	−0.
3	2	2	1.8000	0.	−0.	0.	−0.499444	−0.
3	2	2	2.2000	0.	−0.	0.	0.283946	−0.
3	2	−2	1.8000	0.	−0.	−0.499444	0.	−0.
3	2	−2	2.2000	0.	−0.	0.283947	0.	−0.
7	3	1	3.2000	0.	−0.	−0.096824	0.	−0.
7	3	−1	3.2000	0.	−0.	0.	−0.096824	−0.
7	3	−3	3.2000	−0.000373	−0.127223	0.	0.	−0.
4	0	0	1.9000	0.003492	0.329126	0.	0.	−0.
4	1	1	1.9000	0.	−0.	0.351158	0.	−0.
4	1	−1	1.9000	0.	−0.	0.	0.351158	−0.
Eigenvalues[b]				− 10.909549	−0.613559	−0.262555	−0.262555	0.007237

Electronic energy   = −49.07761574
Nuclear repulsion energy =   9.80425858
Total energy   = −39.27335691

[a] The nuclear configuration is planar with all protons 2.0126 bohrs from the carbon atom and defining an equilateral triangle.

[b] All energies are expressed in hartrees.

TABLE 4

CH₃ RADICAL[a]

N	L	M	Orb. expt.	Eigenvectors				
2	1	0	0.9550	−0.	0.	0.	0.	0.434613
2	1	0	1.4209	−0.	0.	0.	0.	0.438097
2	1	0	2.5880	−0.	0.	0.	0.	0.194056
2	1	0	6.3400	−0.	0.	0.	0.	0.011668
1	0	0	5.3820	0.923115	−0.224419	0.	0.	0.
1	0	0	9.1520	0.083108	0.009848	0.	0.	0.
3	0	0	3.0370	0.012602	−0.018992	0.	0.	0.
2	0	0	1.6840	−0.009307	0.849425	0.	−0.000002	0.
2	1	1	0.9740	−0.	0.	0.118610	0.	0.
2	1	1	1.6840	−0.	0.	0.419318	0.	0.
2	1	1	3.5540	−0.	0.	0.087866	0.	0.
2	1	−1	0.9740	−0.	0.	0.	0.118611	0.
2	1	−1	1.6840	−0.	0.000002	0.	0.419317	0.
2	1	−1	3.5540	−0.	0.	0.	0.087866	0.
3	2	0	1.8000	0.000152	−0.281848	0.	0.	0.
3	2	0	2.2000	−0.000737	0.145971	0.	0.	0.
3	2	2	1.8000	−0.	0.	0.	−0.486012	0.
3	2	2	2.2000	−0.	0.	0.	0.271774	0.
3	2	−2	1.8000	−0.	0.	−0.486012	0.	0.
3	2	−2	2.2000	−0.	0.	0·271774	0.	0.
7	3	1	3.2000	−0.	0.	−0.093917	0.	0.
7	3	−1	3.2000	−0.	0.	0.	−0.093917	0.
7	3	−3	3.2000	−0.000383	−0.126468	0.	0.	0.
4	0	0	1.9000	0.003324	0.205282	0.	−0.000001	0.
4	1	1	1.9000	−0.	0.	0.428020	0.	0.
4	1	−1	1.9000	−0.	0.	0.	0.428019	0.

Eigenvalues[b]   −11.189321   −0.887997   −0.538903   −0.538903   −0.361982

Electronic energy[b] $= -49.13579464$
Nuclear repulsion energy $=$ 9.804255858
Total energy $= -39.33153582$

[a] The nuclear configuration is planar with all protons 2.0126 bohrs from the carbon atom and defining an equilateral triangle.
[b] All energies are expressed in hartrees.

III. Discussion

According to Koopmans' approximation (Koopmans, 1933), the ionization potential is just the orbital energy ε of the pi electrons. In pi-electron theory it is customary to maintain a fixed core in order to calculate two different states or the ionization potential of a system. The fixed core ionization potential of CH_3 is just equal to the orbital energy of the pi-electron. It can be seen that for the system CH_3, the fixed core approximation is in error by 10% of the true HF ionization potential, so that the core readjustment does affect the IP as can be seen by examination of vectors in Tables 1 and 2. The correlation energy of the pi electron with the core is estimated at .934 eV (Hermann, 1965), so that the fixed-core approximation compensates for most of this neglect. The vertical electron affinity for CH_3 was found here in the HF approximation to be slightly positive at $+1.77$ eV. The increment in the total correlation energy of adding a pi electron to planar CH_3 is estimated to be -1.71 eV (Hermann, 1965). It is interesting that here, too, the constant core approximation again partly compensates for the neglect of correlation effects on the electron affinity.

The nature of the basis set used in the representation of one-electron MO's is usually taken to be one STO on each center with the Slater-Zener ζ-value of 1.59 occasionally adjusted to give correct atomic valence state results.

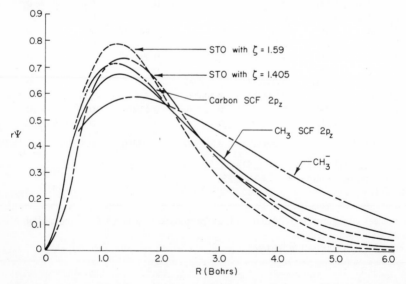

FIG. 1.   The comparison of radial plots of the pi orbitals of the carbon atom in various systems. The STO with $\zeta = 1.405$ is the best compromise STO found empirically by Adams and Miller (1966).

In a pi system the core potential in which the p_z electron moves should be better represented by assuming the core to be locally more similar to the core of CH_3 than a point charge of 3.18.

It is interesting to compare the p_z orbital of the planar methyl radical with that of the Hartree-Fock valence state carbon atom (Fig. 1). If it is assumed that a basis set for pi-electron systems may be constructed from the localized p_z orbital of the planar methyl radical rather than atomic SCF orbitals or atomic Slater-type orbitals, a revision in a number of the one- and two-center integrals used in Pariser Parr theory is implied (Table 5).

TABLE 5

ONE AND TWO CENTER COULOMB-TYPE ELECTRON
REPULSION INTEGRALS (eV)

R (angstroms)	0	1.4	2.425	2.8
STO ($\zeta = 1 \cdot 59$)	16.93	9.03	5.67	4.97
Carbon atom SCF	15.55	8.67	5.57	4.89
CH_3 radical[a]	14.19	8.42	5.50	4.85

OVERLAP INTEGRALS

R (angstroms)	1.4	2.425	2.8
STO ($\zeta = 1 \cdot 59$)	0.26	0.0389	0.0177
Carbon atom SCF	0.3269	0.0839	0.0493
CH_3 radical[a]	0.3797	0.1124	0.0693

[a] These were obtained using the pi orbital defined in Table 4.

For the prediction of ground-state properties of aromatic molecules, such as charge densities and ground-state ionization potentials, CH_3 pi orbitals should make a good basis set. It is conceivable that some sort of interpolation between the systems given here with integer numbers of pi electrons might be effected in order to accommodate carbon atomlike parts of molecules with noninteger numbers of electrons. The results should be compared with HF values rather than exact values because of the neglect of correlation in the one-center repulsion integral and also of right-left correlation. Comparison with exact results may be easier if the (11/11) integral is reduced by the correlation energy present in adding one pi electron to the *entire* atom, or 1.7 eV, and right-left correlation with configuration interaction is included.

IV. Conclusion

Accurate *ab initio* orbital treatment of large asymmetrical molecules is not possible at the present time. Accordingly, semiempirical approaches need to be employed. However, accurate *ab initio* treatment of small molecules is possible at the present time. Accordingly, it is possible to transcend the usual approaches to molecular systems which involve using wave functions for free atoms as a basis for representing molecular orbitals. The work reported here is an illustration of what can be done in this regard and reveals that there can be considerable difference in the atom-like fragment wave functions to be used in a molecule according as these are found for a free atom or a molecular fragment. We wish to acknowledge financial assistance from the United States Public Health Service.

REFERENCES

Adams, O. W., and Miller, R. L. (1966). *J. Chem. Phys.* **44**.
Cusachs, L. C., and Reynolds, J. W. (1965). *J. Chem. Phys.* **43**, S160.
Das, G., and Wahl, A. C. (1966). *J. Chem. Phys.* **44**, 87.
Fischer-Hjalmars, I. (1965). *J. Chem. Phys.* **42**, 1962.
Hermann, R. B. (1965). *J. Chem. Phys.* **41**, 1027.
Joy, H. W., and Handler, G. S. (1965). *J. Chem. Phys.* **42**, 3047.
Koopmans, T. A. (1933). *Physica* **1**, 104.
Lounsbury, J. (1965). Ph.D. Thesis, Illinois Institute of Technology.
Lykos, P. G. (1964). *Adv. Quantum Chem.* **1**, 170.
Moccia, R. (1964). *J. Chem. Phys.* **40**, 2164, 2176, 2186.
Parr, R. G. (1963). "Quantum Theory of Molecular Electronic Structure." Benjamin, New York.
Roothaan, C. C. J. (1960). *Rev. Mod. Phys.* **32**, 179.
Wahl, A. C., and Gilbert, T. L. (1967). *Phys. Rev.* to be published.

Charge Transfer Complexes in Biochemistry*

ALBERTE PULLMAN and BERNARD PULLMAN

INSTITUT DE BIOLOGIE PHYSICO-CHIMIQUE

UNIVERSITÉ DE PARIS, PARIS, FRANCE

I. Introduction

Charge transfer complexes are molecular or supramolecular entities formed from two (sometimes more) ordinarily stable molecular components through a more or less complete transfer of an electron from one of the components (the electron donor) to the other (the electron acceptor). Following the quantum theory of the phenomenon, which is the only satisfactory one (Mulliken, 1952a and b, 1956, 1964, general reviews: McGlynn, 1958, 1960; Briegleb, 1961; Andrews and Keefer, 1964), the interaction of an electron-donor (D) with an electron-acceptor (A) may be described by saying that when D and A combine to form a complex, the wave function for their association may be written approximately:

$$\Psi_N = a\Psi_{(DA)} + b\Psi_{(D^+A^-)}, \quad a > b,$$

for the ground state, and

$$\Psi_E = b^*\Psi_{(DA)} - a^*\Psi_{(D^+A^-)}, \quad a^* > b^*,$$

for the excited state.

In these expressions $\Psi_{(DA)}$ denotes the so called *no-bond* wave function, it means the wave function corresponding to a structure in which the binding of the two components is effected by the "classical" intermolecular forces (the electrostatic, dispersion, H-bonding, etc., forces), while $\Psi_{(D^+A^-)}$ denotes

* This work was supported by Public Health Service Research Grant No. GM 12289-01 from the National Institute of General Medical Sciences.

345

the so-called *dative-bond* wave function, corresponding to a structure of the complex in which one electron has been transferred from D to A and in which besides the forces listed above there is also a weak chemical binding between the odd electrons situated on the two components of the complex. It can be seen that the charge transfer is generally more pronounced in the excited state of the complex than in its ground state. The transition from the ground to the excited state is frequently associated with the appearance of a new absorption band, situated generally toward long wavelengths, which is the essential and practically the only unambiguous indication of the formation of a charge transfer complex, although such a formation may also be associated with the appearance of other new characteristics: dipole moments, enhancements of semiconductivity or of chemical reactivity, etc. In so far as charge transfer complexes may be intermediates in the generation of free radicals, useful information about their formation may be obtained sometimes by electron-spin-resonance spectroscopy (Isenberg, 1964).

The consideration of the energy quantities involved in the formation of the ground state and the transition to the excited state may be obtained by solving the appropriate secular determinant. On writing the expressions for Ψ_N and Ψ_E in the simplified forms

$$\Psi_N = a\Psi_0 + b\Psi_1,$$

$$\Psi_E = b^*\Psi_0 - a^*\Psi_1,$$

this looks as follows:

$$\begin{vmatrix} E_0 - E & H_{01} - ES_{01} \\ H_{01} - ES_{01} & E_1 - E \end{vmatrix} = 0,$$

where

$$E_0 = \int \Psi_0 H \Psi_0 \, d\tau, \qquad E_1 = \int \Psi_1 H \Psi_1 \, d\tau,$$

$$H_{01} = \int \Psi_0 H \Psi_1 \, d\tau, \qquad S_{01} = \int \Psi_0 \Psi_1 \, d\tau = \sqrt{2} \frac{S_{DA}}{(1 + S_{DA}^2)^{1/2}}.$$

E_0 is the energy associated with Ψ_0, i.e., the sum of the separate energies of D and A modified by any energy of attraction arising from forces other than CTC, while E_1 includes the energy of attraction between the charged species and the covalent binding between the odd electrons situated on the two components. H_{01} is the interaction energy of DA with D^+A^-, H being the exact Hamiltonian of the entire set of nuclei and electrons of the complex. $S_{DA} = \int \phi_D \phi_A \, d\tau$ is the overlap integral between the highest filled molecular orbital of the electron donor (ϕ_D) and the lowest empty orbital of the electron acceptor (ϕ_A).

It is easily shown that the energies of the ground and of the excited states can be approximated by

$$E_N = E_0 - \frac{(H_{01} - E_0 S_{01})^2}{E_1 - E_0},$$

$$E_E = E_1 + \frac{(H_{01} - E_1 S_{01})^2}{E_1 - E_0},$$

and the transition energy between them, corresponding to the charge transfer band, is thus

$$\Delta E = E_E - E_N = E_1 - E_0 + \frac{(H_{01} - E_1 S_{01})^2 + (H_{01} - E_0 S_{01})^2}{E_1 - E_0},$$

which in the first approximation may be shown to be reducible to

$$\Delta E = I_D - E_A + \Delta$$

where I_D is the ionization potential of the donor, E_A the electron affinity of the acceptor, and Δ a stabilization term. The equation signifies that if we consider a constant acceptor and vary the electron donors, and provided Δ is approximately constant, we may expect to observe a linear relation between the frequency of the charge transfer band and the ionization potential of the donor. Inversely, under the same conditions, if we have a constant donor and vary the acceptors, a linear relation should exist between the frequency and the electron affinities of the acceptors. In practice, it is the first of these correlations which is most frequently observed.

II. Biochemical Charge Transfer Complexes

During the last few years, numerous authors have postulated the frequent formation of charge transfer complexes between molecules of biochemical interest and in particular conjugated biomolecules (for which relatively low ionization potentials and high electron affinities are expected) and have envisaged the involvement of such complexes both in the mechanism of biochemical reactions and in the structure of certain cellular components (nucleic acids, mitochondria, quantosomes). Szent-Gyorgyi (1960), in particular, has been one of the protagonists of this conception.

Among the biomolecules which have most frequently been considered as possibly implicated in charge transfer complexes are the following (Pullman and Pullman, 1963):

(1) the essential components of the oxidation-reduction coenzymes (if not the coenzymes themselves), in particular the pyridinium (or nicotinamide) ring of the pyridine nucleotides and the isoalloxazine ring of the flavin coenzymes;

(2) the purines;

(3) indolic compounds, in particular tryptophan and serotonine;

(4) quinones.

The associations which have been most extensively studied and considered as charge transfer complexes or at least as involving charge transfer as an important *component* in the overall binding concern the interactions:

(1) between biomolecules containing the indole ring and pyridine nucleotides or flavins,

(2) in or between the oxidation-reduction coenzymes,

(3) between purines and a series of partners such as flavins, aromatic hydrocarbons, steroids, actinomycin, acridines, purines themselves, etc.

The analysis of the principal available data involving such biomolecules and related model compounds indicates (Table 1) that the formation of a

TABLE 1

PRINCIPAL RESEARCHES ON CHARGE TRANSFER COMPLEXES IN BIOCHEMISTRY

Complex	Reference	CTC band
Pyridinium salts with iodine	(Kosower, 1960, p. 171)	+
Indolic compounds and NAD$^+$	(Cilento and Giusti, 1959; Cilento and Tedeschi, 1961)	+
	(Alivisatos *et al.*, 1961)	+
Indoles and flavins	(Isenberg and Szent-Gyorgyi, 1958, 1959; Isenberg *et al.*, 1960)	+[a]
Methyl indoles with quinones	(Foster and Hanson, 1964)	+
Intramolecular complex in indolyl ethylnicotinamide	(Shifrin, 1964a)	+
Intermolecular complexes in a model (*I*, in text) for interactions of aromatic amino acids with the nicotinamide moiety of NAD$^+$	(Shifrin, 1964b)	+
Tryptophan and pteridines	(Fujimori, 1958)	−
Indoles and related heterocycles with T_2 bacteriophage	(Kanner and Kozloff, 1964)	−
Pyridinium cations and aromatic hydrocarbons	(Cilento and Sanioto, 1965)	+
Menadione and aromatic hydrocarbons	(Cilento and Sanioto, 1963)	+
Purines or pyrimidines with chloranil or 1.3.5.-trinitrobenzene	(Beukers and Szent-Gyorgyi, 1962)	+
Nucleic acid bases and chloranil	(Machmer and Duchesne, 1965)	+

Complex	Reference	CTC band
Indole, thymine, and cytosine with chloranil	(LuValle *et al.*, 1963)	[a]
Nucleosides or nucleotides of the nucleic acid bases and chloranil	(Duchesne *et al.*, 1965)	+
Purine and pyrimidine nucléotides with mutagenic acridines	(Duchesne and Machmer, 1965)	+
Mutagenic acridines and tetracyano-ethylene	(Duchesne and Machmer, 1965)	+
Purines and pyrimidines with steroids	(Molinari and Lata, 1962)	−
Aromatic amino acids and purines with isoalloxazine derivatives	(Harbury and Foley, 1958) (Harbury *et al.*, 1959)	−
Interaction of purines and pyrimidines with flavins	(Tsibris *et al.*, 1964)	
Intramolecular complex between adenine and isoalloxazine in FAD	(Weber, 1950)	−
Pyridinium ring and adenine in NADH₂ (intramolecular)	(Weber, 1957)	−
Pyridinium ring and adenine in NAD⁺ (intramolecular)	(Cilento and Schreier, 1964)	−
FMN with FMNH₂	(Gibson *et al.*, 1962)	−
NADH and FMN	(Isenberg *et al.*, 1961)	+
	(Szent-Gyorgyi *et al.*, 1961)	[a]
NAD–NADH	(Cilento and Schreier, 1964)	[b]
Crystals of 8-azaguanine monohydrate	(Macintyre *et al.*, 1965; Macintyre, 1965)	−
Phenols and flavins	(Fleischman and Tollin, 1965a,b)	+
Carcinogenic hydrocarbons and iodine	(Szent-Gyorgyi *et al.*, 1960)	+
Carcinogenic hydrocarbons and acridine	(Szent-Gyorgyi and McLaughlin 1961)	+
Phenothiazines and metals	(Borg, 1961)	+
Aminoacids and proteins with riboflavin, choranil and oxygen	(Slifkin, 1962; Birks and Slifkin, 1963) (Slifkin, 1964) (Slifkin, 1963)	±
Aromatic carcinogens with iodine, chloranil, trinitrobenzene and acridine	(Epstein *et al.*, 1964)	+
β-carotene with iodine	(Lupinski, 1962)	+
Nucleic acid bases with chloranil, iodine and riboflavin	(Slifkin, 1965)	+
Porphyrins with heterocyclic molecules, including purines	(Mauzerall, 1965)	−

[a] Electron spin resonance studies.
[b] No complexation.

charge transfer complex is firmly established in only a limited number of cases, in so far as the existence of a characteristic charge transfer band has been observed only rarely. In fact, such a band seems to occur essentially when one of the partners in the complex consists of a pyridinium or a quinone ring which, as will be seen shortly, are strong electron acceptors. In most of the other cases what is generally observed is a more or less satisfactory correlation between the association constants and the electron donor or acceptor properties of the molecules involved. The correlation is then considered as indicative of a possible involvement of charge tranfer as a significant component in the forces governing the formation of the complex.

III. Electron Donor and Acceptor Properties of Biomolecules

This situation gives rise to a number of problems. In the first place it is obvious that the knowledge of the ionization potentials and electron affinities of biomolecules, which measure respectively their electron donor and acceptor abilities, is of fundamental significance for the appreciation of charge transfer complexations. In view of the complete absence of experimental information about the values of these quantities in biomolecules, the contribution of the theory, even if suggesting only approximate values, is then obviously of particular importance.

The simplest evaluation of these properties may be obtained through the use of the Hückel approximation of the molecular orbital method, it *being understood that such an evaluation is particularly suitable for the determination of the relative electron-donor-acceptor properties of the molecules.* The appropriate indices are the energies of the highest filled molecular orbitals for the electron donor capacity and the energies of the lowest empty molecular orbitals for the electron acceptor abilities. The calculations yield these energies in the forms $E_i = \alpha + K_i\beta$, where α is the coulomb and β the resonance integral of the method. The values of K_i are generally in the range of 0 to 1.5 for the highest filled molecular orbital and of 0 to -1.5 for the lowest empty molecular orbital. The closer to zero the values of the coefficients for both orbitals the greater respectively the electron donor or the electron acceptor properties of the molecules (Pullman and Pullman, 1963). The reliability of these quantities for conclusions in this field is substantiated by correlations obtained between the theoretical and experimental sets of data in series of fundamental molecules in which both are known (Streitwieser, 1961). The possession of such a relative scale is frequently sufficient for the elucidation of the nature of the partnership in the complex and the verification of the aforementioned correlations. The essential results in this field (Pullman and Pullman, 1963) are summed up in Table 2 from the examination of which it appears that, broadly speaking,

TABLE 2

ENERGY COEFFICIENTS OF MOLECULAR ORBITALS (IN β UNITS)

Compound	Highest filled molecular orbital	Lowest empty molecular orbital
Purine	0.69	−0.74
Adenine	0.49	−0.87
Guanine	0.31	−1.05
Hypoxanthine	0.40	−0.88
Xanthine	0.44	−1.01
Uric Acid	0.17	−1.19
Uracil	0.60	−0.96
Thymine	0.51	−0.96
Cytosine	0.60	−0.80
Barbituric acid	1.03	−1.30
Alloxane	1.03	−0.76
Phenylallanine	0.91	−0.99
Tyrosine	0.79	−1.00
Histidine	0.66	−1.16
Tryptophan	0.53	−0.86
Riboflavin	0.50	−0.34
Pteridine	0.86	−0.39
2-Amino-4-hydroxypteridine	0.49	−0.65
2,4-Diaminopteridine	0.54	−0.51
2,4-Dihydroxypteridine	0.65	−0.66
Folic acid	0.53	−0.65
Porphin	0.30	−0.24
1,3-Divinylporphin	0.29	−0.23
1-Vinyl-5-formylporphin	0.30	−0.21
α-Carotene	0.10	−0.19
β-Carotene	0.08	−0.18
Vitamin A_1	0.23	−0.31
Vitamin A_2	0.20	−0.26
Retinene	0.28	−0.26
p-Benzoquinone	1	−0.23
1,4-Naphtoquinone	1	−0.33
9,10-Anthraquinone	1	−0.44
Benzohydroquinone	0.63	−1
Naphtohydroquinone	0.41	−0.71
Anthrahydroquinone	0.23	−0.53
NAD$^+$	1.03	−0.36
NADH	0.30	−0.92
FMN	0.50	−0.34
FMNH$_2$	−0.11	−0.95

the biomolecules may be divided from the point of view under consideration into three groups:

(1) Compounds susceptible to function essentially as electron donors. These include the purines (moderate electron donors with the exception of uric acid which is predicted to be a very good electron donor), pyrimidines (very poor donors, with some of them, e.g. alloxane, even predicted to be rather acceptors), α-aminoacids of proteins (poor donors with the exception of tryptophane which should be a moderate donor), reduced forms of flavins and of pyridine nucleotides (good donors) and some dyes of pharmacological interest, in particular in the series of phenothiazines (very good donors).

(2) Compounds susceptible to function essentially as electron acceptors. These include the oxidized forms of flavins and of pyridine nucleotides, some (but not all) pteridines, quinones, and bile pigments.

(3) Compounds susceptible to function as both electron donors and acceptors, and generally, as both good donors and acceptors. These are essentially the porphyrins, carotenes, and retinenes.

At this point it must usefully be added that in some although still rare cases more refined, self-consistent field calculations have been carried out with the aim of obtaining more precise, absolute values of the ionization potentials of some of the electron donors, quoted above (reliable calculations of electron affinities are, as is well known, very difficult to perform). This is in particular the case of purines and pyrimidines present in the nucleic acids (Pullman and Rossi, 1964). The refined calculations carried out for these particular important biomolecules confirmed the trend predicted by the Hückel method and in particular confirmed that guanine should be the best electron donor among the bases of the nucleic acids. They also confirm the approximate validity of the Wacks-Dibeler (1959) equation:

$$I = (3.14 \pm 0.24)K_i + (6.24 \pm 0.10),$$

which proposes to relate the ionization potentials I (in electron volts) to the coefficients K_i of the highest occupied molecular orbital.

The theoretical predictions have also received a number of striking experimental, although indirect, verifications. This is again, in particular, the case of purines and pyrimidines, and the verifications come essentially from the studies of the electrochemical behavior of these compounds. Table 3 summarizes the results of researches on polarographic oxidability and reducibility of the bases (Smith and Elving, 1962; Struck and Elving, 1964; Elving et al., 1966; Pullman, 1965) and it can be observed that the results are in good agreement with predictions based on the values of the coefficients of the molecular orbitals. Thus, the oxidizable compounds have lower values of the coefficient of their highest filled orbital than the nonoxidizable ones and, similarly, the reducible compounds have smaller absolute values of the

TABLE 3

ELECTRON DONOR AND ACCEPTOR PROPERTIES OF PURINES AND PYRIMIDINES

Compound	Highest filled MO	Polarographic oxidability	Lowest empty MO	Polarographic reducibility
Purine	0.69	−	−0.74	+
Adenine	0.49	+	−0.87	+
Guanine	0.30	+	−1.05	−
Hypoxanthine	0.40	+	−0.88	+
Xanthine	0.44	+	−1.01	−
Uric acid	0.17	+	−1.19	−
Uracil	0.60	−	−0.96	−
Thymine	0.51	−	−0.96	−
Cytosine	0.60	−	−0.80	+
Barbituric acid	1.03		−1.30	
Alloxane	1.03		−0.76	+

coefficients of their lowest empty orbital than do the nonreducible ones. It may be added that in striking agreement with theory uric acid is the most easily oxidized of all the compounds tested. The polarographic results confirm also the prediction that guanine is the most easily oxidized compound among the bases of the nucleic acids.

The good electron donor properties predicted for porphyrins and carotenes are in agreement with the relatively low value of their ionnization potentials (Terenin and Vilessov, 1964) and so is also the case for the very good donor properties predicted for phenothiazine (Kearns and Calvin, 1961, Lyons and Mackie, 1963).

The abilities of the highly conjugated carotenes and retinenes to function also as electron acceptors is substantiated by their easy polarographic reducibility (Kuta, 1964).

IV. Established Charge Transfer Complexes

The results of Table 2 may be used in the study of charge transfer complexations in two ways. In the case of well-defined complexes, characterized by the existence of a charge transfer band, they may lend further support to the general theory by showing the existence of the expected correlations between the frequency of the band and, following the case, the ionization potentials of the donors (when the acceptor is constant) or the electron affinities of the acceptors (when the donor is constant). The following are particularly striking examples of such successful correlations.

(1) The work of Shifrin (1964a,b) on the model compounds (for the study of enzyme coenzyme interactions) of the type I, where the symbol AAC repre-

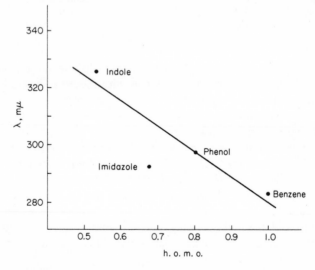

I

sents the conjugated ring of the aromatic amino acid of proteins and in which a correlation appears (Fig. 1) between the frequency of the charge transfer band and the theoretical ionization potential of the aromatic donor as measured by the coefficient of its highest occupied molecular orbital. The

Fig. 1. Wavelength of the charge transfer band *vs* energy of the highest occupied molecular orbital in compounds of Type I.

work confirms the relatively important electron-donor properties of the indole ring. The point representative of imidazole lies, however, somewhat off the curve.

(2) The work of Machmer and Duchesne (1965) on the charge transfer complexes between nucleic acid bases and chloranil, in which a linear correlation can be shown to exist (Fig. 2) between the peak of the charge transfer band and the ionization potentials of the bases. The work confirms the *relatively* important electron-donor properties, among the nucleic bases, of guanine.

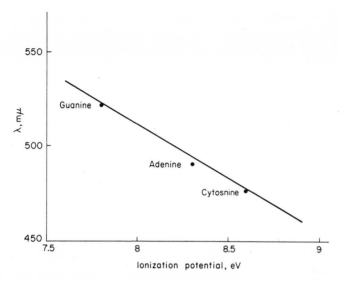

Fig. 2. The wavelength of the charge transfer band *vs* the ionization potential of the bases in complexes of nucleic acid bases with chloranil.

(3) The work of Kosower (1960) on the model complexes between pyridinium compounds and iodine, where it may be shown (Fig. 3) that the wavelength of the charge transfer band is related linearly to the electron affinity of the pyridinium compounds, as measured by the coefficients of their lowest empty molecular orbitals.

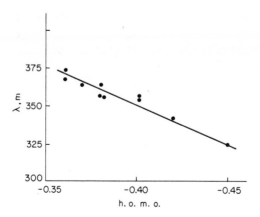

Fig. 3. The wavelength of the charge-transfer absorption band *vs* the energy of the lowest empty molecular orbital in complexes of methylpyridinium compounds with iodine.

V. Dubious (Partial?) Charge Transfer Complexations

On the other hand, in a number of cases in which molecular associations were found but in which no charge transfer band has been observed, correlations have nevertheless been noticed between the association constants and the theoretical data on the electron donor or acceptor properties of the molecules. This is the case, in particular, for a number of associations involving purines and pyrimidines as electron donors with a constant electron acceptor such as e.g. riboflavin (Tsibris *et al.*, 1965), the antibiotic actinomycin (Pullman, 1964a), or the carcinogenic 3,4-benzpyrene (Pullman, 1964b). In such cases, the correlation was considered as signifying that charge transfer forces play a significant role in these associations. The two essential questions which may be raised, of course, are: how signficant? and, what for? Recent general results on the evaluation of the intermolecular forces responsible for the "stacking" type interactions between conjugated aromatic molecules at relatively short distances (to which the above quoted associations probably belong) seem to indicate that in spite of the observed correlations the contribution of charge transfer to the *binding energy* of such complexes may in fact be rather restricted and represent only a relatively small percentage of the over-all interaction energy.

Thus, e.g., calculations indicate (Mantione and Pullman, 1966) that the contribution of the charge transfer forces to the energy of the stacking-type auto-association of the purines and pyrimidines in aqueous solution or to the association of purines with hydrocarbons is relatively small, amounting only to a fraction of the contribution evaluated for the Van der Waals-London forces (Pullman *et al.*, 1965a,b). On the other hand this situation does not preclude the possible importance of the effect on some other physicochemical properties of the complexes, as suggested e.g. by the recent proposition of Macintyre (1965; Macintyre *et al.*, 1965) following which the shortening of the interplane distance in the crystals of 8-azaguanine with respect to the usual separation between the planes of aromatic molecules could be due to charge transfer interactions. Such interactions operating inside the nucleic acids could also be related to the semiconductivity of these macromolecules (Brillouin, 1962; Pullman, 1964c). As to the direct biological significance of such complexes not much seems to be known about it at present and in fact it may be useful to reemphasize the extreme danger of postulating without valid arguments their decisive involvement in biological phenomena. Thus, e.g., a number of authors have postulated in recent years the involvement of electron transfer phenomena in the mechanism of carcinogenesis by aromatic hydrocarbons or heterocyclics. These propositions were all based on some limited correlations between the electron donor or acceptor properties of some selected chemicals and their carcinogenicity. It was very easy to show simply by enlarging the number of chemicals considered that the proposed correlations were fictitious (Pullman, 1964b). Explicit recent experimentation (Epstein *et al.*, 1964) on the ability of the chemical carcinogens to take part in charge transfer complexes with a number of acceptors (iodine, chloranil, trinitrobenzene, acridine) has entirely confirmed the soundness of the critical approach and demonstrated the absence of any correlation between carcinogenicity and charge transfer complexation.

VI. *n-π* and "Local" Charge Transfer Complexations

In the preceding discussion we have been essentially concerned with the electron donating and accepting properties and thus in the possible involvement in charge transfer complexes of the π electrons of biomolecules. The majority of such molecules contain, however, heteroatoms with lone pairs of electrons (*n* electrons) which may also be implicated in "local" charge transfer complexes. Refined, self-consistent field calculations, in so far as they are available, show that in the large conjugated biomolecules of the type that we are interested in, the lowest ionization potential is probably generally that of the π electrons. This is in particular the case for biological purines and pyrimidines (Pullman and Rossi, 1964). Nevertheless, the lone-pairs may be predicted to be of more importance in charge transfer complexes formed with saturated biomolecules and in fact the involvement of the lone pairs in charge transfer complexes has been postulated to occur in the interactions of the α-aminoacids of proteins with different electron acceptors (Slifkin, 1962, 1963; Birks and Slifkin, 1963).

The concept of a "local" charge transfer complex, involving electron transfer through a localized site at the molecular periphery has also been advocated in the case of π-π complexes, in particular of those involving indolic compounds (Szent-Gyorgyi and Isenberg, 1960), whose complexing ability seems to be superior to what might be expected from the electron donor properties of such molecules, as evaluated by the energy of their highest filled molecular orbital. Another interpretation of this situation has, however, also been proposed in terms of the particularly outstanding complementary charge distribution in the linked partners (Karreman, 1961, 1962).

Note added in proof: The list of the principal researches on charge transfer complexes in biochemistry given in Table 1 may be usefully completed with the following recent references: (a) complexes between phenothiazines and acceptors (Foster and Hanson, 1966; Foster and Fyfe, 1966) in which a CTC band is observed; (b) complexes between oxidized flavins and indole derivatives and between both oxidized and reduced flavins and purines (Wilson, 1966), a new absorption band being observed only in the case of the complexes involving indoles; (c) complexes between NAD^+ analogs and reduced flavin mononucleotide (Sakurai and Hosoya, 1966), showing a CTC band, the frequency of which correlates linearly with the energies of the lowest empty molecular orbitals of the NAD^+ analogs.

REFERENCES

Alivisatos, S. G. A., Ungar, F., Jibril, A., and Mourkides, G. A. (1961). *Biochim. Biophys. Acta* **51**, 361.

Andrews, L. J., and Keefer, R. M. (1964). "Molecular Complexes in Organic Chemistry." Holden-Day, San Francisco.

Beukers, R., and Szent-Gyorgyi, A. (1962). *Rec. Trav. Chim.* **81**, 541.

Birks, J. B., and Slifkin, M. A. (1963). *Nature* **197**, 42.

Borg, D. C. (1961). *Fed. Proc.* **20**, Suppl. 10, 104.

Briegleb, G. (1961). "Electronen-Donator-Acceptor-Komplexe." Springer, Berlin.

Brillouin, L. (1962). *In* "Horizons in Biochemistry" (M. Kasha and B. Pullman, eds.), p. 295. Academic Press, New York.

Cilento, G. and Giusti, P. (1959). *J. Am. Chem. Soc.* **81**, 3801.

Cilento, G., and Sanioto, D. L. (1963). *Ber. Bungel. fl. Physik. Chemie* **67**, 426.

Cilento, G., and Sanioto, D. L. (1965). *Arch. Biochem. Biophys.* **110**, 133.

Cilento, G., and Schreier, S. (1964). *Arch. Biochem. Biophys.* **107**, 102.

Cilento, G., and Tedeschi, P. (1961). *Biol. Chem.* **236**, 907.

Duchesne, J., and Machmer, P. (1965). *Compt. Rend.* **260**, 4279.

Duchesne, J., Machmer, P., and Read, M. (1965). *Compt. Rend.* **260**, 2081.

Elving, P. J., Struck, W. A., and Smith, D. L. (1966). In press.

Epstein, S. S., Bulon, I., Koplan, J., Small, M., and Mantel, N. (1964). *Nature* **204**, 750.

Fleischman, D. E., and Tollin, G. (1965a). *Biochim. Biophys. Acta* **94**, 248.

Fleischman, D. E., and Tollin, G. (1965b). *Proc. Natl. Acad. Sci. U.S.* **53**, 38.

Foster, R., and Fyfe, C. A. (1966). *Biochim. Biophys. Acta* **112**, 490.

Foster, R., and Hanson, P. (1964). *Trans. Faraday Soc.* **60**, 2189.

Foster, R., and Hanson, P. (1966). *Biochim. Biophys. Acta* **112**, 482.

Fujimori, E. (1958). *Proc. Natl. Acad. Sci. U.S.* **45**, 133.

Gibson, Q. H., Massey, V., and Atherton, N. M. (1962). *Biochem. J.* **85**, 364.

Harbury, H. A., and Foley, K. A. (1958). *Proc. Natl. Acad. Sci. U.S.* **44**, 662.

Harbury, N. A., La None, K. F., Lorch, P. A., and Anick, R. M. (1959). *Proc. Natl. Acad. Sci. U.S.* **45**, 1708.

Isenberg, I. (1964). *Pharmacol. Rev.* **44**, 487.

Isenberg, I., and Szent-Gyorgyi, A. (1958). *Proc. Natl. Acad. Sci. U.S.* **44**, 857.

Isenberg, I., and Szent-Gyorgyi, A. (1959). *Proc. Natl. Acad. Sci. U.S.* **45**, 1229.

Isenberg, I., Szent-Gyorgyi, A., and Baird, Jr., S. L. (1960). *Proc. Natl. Acad. Sci. U.S.* **46**, 1307.

Isenberg, I., Baird, Jr., S. L., and Szent-Gyorgyi, A. (1961). *Proc. Natl. Acad. Sci. U.S.* **47**, 245.

Kanner, L. C., and Kozloff, L. M. (1964). *Biochemistry* **3**, 215.

Karreman, G. (1961). *Bull. Math. Biophys.* **23**, 135.

Karreman, G. (1962). *Ann. N. Y. Acad. Sci.* **96**, 1029.

Kearns, D. A., and Calvin, M. (1961). *J. Chem. Phys.* **34**, 2026.

Koral, M., and Collins, M. (1963). *J. Phys. Chem.* **67**, 2635.

Kosower, E. M. (1960). *In* "The Enzymes" (P. O. Boyer, H. Lardy, and K. Myrbäck, eds.), Vol. 3, p. 131. Academic Press, New York.

Kuta, E. J. (1964). *Science* **144**, 1130.
Lupinski, J. H. (1962). *J. Phys. Chem.* **67**, 2725.
Lu Valle, J. E., Leifer, A., Koral, M., and Collins, M. (1963). *J. Phys. Chem.* **67**, 2635.
Lyons, L. E., and Mackie, J. C. (1963). *Nature* **197**, 589.
Machmer, P., and Duchesne, J. (1965). *Nature* **206**, 618.
Macintyre, W. M. (1965). *Science* **147**, 507.
Macintyre, W. M., Singh, P., and Werkema, M. S. (1965). *Biophys. J.* **5**, 697.
Mantione, M. J., and Pullman, B. (1966). *Compt. Rend.* **262**, 1492.
Mauzerall, D. (1965). *Biochemistry* **4**, 1801.
McGlynn, S. P. (1958). *Chem. Rev.* **58**, 1113.
McGlynn, S. P. (1960). *Radiation Res. Suppl.* **2**, 300.
Molinari, G., and Lata, G. F. (1962). *Arch. Biochem. Biophys.* **96**, 486.
Mulliken, R. S. (1952a). *J. Phys. Chem.* **56**, 801.
Mulliken, R. S. (1952b). *J. Am. Chem. Soc.* **74**, 811.
Mulliken, R. S. (1956). *Rec. Trav. Chim.* **75**, 845.
Mulliken, R. S. (1964). *J. Chim. Phys.* **61**, 20.
Pullman, A., and Rossi, M. (1964). *Biochem. Biophys. Acta* **88**, 211.
Pullman, B. (1964a). *Biochim. Biophys. Acta* **88**, 440.
Pullman, B. (1964b). *J. Cell. Compar. Physiol.* **64**, Suppl. 1, 91.
Pullman, B. (1964c). *Compt. Rend.* **259**, 3101.
Pullman, B. (1965). *J. Chem. Phys.* **43**, S233.
Pullman, B., and Pullman, A. (1963). "Quantum Biochemistry." Wiley (Interscience), New York.
Pullman, B., Claverie, P., and Caillet, J. (1965a). *Compt. Rend.* **260**, 5387, 5919.
Pullman, B., Claverie, P., and Caillet, J. (1965b). *Science* **147**, 1305.
Sakurai, T., and Hosoya, H. (1966). *Biochim. Biophys. Acta* **112**, 459.
Shifrin, S. (1964a). *Biochim. Biophys. Acta* **81**, 205.
Shifrin, S. (1964b). *Biochemistry* **3**, 829.
Slifkin, M. A. (1962). *Nature* **193**, 464.
Slifkin, M. A. (1963). *Nature* **197**, 275.
Slifkin, M. A. (1964). *Spectrochim Acta* **20**, 1543.
Slifkin, M. A. (1965). *Biochem. Biophys. Acta* **103**, 365.
Smith, D. L., and Elving, P. J. (1962). *J. Am. Chem. Soc.* **84**, 2741.
Streitwieser, Jr., A. (1961). "Molecular Orbital Theory for Organic Chemists." Wiley, New York.
Struck, W. A., and Elving, P. J., (1964). *J. Am. Chem. Soc.* **86**, 1229.
Szent-Gyorgyi, A. (1960). "Introduction to a Submolecular Biology." Academic Press, New York.
Szent-Gyorgyi, A., and Isenberg, I. (1960). *Proc. Natl. Acad. Sci. U.S.* **46**, 1334.
Szent-Gyorgyi, A., and McLaughlin, J. (1961). *Proc. Natl. Acad. Sci. U.S.* **47**, 1397.
Szent-Gyorgyi, A., Isenberg, I., and Baird, Jr., S. L. (1960). *Proc. Natl. Acad. Sci. U.S.* **46**, 1444.
Szent-Gyorgyi, A., Isenberg, I., and McLaughlin, J. (1961). *Proc. Natl. Acad. Sci. U.S.* **47**, 1089.
Terenin, A., and Vilessov, F. (1964). *Advan. Photochem.* **2**, 385.
Tsibris, J. C. M., McCormick, D. B., and Wright, L. D. (1965). *Biochemistry* **4**, 504.
Wacks, M. E., and Dibeler, V. H. (1959). *J. Chem. Phys.* **31**, 1557.
Weber, G. (1950). *Biochem. J.* **47**, 114.
Weber, G. (1957). *Nature* **180**, 1409.
Wilson, J. E. (1966). *Biochemistry* **5**, 1351.

The Augmented Plane Wave Method and the Electronic Properties of Rare-Earth Metals

A. J. FREEMAN

NATIONAL MAGNET LABORATORY*
MASSACHUSETTS INSTITUTE OF TECHNOLOGY, CAMBRIDGE, MASSACHUSETTS

J. O. DIMMOCK

LINCOLN LABORATORY†
MASSACHUSETTS INSTITUTE OF TECHNOLOGY, LEXINGTON, MASSACHUSETTS

R. E. WATSON

BROOKHAVEN NATIONAL LABORATORY‡
UPTON, NEW YORK

I. Introduction

The augmented plane wave (APW) method, originally proposed by Slater (1937) and extended by Slater and Saffren (1953), has in recent years become the leading method for determining theoretically electronic energy-band structures, particularly in metals. The success of the method lies in its ease of application (thanks to the computer techniques developed by Saffren (1959) and Wood (1960), and in the fact that highly accurate solutions of the periodic

* Supported by the U.S. Air Force Office of Scientific Research.
† Operated with support from the U.S. Air Force.
‡ Supported by the U.S. Atomic Energy Commission.

361

potential problem (for a given potential) may be obtained. Well-known applications of the APW method to the determination of the energy-band structure of metals include those of Saffren, Wood, Burdick, Hanus, and Switendick. [An excellent description of the APW method, its relation to other energy-band methods and an extensive review of the literature is given by Slater (1965)]. Loucks' (1965) recently completed relativistic version of the APW scheme has greatly increased the applicability of the method, particularly to those systems where spin-orbit and/or other relativistic terms are important.

In this paper we report on some calculations we have performed, using the nonrelativistic APW method, to obtain the electronic energy bands of the heavy rare-earth metals. This work was undertaken as the first part of a program to investigate, from a theoretical viewpoint, the electronic and magnetic properties of the type 4f hexagonal rare-earth metals. We will be concerned here primarily with the results of these calculations and with their immediate implications in terms of the electric, optical, and magnetic properties of these materials. In addition, we discuss briefly the problems involved in calculating from first principles the electronic energy bands in crystals in general and also specifically in metals. We also discuss the assumptions and approximations peculiar to the APW method as used in current calculations and specifically in the calculations we have performed. Much of what we discuss is well known, but is included here because of its particular relevance to this volume and to viewing the results we shall report. Finally, we discuss the results obtained for the heavy rare-earth metals and our expectations as to their general validity.

II. The Heavy Rare-Metals

The heavy rare-earth metals have been viewed traditionally as consisting of trivalent atomic cores including an unfilled or partially filled 4f shell plus three conduction electrons per atom. Due to the lack of a more detailed model of the conduction bands in rare-earth metals, previous theoretical work has attempted to explain the available experimental data by assuming a simple model in which the three conduction electrons occupy essentially free electron bands perturbed perhaps by a fairly small crystal potential. Much of this theoretical work appears to depend critically on details of the free electron model for the conduction electrons. We undertook to calculate these energy bands in hopes of obtaining a more precise model for the rare-earth metals.

The principal experimental properties of the heavy rare-earth metals in which we are interested fall into three categories—magnetic properties, optical properties, and electric properties. Owing to the partially filled 4f shell, which in all of the heavy rare-earth metals possesses a localized magnetic moment, these materials order at low temperatures to form various magnetic structures. Some of these structures are shown (Koehler, 1965) in Fig. 1. As indicated in the figure, the heavy rare-earth metals possess various magnetic

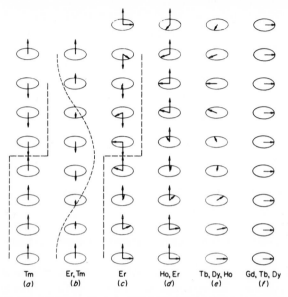

Tm (a)   Er, Tm (b)   Er (c)   Ho, Er (d)   Tb, Dy, Ho (e)   Gd, Tb, Dy (f)

FIG. 1. Schematic representation of magnetic structures of rare-earth metals after Koehler (1965). The moments are supposed to be parallel in a given hexagonal layer.

configurations, and transitions between these configurations occur for any given material at different temperatures. In Table 1, we show some additional

TABLE 1

SOME PHYSICAL PROPERTIES OF THE HEAVY RARE-EARTH METALS[a]

Metal	T_N (°K)	T_c (°K)	$\mu_f(\mu_B)$	$gJ(\mu_B)$
Gd		293.2	7.55	7.0
Tb	229	221	9.34	9.0
Dy	178.5	85	10.20	10.0
Ho	132	20	10.34	10.0
Er	85	19.6	8.0	9.0
Tm	51–60	22(?)	3.4	7.0

[a] As listed by Koehler (1965).

physical properties of the heavy rare-earth metals. Note in particular the measured magnetization per atom as indicated in the fourth column. The expected moment due to the 4f electrons alone is shown in the last column.

In all cases the numbers in these two columns are somewhat different, indicating a contribution from the polarization of the conduction band electrons due to an exchange with the 4f shell is expected. The principal electrical property which we would like to understand at present is the resistivity of these materials measured as a function of temperature. This shows effects due to two causes. First, there is evidence of spin disorder scattering in the strong temperature dependence of the conductivity. Secondly, large discontinuities occur due to the various magnetic transitions which these materials undergo (Hall *et al.*, 1958; Colvin *et al.*, 1960; Hegland *et al.*, 1963). Measurements of the resistivity of single crystals, e.g., erbium, show a strong anisotropy. The discontinuities are present primarily in the resistivity measured along the hexagonal or *c*-axis of the crystal. This anomaly has been interpreted in terms of superzone gaps introduced perpendicular to the *c*-axis at the transition temperature by the onset of long-range magnetic ordering (Mackintosh, 1962; Miwa, 1963; Elliott and Wedgwood, 1963).

III. Approximations Involved in So-Called First Principle Band Calculations

Before discussing our specific results for the rare-earth metals, it is useful to discuss briefly the assumptions and approximations inherent in energy-band calculations. The calculation of electronic eigenstates in crystal and solid is essentially a many-body problem and entails the solution of Schrödinger's equation for approximately 10^{23} nuclei and electrons. Obviously, this is a completely hopeless task without the addition of numerous simplifying approximations.

A. REDUCTION OF MANY-BODY PROBLEM TO ONE-ELECTRON FORM

The first set of approximations are assumed in order to reduce the many-body problem to that of a single electron in a periodic potential. These approximations are serious and are not completely justifiable. The first of these is the Born-Oppenheimer approximation which essentially amounts to neglecting the electron-phonon interaction and reduces the problem to that of an interacting electron system only. Actually, electron-phonon interactions in metals can cause an enhancement of the measured electron mass and the measured oscillator strength for optical transitions by a factor of up to 2.5 for some polyvalent metals. These effects are generally classified as polaron effects. The neglect of the electron-phonon interaction does not appear to be so bad for alkali metals as it is for polyvalent metals and in general it does not appear to seriously affect Fermi surface dimensions even though it modifies the density of states obtained from specific-heat measurements. Effects due to electron-phonon interactions could conceivably be much more serious in insulators where conductivity occurs via a hopping process.

The second assumption is the use of the Hartree-Fock (HF) approximation which reduces the problem to that of an independent electron model and which neglects electron-electron correlations among electrons of opposite spin. Even with this assumption, the problem is still a many-body problem and its exact solution is beyond our present capabilities. It is uncertain at this time if electron-electron correlations play an important role in the electronic band structure of metals. There has, however, been some recent speculation that such effects are important in describing the optical properties of some alkali metals. Electron-electron correlations are quite important in semiconductors and insulators and lead, for example, to the well-known exciton effects in these materials.

The third approximation is that of averaging the exchange term which arises in the Hartree-Fock equations. In order to obtain an effective single electron local potential, it is necessary to average this nonlocal term in one manner or another. It can be averaged over atomic orbitals leading to an ℓ dependent exchange term. However, the more common approach is to use Slater's $\rho^{1/3}$ approximation for the free electron gas. Serious questions have been raised as to the applicability of this approximation to the core (including rare earth 4f) electrons in metals. The principal justification of this approach is that it is simple and relatively easy to use.

B. THE APW "MUFFIN TIN" POTENTIAL

With these three approximations—Born-Oppenheimer, Hartree-Fock, and the Slater average of the exchange term—the many-body problem is reduced to that of a single electron in a periodic potential. The form of this potential in the APW method is that of a "muffin tin," where the potential is made spherically symmetric about each atomic site and is taken to be flat between the APW spheres. The potential is constructed by taking a superposition of spherically averaged atomic charge densities from the neighboring atoms using Löwdin's expansion techniques. The atomic charge densities are obtained from the appropriate atomic wave functions calculated for the free atoms or ions. The potential between the muffin tin spheres is flat and is usually taken as an average of the potential over this region as obtained from the superposition. This potential contains a number of adjustable parameters. In the case of compounds, one can vary the assumed ionicity of the various components and their Madelung energies, since both of these quantities are usually known only within broad limits. In obtaining the atomic charge densities, one can vary the atomic configuration and the state of ionization assumed in the free atom calculations. One can also vary the radii of the APW muffin tins and the potential between the spheres.

C. CRITIQUE OF PROCEDURE

It is now important to ask if there is any justification of the numerous assumptions and approximations which we have described. The answer is that there is at present no real justification of the first three approximations made to reduce the many-body problem to that of a single electron in an effective periodic potential, other than a (dangerous) comparison of the final results of the calculations with experiment. Solutions of the periodic potential problem using an effective one-electron potential can actually be obtained to almost any accuracy desired with the use of modern-day computers. The only real problem which remains is that of obtaining a good self-consistent effective starting potential and of investigating the assumptions made in order to reduce the many-body problem to that of a single electron in a periodic potential.

One approach might be to attempt to achieve self-consistency in the solutions by an iterative process. Here, one can use the calculated wave functions for the crystal to compute a new effective one-electron potential and iterate this process until convergence is achieved. This process, however, is costly in computer time and is still limited by the first three assumptions (mostly that of the averaged exchange) and also by the form assumed for the APW potential. The conclusion is that this procedure may not be worth the trouble, primarily because the answer obtained is probably no better than that arrived at in the first calculation.

Perhaps a more reasonable approach is to systematically vary the several adjustable parameters which enter the APW potential and to investigate the sensitivity of the calculated results to this variation. The range over which the results vary can, in some sense, be considered as a limit to their theoretical validity. One must recognize, however, that this entails only an investigation of the assumed single-electron effective potential and does not really investigate the assumptions necessary to obtain this form for the problem. In the case of compounds, one must vary the ionicity and Madelung energy within a reasonable range about the estimated values of these quantities. One must also investigate the effects due to a variation of the atomic configurations and state of ionization to the extent that these are not known for the solid.

The radii of the muffin tins are chosen to be those values such that the APW spheres for the various constituent atoms touch. The potential between the spheres is usually taken, at least for metals, as some suitable average over the potential in this region obtained from the superposition of the atomic charge densities. Some results of this procedure carried out for a few materials to date can be summarized as follows: for nearly free electron metals for which the energy bands are least sensitive to a variation of the crystal potential, one finds, within the single-electron approximation, that the electronic-band energies are probably good to about 0.2 eV. For transition metals the situation is not nearly so encouraging. Band-energy variations of between 1 and 5 eV have been found to occur using different starting potentials.

The situation in semiconductors is somewhat more difficult to assay since considerable experimental data have been available, usually prior to the theoretical calculations, and in some cases the calculations appear to have been influenced by the experimental results. (Some theoretical procedures are semi-empirical in that the calculations are adjusted to fit existing data. This can be done with the APW method by selectively adjusting the various parameters when there is sufficient experimental data available. This procedure probably results in the most accurate energy band for semiconductors. The pseudopotential method, which is probably the best known of these procedures, appears to have had considerable success in determining energy bands both in semiconductors and in metals. However, we are not considering this procedure here, but instead are concerning ourselves only with so-called first principle calculations. One can question, however, the use of the term " first principle " in any band calculation which includes the numerous assumptions and approximations considered above.) For group IV semiconductors, it appears that the energy bands can be calculated to within about 1 eV without adjustment to fit experimental values for band gaps and other properties. The situation is expected to be somewhat worse in the case of the compound semiconductors.

For the rare-earth metals in the present calculations, we find that the relative band energies can vary as much as 0.5 eV with different potentials. However, as is also true for the other classes of materials, some band gaps are much more sensitive than others. The variations quoted here are, in general, for the more sensitive bands. Nevertheless, one should keep these numbers in mind when assessing the validity of various energy-band calculations.

IV. Electronic Band Structures of Rare-Earth Metals

With this introduction and precaution, we are now in a position to discuss the results of the current energy-band calculations which we have obtained for the rare-earth metals. We discuss here primarily the results obtained for Gd since they are the most complete. The results which we have obtained also for La, Tm, and Lu are substantially the same as those of Gd and differ only in detail.

First, consider the atomic structure of the rare-earth metals. These consist of a xenon core, a partially filled 4f shell (which in Gd contains seven 4f electrons) and three valence electrons in the atomic 5d and 6s states. The relative positions in energy of these states (Herman and Skillman, 1963) are shown in Fig. 2. The atomic 5d and 6s states lie close to one another in energy and are widely separated from the 4f shell. The xenon core states all

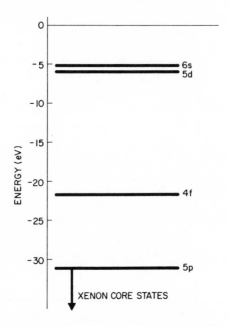

FIG. 2.   Relative positions of the energy of the outermost electrons in atomic Gd.

lie at considerably lower energies and will not be further considered. From the figure one expects the 5d and 6s electrons to contribute to the conduction processes independent of the 4f electrons.

In Fig. 3 we show the relative outer radial extent of the atomic electrons for Gd and also indicate the Wigner-Seitz radius appropriate for Gd metal. As can be seen, the 4f electrons are tightly bound to the atom and do not overlap neighboring atoms appreciably. Consequently in the band model, the 4f electrons will form a very narrow band. The calculations yield a 4f band with a width of about 0.05 eV located approximately 11 eV below the bottom of the 5d–6s bands. This separation, however, is very sensitive to the potential used in the calculations and is consequently unreliable. Furthermore, the energy-band picture for the 4f states essentially neglects the intra-atomic exchange energies of these electrons which amounts in Gd to several electron volts. Consequently, the 4f electrons cannot be treated as band electrons but must be considered as localized and so do not fit within the band picture·at all. This makes their calculated position in energy even more unrealistic than is indicated by the variation obtained with different potentials. As can be

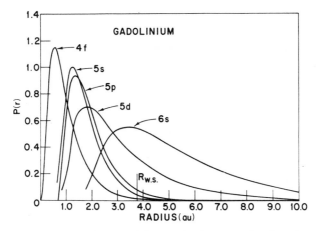

FIG. 3.   Relative outer radial extent of the atomic 4f, 5s, 5p, 5d and 6s electrons in Gd. Also indicated is the Wigner-Seitz radius appropriate for Gd metal.

seen from Fig. 3, the 5d and 6s atomic functions on different atom sites do overlap one another to a considerable extent. Consequently, they will form an s-d conduction band of considerable width. The contribution to this band from the 5d electrons is expected to be somewhat narrower than that of the 6s electrons since the spatial overlap of the 5d functions is somewhat less than that of the 6s functions. Note that this is expected to bear a strong similarity to the situation found to exist in the case of transition metals.

The calculations for Gd have been carried out with a number of starting potentials. These have all been generated by superpositions of atomic charge densities obtained for free Gd atoms in which we have varied the assumed atomic configuration for the free atoms. We have used atomic charge densities obtained by using the Hartree-Fock-Slater (HFS) calculational procedure of Herman and Skillman (1963) applied to the atomic Gd configurations $4f^7 5d^1 6s^2$, $4f^7 5d^2 6s^1$, $4f^7 5d^3 6s^0$, and $4f^8 5d^0 6s^2$. We have also used the atomic Hartree-Fock charge density obtained by Freeman and Watson (1962) for the singly ionized Gd configuration $4f^7 6s^2$ to which was added a 5d function. A plot of these potentials is shown in Fig. 4. Note that as expected, the differences in the potentials occur in the outer regions of the atom since we have varied the configuration of the outer electrons only. All of these potentials gave qualitatively the same results with a maximum variation in the relative energies of the conduction band states of about 0.5 eV. The results which we present are those obtained using the HFS $4f^7 5d^1 6s^2$ potential. These are representative of results obtained using the other potentials.

A histogram of the calculated density of states for Gd metal is shown* in

---

* A preliminary report of this work was given earlier by Dimmock and Freeman (1964).

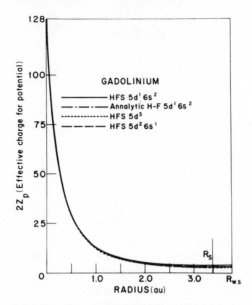

FIG. 4.   Plot of effective nuclear charge for potential $2Z_p(r)$ for the different configurations used in the calculations described in the text.

Fig. 5. The density of states of the conduction bands was obtained by dividing the Brillouin zone into 192 identical hexagons, each characterized by the energies calculated at its center. We show also for comparison the density of states given by the free-electron model. The d-bands originating from the Gd 5d states contribute a high density of states in the vicinity of the Fermi energy with a width of about 0.5 Rydbergs (6 eV). This width is nearly the

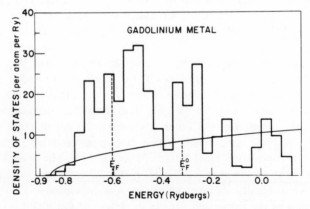

FIG. 5.   A histogram representation of the density of states, in electrons per atom per rydberg. The parabolic curve is the prediction of the free-electron model.

same as that obtained by Wood (1960) for the 3d-bands in iron. Note that the Fermi energy lies at a peak in the density of states. The Fermi energy, for three electrons per atom, is $E_F = 0.25$ measured from the bottom of the band as compared with a value of 0.54 Ry for the free-electron model. At the Fermi energy, the calculated density of states is large, $N(E_F) = 1.8$ electrons per atom per eV compared with the free electron value of $0.6 \, \text{eV}^{-1}$. This is due to the fact that the electron bands in the vicinity of the Fermi surface are of mixed s-d character and are consequently much flatter than would be expected from a free-electron model.

One can note in Fig. 5 a small tail at lower energies in the density of states due to the bottom of the 6s band. This s-band tail can be seen more clearly in Fig. 6 where we plot the energy bands calculated for Gd metal. The high

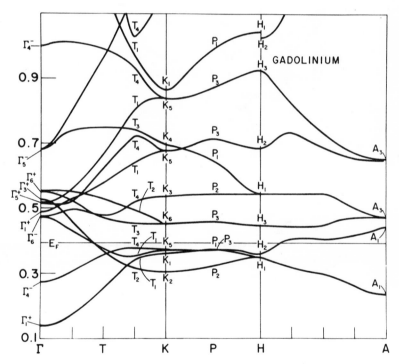

FIG. 6. Calculated $E(k)$ curves for the conduction bands of gadolinium metal along the symmetry directions Γ-K-H-A.

density of flat d-bands in the vicinity of the Fermi energy is very apparent in this figure. One should note that these are actually mixed s-d bands since the s-electrons contribute to the conduction band states throughout the entire region. Further, it should be emphasized at this time that the energy-band calculations which we are reporting are those obtained using a nonrelativistic method. If relativistic effects were included, they would result in two modifications to Fig. 6. The first is that there would be a relative downward shift of the s-bands with respect to the d-bands by about 0.4 eV corresponding to the relativistic shift of the 6s states in Gd with respect to the 5d states. In addition, spin orbit coupling will split the energy bands at Γ, K, H and A and incidentally throughout the ALH plane as well. This splitting is also about 0.4 eV.

The electronic properties of the rare earth metals are determined largely by the shape, form, and topology of their Fermi surface. Figure 7 shows the

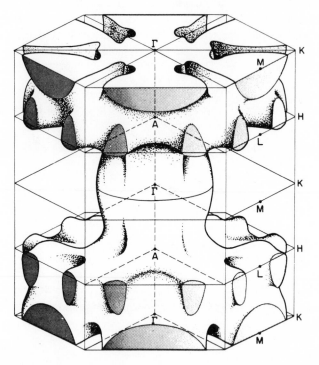

Fig. 7. The complete Fermi surface for holes in Gd metal in the double-zone representation.

complete Fermi surface for holes in gadolinium metal, in the double-zone scheme. As far as we can determine there are no additional pockets of holes or electrons. This Fermi surface permits open orbits both along the c-axis of the crystal and in the plane perpendicular to this axis. One should ask to what extent we consider this Fermi surface reliable. We feel that we have partially answered this question by repeating our calculations with various different Gd starting potentials. Since the qualitative features of the Fermi surface are found not to change with the different potentials used, we feel that these qualitative features are reliable. It should be pointed out that this Fermi surface bears no resemblance at all to the Fermi surface of the free-electron model. Note that we have drawn the Fermi surface in the so-called double-zone scheme. It should be recognized that with the inclusion of relativistic effects, an energy gap, representing itself as a discontinuity in the Fermi surface will occur in the ALH plane of the figure.

V. Comparison with Experiment

One might ask, how well do the calculated results agree with experiment? As stated earlier, much of the previous theoretical work on rare-earths depended critically on the assumed free-electron nature of the conduction bands. There is now mounting evidence that the free-electron model is completely incorrect and that our 5d-6s bands are indeed the correct representation of the conduction bands, as we shall show.

A. MAGNETIZATION AND SPECIFIC-HEAT MEASUREMENTS

As regards experiment, it has been difficult, for example, to explain by means of the free-electron model the large saturation magnetization (Nigh *et al.*, 1963) of Gd (cf. Table 1) and especially the large electronic specific heat (Berman *et al.*, 1958; Jennings *et al.*, 1960; Lounasmaa, 1963, 1964) of the rare-earth metals which indicates a density of states at the Fermi surface some eight times that given by the free-electron model.

Let us first consider the magnetic properties of gadolinium (Dimmock and Freeman, 1964). The saturation magnetization measurements of 7.55 μ_B per Gd atom in the metal is 0.55 μ_B more than expected for an ^8S ion. It is common to assume that this additional moment arises from a polarization of the conduction electrons. Using our computed density of states and a simple model in which the conduction electrons are polarized by exchange with the localized 4f electrons, one may estimate the exchange integral $\mathscr{J}$ required to produce this additional moment. For gadolinium the induced moment is given by $\mu = 7/2 \mathscr{J} N(E_F) \mu_B$. For $N(E_F) = 1.8$ eV^{-1} we find $\mathscr{J} = 0.08$ eV. This $\mathscr{J}$ is about five times smaller than that computed between atomic 4f and 5d electrons but agrees with values of $\mathscr{J}$ (0.05–0.10 eV) calculated between a localized 4f electron and a plane wave. (Orthogonalized plane wave calculations, on the other band give $\mathscr{J} = 0.04$–0.07 eV.) From these estimates, we conclude that the "extra" magnetization in Gd can arise very easily from a reasonable exchange between the magnetic 4f electrons and the s-d conduction electrons at the Fermi energy largely because of the size of our computed $N(E_F)$. Further, with this picture of s-d conduction electrons occupying a band having a high density of states, one sees a strong qualitative resemblance to the transition metals and the role of d electrons in understanding the origin of magnetism in these materials. The difference is that in the rare-earth metals the bulk of the magnetization is carried by the 4f electrons which, however, lie well inside the atom and play no further direct role in interatomic exchange. From our calculated $N(E_F)$ we obtain an electronic specific heat contribution of $\gamma = 4.2$ mJ/mole deg^2, which may be compared with an average measured value of about 10 mJ/mole deg^2 for the 4f rare-earth metals with triply ionized cores, and with a free-electron value of 1.3 mJ/mole deg^2. Thus while our calculated $N(E_F)$ is some three times larger than the free-electron value, the calculated γ is smaller than experiment by about a factor of two. Crude estimates for Gd indicate that this difference could arise from electron-phonon contributions (Krebs, 1963; Prange and Kadanoff, 1964) to an apparent $N(E_F)$ deduced from measured γ values.

B. OPTICAL PROPERTIES

Predictions can be made from the calculated energy bands concerning optical properties. Anomalies in the optical absorption and reflectivity may occur due to interband transitions between occupied and unoccupied energy levels for frequencies at which the bands yield a high joint density of states. These have been discussed elsewhere (Dimmock et al., 1965). In addition to these transitions, interband transitions can also occur between the atomic 4f levels and the electronic energy states above the Fermi energy. Blodgett et al. (1964) have recently measured the photoemission from Gd and have found a high density of states at the Fermi energy and a bandwidth in good agreement with our theoretical predictions. They have also observed emission from 4f levels located about 5.8 eV below the Fermi energy. Since our band calculations yield a high density of states at about 1.2 eV above the Fermi energy (see Fig. 5) we would expect the transitions between the 4f levels and the conduction bands to yield an anomaly in the uv at about 7.0 eV.

There are also optical anomalies which are expected from the fact that the conduction bands in the heavy rare-earth metals will be split at low temperatures through an exchange interaction with the 4f electrons (Miwa, 1963). As shown in Fig. 1, the heavy rare-earth metals exhibit, at low temperatures, some form of magnetic order. This results in an exchange splitting of the s-d conduction bands which may take the form either of energy gaps which occur at superzone boundaries created by an antiferromagnetic superlattice as exists in Tm, or a simple separation into the so-called spin-up and spin-down bands of a ferromagnet as would occur in Gd. Both of these types of exchange splittings are expected to result in optical absorption and reflectivity anomalies due to transitions between the exchange split bands. However, the shape and possibly the position of the absorption band might be expected to be somewhat dependent on the magnetic structure.

The infrared reflectivity of a thin film of antiferromagnetic Ho has been measured by Schüler (1964). His data show a temperature dependent anomaly at about 0.35 eV which has been interpreted as due to interband transitions across the energy gaps created by the antiferromagnetic superlattice. Cooper and Redington (1965) have observed the infrared absorption spectra of a thin film of Dy both with and without an external magnetic field. They observed an anomaly at about 0.44 eV quite similar to that seen by Schüler in Ho. The spectra observed in antiferromagnetic and ferromagnetic Dy were essentially identical. Recently, Schüler has observed a similar anomaly in the reflectivity of thin films of ferromagnetic Gd. The frequency of the anomalies in both Dy and Ho are strongly temperature dependent, becoming lower at higher temperatures. In addition, the anomalies vanish altogether above the Néel points. This indicates that they are probably of magnetic origin, due to the exchange splitting of the s-d conduction bands. The exchange splitting is given for heavy rare-earth metals at $T = 0$ by $\Delta E = 2 \mathscr{J} S$ where $\mathscr{J}$ is an effective s-f exchange energy and S is the spin of the rare-earth ion. We have estimated ΔE, as above, for Gd from our calculated density of states at the Fermi surface and the observed saturation magnetization of 7.55 μ_B/atom. We found that for Gd $\Delta E = 0.61$ eV. Values of ΔE for the heavy rare-earth metals are given in Table 1 from the value for Gd and Eq. (1) assuming $\mathscr{J}$ is the same for all metals in the series. Although the values of ΔE given in Table 2 are to be considered as rough estimates only, the agreement with the position of the absorption anomaly in Dy at about 0.44 eV and with the position of the reflectivity anomaly in Ho at about 0.35 eV is quite encouraging.

TABLE 2

ESTIMATES OF THE VALUES OF ΔE FOR THE
HEAVY RARE-EARTH METALS

	S	ΔE (eV)
Gd	7/2	0.61
Tb	3	0.52
Dy	5/2	0.44
Ho	2	0.35
Er	3/2	0.26
Tm	1	0.17

C. ELECTRICAL RESISTIVITY ANOMALIES

Finally, we discuss briefly the resistivity anomalies observed at the magnetic ordering temperatures of the heavy rare-earths (Colvin *et al.*, 1960; Hall *et al.*, 1958; Hegland *et al.*, 1963; Elliott and Wedgwood, 1963; Mackintosh, 1962; Miwa, 1963). As mentioned in Section II, these anomalies have been successfully interpreted in terms of the magnetic ordering of these materials. As seen in Fig. 1, Tm shows a linear spin wave-type structure between 50° and 40°K in which the magnitude of the z-component of the moments varies sinusoidally with distance along the c-axis. The period of the wave vector is constant at seven (hexagonal) layers over the observed temperature range and differs from that of many of the other rare-earth structures which have periods incommensurate with the lattice and which vary with temperature. As described briefly above, this periodic magnetic structure introduces planes of energy discontinuity (superzone gaps) into the nonmagnetic Brillouin zone structure (Elliott and Wedgwood, 1963; Mackintosh, 1962; Miwa, 1963). These energy gaps may affect drastically the electrical conduction of the metal as the temperature is lowered through the Néel temperature provided one of these superzone boundaries destroys a large part of the Fermi surface. The observation of large anisotropy in the resistivity (maximum along the c-axis) and the reduction of the anomaly in Tb when the sample is cooled in a magnetic field (which suppresses the long-range order and reduces the band gaps) provided confirmation for the validity of the model. The existence of superzone planes which cut large sections of the Fermi surface in the free-electron model led easily to an explanation of the resistivity anomaly along the c-axis and to the variation in resistivity with the variation in magnetic period. This agreement has since been taken as evidence in support of the validity of the free electron model. However, our determination that the conduction bands in Gd resemble those of the transition metals and differ markedly from free electron bands showed that this model was completely invalid for the rare-earth metals. It also raised the question at the same time as to whether agreement between theory and experiment could be restored using the APW band structure and the resulting Fermi surface.

The usual argument, based on first-order perturbation theory, asserts that energy gaps and superzone boundaries occur at values of $\mathbf{k}$ for which

$$E(\mathbf{k}) - E(\mathbf{k} \pm \mathbf{q}) = 0 \tag{1}$$

when the system is subjected to a perturbation of wave vector $\mathbf{q}$. Experimentally, $\mathbf{q}$ lies parallel to the crystal c-axis in the rare-earth metals. Since by symmetry $E(\mathbf{k}) = E(-\mathbf{k})$ this results in planar superzone boundaries at $k_z = \pm\frac{1}{2}q$, or more completely at $k_z = \frac{1}{2}K_z \pm \frac{1}{2}q$ where K_z is the z component of a reciprocal lattice vector. It should be noted that although these are the only superzone boundaries required by symmetry, to this order, in general other boundaries may occur at values of $\mathbf{k}$ which satisfy Eq. (1) and that these values of $\mathbf{k}$ will depend specifically on the energy-band structure or, alternatively, on the particular Fermi surface. Specifically, gaps occur at those values of $\mathbf{k}$ where both $\mathbf{k}$ and $\mathbf{k} \pm \mathbf{q}$ lie on the Fermi surface, that is, where $\mathbf{q}$ spans a section of the Fermi surface.

All of this discussion is limited to first-order perturbation theory, which should be applicable in the vicinity of the ordering temperature where the magnetic moment is small. However, at lower temperatures, if the periodic perturbation is large, compared to the separations between energy bands, a higher order treatment must be considered. Accepting the arguments given above then, from Table 2 we see that in Tm at $T = 0$ the energy gaps introduced at the superzone boundaries should be about 0.17 eV wide. This energy is comparable to the separation between the flat d-bands in the vicinity of the Fermi surface which we have obtained for the rare-earth metals. So-called higher order terms in perturbation theory will introduce energy gaps of magnitude comparable to those at $k_z = \pm\frac{1}{2}q$. Therefore, because of the fact that these bands are relatively flat and closely spaced we must replace Eq. (1) by

$$E(\mathbf{k}) - E(\mathbf{k} \pm n\mathbf{q}) = 0 . \tag{2}$$

This then leads to superzone boundaries at $k_z = \pm\frac{1}{2}nq$.

Our calculated energy bands and Fermi surface for Tm closely resemble those for Gd shown in Figs. 6 and 7. Figure 8 shows several vertical cross

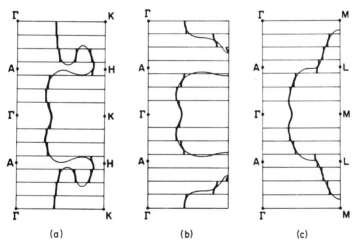

(a)   (b)   (c)

FIG. 8. Some vertical cross sections of the Tm Fermi surface containing the c-axis. The influence of magnetic ordering is demonstrated by comparing the low temperature cross sections, shown as heavy solid curves, with the high temperature cross sections, shown as light solid curves. The horizontal lines denote superzone boundaries at $k_z = \pm n(2\pi/7c)$ introduced by the magnetic ordering.

sections of the Fermi surface calculated for Tm. The horizontal lines denote superzone boundaries at $k_z = \pm n(2\pi/7c)$ introduced by the periodic magnetic ordering. The expected distortion of the Fermi surface at $T = 0$ is given approximately by the heavy solid curves. The largest portions of the Fermi surface are destroyed by the superzone boundary corresponding to $n = 3$. Notice that this effect is a direct consequence of the presence of several relatively flat d-bands in the vicinity of the Fermi energy and would not occur to any extent in the free-electron model. Notice further that the vector $q = 4\pi/7c$ actually spans a section of the calculated Fermi surface as can be seen in Fig. 8(b). This is essential to the resistivity anomaly at the transition temperature as discussed above.

In Fig. 8, we have drawn the perturbed Fermi surface in such a way as to emphasize its relationship to the unperturbed surface (the light solid curves). It should be recognized that the Bloch states which originally had unique k values within the double Brilloiun zone for the hcp structure are now mixtures of k values differing by multiples of q. Therefore, the assignment of a particular one-electron state to a particular point in k space is ambiguous to this degree. However, the essential feature of the result is that, in the magnetic state, the Fermi surface normal to the z-axis is largely destroyed while segments parallel to the axis remain, though somewhat perturbed. This implies a resistance anomaly parallel but not perpendicular to the crystal c-axis in agreement with experiment. It should be pointed out, however, that the calculations we have performed are all nonrelativistic and that relativistic corrections, including spin-orbit effects, will certainly modify, to some extent, the computed Fermi surface. Nevertheless, we feel that the general features of the Fermi surface and of the effects of magnetic ordering, should remain even when the relativistic effects are taken into account.

In summary, we can make the following statements: (1) The observed $\mathbf{q}$ vector spans a section of the calculated Fermi surface of Tm such that a section of this Fermi surface perpendicular to the z-axis is destroyed at the onset of magnetic ordering. This results in the observed resistivity anomaly at T_N. (2) Due to the fact that the energy bands are relatively flat in the vicinity of the Fermi energy, gaps will occur at superzone boundaries for $k_z = \pm\frac{1}{2}nq$ as the temperature is lowered below T_N, destroying large sections of the Fermi surface normal to the z-axis. It appears that the anomalies in the temperature dependence of the resistivity of the heavy rare-earth metals can be understood in terms of the calculated energy bands of these materials, and that qualitative agreement, at least, exists between theory and experiment. A quantitative comparison appears difficult at this time because of the expectation of various relativistic corrections of other uncertainties in the energy-band structure and of the general complex nature of the calculated energy bands.

VI. Conclusion

In conclusion, we emphasize that the computed conduction bands for the rare-earth metals are not at all represented by the free-electron model but instead are of s-d character and strongly resemble the energy bands of transition metals. There occurs a high density of states at the Fermi energy as implied by specific heat and magnetization data and shown by recent photoemission measurements. The additional magnetic moment measured in the rare-earth metals over that expected on the basis of the 4f shell alone is due to an exchange polarization of the s-d conduction bands. We have also shown, using our calculated energy bands and Fermi surfaces, at least qualitative agreement may be obtained between theory and experiment for some optical and electrical properties despite the limitations inherent in the calculations.

Finally, we note that the Fermi surface obtained has many unusual features, such that it would be very interesting to study the de Haas-van Alphen, Schubnikov-de Haas and cyclotron resonance phenomena in these materials. Unfortunately, the purity of the rare-earth metals is not at present sufficiently high to allow one to make these measurements. However, it may be possible to study the Fermi surface topology through magnetoresistance measurements and it is to be hoped that such experiments will be undertaken soon.

ACKNOWLEDGMENTS

We are indebted to Mrs. A. Furdyna who participated fully in many parts of this work. We are grateful to J. H. Wood for making the APW programs available to us and for many helpful discussions, and to A. Furdyna and R. Sheshinski for their help with many phases of the computations.

REFERENCES

Berman, A., Zemansky, M. W., and Boorse, H. A. (1958). *Phys. Rev.* **109**, 70.
Blodgett, A. J., Spicer, W. E., and Yu, A. Y-C. (1966). *In* " Optical Properties and Electronic Structure of Metals and Alloys " (F. Abelés, ed.), p. 246. North-Holland Publ., Amsterdam.
Colvin, R. V., Legvold, S., and Spedding, F. H. (1960). *Phys. Rev.* **120**, 741.
Cooper, B. R., and Redington, R. W. (1965). *Phys. Rev. Letters* **14**, 1066.
Dimmock, J. O., and Freeman, A. J. (1964). *Phys. Rev. Letters* **13**, 750.
Dimmock, J. O., Freeman, A. J., and Watson, R. E. (1966). *In* "Optical Properties and Electronic Structure of Metals and Alloys " (F. Abelés, ed.), p. 237. North-Holland Publ., Amsterdam.
Elliott, R. J., and Wedgwood, F. A. (1963). *Proc. Phys. Soc.* **81**, 846.
Freeman, A. J., and Watson, R. E. (1962). *Phys. Rev.* **127**, 2058.
Hall, P. M., Legvold, S., and Spedding, F. H. (1958). *Phys. Rev.* **109**, 971.
Hegland, D. E., Legvold, S., and Spedding, F. H. (1963). *Phys. Rev.* **131**, 158.
Herman, F., and Skillman, S. (1963). "Atomic Structure Calculations." Prentice-Hall, Englewood Cliffs, New Jersey.
Jennings, L. D., Miller, R. E., and Spedding, F. H. (1960). *J. Chem. Phys.* **33**, 1849.
Koehler, W. C. (1965). *J. Appl. Phys.* **36**, 1078S.
Krebs, K. (1963). *Phys. Letters* **6**, 31.
Loucks, T. L. (1965). *Phys. Rev.* **134**, A1181, A1333.

Lounasmaa, O. V. (1962). *Phys. Rev.* **126.**
Lounasmaa, O. V. (1963). *Phys. Rev.* **129,** 2460.
Lounasmaa, O. V. (1964). *Phys. Rev.* **133,** A219.
Mackintosh, A. R. (1962). *Phys. Rev. Letters* **9,** 90.
Miwa, H. (1963). *Progr. Theor. Phys. Japan* **29,** 477.
Nigh, H., Legvold, S., and Spedding, F. H. (1963). *Phys. Rev.* **132,** 1092.
Prange, R. E., and Kadanoff, L. P. (1964). *Phys. Rev.* **134,** A566.
Saffren, M. M. (1959). Ph.D. Thesis, M.I.T., Physics Department.
Schüler, C. C. (1964). *Phys. Letters* **12,** 84.
Schüler, C. C. (1966). To be published.
Slater, J. C. (1937). *Phys. Rev.* **51,** 846.
Slater, J. C. (1963). *Phys. Rev.* **92,** 603.
Slater, J. C. (1965). "Quantum Theory of Molecules and Solids," Vol. II. McGraw-Hill, New York.
Slater, J. C., and Saffren, M. M., (1953). *Phys. Rev.* **92,** 603, 1126.
Wood, J. H. (1960). *Phys. Rev.* **117,** 714.

New Studies of the Band Structure of Silicon, Germanium, and Grey Tin*

F. HERMAN, R. L. KORTUM, C. D. KUGLIN, and R. A. SHORT

LOCKHEED PALO ALTO RESEARCH LABORATORY, PALO ALTO, CALIFORNIA

I. Introduction

Although a vast amount of experimental and theoretical information is now available concerning the valence and conduction band edges of silicon and germanium—and to a lesser extent grey tin—our detailed knowledge of the energy band structure of these crystals away from the band edges is still

* Supported by the Lockheed Independent Research Fund.

surprisingly incomplete. The object of the present study is to elucidate, in quantitative terms, the nature of these relatively unexplored regions of the band structure, and thereby to provide a reliable theoretical guide for experimental investigations of optical, photoemissive, and pressure-sensitive properties that depend on the band structure away from the band edges.

It is possible to obtain a reasonably good qualitative picture of the band structure over a 10–20 eV range by carrying out first-principles energy band calculations, but the accuracy of such calculations is often not high enough for detailed analyses of experimental spectra. Another approach is represented by the empirical pseudopotential method (Brust, 1964; Cohen and Bergstresser, 1966), and by the empirical full zone $k \cdot p$ method (Cardona and Pollak, 1966). The idea here is to set up a parametric model of the energy band structure, and then to adjust the parameters so that the calculated band structure agrees with the few known features of the experimental band structure. The task of fitting the experimental band structure over a 10–20 eV range with an empirical model is a very difficult one, and some sacrifice in local accuracy in the interest of a good overall fit is probably unavoidable. In spite of their convenience, empirical band models are not nearly as accurate as some of their advocates (cf. Phillips, 1966) would have us believe. The marked discrepancies between experimental and computed values for the imaginary part of the complex dielectric response function for silicon and germanium (cf. Brust, 1964, especially Fig. 16) should serve as a warning to those who would accept empirical pseudopotential band models uncritically.

In view of the recent development of high-resolution experimental techniques for studying band structure, such as modulated electroreflectivity (Seraphin, 1964, 1965) and modulated piezoreflectivity (Engeler et al., 1965; Gobeli and Kane, 1965), the need for high-accuracy band calculations is now more acute than ever. We believe that recent attempts to interpret electroreflectivity and piezoreflectivity spectra for silicon and germanium in terms of pseudopotential band models have been only partially successful because these models are not sufficiently accurate for such an exacting task.

In this article, we describe a method for determining the band structure of crystals which is designed to have a higher accuracy than purely first-principles or purely empirical (pseudopotential or $k \cdot p$) methods. The first step in our approach is a nonrelativistic self-consistent energy band calculation which is carried out with far greater care than is customary. In the second step, we depart from a purely first-principles approach, and introduce a small empirical adjustment which serves to bring key features of the theoretical energy level scheme into exact agreement with the most reliably established features of the experimental level scheme. Our approach to superior accuracy, then, is based on the addition of a small, carefully chosen empirical adjustment to an otherwise first-principles band calculation. The empirical adjustment proves to be quite small: it is usually sufficient to change a few of the leading Fourier coefficients of the self-consistent crystal potential by a few percent each.

Although the study of crystals whose band structures are poorly understood was foremost in our minds when we set out to develop this *empirically perturbed self-consistent field method*, it seemed worthwhile to test our approach on the well-studied diamond-type crystals before attempting the study of other, less familiar, crystals. In addition to testing out our method on these crystals, we have succeeded in obtaining a considerable amount of new and hopefully accurate information about (a) key features of the energy band structure of silicon, germanium, and grey tin away from the valence and conduction band edges; (b) systematics of the energy band structure of the germanium-silicon alloy system away from the band edges; (c) net deformation potential differences for many important interband transitions; and (d) systematics of the band structure of germanium as a function of lattice constant over an extreme lattice constant range.

We have also examined a number of previous theoretical ideas (cf. Phillips, 1966) concerning energy level assignments and the identification of interband transitions principally responsible for characteristic features of optical spectra. We have examined these ideas in the light of the experimental evidence itself, in the light of our new energy band models, and in the light of our new deformation potential calculations. For example, our calculated deformation potentials for specific interband transitions were compared with the measured deformation potentials for supposedly related optical reflectivity peaks.

Our new results confirm many of the earlier energy level assignments, but show, for example, that the $X_1 - X_4{}^*$ transition is not really representative of the main optical reflectivity peak, a conclusion that has also been reached by Kane (1966) on the basis of other considerations. Our results are at variance with the common identification of the 3.4 eV reflectivity peak in silicon with $\Gamma_{15} - \Gamma_{25'}$ or closely related $\Delta_1 - \Delta_5$ transitions (Phillips, 1962, 1964, 1966; Cardona and Pollak, 1966; Brust, 1964; Cohen and Bergstresser, 1966).

In fact, our results suggest that the $\Gamma_{15} - \Gamma_{25'}$ transition has not been properly identified previously, not only in silicon, but also in germanium and grey tin. In all three of these crystals, we find that this important transition lies at least 0.5 eV lower in energy than is currently believed. This conclusion has an important bearing on current interpretations of reflectivity, electroreflectivity, piezoreflectivity, and photoemission spectra since a change in $\Gamma_{15} - \Gamma_{25'}$ by even 0.5 eV would have a profound effect on the structure of three of the four lowest conduction bands in the central region of the reduced zone, and on the detailed nature of interband transitions in the range between 2 and 4 eV.

---

* Contrary to common usage, we will denote the transition $A \to B$ as B–A since B–A is closer in form to the expression for the transition energy, $E(B) - E(A)$.

II. Theoretical Approach

A. SELF-CONSISTENT ENERGY BAND CALCULATIONS

Our nonrelativistic self-consistent (NRSC) band calculations are based on the orthogonalized plane wave (OPW) method (for a review, see Herman, 1958), and on Slater's simplified version of the Hartree-Fock equations (Slater, 1951). The present calculations are based primarily on the free-electron exchange approximation proposed by Slater in his 1951 paper, though other exchange approximations are used in selected portions of our work. The free-electron exchange approximation has the dual virtue of being physically realistic and computationally tractable.

The mathematical approximations and numerical procedures used in the present study are identical to those already described in our 1964 Paris Semiconductor Conference paper (Herman, 1964), except that a greatly improved set of computer codes are now used in place of the earlier set. Most of the differences between theory and experiment noted in our preliminary account (Herman, 1964) can be attributed to the use of orthogonality coefficients that were not computed with sufficiently high accuracy. Because of cancellation effects, a slight inaccuracy (even 1 %) in one term of an OPW matrix element can have serious repercussions. In the present work, all terms appearing in the OPW matrix elements are accurate to five significant figures.

We begin our NRSC band calculations by computing preliminary energies and wave functions at a set of 32 sample points in the reduced zone on the basis of a trial crystal potential. The crystal charge density is then determined from this set of sample wave functions. We then iterate, calculating a new crystal potential each time from the previously determined crystal charge density. The iteration is continued until the crystal charge density is self-consistent to better than one part in 10^3, often to better than one part in 10^4. In our standard NRSC band calculation, the OPW expansion includes about 120 terms at each of the 32 sample points, which are as follows: 1 (0 0 0)+ 6 ($\frac{1}{2}$ 0 0) + 12 ($\frac{1}{2}$ $\frac{1}{2}$ 0) + 4 ($\frac{1}{2}$ $\frac{1}{2}$ $\frac{1}{2}$) + 3 (1 0 0) + 6 (1 $\frac{1}{2}$ 0), where a common factor of $(2\pi/a)$ has been omitted. The overall precision of our standard NRSC energy level scheme is estimated to be about ± 0.05 eV.

We have checked the convergence of our NRSC calculations by doubling the number of sample points [this is accomplished by adding 8 ($\frac{1}{4}$ $\frac{1}{4}$ $\frac{1}{4}$) + 24 ($\frac{3}{4}$ $\frac{1}{4}$ $\frac{1}{4}$) to the previous list], and also by increasing the number of OPWs per point from about 120 to about 180. Each of these refinements affected the NRSC energy level scheme only slightly: energy level separations were usually changed by less than ± 0.0025 eV.

B. EMPIRICAL PERTURBATION SCHEME

Instead of attempting to improve the physical rigor of the NRSC energy band calculation– by using a more refined exchange approximation, or possibly even by including relativistic, spin-orbit coupling, and electron correlation effects—we will take a shortcut, and compensate for our shortcomings in physical rigor by means of a crystal potential perturbation ΔV which is to be determined empirically. This perturbation—which may be represented formally by nonlocal as well as by local operators—is designed to bring key features of the theoretical energy level spectrum into agreement with the most reliably established features of the experimental spectrum. In effect, ΔV will be used to generate a set of energy level shifts $\Delta E(\Delta V)$ which transform the NRSC energy level scheme, $E(\text{NRSC})$, into a modified (or perturbed) scheme, $E(\text{PERT})$, according to the defining relation:

$$E(\text{PERT}) = E(\text{NRSC}) + \Delta E(\Delta V).$$

For convenience, we choose to classify all energy levels according to the irreducible representations of the single group. Accordingly, the spin-orbit coupling corrections $\Delta E(\text{SO})$ will not be included in $\Delta E(\Delta V)$. Instead, these corrections will be subtracted from the (actual) experimental energy level spectrum, $E(\text{EXPT})$, thereby generating the (single group) experimental spectrum, $E^*(\text{EXPT})$:

$$E^*(\text{EXPT}) = E(\text{EXPT}) - \Delta E(\text{SO}).$$

At this stage, our objective is to adjust $E(\text{PERT})$ to $E^*(\text{EXPT})$ by a suitable choice of ΔV. Since we are not yet in a position to calculate $\Delta E(\text{SO})$ from first principles, we are obliged to use experimental values for $\Delta E(\text{SO})$ in the present work.

The success of our plan depends on our ability to devise a suitable ΔV. It is instructive to make a formal decomposition of ΔV and then study the effect each individual part has on the band structure. If ΔV is regarded as a local function, a Fourier decomposition is appropriate:

$$\Delta V(\mathbf{r}) = \Sigma(\mathbf{h})\, \Delta v(\mathbf{h}) \exp i\mathbf{h} \cdot \mathbf{r}.$$

By first-order perturbation theory, we can determine the energy level shifts $\Delta E(\mathbf{h})$ produced by the leading Fourier coefficients, $\Delta v(\mathbf{h})$. Each symmetrically equivalent set of $\Delta v(\mathbf{h})$—denoted for short by $\Delta v(\mathbf{h})$—can be treated as an adjustable parameter. In deciding which $\Delta v(\mathbf{h})$ to concentrate on, we can be guided to some extent by the relative magnitude of the estimated uncertainties in the corresponding self-consistent $v(\mathbf{h})$. For example, an improvement in our treatment of valence–valence exchange would have the most profound effect on $v(111)$, so that $\Delta v(111)$ can be regarded as a prime adjustment parameter.

By modifying the nonlocal repulsive potential arising from the orthogonality terms in the OPW matrix elements, a nonlocal ΔV can be simulated. This is most readily accomplished by altering the various core energy levels, either individually or in selected combinations: $E_\alpha(\text{NRSC}) \rightarrow E_\alpha(\text{NRSC}) + \Delta E_\alpha^{\text{core}}$, where $\alpha = 1s, 2s, 2p \ldots$. If all the core levels are shifted by a common amount, ΔE^{core}, the valence and conduction band levels will be shifted in a manner described by the symbol $\Delta E(CORE)$. If only the s core levels (1s, 2s ...) are displaced from their NRSC values, the shift pattern $\Delta E(CORE/s)$ is obtained, and similarly for selective shifts of p and d core levels.

The relativistic (mass-velocity and Darwin) correction, $\Delta E(REL)$, is a special case of $\Delta E(\Delta V)$ which can be evaluated by first-order perturbation theory (Herman et al., 1963). For germanium and grey tin, it is found that $\Delta E(REL)$ is nearly proportional to $\Delta E(CORE)$, suggesting that $\Delta E(CORE)$ is also a prime adjustment parameter. In these crystals, and presumably in others, $\Delta E(CORE)$ can be used to simulate the relativistic correction, as well as other corrections associated with the ion core region.

A typical two-parameter adjustment scheme is based on the two parameters $\Delta v(111)$ and ΔE^{core}, and has the form

$$E(PERT) = E(NRSC) + \Delta E(111) + \Delta E(CORE).$$

In practice, a satisfactory adjustment can be carried out by using a $\Delta v(111)$ of the order of $0.03v(111)$, and a core shift ΔE^{core} of the order of 0.2 Ry. Another two-parameter scheme is based on $\Delta v(111)$ and $\Delta v(220)$ and has the form

$$E(PERT) = E(NRSC) + \Delta E(111) + \Delta E(220).$$

In this case, a satisfactory adjustment usually involves a $\Delta v(111)$ of the order of $0.03v(111)$, and a $\Delta v(220)$ of the order of $0.03v(220)$; here $v(111)$ and $v(220)$ are the NRSC Fourier coefficients of crystal potential.

As will be indicated more fully in our subsequent treatment of germanium, the adjusted energy level scheme $E(PERT)$ proves to be relatively insensitive to the exact form of the starting point $E(NRSC)$, provided this starting point is already in reasonable qualitative agreement with experiment [as all our $E(NRSC)$ are]. Moreover, $E(PERT)$ proves to be relatively insensitive to the particular adjustment parameters employed, provided these are chosen in a reasonable manner. Therefore, $E(PERT)$ is determined primarily by the qualitative features of $E(NRSC)$, and by the specific features of $E^*(EXPT)$ with which $E(PERT)$ is brought into register. In order to obtain the most reliable adjusted energy level scheme, the most sensitive features of $E(PERT)$, rather than the least sensitive, should be adjusted to $E^*(EXPT)$. This important practical consideration will be amply illustrated in our subsequent treatments of germanium and silicon.

C. THE KOOPMANS CORRECTION

It must be emphasized that exact agreement between $E(NRSC)$ and $E^*(EXPT)$ should not be expected, because the NRSC calculations are based on a simplified model. Apart from the neglect of relativistic and correlation effects, the approximate treatment of exchange leads to two separate difficulties. In the first place, electron exchange effects are not treated exactly. In the second place, and this is not generally appreciated, Koopmans' theorem is no longer strictly obeyed when a simplified version of the Hartree-Fock exchange operator is used (Lindgren, 1965a,b). Consequently, one-electron energy eigenvalues do not correspond (exactly) to one-electron binding energies (orbital energies), as they do in the rigorous Hartree-Fock formalism. In our treatment, the change in the total energy of the system produced by an inter-band electronic transition—the true measure of the experimental transition energy—is only *approximately* equal to the difference between the initial and final NRSC one-electron energy eigenvalues.

Theoretically, we can introduce a correction—the Koopmans correction, $\Delta E(\text{KOOP})$—which converts one-electron energy eigenvalues into one-electron binding energies. If we could actually evaluate this correction, or even estimate it reasonably well, our empirical adjustment scheme could be improved considerably, for $\Delta E(\Delta V)$ would no longer have to include $\Delta E(\text{KOOP})$ implicitly. We could replace $E(\text{PERT}) = E(\text{NRSC}) + \Delta E(\Delta V)$ by $E(\text{PERT}) = E(\text{NRSC}) + \Delta E(\text{KOOP}) + \Delta E'(\Delta V)$, where $\Delta E'(\Delta V)$ is (hopefully) smaller than $\Delta E(\Delta V)$.

In the case of atoms and molecules, the Koopmans correction is readily determined, since this is essentially the expectation value of the difference between the exact Hartree-Fock exchange operator and the approximate exchange operator. For systems such as atoms and molecules, the exact Hartree-Fock exchange operator can be computed, but for a system as complicated as a crystal, this operator is not easily calculated. Therefore, the task of determining the Koopmans correction as part of a crystal calculation seems quite formidable. With further study, however, ways may be found to obtain good estimates for $\Delta E(\text{KOOP})$, but for the present, we are compelled to include $\Delta E(\text{KOOP})$ implicitly in our empirical energy level shift $\Delta E(\Delta V)$.

D. ADJUSTMENT STRATEGY

Since a principal objective of the present study is the confirmation or contradiction of previous theoretical ideas concerning the nature of the band structure away from the valence and conduction band edges, it is obviously desirable to ignore these ideas (cf. Phillips, 1962, 1964, 1966; Cardona, 1965; Brust *et al.*; 1962a,b; Brust, 1964; Cohen and Bergstresser, 1966; Cardona and Pollak, 1966; Saslow *et al.*, 1966) in setting up our own energy band models. Therefore, in attempting to fit theory to experiment, we will rely most heavily on well-authenticated experimental information bearing on the direct and indirect band gaps.

In grey tin and germanium, we are fortunate that the direct and indirect band gaps are fairly well understood, and that these band gaps happen to be defined by the two most sensitive transitions in the $E(\text{PERT})$ scheme, namely,

$\Gamma_{2'}-\Gamma_{25'}$ and $L_1-\Gamma_{25'}$ (cf. Herman and Skillman, 1961). For these two crystals, we will use a variety of two-parameter adjustment schemes, obtaining values for the two parameters by bringing $\Gamma_{2'}-\Gamma_{25'}$ and $L_1-\Gamma_{25'}$ in the $E(\text{PERT})$ scheme into exact register with their counterparts in the $E^*(\text{EXPT})$ scheme.

In silicon, we must adopt a different strategy, since the direct band gap has not yet been established experimentally, and since the indirect band gap is not defined by either of the two most sensitive transitions, but rather by a transition of lesser sensitivity, $\Delta_1^m-\Gamma_{25'}$, where m denotes conduction band minimum. Our strategy here will be to use the well-known indirect band gap as one constraint on a two-parameter adjustment scheme, and then to determine the remainder of the band structure as a function of one of the more sensitive transitions. In practice, this approach pins down the insensitive transitions quite nicely, and leaves only the sensitive transitions somewhat uncertain. Recent electroreflectivity measurements (Seraphin, 1965) will then be examined for possible clues concerning the sensitive transitions. It happens that among our one-parameter family of possible energy band models, there are two particular models that are favored by alternate theoretical interpretations of these measurements.

III. Grey Tin

A. ENERGY BAND MODEL

Until the recent work of Groves and Paul (1964), grey tin was thought to be a direct band gap semiconductor with a band gap of about 0.08 eV. By a careful analysis of transport measurements, Groves and Paul were able to show that grey tin is actually a semimetal. For our purposes, it is sufficient to make use of Groves and Paul's experimental results in assigning values to the direct and indirect band gaps (the former is negative, incidentally).

In obtaining our results for $E(\text{PERT})$ listed in Table 1, we used the arithmetic average of four different two-parameter adjustment schemes. In two of these schemes, the relativistic corrections were included implicitly in the two $\Delta E(\Delta V)$ terms, so that $E(\text{PERT})$ had the form $E(\text{PERT}) = E(\text{NRSC}) + \Delta E(\Delta V_1) + \Delta E(\Delta V_2)$. In the remaining two schemes, these corrections were taken into account explicitly by writing $E(\text{PERT}) = E(\text{NRSC}) + \Delta E(\Delta V_1) + \Delta E(\Delta V_2) + \Delta E(\text{REL})$, and using calculated values for $\Delta E(\text{REL})$. In one pair of schemes, $\Delta E(111)$ and $\Delta E(\text{CORE})$ were used as energy level shifts; in the other pair, we used one core shift for valence band levels and another core shift for conduction band levels. In spite of considerable differences among the four adjustment schemes:

(a) $E(\text{PERT}) = E(\text{NRSC}) + \Delta E(111) \quad + \Delta E(\text{CORE})$

(b) $E(\text{PERT}) = E(\text{NRSC}) + \Delta E(111) \quad + \Delta E(\text{CORE}) + \Delta E(\text{REL})$

(c) $E(\text{PERT}) = E(\text{NRSC}) + \Delta E_v(\text{CORE}) + \Delta E_c(\text{CORE})$

(d) $E(\text{PERT}) = E(\text{NRSC}) + \Delta E_v(\text{CORE}) + \Delta E_c(\text{CORE}) + \Delta E(\text{REL}),$

where v and c refer to valence and conduction band levels, the deviations from the average $E(\text{PERT})$ solution were usually less than 0.1 eV. This remarkable insensitivity of $E(\text{PERT})$ to the choice of specific adjustment parameters will be considered further in the section on germanium.

It is noteworthy that the difference between $E(\text{NRSC})$ and $E(\text{PERT})$ is about 0.3 or 0.4 eV for most of the transitions listed. Although the relativistic corrections are quite large, $\Delta E(\text{REL})$ for $\Gamma_2{-}\Gamma_{25'}$ being nearly -1.4 eV, these corrections are largely offset by other ion-core-type corrections which enter through the core shift terms. For example, in scheme (b), it is found that $\Delta E(\text{CORE})$ and $\Delta E(\text{REL})$ are nearly proportional to one another, so that the sum $\Delta E(\text{CORE}) + \Delta E(\text{REL})$ plays the same role in scheme (b) that the term $\Delta E(\text{CORE})$ plays in scheme (a). We will say more about such questions in Section IV,C.

In Table 1, our average $E(\text{PERT})$ solution for grey tin is compared with the corresponding empirical pseudopotential solution $E(\text{PSEUDO})$ recently reported by Cohen and Bergstresser (1966). The two solutions are quite similar, the principal difference being in the values of the transition $\Gamma_{15}{-}\Gamma_{25'}$.

In germanium and silicon, as well as in grey tin, our predicted value for this transition is consistently lower than Cohen and Bergstresser's calculated value by at least 0.5 eV, which is outside the ± 0.05 eV numerical uncertainties associated with $E(\text{PERT})$ or $E(\text{PSEUDO})$. We believe that our results are more reliable than Cohen and Bergstresser's on the basis of internal evidence, such as the insensitivity of $E(\text{PERT})$ to changes in the detailed nature of the adjustment procedure, the insensitivity of $E(\text{PERT})$ to changes in the detailed nature of $E(\text{NRSC})$ (see the discussion on germanium), and the relative magnitudes of our $\Delta E(\Delta V)$ and those of Cohen and Bergstresser (see the discussion on silicon).

B. SPIN-ORBIT SPLITTING

Since the spin-orbit splitting of the $\Gamma_{25'}$ level in grey tin is about 0.7 eV (Groves and Paul, 1964), it is expected that the p-like valence and conduction bands passing through $\Gamma_{25'}$ and Γ_{15} will be spin-orbit split in different regions of the reduced zone by amounts varying from 0 to about 0.7 eV. The present study of grey tin—and that of Cohen and Bergstresser (1966)—merely map

TABLE 1

Comparison of Theoretical and Experimental Transition Energies for Germanium and Grey Tin[a]

Transition	Germanium					Grey tin				
	Present work			Cohen-Bergstresser		Present work			Cohen-Bergstresser	
	E(NRSC)	E(PERT)	E^*(EXPT)	E_0^*(EXPT)	E(PSEUDO)	E(NRSC)	E(PERT)	E^*(EXPT)	E_0^*(EXPT)	E(PSEUDO)
$L_1-\Gamma_{25'}$	0.7	0.76^b	0.76^c	0.8	0.9	0.7	0.32^b	0.32^i	0.3	0.6
$\Gamma_{2'}-\Gamma_{25'}$	0.2	0.90^b	0.90^c	1.0	1.2	0.3	-0.16^b	-0.16^i	-0.2	-0.1
$\Delta_1^m-\Gamma_{25'}$	1.3	1.0	0.96^d	1.0	1.0	1.3	0.9			1.1
$X_1-\Gamma_{25'}$	1.5	1.2	$\sim1.2^d$			1.5	1.1			
$L_1-L_{3'}$	1.9	2.05	$\sim2.1^e$	2.1	2.0	1.7	1.4		1.4	1.4
$\Lambda_1-\Lambda_3$			2.2^f					1.5^j		
$\Gamma_{15}-\Gamma_{25'}$	3.0	2.7	$(3.4)^g$	3.4(?)	3.5	2.5	2.2	$(2.8)^j$	2.9(?)	3.0
Extended										
X_1-X_4	4.2	4.1	$\sim4.1^h$	4.3	3.8	3.7	3.4	$(3.7)^j$	3.5	3.1
$L_3-L_{3'}$	5.6	5.3	$(5.4)^h$	5.4	5.4	4.7	4.4	$(4.4)^j$	4.2	4.4

[a] Nonrelativistic self-consistent solutions are denoted by E(NRSC), perturbed (adjusted) solutions by E(PERT), and experimental values by E^*(EXPT). Room temperature values are used for germanium, and 200°K values for grey tin. Experimental estimates for E^*(EXPT) which are uncertain to a few tenths of an electron volt are enclosed in parentheses. The experimental estimates (0°K) of Cohen and Bergstresser are denoted by E_0^*(EXPT), and their pseudopotential solutions by E(PSEUDO). Doubtful identifications are indicated by question marks. All energies are in electron volts. Differences between E^*(EXPT) and E_0^*(EXPT) for $L_1-\Gamma_{25'}$, and $\Gamma_{2'}-\Gamma_{25'}$, reflect the temperature dependence of the indirect and direct band gaps. Differences between E^*(EXPT) and E_0^*(EXPT) for other transitions usually reflect different interpretations of experimental information as well as the temperature dependence of the band structure.

[b] Adjusted to $E^*(\text{EXPT})$, where $E^*(\text{EXPT}) = E(\text{EXPT}) - \Delta E(\text{SO})$.

[c] From MacFarlane *et al.* (1958). For $L_1 - \Gamma_{25'}$, $E^*(\text{EXPT}) = 0.66 + 0.10 = 0.76$ eV, where 0.10 eV is one-third the spin-orbit splitting of $\Gamma_{25'}$. For $\Gamma_2 - \Gamma_{25'}$, $E^*(\text{EXPT}) = 0.80 + 0.10 = 0.90$ eV.

[d] From Braunstein *et al.* (1958). According to Fig. 17 of Braunstein *et al.*, Δ_1^m lies 0.20 eV above L_1. In the $E(\text{PERT})$ scheme, Δ_1^m lies 0.79 of the way from Γ to X. According to Professor William Paul (private communication), the energy separation between the Δ_1 minimum and L_1 in germanium is (a) 0.18 ± 0.03 eV, according to an analysis of pressure data by Nathan; (b) 0.21 ± 0.03 eV, according to an analysis of magneto-conductance pressure data by Howard; and (c) 0.194 ± 0.007 eV, according to an analysis of free carrier absorption data by Meyer *et al.* Thus, our estimate $\Delta_1^m - L_1 = 0.20$ eV appears to be trustworthy. Since we find that $X_1 - \Delta_1^m = 0.20$ eV, we write $X_1 - \Gamma_{25'} = \sim 1.2$ eV.

[e] Since our theoretical value for $L_1 - L_3$ is 0.10 ± 0.05 eV less than our theoretical value for $\Lambda_1 - \Lambda_3$ (critical point transition), and the experimental value for $\Lambda_1 - \Lambda_3$ is 2.2 eV (cf. footnote *f* below), our estimate for $L_1 - L_3$ is $2.20 - 0.10 \pm 0.05 = 2.10 \pm 0.05$ eV, which we render above as ~ 2.1 eV. Potter (1966) has recently observed structure in the optical spectrum of germanium at 1.74 ± 0.02 and 1.94 ± 0.02 eV which he tentatively assigns to the $L_1 - L_3$ (spin-orbit split) doublet. The center of gravity of Potter's doublet is 1.84 ± 0.02 eV, which is to be contrasted with our estimate of ~ 2.1 eV. It is quite possible that what Potter is observing is not the $L_1 - L_3$ doublet: see "Note added in proof", p. 427.

[f] From Gerhardt (1965a). The centre of gravity of the 2.1, 2.3 eV doublet is 2.2 eV.

[g] From Sobolev (1965).

[h] From Philipp and Taft (1959); See also Philipp and Ehrenreich (1963). According to Kane (1966), $X_1 - X_4$ is estimated to lie 0.2 eV below the $\varepsilon_2(\omega)$ peak at 4.3 eV in silicon. In view of the similarity in the band structures of silicon and germanium in the neighborhood of X, Kane's result is applied here to germanium. See also Table, 5, footnote *g*.

[i] From Groves and Paul (1964). For $L_1 - \Gamma_{25'}$, $E^*(\text{EXPT}) = 0.08 + 0.24 = 0.32$ eV, where 0.24 eV is one-third the spin-orbit splitting of $\Gamma_{25'}$. For $\Gamma_2 - \Gamma_{25'}$, $E^*(\text{EXPT}) = -0.40 + 0.24 = -0.16$ eV.

[j] From Cardona and Greenaway (1962). The center of gravity of the 1.28, 1.75 eV doublet is 1.5 eV. The numbers quoted are reflectivity peak energies. For more up-to-date information, see the recent electroreflectivity measurements by Cardona *et al.* (1966).

out the centers of gravity of the various spin-orbit split bands. In order to obtain a more realistic picture of the band structure of grey tin, it is obviously necessary to take the spin-orbit interaction into account (Herman *et al.*, 1966).

We are presently developing computer codes for calculating the spin-orbit splitting at selected points in the reduced zone by first-order perturbation theory. Our projected method for calculating the spin-orbit splitting—or what amounts to the same thing, the spin-orbit coupling corrections $\Delta E(\text{SO})$— will parallel the method we are already using for computing the relativistic corrections $\Delta E(\text{REL})$ from first principles.

Until such time as these computer codes become operational, we are planning to determine the spin-orbit splitting by a simpler, but less comprehensive, method. In particular, we are adopting the extended **k·p** representation of Cardona and Pollak (1966), but we are fitting the parameterized **k·p** energy band model (with spin-orbit splitting ignored) to our own energy level scheme, $E(\text{PERT})$, rather than to fragmentary experimental information. One of the most useful features of the extended **k·p** representation is the ease with which the spin-orbit interaction can be taken into account. In its present form, however, the **k·p** treatment of spin-orbit interaction is somewhat oversimplified, in that the number of relevant parameters must be reduced to as few as can be fitted to experiment (or judiciously estimated). We plan to determine the spin-orbit splitting in grey tin in the same manner that Cardona and Pollak (1966) determined this splitting in germanium—at least for the present. In due course, we will be able to determine the spin-orbit splitting throughout the reduced zone by using the extended **k·p** representation as an interpolation scheme: The relevant parameters will be determined partly by adjusting the **k·p** energy band model to experiment (transition energies and spin-orbit splitting), and partly by adjusting this model to our own $E(\text{PERT})$ and $\Delta E(\text{SO})$ results. At any rate, our understanding of the band structure of grey tin will remain somewhat rudimentary until the spin-orbit splitting throughout the zone is taken into account.

It would also be highly desirable to have additional experimental information concerning the band structure, so that current theoretical estimates of various interband transitions could be checked.

We have learned only recently that the electroreflectivity spectrum of grey tin has been determined by Cardona, McElroy, Pollak, and Shaklee using their electrolytic technique* (M. Cardona, invited paper, Durham Meeting of the American Physical Society, March 31, 1966). Since the successful interpretation of this spectrum would resolve many current questions concerning the band structure of grey tin away from the band edges, we are awaiting further developments with keen anticipation.

---

* Shaklee *et al.*, 1965, 1966; Cardona *et al.*, 1966.

IV. Germanium

A. ENERGY BAND MODEL

Since the direct and indirect band gaps of germanium are accurately known, and since they are defined by the two most sensitive transitions, $\Gamma_2{}'-\Gamma_{25}{}'$ and $L_1-\Gamma_{25}{}'$, it is expedient to proceed just as we did in the case of grey tin, and obtain exact fits for these two transitions by using two-parameter adjustment schemes. In studying germanium, we examined an even larger number of two-parameter schemes than we did in studying grey tin. In Table 1, under the heading $E(\text{PERT})$, we have displayed the arithmetic average of twelve different two-parameter $E(\text{PERT})$ solutions. The individual solutions usually deviated from the average solution by less than 0.1 eV, though in a few scattered instances the variation was as large as ± 0.2 eV.

Having established our own energy band model, let us now compare our results for germanium with those obtained by Cohen and Bergstresser (1966). These authors adjusted their empirical pseudopotential model, $E(\text{PSEUDO})$, to their best estimate of the experimental energy level scheme at absolute zero temperature, $E_0^*(\text{EXPT})$. In our work, $E(\text{PERT})$ was adjusted to two transitions in $E^*(\text{EXPT})$, the room temperature experimental scheme. This slight difference of approach is of minor importance in any comparison of $E(\text{PERT})$ with $E(\text{PSEUDO})$, since the difference between $E^*(\text{EXPT})$ and $E_0^*(\text{EXPT})$ is at most 0.1 eV, a value comparable to the combined numerical uncertainties in $E(\text{PERT})$ and $E(\text{PSEUDO})$.

Cohen and Bergstresser obtain the best compromise fit they can using three empirical pseudopotential parameters analogous to our empirical crystal potential perturbations $\Delta v(111)$, $\Delta v(220)$, and $\Delta v(311)$. We wish to emphasize that our $\Delta v(\mathbf{h})$ are not pseudopotential coefficients, but rather empirical modifications of our NRSC crystal potential. Since the starting point of their empirical adjustment procedure is considerably different from our own, as will be explained more fully in our subsequent discussion of silicon (cf. Section V,B), it is doubtful whether nearly identical $E(\text{PERT})$ and $E(\text{PSEUDO})$ schemes could be generated by the use of analogous adjustment parameters, even if there were complete agreement on both sides concerning the experimental band scheme. In practice, $E(\text{PERT})$ and $E(\text{PSEUDO})$ are somewhat different, partly because the adjustment procedures and starting points are different, and partly because the physical assumptions concerning the experimental situation are different.

As can be seen from Table 1, and also from Fig. 1, $E(\text{PERT})$ and $E(\text{PSEUDO})$ are qualitatively similar, but quantitatively different in detail, particularly in the neighborhood of the important conduction band state Γ_{15}, whose location determines the disposition of three of the four lowest conduction bands in the central region of the reduced zone. Even though

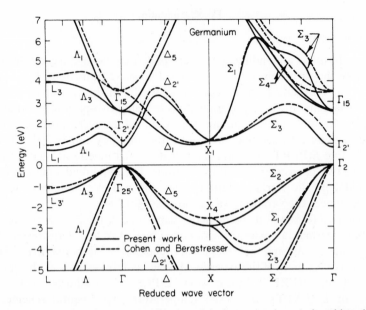

FIG. 1.   Comparison of two energy band models for germanium (spin-orbit splitting neglected). The present solution, E(PERT), is based on a two-parameter adjustment, with $L_1-\Gamma_{25'} = 0.76$ eV, and $\Gamma_{2'}-\Gamma_{25'} = 0.90$ eV. The Cohen and Bergstresser (1966) solution is based on a three-parameter pseudopotential band model. In both models, spin-orbit split levels are represented by their weighted means.

E(PSEUDO) has been fitted to all known or estimated transitions, while E(PERT) has been fitted only to the two most precisely known (and most sensitive) transitions, E(PERT) provides at least as good a representation of the overall energy band structure as does E(PSEUDO), judging from Table 1. In view of our adjustment procedure, E(PERT) provides a better account of the direct and indirect band gaps than does E(PSEUDO), and judging from Fig. 1, a better account of the highest valence band and the lowest conduction band throughout the entire reduced zone as well.

After commenting briefly on the experimental evidence bearing on the $\Gamma_{15}-\Gamma_{25'}$ transition, we will examine the energy level shifts $\Delta E(\Delta V)$ in somewhat greater detail than previously, and indicate that an extremely flexible adjustment scheme can be developed in terms of only three parameters, such as $\Delta v(111)$, $\Delta v(220)$, and $\Delta v(311)$. We will then demonstrate that an adjustment scheme based on these three parameters favors our value of 2.7 ± 0.2 eV for $\Gamma_{15}-\Gamma_{25'}$, rather than Cohen and Bergstresser's considerably higher value of 3.5 eV. After presenting further theoretical arguments in support of our two-parameter E(PERT) solution, we will turn to deformation potential calculations and related matters.

B. EXPERIMENTAL EVIDENCE

In view of the significant difference between our predicted value for the $\Gamma_{15}-\Gamma_{25'}$ transition, 2.7 $\pm$ 0.2 eV, and Cohen and Bergstresser's value of 3.5 eV, which was obtained with an eye on their experimental assignment, 3.4 eV, we have reviewed the experimental evidence bearing on this transition, and we find no conclusive evidence supporting the 3.4-eV assignment. For example, in a theoretical paper discussing the photoelectric yield from cesium covered germanium, Cohen and Phillips (1965) show an experimental curve (due to Allen and Gobeli) and indicate where the spin-orbit split $\Gamma_{15}-\Gamma_{25'}$ transition is expected to lie. The experimental evidence supporting this "expectation" is obscure, and what is more, only the spin-orbit splitting of $\Gamma_{25'}$ is taken into account, and that of Γ_{15}, which is of the same order of magnitude as the $\Gamma_{25'}$ spin-orbit splitting, is ignored.

The modulated electroreflectivity spectrum of germanium, as determined by Seraphin (1964) in his pioneering studies, exhibits four peaks in the range from 2.8 to 4.0 eV, the principal peak being at 3.65 eV. Seraphin has tentatively suggested that these four peaks are somehow related to interband transitions between spin-orbit split $\Gamma_{25'}$ and Γ_{15} states (or closely related ones). In the light of our model, the weaker structure between 2.8 and 3.3 eV could be attributed to such transitions, but the principal peak at 3.65 eV would have to be assigned to interband transitions not directly related to $\Gamma_{15}-\Gamma_{25'}$.

As will be indicated more fully in our subsequent discussion of silicon, current theories of electroreflectance are not sufficiently comprehensive to provide clearcut and unambiguous interpretations of many features of electroreflectivity spectra. Moreover, the intrinsic nature of some characteristic features of such spectra can be obscured by unfavorable experimental conditions. Therefore, we must await further theoretical and experimental developments before attempting to decide the question of the $\Gamma_{15}-\Gamma_{25'}$ transition on the basis of Seraphin's exploratory electroreflectivity measurements. In any event, Seraphin's work has paved the way for a host of high-resolution optical studies which should contribute greatly to our understanding of the band structure of germanium and other crystals away from their band edges. (See Note Added in Proof.)

C. FURTHER REMARKS ABOUT $\Delta E(\Delta V)$

We noted earlier that the deviations of twelve different two-parameter E(PERT) solutions from their arithmetic average were usually less than 0.1 eV. This is indeed a remarkable result, since it suggests that the detailed form of E(PERT) is not critically dependent on the choice of adjustment parameters. Actually, this result is partly due to our fitting the most sensitive

TABLE 2

NORMALIZED TRANSITION ENERGY SHIFT PATTERNS FOR GERMANIUM[a,b]

Transition	Pattern 1		Pattern 2					Pattern 3					Pattern 4
	111	333	220	422	CORE/s	CORE[c]	REL	311	222	400	331	CORE/p	CORE/d
$\Gamma_{2'}$–$\Gamma_{25'}$	1.00	1.00	1.00	1.00	1.00	1.00	1.00	1.00	1.00	1.00	1.00	1.00	1.00
L_1–$\Gamma_{25'}$	−3.04	−2.55	0.38	0.41	0.33	0.40	0.41	0.80	0.90	1.27	0.76	0.79	0.28
X_1–$\Gamma_{25'}$	−6.40	−4.61	0.04	−0.03	0.15	0.00	0.04	0.67	0.88	1.49	0.54	0.73	−0.48
X_1–X_4	−4.39	−2.62	0.27	0.06	0.15	0.10	0.08	0.48	0.49	0.77	0.18	0.48	−1.38
L_1–$L_{3'}$	−2.21	−0.56	0.50	0.35	0.48	0.48	0.44	0.72	0.67	0.97	0.54	0.66	−0.30
L_3–$L_{3'}$	−3.69	−5.33	−0.18	−0.16	0.00	−0.05	−0.07	0.56	0.80	1.16	0.52	0.35	−1.50
Γ_{15}–$\Gamma_{25'}$	−3.39	−7.47	−0.21	0.02	0.00	−0.07	−0.06	0.59	1.15	1.40	0.88	0.29	−0.30

[a] All columns have been normalized to a change of 1 eV in the transition $\Gamma_{2'}$–$\Gamma_{25'}$. The $\Delta E(\mathbf{h})$ patterns are identified by $\mathbf{h}$, the full core shift[c] pattern $\Delta E(\text{CORE})$ by CORE, and the selective s, p, and d core shift patterns by CORE/s, CORE/p, and CORE/d. The normalized relativistic correction is denoted by REL. The unnormalized version of $\Delta E(\text{REL})$ can be obtained by multiplying the REL column by −1.05. All entries are in electron volts.

[b] The energy level shift patterns $\Delta E(\Delta V)$ can be calculated at three different levels of sophistication. At the simplest level, the $\Delta E(\Delta V)$ are determined by first-order perturbation theory. This approach is satisfactory provided ΔV is sufficiently small and provided the levels being perturbed are sufficiently far apart. The information contained in Table 2 was generated by first-order perturbation theory since the two conditions just mentioned are satisfied in practice. When one or both of these conditions breaks down, it is necessary to proceed to the inter-mediate level. Here ΔV is added to the crystal potential V, and the OPW secular equations are diagonalized for $V + \Delta V$. The E(PERT) scheme is then given directly by the new set of energy eigenvalues. At the third level of sophistication ΔV is added to V and a self-consistent version of E(PERT) is obtained by successive iteration. In this mode, it is convenient to keep ΔV fixed from iteration to iteration. Alternatively, with $V + \Delta V$ expressed in the Fourier series representation, $v(\mathbf{h}) + \Delta v(\mathbf{h})$ can be replaced by $v(\mathbf{h})/\varepsilon(\mathbf{h})$, where $\varepsilon(\mathbf{h})$ is an *empirical* wave-vector dependent dielectric function which can also be held fixed from iteration to iteration. All E(PERT) solutions quoted in the present paper were obtained by first-order perturbation theory. The adequacy of this approach was confirmed by repeating selected calculations at the inter-mediate level. So long as we are content with precisions of the order of ± 0.05 eV, third-level (self-consistent) E(PERT) calculations do not appear necessary.

[c] The concept of a core shift was introduced by Herman and Skillman (1961) in a paper which also clearly demonstrated the relative sensitivity of different interband transition energies to changes in the core shift parameter. Phillips (1962) and also Lin and Phillips (1965) have noted that the poor agreement between experiment and the self-consistent energy band calculations by Kleinman and Phillips (1960) on silicon can be attributed to an error in the determination of $v(000)$, which was equivalent to a core shift of about -1.2 Ry. Lin and Phillips have given to the core shift a far more important role than it really deserves. While a change in the core shift can indeed be used to improve the agreement between theory and experiment, this represents only one of several possible adjustments that would have nearly the same effect: note that the core shift (CORE) is only one representative of pattern 2. We feel that the present analysis in terms of energy level shift patterns is decidedly more informative than the over-simplified analysis of Lin and Phillips (1965).

transitions to experiment: the remaining transitions, being less sensitive than the fitted ones, are affected only slightly—but often significantly—by the energy shifts $\Delta E(\Delta V)$. For example, $\Gamma_{15}-\Gamma_{25'}$ is shifted from the E(NRSC) value of 3.0 eV to the E(PERT) value of 2.7 $\pm$ 0.2 eV.

Further insight into the nature of the $\Delta E(\Delta V)$ energy shifts can be gained by studying Table 2, where the key transition energy shift patterns for germanium, suitably normalized, are arranged into four classes according to their broad qualitative features. The patterns within any one class are more nearly alike than are patterns belonging to different classes. Since we are primarily concerned with valence and conduction band levels derived from atomic s and p states, and since these levels are not particularly sensitive to physically reasonable changes in the 3d core level, the ΔE(CORE/d) pattern can be ignored, leaving only three classes to be considered further.

If two $\Delta E(\Delta V)$ terms associated with the same shift pattern are employed in a two-parameter adjustment to two experimental transitions, a physically reasonable fit involving small ΔV cannot be obtained, since the two $\Delta E(\Delta V)$ terms are too nearly alike, i.e., too nearly linearly dependent. [The question of linear dependence in empirical pseudopotential adjustment schemes has been studied by Kane (1966) in an informative paper.] On the other hand, quite reasonable fits involving small ΔV can be obtained by using two $\Delta E(\Delta V)$ terms associated with different shift patterns. Since it is primarily the pattern that counts, rather than the specific member of the pattern, it can be seen that many different two-parameter schemes can be devised, but that they all represent essentially three different combinations: patterns 1 and 2, patterns 2 and 3, and patterns 3 and 1. In setting up twelve different two-parameter adjustment schemes for germanium, we used representatives of all three combinations.

We are now in a position to choose the most flexible adjustment scheme involving the minimum number of adjustment parameters: we simply have to include one representative from each of the three major patterns. Accordingly, let us set up a three-parameter scheme based on $\Delta v(111)$, $\Delta v(220)$, and $\Delta v(311)$. Not only do these three parameters belong to different patterns, but they also happen to be analogous to the three pseudopotential parameters used by Cohen and Bergstresser. Since we now have three parameters at our disposal, we will adjust $\Gamma_{2'}-\Gamma_{25'}$ and $L_1-\Gamma_{25'}$ to their proper E^*(EXPT) values as before, and we will use an assumed value for $\Gamma_{15}-\Gamma_{25'}$ as our third constraint. In order to compare our previous average two-parameter E(PERT) solution with Cohen and Bergstresser's three-parameter E(PSEUDO) solution, we will choose values for $\Gamma_{15}-\Gamma_{25'}$ which correspond to these two solutions. However, we will use 2.8 rather than 2.7 eV for E(PERT) for a reason that will be indicated shortly. Setting $\Gamma_{15}-\Gamma_{25'}$ first to 2.8 and then to 3.5 eV, we obtain the following three-parameter E(PERT) solutions:

	$\Gamma_{15}-\Gamma_{25'}$	$\Delta_1^m-\Gamma_{25'}$	$L_1-L_{3'}$	X_1-X_4	$L_3-L_{3'}$
E(PERT) =	2.80	0.99	2.05	4.07	5.33 eV
E(PERT) =	3.50	0.74	1.88	3.48	5.87 eV
For comparison:					
E^*(EXPT) =		0.96	~ 2.1	~ 4.1	(5.4) eV

It is now clear that an exact fit to the direct and indirect band gaps, coupled with a choice of 2.8 eV for $\Gamma_{15}-\Gamma_{25'}$, leads to a three-parameter E(PERT) model which is nearly identical to our previous average two-parameter E(PERT) model, and far more important, which is in excellent agreement with experiment. On the other hand, when we adjust the direct and indirect band gaps to experiment, and then adjust $\Gamma_{15}-\Gamma_{25'}$ to 3.5 eV—Cohen and Bergstresser's value—the agreement between theory and experiment for some of the other key transitions is ruined. In view of the flexible nature of our three-parameter fit, we take this comparison as a strong argument in favor of our value of 2.8 eV for this transition.

As a further argument, we observe that if the magnitude of ΔV is plotted as a function of the value assigned to $\Gamma_{15}-\Gamma_{25'}$, this curve has a sharp *minimum* at $\Gamma_{15}-\Gamma_{25'} = 2.8$ eV. (This is why we used 2.8 rather than 2.7 eV in the above comparison.) In other words, if we accept E(NRSC) as a sound starting point for a small empirical adjustment, if we use a very flexible three-parameter adjustment scheme, and if we require the adjustment to give the correct experimental values for the direct and indirect transitions, then the *smallest* empirical adjustment consistent with these considerations is one giving a value of 2.8 eV for the $\Gamma_{15}-\Gamma_{25'}$ transition.

D. FURTHER REMARKS ABOUT E(NRSC)

Having already indicated that the route from E(NRSC) to E(PERT) via $\Delta E(\Delta V)$ is not critically dependent upon the detailed nature of ΔV, we will now indicate, more by way of example than in general terms, that the choice of E(NRSC) is also not critical, provided E(NRSC) is already in good qualitative agreement with experiment in its own right. In particular, we will show what happens when the NRSC energy band structure of germanium is recalculated using the free-electron exchange approximation recently proposed by Kohn and Sham (1965) in place of Slater's. The Kohn-Sham exchange term, which is derived from a variational principle, is proportional to Slater's, but only 2/3 as large, so that the substitution of the former for the latter leads to a significant change in E(NRSC), as can be seen from Table 3. However, even though the E(NRSC) scheme based on the Kohn-Sham exchange term differs from that based on Slater's by as much as 1 eV, both schemes lead to adjusted E(PERT) schemes which differ from one another by less than 0.1 eV. Thus our point is illustrated.

As a brief digression, we observe that the E(NRSC) scheme based on the Kohn-Sham exchange term compares as well with E^*(EXPT) as the E(NRSC) scheme based on Slater's, but that an intermediate scheme compares more favorably with experiment than either of the others. This suggests a generalization of our adjustment scheme according to which the Slater free-electron exchange term is multiplied by a factor λ which is to be determined empirically. (The Kohn-Sham exchange approximation, based on theoretical considerations, corresponds to $\lambda = 2/3$.) We can obtain a family of NRSC

TABLE 3

EFFECT OF CHANGING THE MAGNITUDE OF THE FREE-ELECTRON EXCHANGE TERM ON THE NONRELATIVISTIC SELF-CONSISTENT (NRSC) ENERGY BAND STRUCTURE OF GERMANIUM[a]

	Nonrelativistic self-consistent solution, E_λ(NRSC)			Adjusted solution E(PERT)	Experiment E^*(EXPT)
Transition	$\lambda = 2/3$ Kohn-Sham	$\lambda = 5/6$ Intermediate	$\lambda = 1$ Slater		
$L_1 - \Gamma_{25'}$	0.44	0.54	0.66	0.76	0.76
$\Gamma_{2'} - \Gamma_{25'}$	0.80	0.50	0.18	0.90	0.90
$X_1 - \Gamma_{25'}$	0.60	1.06	1.52	1.2	~ 1.2
$L_1 - L_{3'}$	1.82	1.82	1.85	2.1	~ 2.1
$\Gamma_{15} - \Gamma_{25'}$	2.50	2.75	3.01	2.7	
$X_1 - X_4$	3.70	3.94	4.20	4.1	~ 4.1
$L_3 - L_{3'}$	5.07	5.31	5.56	5.3	(5.4)

[a] The purpose of this comparison is not to judge the relative merits of the Kohn-Sham and Slater free-electron exchange approximations, but rather to show that the magnitude of the free-electron exchange term can be modified empirically, through the use of the λ factor, so as to bring E_λ(NRSC) closer to E^*(EXPT). A number of previous authors have used λ factors other than 1 to improve the agreement between theory and experiment; see, for example, Lindgren (1965b). The reader should bear in mind that the optimum value of λ may be different from crystal to crystal. For example, preliminary studies indicate that the optimum value of λ is closer to unity in silicon than in germanium. The column E_λ(NRSC), $\lambda = 1$, corresponds to the germanium E(NRSC) column in Table 1. The columns E(PERT) and E^*(EXPT) have the same meanings and values here as in Table 1. All energies are in electron volts.

solutions by using different values of λ, as well as a corresponding family of adjusted solutions:

$$E_\lambda(\text{PERT}) = E_\lambda(\text{NRSC}) + \Delta E_\lambda(\Delta V).$$

E_λ(PERT) can now be adjusted to E^*(EXPT) partially by the choice of λ, and partially by the choice of ΔV. The greater the fractional role played by λ in bringing E_λ(PERT) close to E^*(EXPT), the smaller the role that ΔV itself must play. In many respects, it would be advantageous to minimize $\Delta E_\lambda(\Delta V)$ by a suitable choice of λ, so that E_λ(NRSC) itself is as close to E^*(EXPT) as possible. Preliminary studies indicate that λ serves well as an adjustment parameter in its own right, but that all the key transitions in the E_λ(PERT) scheme cannot be brought into exact register with their experimental counterparts by the use of the λ adjustment alone. At any rate, we see that a reduction in $\Delta E_\lambda(\Delta V)$ goes hand in hand with a shift of the Γ_{15}–$\Gamma_{25'}$ transition from 3.0 to 2.75 eV. This is one further indication of the most likely value for this transition; cf. Table 3.

E. Deformation Potential Studies

As an application of our perturbed self-consistent field approach to energy band calculations, we undertook a study of the effect of hydrostatic pressure on the energy band structure of germanium, hoping to improve upon an earlier and somewhat unsatisfactory pseudopotential study by Bassani and Brust (1963). Having obtained E(NRSC), $\Delta E(\Delta V)$, and E(PERT) for germanium at normal pressure (lattice constant $= a_0$), we proceeded to obtain E(NRSC) for a number of other lattice constants; expressed in units of a_0, these included: $a/a_0 = 0.90$, 0.95, 1.05, and 1.10. Using three-point interpolation ($a/a_0 = 0.95$, 1.00, 1.05), we obtained values for the deformation potentials D (change in energy per unit dilatation) for the various energy levels of interest (cf. Bardeen and Shockley, 1950). These deformation potentials will be denoted by the symbol D(NRSC) to indicate that they are based on the E(NRSC) scheme. To check the numerical accuracy of the three-point interpolation, we repeated the deformation potential calculations using five-point interpolation ($a/a_0 = 0.90$, 0.95, 1.00, 1.05, 1.10). The five-point results agreed with the three-point results to a few percent.

Since we have made no serious attempt to determine how the zero of energy changes with lattice constant, it would not be particularly meaningful to quote our absolute deformation potential values for individual levels. Instead, we will list the net deformation potential differences—also denoted by D(NRSC)—for several key transitions, and compare them with experiment, as well as with other theoretical results. All of this is shown in Table 4.

Our present deformation potential values could be improved by taking the lattice-constant dependence of $\Delta E(\Delta V)$ into account, and basing the deformation potential calculation on the E(PERT) scheme rather than on the E(NRSC) scheme. The work of Kleinman (1963) suggests that the lattice-constant dependence of the spin-orbit corrections ΔE(SO) should also be taken into account in any serious treatment of deformation potentials. In the case of germanium, we estimate that the inclusion of these two refinements could change our D(NRSC) values by as much as 10%. Of course, our

TABLE 4

COMPARISON OF THEORETICAL AND EXPERIMENTAL NET DEFORMATION POTENTIAL DIFFERENCES FOR SILICON AND GERMANIUM, IN eV PER UNIT DILATATION[a]

Transition	Silicon			Germanium		
	Theory: Goroff and Kleinman[e]	Present theory D(NRSC)	Experiment D(EXPT)	Theory: Cardona and Pollak[h]	Present theory D(NRSC)	Experiment D(EXPT)
L_1–$\Gamma_{25'}$	−4.1	−4.1		−3.3	−3.5	−3.8[f]
X_1–$\Gamma_{25'}$	+0.3	+1.4		+1.2	+0.8	0 to +1.5[f]
Δ_1^m–$\Gamma_{25'}$		+1.4	+1.5[f]		+0.7	
Δ_1^b–$\Gamma_{25'}$		+0.7			−0.7	
Γ_{15}–$\Gamma_{25'}$	−1.35	−0.6		−2.6	−1.7	
Δ_1^b–Δ_5		−1.3			−2.5	
X_1–X_4	−2.3	−1.4	-2.8 ± 0.5[g]	−1.7	−4.4	-4.2 ± 0.4[j]
4.3-eV peak					−10.3	
Σ_3–Σ_2[c]		−3.1			−5.8[i]	
$\Gamma_{2'}$–$\Gamma_{25'}$	−8.6	−11.9		−9.6	−5.0	-9.6 ± 0.8[k]
2.2-eV peak[d]	−4.5	−5.2		−5.2		-5.7 ± 0.3[g]
L_1–$L_{3'}$			-5.0 ± 0.5[g]			
3.4-eV peak						
W_1–W_2		−5.7			−9.1	
L_3–$L_{3'}$		−1.1			−2.3	

[a] D(NRSC) goes along with all E(PERT) solutions presented in Tables 1 and 5 since D(NRSC) depends only on E(NRSC).

[b] Conduction band level Δ_1 and valence band level Δ_5 are located at $(2\pi/a)$ (0.5 0 0). The (100) conduction band edge is identified by Δ_1^m. In the E(PERT) scheme, Δ_1^m is located at $(2\pi/a)$(0.81 0 0) in silicon, and at $(2\pi/a)$ (0.79 0 0) in germanium.

[c] Conduction band level Σ_3 and valence band level Σ_2 are located at $(2\pi/a)$ (0.5 0.5 0).

[d] Actually 2.1, 2.3 eV doublet. Nominal symmetry classification is Λ_1–Λ_3.

[e] From Goroff and Kleinman (1963). The conversion from their units to ours is based on the following identity: -1.88 eV per unit dilatation $= 1.95 \times 10^{-6}$ eV per atmosphere, which is quoted by Kleinman (1963). It had already been noted by Goroff and Kleinman that the experimental deformation potential for the 3.4-eV reflectivity peak was considerably closer to their theoretical value for the L_1–L_3, transition than for the Γ_{15}–$\Gamma_{25'}$ transition. This led them to doubt the common identification of the 3.4-eV reflectivity peak with the Γ_{15}–$\Gamma_{25'}$ transition, and to suspect that this peak is actually to be identified with the L_1–L_3, transition.

[f] From Paul and Brooks (1963). Somewhat different values of D(EXPT) for the indirect band gaps of silicon and germanium have recently been reported by Balslev (1966). We use the values quoted by Paul and Brooks since we believe these are more reliable than Balslev's values.

[g] From Zallen (1964) and Gerhardt (1966).

[h] From Cardona and Pollak (1966). The conversion from their units to ours is based on the identity: -1.00 eV per unit dilatation $= 1.35 \times 10^{-6}$ eV per atmosphere.

[i] This is the value calculated $\frac{1}{4}$ of the way from Γ to L. The Λ_1–Λ_3 critical point transition is estimated to lie in this neighborhood.

[j] From Zallen (1966).

[k] From Cardona and Paul (1960). The pressure coefficient for the direct energy gap is $1.3 \pm 0.1 \times 10^{-5}$ eV cm^2/kg.

D(NRSC) for the direct $\Gamma_2-\Gamma_{25'}$ and indirect $L_1-L_{25'}$ and $\Delta_1^m-\Gamma_{25'}$ transitions are sufficiently close to the corresponding experimental values to give us some measure of confidence in the quantitative validity of our (simplified) deformation potential calculations.

Zallen (1964) has measured the pressure dependence of a number of optical reflectivity peaks in germanium, silicon, and several other semiconductors. From these measurements he is able to deduce the deformation potentials associated with these peaks. Some of his results are listed in Table 4. In more recent work, Zallen (private communication) has obtained the value D(EXPT) $= -4.2 \pm 0.4$ eV for the main reflectivity peak in germanium, which occurs at an energy of 4.5 eV. Even though it is known from the detailed survey of the reduced zone carried out by Brust (1964, 1965), and from related studies by Kane (1966), that an extended region of the reduced zone contributes to this peak, it is convenient, though somewhat misleading, to associate this peak with the X_1-X_4 transition.

According to Kane, whose study was confined to silicon but whose results are also applicable to germanium, the X_1-X_4 transition is 0.2 eV lower in energy than the $\varepsilon_2(\omega)$ peak, which in turn is 0.2 eV lower in energy than the main reflectivity peak. [This places the X_1-X_4 transition energy (in both germanium and silicon) at about 4.1 eV, in excellent agreement with our theoretical predictions (cf. Tables 1 and 5).] Kane also finds that the region in the reduced zone near the X point makes only a small contribution to the main reflectivity peak and to the imaginary part of the complex dielectric constant, $\varepsilon_2(\omega)$, which is a more direct measure of the joint interband density of states. Therefore, even though the X_1-X_4 transition may lie close in energy to the main peak, this transition should not be regarded as representative. It is hardly surprising, then, that our theoretical deformation potential value for X_1-X_4 in germanium, D(NRSC) $= -2.5$ eV, is considerably different from Zallen's experimental value, D(EXPT) $= -4.2 \pm 0.4$ eV. The magnitude of this difference merely serves to emphasize how nonrepresentative of the main peak the X_1-X_4 transition really is. In order to account properly for the experimental deformation potential value for the 4.5-eV reflectivity peak, it would be necessary to make a detailed survey of the reduced zone, in the manner of Brust (1964, 1965), and to weigh the deformation potentials of the various contributing interband transitions according to their importance.

The experimental deformation potential for the 2.2-eV reflectivity peak— this is really a 2.1, 2.3 eV doublet—is -5.7 ± 0.3 eV (Zallen, 1964; Gerhardt, 1965a,b). The 2.2-eV peak is nominally assigned to a $\Lambda_1-\Lambda_3$ transition associated with a critical point lying along the [111] axis, somewhere between L and Γ, but closer to Γ than to L (Brust, 1964; Cardona and Pollak, 1966). According to our calculations, D(NRSC) remains close to -5.0 eV most of the way from L to Γ, changing rapidly to -10.3 eV only in the neighborhood of Γ. [Note that $D(\text{NRSC}) = -10.3$ eV is our value for the $\Gamma_2{}'-\Gamma_{25'}$ transition (cf. Table 4.)] Since the $\Lambda_1-\Lambda_3$ critical point is located in the range where $D(\text{NRSC})$ is close to -5.8 eV, our calculations are consistent with experiment so far as the 2.2-eV peak is concerned.

In any event, it is clear that accurate and comprehensive deformation potential information—both theoretical and experimental—could be used to considerable advantage in checking the identity of interband transitions principally responsible for characteristic features of optical spectra. One of the most exciting prospects for future research is the determination of the deformation potential of an individual transition, rather than the integral value of the deformation potential taken over all the transitions that contribute to a broad optical reflectivity peak. Since critical point transitions are brought out quite clearly in electroreflectivity spectra, the deformation potentials of such transitions could be determined by measuring the hydrostatic pressure dependence of the electroreflectivity spectrum.

F. EXTREME PRESSURE STUDIES

Just as the study of the pressure (or lattice constant) dependence of the band structure in the neighborhood of a_0 leads to information concerning deformation potentials, so the same study over an extended lattice constant range casts fresh light on the dramatic changes in band structure that would be produced by extreme pressures, say millions of atmospheres (assuming germanium retained the diamond structure at these pressures). The connection between the energy band spectrum and the free atom energy levels is also illuminated by such a study.

It is known that there are at least three high-pressure modifications of germanium (Bates *et al.*, 1965), namely, Ge II (white tin structure); Ge III (body-centered tetragonal structure), and Ge IV (modified body-centered cubic structure). In this notation, ordinary germanium is called Ge I (diamond structure). For a discussion of the crystal structures of some high-pressure modifications of silicon and germanium, see, for example, Kasper and Richards (1964). At room temperature, and under equilibrium conditions, Ge I converts to Ge III at about 25,000 atm, while Ge III converts to Ge IV at about 120,000 atm. Under nonequilibrium conditions, Ge I can persist in a metastable form above 25,000 atm, but at about 120,000 atm, Ge I converts to Ge II.*

In the present study, we shall consider only diamond-type germanium, Ge I, though we hope to study some of the high pressure modifications at a later

* In view of the experimental difficulties associated with high pressure measurements, particularly the establishment of pure hydrostatic pressure, the stability ranges of Ge I through IV are not known with certainty. The values quoted above seem to be the best available at this time, but they should be accepted with caution. The authors wish to acknowledge an informative correspondence with Professor William Klement on this point.

date. It is beyond the scope of our present treatment, of course, to predict the critical pressures at which phase transitions occur. Our attention will be focused primarily on the pressure dependence of the electronic energy level scheme.

The energy level scheme of Ge I at six different points in the reduced zone is depicted as a function of lattice constant in Figs. 2 and 3. At the normal lattice constant, $a = a_0 = 5.657$ Å, the band structure shown in Figs. 2 and 3 corresponds to the E(PERT) band structure displayed previously in Fig. 1. The band structure in the range $0.6 \leqq a/a_0 \leqq 1.1$ was determined from the relation

$$E(\text{PERT}; a) = E(\text{NRSC}; a) + \Delta E(\Delta V; a_0),$$

where $E(\text{NRSC}; a)$ is the NRSC solution for lattice constant a, and $\Delta E (\Delta V; a_0)$ is the energy level shift pattern obtained previously by fitting

$$E(\text{PERT}) = E(\text{PERT}; a_0) = E(\text{NRSC}; a_0) + \Delta E(\Delta V; a_0)$$

to E*(EXPT). Since the difference between $\Delta E(\Delta V; a)$ and $\Delta E(\Delta V; a_0)$ is estimated to be reasonably small in this range, $\Delta E(\Delta V; a_0)$—which we know—is used in place of $\Delta E(\Delta V; a)$ throughout this range. In order to insure the proper asymptotic behavior of the energy band structure at large values of a/a_0, i.e., a gradual approach to the atomic energy level scheme, it was necessary to assume that $\Delta E(\Delta V; a)$ approached zero as a/a_0 approached infinity. In practice, $\Delta E(\Delta V; a)$ was required to vary linearly from $\Delta E(\Delta V; a_0)$ at $a/a_0 = 1.1$ to zero at $a/a_0 = 1.7$.

Our band calculations were carried out for several values of a/a_0. Since Ge I converts to Ge II at about $a/a_0 = 0.95$, there is no practical need to study Ge I for values of a/a_0 much below say 0.9. However, for the sake of completeness, we carried our calculations down to values of a/a_0 as small as 0.6. At this ratio, the 3d core band begins to overlap the 4s valence band.

At $a/a_0 = 1$, the core band atomic orbitals located on adjacent lattice sites do not overlap each other to any significant extent. As a/a_0 is reduced below 1, the nearest neighbor overlap increases gradually, most noticeably among the 3d atomic orbitals. For the purposes of the present study, it did not appear necessary to take this overlap into account. If we were seriously interested in obtaining quantitatively reliable results for a/a_0 below about 0.8, core orbital overlap effects would have to be included in our theoretical treatment.

Our calculations were carried up to a/a_0 ratios as large as 1.8, where it became apparent that OPW expansions containing more than our 120 terms would be required to represent the valence and conduction band wave functions properly. We believe that Figs. 2 and 3 are qualitatively reliable over the entire range shown, and quantitatively reliable in the restricted range between $a/a_0 = 0.8$ and 1.2. It is indeed gratifying that the OPW method can be used so effectively over so broad a lattice constant range.

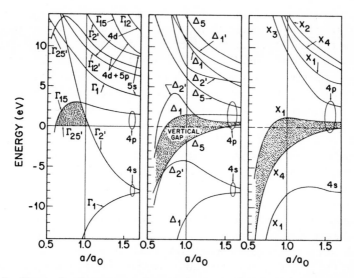

FIG. 2. Energy band structure of germanium as a function of lattice constant at $\Gamma(0\,0\,0)$, $\Delta(\frac{1}{2}\,0\,0)$, and $X(1\,0\,0)$. The lattice constant at normal pressure is denoted by a_0. The zero of energy is placed at the $\Gamma_{25'}$ level.

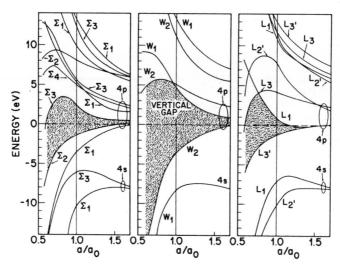

FIG. 3. Energy band structure of germanium as a function of lattice constant at $\Sigma(\frac{1}{2}\,\frac{1}{2}\,0)$, $W(1\,\frac{1}{2}\,0)$, and $L(\frac{1}{2}\,\frac{1}{2}\,\frac{1}{2})$. The lattice constant at normal pressure is denoted by a_0. The zero of energy is placed at the $\Gamma_{25'}$ level.

Let us now examine Figs. 2 and 3 in some detail. As the lattice constant is reduced (from large values), there is no forbidden band across the entire Brillouin zone until the lowest conduction band level, $\Gamma_{2'}$, is swept above the highest valence band level, $\Gamma_{25'}$, at about $a = 1.04a_0$. As the lattice constant is reduced further, the distinction of being the lowest conduction band level switches from $\Gamma_{2'}$ to L_1 just slightly above $a = a_0$. At the normal lattice constant, $\Gamma_{2'}$ lies only 0.14 eV above L_1, while Δ_1^m lies only 0.06 eV above $\Gamma_{2'}$ (cf. Table 1 and Fig. 1). As the lattice constant is reduced still further, L_1 rises above Δ_1^m at about $a = 0.98a_0$, and the conduction band edge switches once more. According to our theoretical work, the switch from [111] to [100] conduction band minima occurs at about 50,000 atm, which is consistent with experiment (Slykhouse and Drickamer, 1958), and with earlier theoretical discussions (see, for example, Herman, 1954). Of course, Slykhouse and Drickamer were studying Ge I in a metastable form, rather than Ge III, which can also exist at 50,000 atm.

It has been suggested by Musgrave (1964) that there is a relationship between the critical (phase transition) pressure and the energy gap in germanium and related semiconductors. In his view, the change from semiconducting to metallic behavior, associated with the change in crystal structure at the critical pressure, is brought about by a destabilizing electronic configuration which can occur when the conduction band becomes critically populated, presumably due to an overlap or near overlap of valence and conduction bands. Our results do not support this view; we find that the conduction band does not begin to overlap the valence band until the lattice constant is reduced to about $0.8a_0$, which corresponds to a pressure of about 475,000 atm, or nearly four times the pressure required to transform Ge I to Ge II. As we have already said, Ge I can be transformed into Ge III at only 25,000 atm under equilibrium conditions (at room temperature). Thus, there appears to be no direct connection between the occurrence of phase transformations and the incipient overlap of valence and conduction bands, at least in germanium.

When energy level vs. lattice constant diagrams are derived using the Wigner-Seitz cellular method, the zero of energy at different lattice constants is determined by the cellular boundary conditions, as is noted by Kimball (1935) in his paper on diamond, and also by Bardeen and Shockley (1950) in their paper on deformation potentials in diamond-type crystals. The variation of the zero of energy with lattice constant is therefore automatically included in such diagrams, but this variation does not necessarily have any precise physical significance. In our own work, we decided to use the $\Gamma_{25'}$ level, which defines the top-most valence band level at a_0, as the zero of energy at all lattice constants. This representation was found to be particularly suitable for delineating the variation of transition energies with lattice constant.

With this choice of reference level, some energy levels such as $\Gamma_{2'}$ and L_1 rise monotonically as the lattice constant is reduced, while others such as Γ_{15} and L_3 first rise, then reach a plateau, and finally fall. Nonmonotonic behavior of this type can often be traced to a changing admixture of s, p, and d character in the crystal wave functions within the ion core regions. For example, at very large interatomic distances, the wave functions for the lower and upper Γ_{15} states shown in Fig. 2 can be represented by linear combinations of 4p and 4d atomic orbitals, respectively. As the interatomic distance is decreased, these two states interact more and more strongly, until at sufficiently small interatomic distances the lower state is so strongly repelled by the upper that its previous upward trend is arrested and ultimately reversed. At the same time, the lower Γ_{15} state gains more and more 4d atomic character at the expense of the 4p.

Even though the upper valence bands and the lower conduction bands are derived primarily from atomic 4s and 4p levels, their detailed form at a_0 is strongly influenced by their proximity to the higher-lying conduction bands derived from atomic 4d (and also 5s and 5p) levels. This influence is most apparent when the lattice constant is changed, since this leads to changes in the fractional 4s, 4p, and 4d atomic characters of the states bordering the forbidden band. The upper valence bands, like the conduction bands passing through the state Γ_{15}, gain 4d atomic character at the expense of 4p atomic character, as a/a_0 is reduced below 1. It remains to be seen whether this dramatic change in the orbital character of the upper valence band states is an important factor in favoring the transformation of germanium from tetrahedrally coordinated Ge I to the high-pressure modifications (Ge II, III, IV), which have distorted tetrahedral coordination.

V. Silicon

A. PRELIMINARY REMARKS

Although our knowledge of the valence and conduction band edges in silicon is quite extensive, the remainder of the band structure is understood more in a qualitative than a quantitative sense. There has been considerable speculation about energy level assignments and the interpretation of the optical reflectivity spectrum (for a review, see Phillips, 1966), but our detailed understanding of the relationship between the energy band structure and reflectivity spectrum remains incomplete. The theoretical studies of Brust (1964, 1965) and Kane (1966) have provided a good picture of the interband transitions primarily responsible for the main reflectivity peak at 4.5 eV and the broad but weaker peak at about 5.3 eV. These authors have also been able to generate a 3.4-eV peak in their theoretical spectrum, but since this result is much more sensitive to details of their energy band model than are their other results, we do not believe that their theoretical 3.4-eV peak is necessarily related to its experimental counterpart. In short, we still regard the nature of the 3.4-eV reflectivity peak as an open question.

Most authors (Phillips, 1962, 1966; Brust, 1964, 1965; Cohen and Bergstresser, 1966; Cardona and Pollak, 1966; Kane, 1966) assign the 3.4-eV reflectivity peak to the $\Gamma_{15}-\Gamma_{25'}$ transition (or to closely related $\Delta_1-\Delta_5$ transitions). The $\Gamma_{15}-\Gamma_{25'}$ assignment is of course nominal, since such a transition would give rise to an edge rather than a peak in the reflectivity spectrum. The general consensus seems to be that interband transitions near the zone center, of the $\Delta_1-\Delta_5$ type, are the primary contributors to the 3.4-eV peak.

Since we regard the experimental evidence bearing on this assignment as inconclusive, we will simply ignore the 3.4-eV peak in the initial stages of our investigation, and develop a model for the band structure without explicit reference to this peak. With our energy band model in hand, we will review relevant experimental evidence and draw our own conclusion concerning the nature of the 3.4-eV reflectivity peak.

B. ENERGY BAND MODEL

In view of our satisfactory treatment of grey tin and germanium in terms of two-parameter empirical adjustments, we will also attempt a two-parameter treatment of silicon. Since the energies of the two most sensitive transitions in silicon are not as firmly established as they are in germanium and grey tin, we must now proceed somewhat differently. In silicon, the only key transition whose energy and symmetry assignment are beyond question is the indirect band gap, $\Delta_1^m-\Gamma_{25'}$, where the superscript m denotes conduction band minimum. In order to bring out a number of important features of the band structure of silicon, we will adjust $E(\text{PERT})$ to the experimental indirect band gap, and to a series of *assumed* values for $L_1-L_{3'}$. We have obtained $E(\text{PERT})$ solutions for several choices of $L_1-L_{3'}$. For each choice, a number of different two-parameter adjustments were carried out. The average $E(\text{PERT})$ solutions for three particularly instructive choices of $L_1-L_{3'}$ are listed in Table 5. The individual fits rarely differed from their respective averages by more than ± 0.10 eV. Note that the $E(\text{PERT})$ entries in Table 5 are given to the nearest 0.05 eV.

It is obvious from Table 5 that insensitive transitions such as $L_3-L_{3'}$, X_1-X_4, and $\Gamma_{15}-\Gamma_{25'}$ are pinned down quite nicely by our adjustment procedure. Even if we could not specify the exact value of $L_1-L_{3'}$, we would still have a fairly good idea of the magnitudes of the insensitive transition energies. For example, if we make the rather weak assumption that $L_1-L_{3'}$ lies somewhere between 2.6 and 3.8 eV, we find that $L_3-L_{3'} = 5.0 \pm 0.15$ eV; $X_1-X_4 = 4.05 \pm 0.15$ eV; and most important of all, $\Gamma_{15}-\Gamma_{25'} = 2.75 \pm 0.15$

TABLE 3. COMPARISON OF THEORETICAL AND EXPERIMENTAL ...

Transition[b]	Present work					Cohen-Bergstresser	
	E(NRSC)	E(PERT)	E(PERT)	E(PERT)	E^*(EXPT)	E_0^*(EXPT)	E(PSEUDO)
Δ_1^m–$\Gamma_{25'}$	1.4	1.13[c]	1.13[c]	1.13[c]	1.13[e]	1.1	0.8
X_1–$\Gamma_{25'}$	1.65	1.3	1.3	1.3			
L_1–$\Gamma_{25'}$	1.8	1.85	2.05	2.25			1.9
Γ_{15}–$\Gamma_{25'}$	3.05	2.8	2.75	2.7		3.4?	3.4
L_1–$L_{3'}$	2.9	3.0[d]	3.2[d]	3.4[d]		3.2	3.1
Λ_1–Λ_3	3.0	3.1	3.3	3.5			
Δ_1–Δ_5	3.5	3.3	3.35	3.4			
See text					(3.4)[f]		
$\Gamma_{2'}$–$\Gamma_{25'}$	2.8	3.35	3.8	4.2			3.8
X_1–X_4	4.2	4.0	4.05	4.1	~4.1[g]	4.3	4.0
Σ_3–Σ_2	4.3	4.0	4.15	4.3	(4.3)[g]		
L_3–$L_{3'}$	5.3	5.05	5.0	4.95	(5.3)[g]	5.3	5.2

[a] The three E(PERT) solutions were all adjusted to the experimental indirect band gap, but to different assumed values for the L_1–$L_{3'}$ transition energy, namely, 3.0, 3.2, and 3.4 eV. The remaining E(PERT) transition energies are to be regarded as predictions. Room temperature values are used for E^*(EXPT) which are uncertain to a few tenths of an electron volt are enclosed in parentheses. The experimental estimates (0°K) of Cohen and Bergstresser are denoted by E_0^*(EXPT), and their pseudopotential solutions by E(PSEUDO). A doubtful identification is indicated by a question mark. All energies are in electron volts.

[b] Since a detailed survey of the reduced zone has not been carried out, the exact location of critical points is not known. Here we merely list the transition energies at points we have actually studied; these include Λ(0.25 0.25 0.25); Δ(0.5 0 0); and Σ(0.5 0.5 0), all in units of $(2\pi/a)$.

[c] Indirect band gap. Adjusted to E^*(EXPT) $= 1.13$ eV. In the E(PERT) scheme. Δ_1^m lies at $(2\pi/a)(0.81\ 0\ 0)$.

[d] Adjusted to different assumed values for the L_1–$L_{3'}$ transition energy.

[e] From Frova and Handler (1965). Note that E^*(EXPT) $= E$(EXPT) $- \Delta E$(SO) $= 1.115 + 0.015 = 1.13$ eV.

[f] From Gerhardt (1965a). The reflectivity peak falls at 3.4 eV. Modulated electroreflectivity measurements indicate the presence of three peaks within a 0.1-eV range near 3.4 eV; see Seraphin and Bottka (1965b) and Seraphin (1965).

[g] From Philipp and Ehrenreich (1963); also Cohen and Phillips (1965). The main reflectivity peak occurs at 4.5 eV, while the corresponding peak in $\varepsilon_2(\omega)$, which is a better measure of interband transition energies, occurs at 4.3 eV. According to Kane (1966), the X_1–X_4 transition energy is 0.2 eV less than the $\varepsilon_2(\omega)$ peak energy, or 4.1 eV. It is difficult to say exactly where the uppermost reflectivity peak occurs; the corresponding $\varepsilon_2(\omega)$ peak lies somewhere between 5.0 and 5.5 eV. The $\varepsilon_2(\omega)$ peak is estimated to lie at 5.3 eV, which is only a rough measure of the L_3–$L_{3'}$ transition energy.

eV. (These results can be obtained from Table 5 by tripling the excursion of L_1-L_3', and extrapolating the other transitions.) In short, there is no way of bringing $\Gamma_{15}-\Gamma_{25'}$ close to 3.4 eV within the framework of any one of several two-parameter adjustments.

Our earlier study of adjustment procedures (cf. Section IV,C) suggests that we can place considerable confidence in our predicted value for the insensitive transition $\Gamma_{15}-\Gamma_{25'}$, but that the value of the sensitive transition $\Gamma_{2'}-\Gamma_{25'}$ is best determined by comparision of theory with experiment. In subsequent sections, we will examine a variety of experimental evidence, partly to check our theoretical predictions concerning the insensitive transitions, and partly to discover clues concerning the sensitive ones. In the remainder of the present section, we will compare our theoretical results with those of Cohen and Bergstresser (1966). We hope to compare our results with those of Cardona and Pollak (1966) in a separate publication.

It is noteworthy that our empirical solution starts from a first-principles energy band model, $E(\text{NRSC})$, which is already in good qualitative agreement with experiment (cf. Table 5). In contrast, the empirical pseudopotential solution of Cohen and Bergstresser starts from the empty-lattice or free-electron gas model, which must be grossly distorted before it can approximate the experimental energy level scheme of a nonmetallic crystal such as silicon. This distortion is illustrated (for germanium) in an earlier paper by one of the present authors (Herman, 1958). In practice, we can bring key features of $E(\text{NRSC})$ into agreement with $E^*(\text{EXPT})$ by using empirical energy level shifts $\Delta E(\Delta V)$ which are an order of magnitude smaller than their pseudopotential counterparts, as can be seen from Table 6. Therefore, in the $E(\text{PERT})$ scheme, the uncertainties and ambiguities associated with the empirical adjustment are an order of magnitude smaller than they are in the $E(\text{PSEUDO})$ scheme. When one is attempting to fit theory to a limited amount of incisive experimental information—as is the case in silicon—our approach has obvious advantages over the pseudopotential approach.

Our $E(\text{PERT})$ solution for silicon $(L_1-L_{3'} = 3.0$ eV) is compared with Cohen and Bergstresser's $E(\text{PSEUDO})$ solution in Table 5, and also in Fig. 4. The two solutions are clearly quite different in the vicinity of the conduction band states Γ_{15} and $\Gamma_{2'}$. Part of the reason for the difference is that Cohen and Bergstresser adjusted $E(\text{PSEUDO})$ to a $\Gamma_{15}-\Gamma_{25'}$ transition energy of 3.4 eV, in accordance with Phillip's earlier " categorical " classification of principal energy levels in silicon and related semiconductors (Phillips, 1962).

In the following, we will consider the experimental evidence for ourselves, and explain why we believe there is no connection between the 3.4-eV peak and $\Gamma_{15}-\Gamma_{25'}$ or related transitions. We believe the correct value for $\Gamma_{15}-\Gamma_{25'}$ is about 2.8 eV, the value given by our $E(\text{PERT})$ solution.

TABLE 6

COMPARISON OF EMPIRICAL ENERGY LEVEL SHIFTS $\Delta E(\Delta V)$ FOR KEY
TRANSITIONS IN SILICON, GERMANIUM, AND GREY TIN[a]

Transition	Silicon[b]		Germanium[d]		Grey tin[e]	
	Present work	Pseudo-potential[c]	Present work	Pseudo-potential[c]	Present work	Pseudo-potential[c]
$\Gamma_1-\Gamma_{25'}$	−0.4	8.6	−0.2	7.3	−0.4	5.7
$\Gamma_{2'}-\Gamma_{25'}$	0.55	3.35	0.7	0.9	−0.46	−0.2
$\Gamma_{15}-\Gamma_{25'}$	−0.25	2.8	−0.3	2.7	−0.3	2.2
X_1-X_4	−0.2	4.0	−0.1	4.1	−0.3	3.4
$L_{2'}-L_{3'}$	−0.4	9.5	−0.4	9.0	−0.3	7.3
$L_3-L_{3'}$	−0.25	5.05	−0.3	5.3	−0.3	4.4
$L_1-L_{3'}$	0.1	3.0	0.2	2.1	−0.3	1.4

[a] In the present work, $\Delta E(\Delta V)$ is defined as $E(\text{PERT})-E(\text{NRSC})$, where $E(\text{PERT})$ is intended to be a close approximation to $E^*(\text{EXPT})$. Since all transition energies shown above are zero in the free-electron gas or empty-lattice model (cf. Herman, 1958), and since $E(\text{PERT}) \approx E^*(\text{EXPT})$, the analogues of $\Delta E(\Delta V)$ in the empirical pseudopotential method of Brust (1964) and of Cohen and Bergstresser (1966) can be represented by the corresponding values of $E(\text{PERT})$. In our approach, $\Delta E(\Delta V)$ can be determined in most circumstances by first-order perturbation theory. In the Brust-Cohen-Bergstresser approach, the major portion of $\Delta E(\Delta V)$ must be determined by solving high-order secular equations; the remaining portion can then be determined by perturbation theory. All entries are in electron volts.

[b] Based on Table 5, for $L_1-L_{3'} = 3.0$ eV.

[c] Here $\Delta E(\Delta V) = E^*(\text{EXPT}) - $ (free-electron gas transition energy) $= E^*(\text{EXPT}) - 0 \approx E(\text{PERT})$. Note that in the free-electron gas model for diamond-type crystals, the valence band level $\Gamma_{25'}$ and the conduction band levels Γ_{15}, $\Gamma_{2'}$, and Γ_1 are all degenerate; similarly for X_4 and X_1; and similarly for $L_{3'}$, L_1, L_3, and the higher-lying conduction band level $L_{2'}$.

[d] Based on Table 1. Still smaller $\Delta E(\Delta V)$ can be obtained by our method: cf. Table 3. (This remark also applies to other crystals.)

[e] Based on Table 1.

C. PIEZOREFLECTANCE STUDIES

Using plane polarized light, Gerhardt (1965a,b) has measured the strain-induced changes in the reflectivity peak of silicon near 3.4 eV produced by uniaxial deformation along the [111] and [100] axes. For compression (or extension) along the [100] axis, the sign of the energy shift of the peak is different for light polarized parallel and perpendicular to the [100] axis, whereas compression along the [111] axis always shifts the peak to higher energies. On the basis of qualitative arguments, Gerhardt comes to the conclusion that transitions clustered along the [100] axes rather than along the [111] axes are the main contributors to the 3.4-eV reflectivity peak.

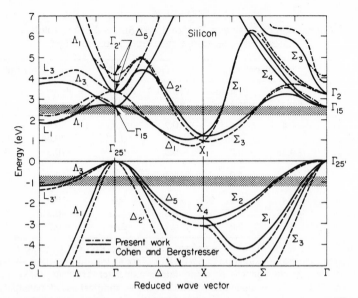

FIG. 4. Comparison of three energy band models for silicon (spin-orbit splitting neglected). One of our two-parameter E(PERT) models is represented by the solid lines, while another is represented by the dash-dot lines. Both of these models have been adjusted to the experimental indirect band gap, $\Delta_1^m - \Gamma_{25'} = 1.13$ eV, but the former has been adjusted to the assumed value $L_1 - L_{3'} = 3.0$ eV, while the latter has been adjusted to the assumed value $L_1 - L_{3'} = 3.4$ eV. In the interest of clarity, the dash-dot lines are not shown where they nearly coincide with the solid lines. The light dashed lines represent the three-parameter pseudopotential model of Cohen and Bergstresser (1966). The lower and upper shaded regions correspond to the initial and final state energy ranges associated with the 3.4-eV reflectivity peak, as given by the photoemission studies of Spicer and Simon (1962); see also Table 7.

This conclusion is compatible with the results of earlier pseudopotential band calculations by Brust (1964), and with the results of the more recent pseudopotential calculations by Cohen and Bergstresser (1966), but not with our own results. Since the interpretation of Gerhardt's measurements is open to question,* let us now turn to deformation potential measurements, which are considerably easier to interpret theoretically.

* In principle, Gerhardt's measurements can be interpreted in terms of a model which specifies (a) the geometrical shape and location in the reduced zone of the region primarily responsible for the 3.4-eV reflectivity peak; (b) the changes in shape and location of this region produced by uniaxial deformation; (c) the changes in the polarization-dependent interband matrix elements produced by uniaxial deformation. Although Gerhardt postulates a model for the 3.4-eV reflectivity peak and proceeds to interpret his data in terms of this model, it is not clear that his model is unique. His conclusions are not based on a set of selection rules which can be justified theoretically, but rather on a set of assumed selection rules. Unless his selection rules and other features of his model can be validated by further

D. DEFORMATION POTENTIAL STUDIES

Zallen's experimental deformation potential value for the 3.4-eV reflectivity peak in silicon is -5.0 ± 0.5 eV (cf. Table 4). Referring to our theoretical deformation potential values in Table 4, and to our theoretical transition energies in Table 5, we see that at the midpoint of the [100] axis, where $\Delta_1-\Delta_5$ is 3.3 eV, the corresponding net deformation potential difference, or deformation potential for short, is -1.3 eV. If we move inward along the [100] axis from the midpoint to the zone center, $\Delta_1-\Delta_5$ decreases from 3.3 to 2.8 eV, while the deformation potential changes from -1.3 to -0.6 eV. If we reverse direction, and move outward along the [100] axis from the midpoint to the zone face, $\Delta_1-\Delta_5$ increases from 3.3 to 4.0 eV, while the deformation potential changes from -1.3 to -1.4 eV.

If we assume that the 3.4-eV reflectivity peak is due primarily to $\Delta_1-\Delta_5$ transitions, as Gerhardt suggests, we run into two difficulties: First, our Δ_1 and Δ_5 bands are not parallel in the region where their energy separation is about 3.4 eV, so that $\Delta_1-\Delta_5$ transitions from this region would not make a large contribution to the joint interband density of states in the neighborhood of 3.4 eV. Second, our theoretical deformation potential value for this region is different by a factor of 4 from Zallen's experimental value.

The situation for the 3.4-eV reflectivity peak in silicon may well be similar to that for the 4.5-eV reflectivity peak in silicon (and also in germanium). As Kane (1966) has shown theoretically, the 4.5-eV reflectivity peak in silicon is produced by transitions associated with an extended region of the reduced zone, rather than by transitions located exclusively in the neighborhood of the X point. This accounts, for example, for the difference between the experimental deformation potential value for the 4.5-eV silicon peak, $D(\text{EXPT}) = -2.8 \pm 0.5$ eV, and our theoretical value for the X_1-X_4 transition, $D(\text{NRSC}) = -1.4$ eV (cf. Table 4).

It is quite possible, and in fact likely, that the 3.4-eV reflectivity peak in silicon is also due to transitions associated with an extended region of the reduced zone, though this region would be less extended than that associated with the 4.5-eV reflectivity peak, which is considerably stronger. If this conjecture is correct, the extended region for the 3.4-eV peak should coincide with a region in the zone where the deformation potential is close to the experimental value for this peak, -5.0 ± 0.5 eV.

theoretical analysis, Gerhardt's conclusions must be regarded as tentative. The situation here may be analogous to the interpretation of magnetoresistance data for p-type germanium on the basis of a many-valley valence band model. An analysis of such experimental data in terms of this model would point to [111] valence band maxima, but this is not the correct model. In order to interpret the data properly, it is necessary to begin with warped or fluted constant energy surfaces, rather than with disconnected clusters of ellipsoidal constant energy surfaces.

We have attempted to visualize the 3.4-eV region by studying the deformation potentials and interband transition energies at the points listed in Tables 4 and 5, and at a few other key points. So far as we can tell, the region of interest includes a section near the [110] axis about $\frac{1}{3}$ of the way from Γ to the zone boundary, as well as a cylindrical section which surrounds the [111] axis most of the way from L to Γ. It is difficult to visualize the precise location and form of this region without carrying out a detailed survey of the reduced zone in the manner of Brust (1964, 1965). We are planning to undertake such a survey in the near future, but we expect to be able to map out the constant energy (and deformation potential) profiles in the reduced zone more efficiently by utilizing recently developed visual display techniques (cf. Wahl, 1966).

E. PHOTOEMISSION STUDIES

Vital evidence concerning the *absolute energies* of the initial and final states of the interband transitions giving rise to the 3.4-eV reflectivity peak in silicon is provided by the photoemission studies of Spicer and Simon (1962). This evidence is obtained by studying the energy distribution of the photoemitted electrons as a function of the energy of the exciting photons, and also by comparing the spectral distribution of the photoelectron quantum yield with the optical reflectivity spectrum.

Briefly, Spicer and Simon find that 3.4-eV incident photons produce a broad peak in the energy distribution of the photoemitted electrons centered 1.0 ± 0.2 eV above the vacuum level, while 5.3-eV incident photons produce a broad peak centered 2.3 ± 0.2 eV above the vacuum level. These two peaks can be correlated with the 3.4- and 5.3-eV peaks which occur both in the optical reflectivity spectrum and in the photoelectron quantum yield spectrum. The experimental evidence is consistent with the view that the same two sets of initial valence band states and final conduction band states play a dominant role in determining the 3.4- and 5.3-eV reflectivity peaks on the one hand, and the 1.0 ± 0.2 and 2.3 ± 0.2 eV photoelectron peaks on the other. Since most of the photoemission takes place from a region of the crystal in which the highest valence band level lies 1.5 eV below the vacuum level, it can be inferred that the two photoelectron peaks lie 2.5 ± 0.2 and 3.8 ± 0.2 eV above $\Gamma_{25'}$. According to Spicer (private communication), there is good evidence that the photoelectrons first make a vertical transition from valence band to conduction band states, and then are emitted from the crystal without any appreciable loss of energy. It follows that the two final state energies are 2.5 ± 0.2 and 3.8 ± 0.2 eV, while the corresponding initial state energies are $2.5 \pm 0.2 - 3.4 = -0.9 \pm 0.2$ and $3.8 \pm 0.2 - 5.3 = -1.5 \pm 0.2$ eV, all relative to $\Gamma_{25'}$.

In Table 7, Spicer and Simon's initial and final state energies for the two sets of transitions are compared with relevant features of our energy level scheme (cf. also Fig. 4). The higher energy peak can be identified with transitions closely related to the L_3-L_3, transition. Since the (so-called) 5.3-eV optical reflectivity peak is quite broad, it is likely that an extended region near the L point is associated with this peak; this is indeed indicated by Kane's (1966) calculations. There may also be a significant contribution to the 5.3-eV peak from $\Delta_2,-\Delta_5$ transitions near the [100] axis midpoint. The breadth of this peak may also be related to the presence of these additional transitions.

TABLE 7

SPICER AND SIMON'S PHOTOEMISSION RESULTS FOR SILICON[a]

Energy level scheme for Silicon			Spicer and Simon[c] (experiment)	
Initial state	Final state	$E(\text{PERT})^b$	3.4 eV peak	5.3 eV peak
	Near L_3			3.8 ± 0.2
	L_3	3.85 ± 0.05		
	$\Gamma_{2'}$	3.8 ± 0.4		
	Γ_{15}	2.75 ± 0.05		
	Extended		2.5 ± 0.2	
	L_1	2.05 ± 0.2		
$\Gamma_{25'}$		0.0		
Extended			-0.9 ± 0.2	
$L_{3'}$		-1.15		
Near $L_{3'}$				-1.5 ± 0.2^d

[a] All entries are in electron volts.
[b] Based on $L_1-L_{3'} = 3.2 \pm 0.2$ eV. See Table 5 for further details.
[c] From Spicer and Simon (1962).
[d] If the interband transition energy is taken as 5.1 rather than 5.3 eV, this entry would read: -1.3 ± 0.2 (eV).

More important for our immediate purpose, however, is the identification of the lower energy peak. With the initial state energy pinned down to the range -0.9 ± 0.2 eV, transitions at or very near the center of the zone are ruled out as principal contributors to the 3.4-eV reflectivity peak. This range could probably be stretched out slightly, say to -0.9 ± 0.3 eV, but this would still exclude Γ and its neighborhood. Therefore, the association of $\Gamma_{15}-\Gamma_{25'}$ or closely related transitions with the 3.4-eV reflectivity peak appears to be ruled out not only by the deformation potential evidence, but also by the photoemission evidence. The region in the reduced zone compatible with the initial state energy range -0.9 ± 0.2 (or 0.3) eV includes the [110] section and the cylindrical section surrounding the [111] axis already suggested by the deformation potential evidence.

For further discussions of photoemission studies of the band structure of silicon, the reader is referred to papers by Brust (1965), Cohen and Phillips (1965), and Allen and Gobeli (1966).

Having stated our reasons for believing (a) that the 3.4-eV reflectivity peak is *not* associated with $\Gamma_{15}-\Gamma_{25'}$ or closely related transitions, and (b) that this peak is associated with interband transitions belonging to an extended region in the reduced zone, most likely a region encircling the [111] axis, and even extending as far as the [110] axis, our discussion of the 3.4-eV reflectivity peak in silicon is concluded. In the next section, we will consider some experimental evidence which may help us pin down one of the sensitive transitions ($\Gamma_{2'}-\Gamma_{25'}$ or $L_1-L_{3'}$) and thereby eliminate the residual uncertainty in our energy band model for silicon (cf. Table 5 and Fig. 4).

F. ELECTROREFLECTANCE STUDIES

Before turning to the electroreflectance studies of Seraphin (1964, 1965), we wish to remind the reader that the standard reflectivity spectrum is closely related to the joint interband density of states, and that under ideal conditions characteristic features in the reflectivity spectrum can be related to critical points (Phillips, 1966). Shoulders or edges are identified with M_0 or M_3 critical points (parabolic band edges), while peaks are identified with pairs of M_1, M_2 critical points (saddle-point band edges). In practice, however, a reflectivity peak may be produced by a set of interband transitions whose high density is not due to a specific critical point, but rather to an extended region of the reduced zone. Such a reflectivity peak may or may not be accompanied by a corresponding electroreflectivity peak (ER-peak): The electroreflectivity spectrum is not so much a measure of the joint interband density of states as it is a measure of the change in this density produced by an electric field. Since electric-field induced changes in the joint density of states are singular at critical points, critical points show up more clearly in electroreflectivity spectra than they do in standard optical spectra. It is for this reason that electroreflectance studies, pioneered by Seraphin and now being vigorously pursued by the Brown University group under Cardona, are expected to play a prominent role in future band structure determinations.

Using high-resolution modulated electroreflectivity techniques, Seraphin (1965) has resolved three ER-peaks within a 0.1-eV range near the 3.4-eV reflectivity peak in silicon. The height of the ER-peak at 3.34 eV is independent of the crystalline orientation of the reflecting surface, while the height of the ER-peak at 3.45 eV is markedly dependent on crystalline orientation. On the basis of these orientation effects, he assigns the 3.34-eV ER-peak to a critical-point transition at the central point of the zone, and the 3.45-eV ER-peak to a critical-point transition elsewhere in the zone. He has also studied the temperature dependence of the two ER-peaks already mentioned, as well as that of the third ER-peak, which lies between the other two at lower temperatures, but disappears at higher temperatures. In view of its pronounced temperature dependence, this intermediate ER-peak has been attributed to an exciton. When the average electric field in the surface is changed by varying the dc bias, the 3.34- and 3.45-eV ER-peaks shift in energy in opposite directions. According to the duality theorem (Phillips and Seraphin, 1965), these opposite spectral shifts indicate that one ER-peak must be assigned to a parabolic band edge, where the band separation is an extremum, while the other ER-peak must be assigned to a saddle-point band edge, where the gradient of the band separation is zero.

Combining the crystal orientation and spectral shift deductions, Seraphin concludes that the 3.34-eV ER-peak is associated with a critical-point transition at a parabolic band edge at the central point of the zone, and that the 3.45-eV ER-peak is associated with a critical-point transition at a saddle-point band edge elsewhere in the zone, possibly along the [111] axis.

As Seraphin himself emphasizes, current interpretations of electroreflectivity spectra should be treated with caution, since our theoretical ability to analyze spectral information is still rather limited. For example, Seraphin's analysis of his spectral data does not show up the spin-orbit splitting in the valence band, which is 0.044 eV at the center of the zone, but smaller elsewhere. Also, it appears to be difficult to understand the temperature dependence of the various ER-peaks. Therefore, the above conclusions reached by Seraphin should be regarded as provisional.

If one or more of the ER-peaks near 3.4 eV is ultimately identified with a critical-point transition at the center of the zone, we would expect this transition to be $\Gamma_{2'}-\Gamma_{25'}$, rather than $\Gamma_{15}-\Gamma_{25'}$, since our two-parameter $E(\mathrm{PERT})$ model places $\Gamma_{15}-\Gamma_{25'}$ at about 2.8 eV whatever we choose for $L_1-L_{3'}$ within reasonable limits (cf. Table 5). We have anticipated the possibility that $\Gamma_{2'}-\Gamma_{25'} = 3.35 \pm 0.05$ eV by pegging one of our three $E(\mathrm{PERT})$ models to this value. This model, which corresponds to the choice $L_1 - L_{3'} = 3.0$ eV, is displayed in Table 5 and in Fig. 4 as well. We have also anticipated the possibility that one or more of the ER-peaks near 3.4 eV will ultimately be identified with a critical-point transition somewhere along (or near) the [111] axis by using $L_1-L_{3'} = 3.4$ eV as the basis for another $E(\mathrm{PERT})$ model: this is also displayed in Table 5 and Fig. 4.

However, we can definitely rule out the possibility that $\Gamma_{2'}-\Gamma_{25'}$ and $L_1-L_{3'}$ are 3.4 eV simultaneously: Setting up a three-parameter $E(\mathrm{PERT})$ model based on $\Delta v(111)$, $\Delta v(220)$, and $\Delta v(311)$, and adjusting these three parameters to $\Delta_1^m-\Gamma_{25'} = 1.13$ eV, $\Gamma_{2'}-\Gamma_{25'} = 3.4$ eV, and $L_1-L_{3'} = 3.4$ eV, we obtain totally unacceptable values for the other key transitions, e.g., $\Gamma_{15}-\Gamma_{25'} = 0.06$ eV; $X_1-X_4 = 1.3$ eV; and $L_3-L_{3'} = 2.8$ eV.

It is unfortunate that no definite conclusions concerning the proper assignments of the 3.34- and 3.45-eV ER-peaks can be drawn at this time. There is good reason, however, to believe that future theoretical analyses of Seraphin's measurements will lead to definite assignments for these ER-peaks, and, hopefully, to definite information concerning one or another of the sensitive transitions.

Recent theoretical work by Aspnes (reported by P. Handler, invited paper Durham Meeting of the American Physical Society, March 31, 1966) indicates that the duality theorem (Phillips and Seraphin, 1965) has only limited applicability, and does not provide a clear-cut basis for interpreting electroreflectivity spectra in general. The transition energy in the neighborhood of a critical point can be expanded in a Taylor series (E vs. $\mathbf{k}$) provided the initial and final states are nondegenerate. The three reduced masses of an M_0 critical point (in a principal axis coordinate system) are all positive; one or two of these three masses is (are) negative for M_1 or M_2 critical points; and all three of these masses are negative for an M_3 critical point. According to the work of Aspnes, the electroreflectivity spectrum associated with a saddle-point band edge (M_1 or M_2) can be decomposed into longitudinal and transverse components, corresponding to the electric field being oriented parallel and perpendicular to the odd sign reduced mass. The duality theorem of Phillips and Seraphin relates the spectral shift at a parabolic band edge to the longitudinal *but not to the transverse* spectral shift at a saddle-point band edge. This omission, which has been remedied by Aspnes, invalidates the arguments that Phillips and Seraphin have used in interpreting Seraphin's spectral shifts. By obtaining a more general solution for the interrelationships among ER-peaks associated with different types of critical points, Aspnes (1966) has paved the way for future theoretical interpretations of measurements such as Seraphin's.

VI. Germanium-Silicon Alloys

Considerable insight into the nature of the energy band structure of pure germanium and pure silicon can be gained by a careful study of the composition dependence of the optical reflectivity spectrum of the germanium-silicon alloy system. According to the measurements of Tauc and Abraham (1961), the 2.2-eV reflectivity peak in germanium—this is actually a 2.1, 2.3 eV doublet—shifts to higher energy as silicon is added to germanium. In the range from 0 to 35 at.% silicon, the doublet splitting decreases linearly from 0.2 to 0.1 eV. The doublet cannot be resolved above 35 at.% Si, but the unresolved peak can be followed experimentally up to about 55 at.% Si, where it lies at about 2.9 eV. In the range between 75 and 100 at.% Si, there is another reflectivity peak which shifts from 3.25 to 3.4 eV in this range. If one extrapolates the composition dependence of the energy of the (2.2 eV) germanium peak, this line passes through the 3.25-eV experimental point at

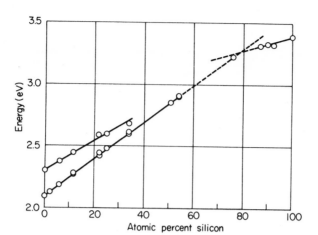

FIG. 5. Composition dependence of the energy of the first reflectivity peak in the germanium-silicon alloy system, according to Tauc and Abraham (1961). In the germanium-rich alloys, this peak is actually a spin-orbit split doublet.

75 at. % Si. However, it seems more reasonable to associate the 3.25-eV point with the 3.4-eV silicon peak than with the 2.2-eV germanium peak (cf. Fig. 5). In any event, there is a sharp break in the curve giving the composition dependence of the energy of the first reflectivity peak at 75 at. % Si, suggesting that the 3.4-eV silicon peak is unrelated to the 2.2-eV germanium peak. This is reminiscent of the sharp break in the composition dependence of the fundamental absorption edge in the germanium-silicon alloy system at 15 at. % Si which one of us explained some time ago (Herman, 1954).

We would now like to offer an interpretation of the sharp break in the Tauc and Abraham curve in terms of our energy band models for germanium and silicon, which are shown superimposed in Fig. 6. It will be noted that certain energy band profiles appear virtually identical in both crystals, while others shift drastically between germanium and silicon. In particular, the $L_3-\Lambda_3-\Gamma_{15}-\Delta_1-X_1-\Sigma_1$ conduction band profile remains nearly stationary, while the $L_1-\Lambda_1-\Gamma_{2'}-\Delta_{2'}-X_1-\Sigma_3$ conduction band profile shows the greatest change.

There is an obvious correlation between the magnitude of the deformation potential and the magnitude of the chemical shift (alloy effect) for the various interband transitions, but we will not pause to discuss this correlation further.

As is known from Brust's detailed studies (Brust, 1964), the 2.2-eV reflectivity peak in germanium is associated with a $\Lambda_1-\Lambda_3$ critical-point transition in the neighborhood of the Λ_1 arch (see also Cardona and Pollak, 1966). As silicon is added to germanium, the 2.2-eV peak obviously shifts to higher energies because of the upward motion of Λ_1, and the doublet splitting

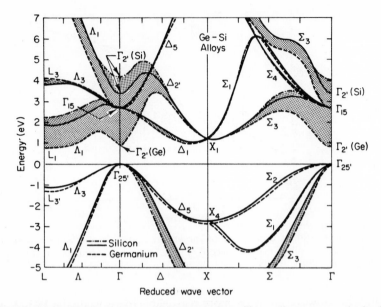

FIG. 6. Energy band structure of the germanium-silicon alloy system, obtained by superimposing the present energy band models for germanium (cf. Fig. 1) and silicon (cf. Fig. 4). As silicon is added to germanium, the germanium energy band profiles (shown dashed) sweep through the shaded regions, and approach the silicon energy band profiles. The latter are shown by solid lines, corresponding to the assumption that $L_1-L_{3'} = 3.0$ eV, and by dash-dot lines, corresponding to the alternate assumption that $L_1-L_{3'} = 3.4$ eV. In the interest of clarity, the dash-dot lines are not shown where they nearly coincide with the solid lines.

obviously decreases because the spin-orbit splitting in the Λ_3 valence band decreases. As the $L_1-\Lambda_1-\Gamma_{2'}$ conduction band profile rises in energy, a composition is reached at which the $\Gamma_{2'}$ level crosses the nearly stationary Γ_{15} level. The lower Λ_1 conduction band, formerly attached to $\Gamma_{2'}$, now becomes attached to Γ_{15} and rises no higher, while the upper Λ_1 conduction band, formerly attached to Γ_{15}, now becomes attached to $\Gamma_{2'}$ and begins to rise with $\Gamma_{2'}$.

The sharp break in the Tauc and Abraham curve at 75 at. % silicon is undoubtedly related to the changes in the conduction band structure away from the center of the zone induced by the cross-over of $\Gamma_{2'}$ and Γ_{15} at a composition not far removed from 75 at. % silicon. Below this critical composition, the spectral shift of the first reflectivity peak is large because the upward motion of the Λ_1 conduction band is unimpeded by the anchoring of this band to Γ_{15} at the zone center. Above this critical composition, the spectral of this peak is small because the upward motion of the Λ_1 conduction band is arrested by the anchoring at the zone center. It would not be too surprising if this anchoring produced a significant change in the shape and location of the region in the reduced zone which contributes most heavily to the first reflectivity peak. While the region associated with the first reflectivity peak may well have a different shape and location in pure germanium and pure silicon, we would expect this region to change continuously, if not uniformly, as we pass through the critical composition in the neighborhood of 75 at. % silicon.

We have recently learned (M. Cardona and F. H. Pollak, private communication) that electroreflectivity studies of the germanium-silicon alloy system are now in progress. It will be interesting to see whether the cross-over of $\Gamma_{2'}$ and $\Gamma_{25'}$ can be observed. It will also be interesting to see whether the $\Lambda_1-\Lambda_3$ critical-point transition, which shows up so clearly in the electro-reflectivity spectrum of pure germanium (Seraphin, 1964), can be traced through the entire composition range from pure germanium to pure silicon, and how the composition dependence of this transition compares with that of the first reflectivity peak.

Many of the questions raised by the present paper would be resolved if the $\Gamma_{15}-\Gamma_{25'}$ transition could be detected (and unambiguously identified) in pure germanium, in pure silicon, or in any of the intermediate germanium-silicon alloys. At present, it is not clear whether $\Gamma_{15}-\Gamma_{25'}$—like $\Gamma_{2'}-\Gamma_{25'}$ in germanium—can be detected by electroreflectivity measurements, or whether $\Gamma_{15}-\Gamma_{25'}$—like $L_1-L_{3'}$ in germanium—cannot be detected by such measurements (Seraphin, 1964, 1965). (See Note added in proof.)

VII. Concluding Remarks

We have developed a method for determining the energy band structure of crystals which is designed to be more reliable than purely first-principles or purely empirical (pseudopotential or $\mathbf{k} \cdot \mathbf{p}$) methods. Superior accuracy is attained by adding a small, carefully chosen empirical correction to an otherwise first-principles band calculation. By carefully examining the nature of empirical corrections, we have learned how to construct optimally flexible adjustment schemes based on a minimum number of adjustable parameters, and how otherwise to enhance the effectiveness and reliability of our small empirical correction (cf. Table 2). Relativistic and spin-orbit coupling corrections can be taken into account by a first-principles calculation, by an empirical correction, or by a combination of the two. In practice, our overall energy band solution is based almost entirely on first-principles considerations, and only slightly on empirical considerations.

At present, our first-principles band calculations are based on Slater's free-electron exchange approximation, though we have experimented with other exchange approximations (cf. Table 3). Although we are attempting to improve our treatment of exchange effects by going beyond the free-electron exchange approximation and variations thereof, the ultimate accuracy of our method is not critically dependent on the exact choice of exchange approximation: in practice, shortcomings in our treatment of exchange (and correlation) effects are largely compensated by the empirical correction.

Our motivation for developing an empirically perturbed self-consistent field method may be summarized as follows. First, we recognized that it was impractical to treat exchange, correlation, and relativistic effects rigorously, and that some form of empirical correction was necessary if the difficulties associated with treating these effects rigorously were to be circumvented. Second, we recognized that purely empirical methods were not nearly as reliable as some of their advocates would have us believe (cf. Phillips, 1966), and that it would be far better to add a small empirical correction to a physically reliable first-principles band calculation than to depend entirely on the caprices of an empirical adjustment (cf. Table 6). Third, we recognized that the small empirical correction required to bring our first-principles theory into agreement with experiment was in effect a quantitative measure of the shortcomings of our first-principles band calculations, and that we might be able to eliminate at least some of these shortcomings if we could study them systematically, and on a quantitative basis. In fact, we have already discovered a number of ways for improving our first-principles band calculations and concurrently reducing the magnitude of the empirical correction required to bring theory and experiment into agreement. Some of these ways have already been incorporated in the present work, while others are still being explored with a view to future incorporation. (See also Herman et al., 1966.)

Instead of attempting to fit our theoretical energy band models to a mixture of precisely and imprecisely known experimental information, as is the common practice in purely empirical band calculations (Brust, 1964; Cohen and Bergstresser, 1966; Cardona and Pollak, 1966), we have adjusted our band models only to the most firmly established experimental information, namely, the direct and indirect band gaps in grey tin and germanium, and the indirect band gap in silicon. By using two-parameter adjustment schemes, we were able to obtain unique solutions for grey tin and germanium, and a one-parameter family of possible solutions for silicon. Many of the essential features of the silicon band structure, namely, the insensitive transitions, are actually pinned down quite nicely by this type of solution. In order to pin down the sensitive transitions, it is necessary to make a further appeal to experiment. Even though definite conclusions have not yet been reached concerning the interpretation of recent electroreflectivity measurements (Seraphin, 1965), we have anticipated two possible interpretations by paying special attention to two energy band models which correspond to these interpretations.

In addition to obtaining new energy band solutions for silicon, germanium, and grey tin (cf. Tables 1 and 5, Figs. 1 and 4), we have calculated deformation potentials for most of the key interband transitions in silicon and germanium, and compared these calculated values with the measured values for supposedly related optical reflectivity peaks (cf. Table 4). Such comparisons show that the key X_1-X_4 transition is not really representative of the main reflectivity peak, even though it is commonly identified as such (Phillips, 1962, 1964, 1966). This particular conclusion has also been reached by Kane (1966) on the basis of a careful analysis of the joint interband density of states.

We have also determined the changes in the band structure of germanium produced by major as well as minor changes in the lattice constant (cf. Figs. 2 and 3), and examined the composition dependence of the band structure of the germanium-silicon alloy system (cf. Fig. 6).

By fitting our theoretical models only to well-established experimental information, thereby freeing ourselves from previous speculations (Phillips, 1962, 1964, 1966) concerning the nature of the band structure away from the band edges, we have been able to take a fresh look at the entire band structure, including such poorly understood regions as the conduction band structure associated with the triply-degenerate state Γ_{15}. Since $\Gamma_{15}-\Gamma_{25'}$ is an insensitive transition, we have been able to pin down this transition in silicon, as well as in germanium and grey tin. In all three of these crystals, our estimates for the $\Gamma_{15}-\Gamma_{25'}$ transition energy are consistently lower than previous estimates (e.g., Cohen and Bergstresser, 1966; Cardona and Pollak, 1966) by at least 0.5 eV. These revised estimates lead to significant changes in the band structure, as can be seen from Figs. 1 and 4.

Since the disposition of three of the four lowest conduction bands in the central region of the reduced zone is determined by $\Gamma_{15}-\Gamma_{25'}$, the value chosen for this transition has an important bearing on theoretical interpretations of ordinary reflectivity spectra, electroreflectivity spectra, piezoreflectivity spectra, and photoemission spectra, particularly in the range between 2 and 4 eV, where $\Gamma_{15}-\Gamma_{25'}$ and related transitions are most prominent. Our present work casts doubt on theoretical interpretations of such spectra based on previous estimates of $\Gamma_{15}-\Gamma_{25'}$, and suggests that it would be desirable to reinterpret these spectra in the light of our estimates for this transition.

ACKNOWLEDGMENTS

During the course of this investigation, the authors have benefited from correspondence and discussions with Professor Joseph L. Birman, Professor David Brust, Professor Marvin L. Cohen, Dr. Kermit F. Cuff, Professor Walter A. Harrison, Dr. Evan O. Kane, Professor James C. Phillips, Professor William E. Spicer, and Dr. Richard Zallen. The authors are grateful to Dr. Edmund C. Burke, Dr. Wayland C. Griffith, Mr. William F. Main, Dr. John P. Nash, and Dr. Morris A. Steinberg for their interest, encouragement, and support.

REFERENCES

Allen, F. G., and Gobeli, G. W. (1966). *Phys. Rev.* **144**, 558.

Aspnes, D. E. (1966). *Phys. Rev.* **147**, 554.

Balslev, I. (1966). *Phys. Rev.* **143**, 636.

Bardeen, J., and Shockley, W. (1950). *Phys. Rev.* **80**, 72.

Bassani, F., and Brust, D. (1963). *Phys. Rev.* **131**, 1524.

Bates, C. H., Dachille, F., and Roy, R. (1965). *Science* **147**, 860.

Braunstein, R., Moore, A. R., and Herman, F. (1958). *Phys. Rev.* **109**, 695.

Brust, D. (1964). *Phys. Rev.* **134**, A1337.

Brust, D. (1965). *Phys. Rev.* **139**, A489.

Brust, D., Phillips, J. C., and Bassani, F. (1962a). *Phys. Rev. Letters* **9**, 94.

Brust, D., Cohen, M. L., and Phillips, J. C. (1962b). *Phys. Rev. Letters* **9**, 389.

Cardona, M. (1965). *J. Appl. Phys.* **36**, 2181.

Cardona, M., and Grennaway, D. L. (1962). *Phys. Rev.* **125**, 1291.

Cardona, M., and Paul, W. (1960). *J. Phys. Chem. Solids* **17**, 138.

Cardona, M., and Pollak, F. H. (1966). *Phys. Rev.* **142**, 530.

Cardona, M., McElroy, P., Pollak, F. H., and Shaklee, K. L. (1966). *Phys. Rev. Letters.* To be published.

Cohen, M. L., and Bergstresser, T. K. (1966). *Phys. Rev.* **141**, 789.

Cohen, M. L., and Phillips, J. C. (1965). *Phys. Rev.* **139**, A912.

Engeler, W. E., Fritzche, H., Garfinkel, M., and Tiemann, J. J. (1965). *Phys. Rev. Letters* **14**, 1069.

Frova, A., and Handler, P. (1965). *Phys. Rev. Letters* **14**, 178.

Gerhardt, U. (1964). *Phys. Letters* **9**, 117.

Gerhardt, U. (1965a). *Phys. Stat. Solidi* **11**, 801.

Gerhardt, U. (1965b). *Phys. Rev. Letters* **15**, 401.

Ghosh, A. K. (1966a). *Phys. Rev. Letters.* To be published.

Ghosh, A. K. (1966b). *Phys. Rev. Letters.* To be published.

Gobeli, G. W., and Kane, E. O. (1965). *Phys. Rev. Letters.* **15**, 142.

Goroff, I., and Kleinman, L. (1963). *Phys. Rev.* **132**, 1080.

Groves, S., and Paul, W. (1964).*Proc. Intern. Conf. Phys. Semicond., Paris, 1964*, pp. 41–50. Dunod, Paris.

Herman, F. (1954). *Phys. Rev.* **95**, 847.

Herman, F. (1958). *Rev. Mod. Phys.* **30**, 102; see, in particular, Figs. 2–4.

Herman, F. (1964). *Proc. Intern. Conf. Phys. Semicond., Paris, 1964*, pp. 3–22. Dunod, Paris. Tables I and II of this reference are superseded by Tables 1 and 5 of the present article.

Herman, F., and Skillman, S. (1961). *Proc. Intern. Conf. Semicond.,Phys. Prague, 1960* pp. 20–28. Czech. Acad. of Sci., Prague. The term "sensitive transitions" originally referred to transitions which are most strongly affected by changes in the core shift parameter. In the light of the present work (cf. Table 2), sensitive transitions are ones which are affected most strongly by any of the pattern 2 corrections, for example, the relativistic correction. Moreover, sensitive transitions will have larger deformation potentials and larger chemical (alloying) shifts than insensitive ones. See also Phillips (1962).

Herman, F., Kuglin, C. D., Cuff, K. F., and Kortum, R. L. (1963). *Phys. Rev. Letters.* **11**, 541.

Herman, F., Kortum, R. L., Kuglin, C. D., and Short, R. A. (1966). *Proc. Intern. Conf. Phys. Semicond., Kyoto, 1966.* To be published.

Kane, E. O., (1966). *Phys. Rev.* **146**, 558.

Kasper, J. S., and Richards, S. M. (1964). *Acta Cryst.* **17**, 752.
Kimball, G. E. (1935). *J. Chem. Phys.* **3**, 560.
Kleinman, L. (1963). *Phys. Rev.* **130**, 2283.
Kleinman, L., and Phillips, J. C. (1960). *Phys. Rev.* **118**, 1153.
Kohn, W., and Sham, L. J. (1965). *Phys. Rev.* **140**, A1133.
Lin, P. J., and Phillips, J. C. (1965). *Advan. Phys.* **14**, 257.
Lindgren, I. (1965a). *Phys. Letters* **19**, 382.
Lindgren, I. (1965b). *Arkiv Fysik* **31**, 59.
MacFarlane, G. G., McLean, T. P., Quarrington, J. E., and Roberts, V. (1958). *Proc. Phys. Soc.* (*London*) **71**, 863.
Musgrave, M. J. P. (1964). *Proc. Phys. Soc.* (*London*) **84**, 585.
Paul, W., and Brooks, H. (1963). *Progr. Semicond.* **7**, 135.
Philipp, H. R., and Ehrenreich, H. (1963). *Phys. Rev.* **129**, 1550.
Philipp, H. R., and Taft, E. A. (1959). *Phys. Rev.* **113**, 1002.
Phillips, J. C. (1962). *Phys. Rev.* **125**, 1931.
Phillips, J. C. (1964). *Phys. Rev.* **113**, A452.
Phillips, J. C. (1966). *Solid State Phys.* **18**, 55.
Phillips, J. C., and Seraphin, B. O. (1965). *Phys. Rev. Letters* **15**, 107.
Potter, R. F. (1966). *Proc. Intern. Conf. Phys. Semicond., Kyoto, 1966.* To be published.
Saslow, W., Bergstresser, T. K., and Cohen, M. L. (1966). *Phys. Rev. Letters* **16**, 354.
Seraphin, B. O. (1964). *Proc. Intern. Conf. Phys. Semicond., Paris, 1964,* pp. 165–170. Dunod, Paris.
Seraphin, B. O. (1965). *Phys. Rev.* **140**, A1716.
Seraphin, B. O., and Bottka, N. (1965a). *Phys. Rev.* **139**, A560.
Seraphin, B. O., and Bottka, N. (1965b). *Phys. Rev. Letters* **15**, 104.
Seraphin, B. O., Hess, R. B., and Bottka, N. (1965). *J. Appl. Phys.* **36**, 2242.
Shaklee, K. L., Pollak, F. H., and Cardona, M. (1965). *Phys. Rev. Letters* **15**, 883.
Shaklee, K. L., Cardona, M., and Pollak, F. H. (1966). *Phys. Rev. Letters* **16**, 48.
Slater, J. C. (1951). *Phys. Rev.* **81**, 385.
Slykhouse, T. E., and Drickamer, H. G. (1958). *J. Phys. Chem. Solids* **7**, 210.
Sobolev, V. V. (1965). *Soviet Phys. Solid State* (*English Transl.*) **6**, 2488.
Spicer, W. E., and Simon, R. E. (1962). *Phys. Rev. Letters* **9**, 385.
Tauc, J., and Abraham, A. (1961). *J. Phys. Chem. Solids* **20**, 190.
Wahl, A. C. (1966). *Science* **151**, 961.
Zallen, R. (1964). Gordon McKay Laboratory of Applied Science, Harvard University, Tech. Rept. HP–12, unpublished.
Zallen, R. (1966). *Phys. Rev.* To be published.

Note Added in Proof

Ghosh (1966a) has recently remeasured the electroreflectivity spectrum of germanium using the electrolytic technique. In addition to peaks at 2.12 and 2.32 eV which he attributes to the $\Lambda_1-\Lambda_3$ doublet, Ghosh also observes structure at 2.05 and 2.24 eV which he attributes to the $L_1-L_{3'}$ doublet. The center of gravity of the 2.05, 2.24 eV doublet is 2.15 eV, which is in excellent agreement with our estimate, 2.1 ± 0.1 eV. Ghosh also observes structure between 2.6 and 2.9 eV which is not well resolved but otherwise quite definite. From our point of view, this last observation is very encouraging, since 2.6

to 2.9 eV is just the spectral range where we believe the controversial $\Gamma_{15}-\Gamma_{25'}$ transition lies. Our best estimate for the center of gravity of the spin-orbit split $\Gamma_{15}-\Gamma_{25'}$ multiplet is 2.8 eV (cf. Section IV,C). It would be premature, of course, to suggest that Ghosh has actually confirmed our prediction that $\Gamma_{15}-\Gamma_{25'}$ is about 2.8 eV. Ghosh has observed two peaks at 5.35 and 5.52 eV which may correspond to members of the spin-orbit split $L_3-L_{3'}$ multiplet, whose center of gravity we estimate to be about 5.4 eV (cf. Table 1). Ghosh (1966b) has also remeasured the electroreflectivity spectrum of silicon using the electrolytic technique, but his experimental curve falls just short of the 2.7 to 2.8 eV region where we believe the silicon $\Gamma_{15}-\Gamma_{25'}$ transition lies.

The Materials Game—An APW Analysis of the Lead Salts

GEORGE W. PRATT, Jr.

MATERIALS THEORY GROUP, DEPARTMENT OF ELECTRICAL ENGINEERING
MASSACHUSETTS INSTITUTE OF TECHNOLOGY
CAMBRIDGE, MASSACHUSETTS

I. Introduction

It was roughly thirty years ago that the essentials of energy band theory were worked out. However, only in recent years has computer technology and the preparation of single crystal materials of controlled composition advanced to the point that can now match the imagination of the band theorist. Indeed, even though refinements in technique, investigation of self-consistency and correlation effects are still receiving considerable attention, one can now regard an energy band analysis as an incisive tool to be used in understanding the electrical, optical, and magnetic properties of a material or family of materials. Of all the various approaches suggested to the energy band problem, only two seem to have survived. First, there is the augmented plane wave or APW method devised by Slater (1937) and carefully investigated and applied by many of his students. Secondly, there is the orthogonalized plane wave or OPW method developed by Herring (1950) and more recently in several works by Kleinman and Phillips (1959). Both methods have their advantages and difficulties. However, our purpose here is to focus, not on the details of band calculation, but rather on the capabilities of band theory in materials research. Thus we will play the "materials game" which consists of the following four parts.

A. Select a material or family of materials with exciting physical and electronic properties.

B. Carry through an APW analysis and determine the Bloch functions and energies throughout the Brillouin zone.

C. Apply the theoretical model found to the entire gamut of physical properties.

D. Try to use the deduced model to predict new physical effects.

II. "Materials Game"

A. Selection of a family of materials

The choice of the lead salts for a detailed energy band analysis is based on the remarkable physical properties of these materials. PbTe has for many years been among the most efficient of thermoelectric materials and it sparked the hope of direct, practical conversion of heat into electric power or of electronic cooling. One measures in these lead salts some of the highest carrier mobilities of any known materials. The static dielectric constants are very large with the value for PbTe being reported from 400 to several thousand. The lead salts have long been important as infrared detectors and recently they have been operated as lasers both as semiconductor diodes and by direct optical pumping. Finally, it is believed that under some circumstances PbTe may have a superconducting phase. Clearly this family of materials must be regarded as an interesting challenge to the energy band method.

B. The energy band determination

Relativistic Effects on the Band Structure. We consider here the question of what dynamical interactions are to be included in the one-electron Hamiltonian from which the Bloch functions $\psi_n(k, r)$ and band energies $\varepsilon_n(k)$ are determined. This is a straightforward question in so far as we can use an energy gap as a yardstick of importance. Any interactions comparable to ε_g must, of course, be retained and including those small in relation to ε_g will very likely be of no physical interest. It is a well-known fact that spin-orbit effects in solids can be very important if the atomic number is large. In the case of Ge with atomic number 32, the spin-orbit splitting of the valence band at $k = 0$ is 0.30 eV which is to be compared with the direct gap of 0.89 eV. Since this interaction is a strongly increasing function of atomic number, it is immediately obvious that spin-orbit effects will be absolutely essential to the description of the lead salts since $z_{Pb} = 82$ and the energy gap in this set of materials is of the order of 0.2 eV.

Since we are dealing with an element of such a high atomic number, let us consider the derivation of the spin-orbit interaction as usually encountered in atomic or solid-state problems in a two-component scheme from the original four-component relativistic theory. The purpose is to ask if the derivation gives rise to any other interactions that might be discarded in a theory aimed at explaining the spin-orbit splitting of atomic levels, but which could play an essential role in a band analysis. As will be explained below, it was originally found by Johnson *et al.* (1963) during the investigation of PbTe that the long known but universally overlooked mass-velocity and Darwin corrections to the energy were of enormous importance.

The mass-velocity correction can be discussed from the following simple point-of-view. Consider an electron associated with an atom in some state of fixed energy ε which we will write simply as

$$\varepsilon = \frac{p^2}{2m} - \frac{ze^2}{r} + V_{el}(r). \tag{1}$$

In order for the energy ε of the electron to remain constant when it is near the nucleus the kinetic energy must become large enough to balance the singular nuclear attraction ze^2/r which completely dominates the potential due to other electrons $V_{el}(r)$. We can define a "relativistic region" about a nucleus by a radius R_0 such that

$$\frac{ze^2}{R_0} = m_0 c^2, \tag{2}$$

which for Pb turns out to be approximately $R_0 = 10^{-12}$ cm. It is an interesting fact that an electron spending only a small fraction of its time inside this relativistic region suffers a substantial change in energy. However, only those Bloch functions with some *s*-like character will have a significant charge density at such small distances from a nuclear site. Furthermore, the *s*-character of an energy band depends on the location in *k*-space, e.g., a band could have pure *s*-character at one symmetry point, but lose it completely at another. Therefore, the relativistic corrections are *k*-dependent and will contribute not only to the value of the band separations but to the effective masses as well. Let ε be written near the nucleus as

$$\varepsilon = \frac{m_0 c^2}{[1 - (v^2/c^2)]^{1/2}} - \frac{ze^2}{r}, \tag{3}$$

expanding the square root and using the relativistic relation between momentum and velocity one finds

$$\varepsilon = m_0 c^2 - \frac{ze^2}{r} + \frac{p^2}{2m} - \frac{1}{8} m_0 c^2 (p^4/m_0 c) + \cdots. \tag{4}$$

The final form of the one-electron Hamiltonian obtained from the Dirac equation by two successive applications of the Foldy-Wouthuysen transformation is in atomic units

$$\mathcal{H} = -\nabla^2 + V - (\tfrac{1}{4}\alpha^2)p^4 + \tfrac{1}{8}\alpha^2\nabla^2 + \tfrac{1}{4}\alpha^2\boldsymbol{\sigma}\cdot[\nabla V x p]. \tag{5}$$

An excellent account of the mass-velocity and Darwin interactions will be found in Bethe and Salpeter (1957) and a discussion of the derivation of Eq. (5) for a many-electron system is given by Pratt (1963).

The relativistic corrections were included in the band analysis of the lead salts by first finding the Bloch functions in terms of APW's and the corresponding energies for the nonrelativistic Hamiltonian $\mathcal{H}_0 = -\nabla^2 + V$. Then the basis functions for the double group states were constructed from these states and the matrix elements of the full relativistic Hamiltonian calculated and this matrix diagonalized. A detailed discussion is given by Conklin $et\ al.$ (1965). Both the valence band maximum and conduction band minimum occurs at the π/a (111) or $k = L$ edge of the Brillouin zone. In Figure 1 the

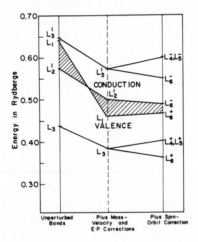

FIG. 1.   Energy band results at the (111) zone edge for PbTe.

results at $k = L$ are shown for $\mathcal{H}_0$, then $\mathcal{H}_0$ plus the mass-velocity and Darwin corrections, and finally including spin-orbit coupling. Note how the L_1 band has a major change in energy due to the mass-velocity and Darwin terms while the L_2^- band is less affected and the $L_3^\pm$ bands still less. This is due to the fact that only the L_1 band has s-like symmetry about the Pb sites, while the L_2^- is s-like only at the Te sites and the $L_3^\pm$ have no s-character at all.

It is quite clear that agreement of the band structure with experiment would be hopeless if the relativistic corrections were ignored. Since the discovery of their marked effect in PbTe they have been included in the band investigations of several other cases. Herman *et al.* (1963) have estimated their importance in several families of materials and Loucks (1965) has set up the energy band problem on a four-component basis, essentially solving the Dirac equation in a solid.

C. COMPARISON WITH EXPERIMENT

The only ambiguous feature of the APW method is the choice of sphere radii surrounding the constituent atoms and the value of the constant potential in the region between the spheres. In fact by varying the constant potential it is possible to make considerable changes in the energy gap, even reducing it to zero. Only the lowest conduction band at L of PbTe exhibited a strong sensitivity and the constant potential was determined by trial and error in order to fit the gap. This represents the only use of experimental information in an otherwise *ab initio* investigation. A detailed presentation of the APW results is given by Conklin *et al.* (1965) and Rabii (1966). Not only does one obtain a semiconductor, but the energy gap occurs at the correct place in k-space, i.e., $k = L$ as dictated by experiment. However, band theory can give a great deal more information than this. Applying $\mathbf{k}\cdot\mathbf{p}$ perturbation theory Kane (1956) and Roth (1960) yields the effective mass tensors and g-factor tensors for the various bands. This perturbation scheme was used on PbTe by Pratt and Ferreira (1964) and by Rabii (1966) for PbSe and PbS and the results are shown in Table 1.

TABLE 1

A COMPARISON BETWEEN THEORY AND EXPERIMENT FOR THE LEAD SALTS[a]

	m_t		m_e		g_{11}		
PbTe {	0.031	(0.024)	0.238	(0.24)	−29.16	(∼ −47.0)	Conduction
	0.034	(0.022)	0.426	(0.31)	31.36	(∼ +47.0)	Valence
	↑	↑					
	theory	experimental					
	↓	↓					
PbSe {	0.064	(0.040)	0.081	(0.070)	−11.57	(∼ +37.0)	Conduction
	0.068	(0.034)	0.095	(0.068)	21.06	(∼ +37.0)	Valence
PbS {	0.150	(0.080)	0.183	(0.105)	−5.20	−11.5	Conduction
	0.203	(0.075)	0.288	(0.105)	6.82	7.0	Valence

[a] The experimental values are given in parentheses beside the corresponding results.

In addition, since the $\mathbf{k}\cdot\mathbf{p}$ results are based on interband momentum matrix elements, one can predict the oscillator strength and relative polarization of the interband optical transitions. This will be applied below to the properties of Pb salt lasers.

One must view these results with some satisfaction. Although the effective masses tend to be too heavy and the g-factors too small, these numerical results come from a very sensitive calculation and there is certainly good overall agreement with experiment. There is another side to this coin. Let us imagine that theoretical considerations indicate that some material should have interesting electronic or optical properties. In addition let this be a material for which there are no suitable single crystals available. Then instead of being forced to develop the preparation techniques and embark on an experimental program, a band analysis can be completed in a matter of weeks and at very small expense that will be able to predict with a very reasonable degree of accuracy the results of such measurements.

These numerical values for the masses and g-factors obtained from the APW work on the Pb salts represent the present day "state of the art." Lin and Kleinman (1966) have obtained very similar results using the OPW scheme. It is very likely that the major source of disagreement with experiment lies in the non-self-consistent crystal potential and probably not in more esoteric areas such as correlation corrections.

One can go still further in relating the band results to experiment. A determination of the deformation potential tensors for the bands at various points in k-space will suffice to describe the effect of isotropic or uniaxial applied stress on the band energies. Furthermore, one can calculate all those transport properties which are dominated by acoustic rather than optical phonon processes. Thus the piezoresistance, low-temperature mobility, etc., can be evaluated theoretically. The deformation potentials for PbTe were found by Ferreira (1965) along the lines of the theory of Picus and Bir (1959). Rabii (1966) applied the same computer programs to PbSe and PbS. Once again agreement with experiment was excellent, usually lying within the experimental uncertainty.

D. SPECULATIONS ON NEW PHYSICAL EFFECTS

This final phase of the " Materials Game " is perhaps the most interesting. Our speculations will be confined to two areas; stress effects on Pb salt lasers and a Jahn-Teller effect for many valley semiconductors.

Shortly after Ferreira had completed his deformation potential work, PbTe and PbSe diodes were operated as lasers. This suggested the possibility of applying uniaxial or hydrostatic stress and studying the change of frequency and polarization. The use of hydrostatic pressure had already been used on GaAs diode lasers by Feinleib et al. (1963) and uniaxial stress by Meyerhofer and Braunstein (1963). It was known, furthermore, that the energy gap decreased in the Pb salts under hydrostatic pressure, Paul (1961). Besson et al. (1965) have continuously tuned a PbSe diode from 8.5 microns to over 20 microns which is certainly an important technical achievement. Pratt and

Ripper (1965) studied the effect of hydrostatic and uniaxial stress on the lasers radiation. Since the output follows changes in the energy gap, one can use the laser to make a very precise check on the deformation potentials. Consider the conduction and valence bands at L. They are found to be

$$|v\rangle = 0.943L_6^+(L_1^+) + (0.228/\sqrt{2})\{-iL_{31}^+ + L_{32}^+\}$$

and   (6)

$$|c\rangle = 0.807L_6^-(L_2^-) - (0.568/\sqrt{2})\{L_{32}^- + iL_{31}^-\}.$$

Thus the valence bandwave function at L has L_6^+ symmetry and due to spin-orbit mixing, it derives partially from the L_1^+ level and partially from the L_3^+ level. The change of the valence band per unit strain ε in the (100) direction is given by

$$\langle v|H_{\text{strain}}(100)|v\rangle = (.943)^2\langle L_1^+|100|L_1^+\rangle + \frac{(.228)^2}{2}[\langle L_{31}^+|100|L_{31}^+\rangle$$

$$+ \langle L_{32}^+|100|L_{32}^+\rangle] + \sqrt{2}(.943)(.228)\langle L_1^+|100|L_{32}^+\rangle. \quad (7)$$

The matrix elements of the (100) strain Hamiltonian are given by Ferreira (1965) as -5.444, -4.449, $+1.131$, and -7.191 in the order they occur in the right-hand side. The matrix element $\langle L_1^+|100|L_{31}^+\rangle$ is identically zero since these states belong to different representations of the group of the *strained* crystal. Carrying through the evaluation of this expression one finds the valence band changes by -7.12 eV per unit strain. A similar calculation for the conduction band shows that it changes by $+1.28$ eV per unit strain and, consequently, the gap changes by 8.40 eV per unit (100) strain.* Obviously, a great deal can be learned concerning the deformation potential tensors for the various bands and about the effect of spin-orbit mixing of the bands by studying uniaxial pressure tuning and the first work of this type has been done by Calawa *et al.* (1965).

The above remarks assume only that the laser output follows changes in the energy gap regardless of the exact nature of the optical transitions involved. If they are band-to-band transitions, it is possible to use the momentum matrix elements required for the $\mathbf{k} \cdot \mathbf{p}$ study to predict the effect of strain on the polarization of the laser output. This is described by Pratt and Ripper (1965) and may prove to be an important technique for investigating the basic laser mechanism.

In addition to the effects of static stress, very interesting possibilities exist in the application of time-dependent stress via sound waves. A compressional

---

* This result differs from that given in Pratt and Ripper (1965) where a numerical error was discovered. A corrected version of those results and an extension to PbSe, PbS, and SnTe will be published shortly.

wave will modulate the index of refraction at the sound frequency ω_s. Since the frequency of the cavity modes of a small chip of semiconductor with two cleaved and parallel faces depends on the refractive index, the mode frequency will be modulated as well. Therefore, we get direct frequency modulation of the laser. Solving Maxwell's equations for this case shows that the modulation index is proportional to (ω_0/ω_s) $(\delta\varepsilon/\varepsilon)$ where ω_0 is the frequency of the un-modulated laser and $\delta\varepsilon/\varepsilon$ is the fractional change in dielectric constant due to the sound waves. Since ω_0/ω_s is of the order of 10^8, only a very small change in ε is required to achieve a modulation index in excess of unity. As a result, it should be possible to divert a considerable amount of energy into the frequency modulation side bands. Work is now underway in this laboratory on this project.

As a final topic let us consider the possibility of a spontaneous Jahn-Teller distortion in a multivalley semiconductor. The usual application of the Jahn-Teller effect is to a paramagnetic salt in which the paramagnetic ion has an orbitally degenerate ground state in the undistorted crystal. For example, the Cu^{++} ion in $CuSO_4 \cdot 5\ H_2O$ has a doubly degenerate ground state of Γ_{12} symmetry in the cubic configuration. This crystal suffers a spontaneous tetragonal distortion which splits the ground state. This splitting is linearly dependent on the strain ε while the elastic energy is a quadratic function of the strain. Writing the total energy as

$$E = \tfrac{1}{2}K\varepsilon^2 - A\varepsilon \tag{8}$$

leads to a value of $\varepsilon = A/K$ for the minimum energy. According to standard first-order perturbation theory the electronic energy in a solid will vary linearly with strain for small ε and again the elastic energy will go as ε^2. Therefore, we suggest that exactly the same mechanism for spontaneous distortion should prevail in a multivalley semiconductor.

Keyes (1961) has already pointed out that the lattice constant c should be a function of carrier concentration N. Thus he writes the total energy E as

$$E = (9/2)B(\delta c/c)^2 + N D_{iso}(\delta c/c). \tag{9}$$

Here B is the bulk modulus and the first term is the elastic energy. The second term is the electronic energy. D_{iso} is the isotropic deformation potential for the band occupied by the N carriers. Keyes predicts the lattice constant behavior for N-type Ge to be

$$\delta c/c = 1.4 \times 10^{-24} N. \tag{10}$$

Therefore, one would require N to be of the order of 10^{20} to get a measurable effect. For p-type PbTe the same calculation gives

$$\delta c/c = 1.42 + 10^{-23} N, \tag{11}$$

an order of magnitude larger. The effect has been observed in n-type Ge by Bruner and Keyes (1961) and Hall (1965) has measured the change with doping of the third-order elastic constants.

The proposed Jahn-Teller effect thus goes one step beyond the Keyes proposal and suggests that the lattice constant will not vary isotropically with carrier concentration. It will be recalled that the mechanism responsible for piezoresistance in a multivalley semiconductor involves a splitting in energy of these valleys by an applied strain followed by a redistribution of carriers among the valleys. This Jahn-Teller effect suggests that this splitting and redistribution occurs spontaneously. The Keyes effect mentioned above is clearly only observable in highly doped materials and the same would be true of this Jahn-Teller distortion.

III. Summary

We have attempted to show in this paper how energy band theory has become an instrument in materials research. In the first place, it provides a theoretical model which can be used to interpret and unify a wide variety of experimental results. Secondly, the calculated effective masses, g-factors, and deformation potentials can be expected to be in reasonable qualitative agreement with experiment. Finally, one can make at least educated guesses as to how a material might behave under new circumstances. In this vein we have speculated about a possible frequency modulation of a semiconductor laser by sound waves and a Jahn-Teller effect in a multivalley material.

There certainly are theoretical frontiers remaining in band theory such as self-consistency, correlation, and electron-phonon effects. However, the field has matured and is now bearing fruit in many areas. This harvest would never have been realized at this time had it not been for the enormous contribution of Professor John C. Slater. Since roughly 1930, he has mounted a sustained effort that has almost singlehandedly carried energy band theory to its present level of success.

REFERENCES

Besson, J. M., Butler, J. F., Calawa, A. R., Paul, W., and Rediker, R. H. (1965). *Appl. Phys. Letters*, Oct. 15.
Bethe, H. A., and Salpeter, E. E. (1957). "Quantum Mechanics of One- and Two-Electron Atoms." Academic Press, New York.
Bruner, L. J., and Keyes, R. W. (1961). *Phys. Rev. Letters* **7**, 55.
Calawa, A. R., Butler, J. F., and Rediker, R. H. (1965). *Bull. Am. Phys. Soc.* **10**, 84.
Conklin, Jr., J. B., Johnson, L. E., and Pratt, Jr., G. W. (1965). *Phys. Rev.* **137**, A1282.
Feinleib, J., Groves, S., Paul, W., and Zallen, R. (1963), *Phys. Rev.* **131**, 2070.
Ferreira, L. G. (1965). *Phys. Rev.* **137**, A1601.
Hall, J. J. (1965). *Phys. Rev.* **137**, A960.

Herman, F., Kuglin, C. D., Cuff, K. F., and Kortum, R. L. (1963). *Phys. Rev. Letters* 11, 541.
Herring, C. (1940). *Phys. Rev.* 57, 1169.
Johnson, L. E., Conklin, Jr., J. B., and Pratt, Jr., G. W. (1963). *Phys. Rev. Letters* 11, 538.
Kane, E. O. (1956). *J. Chem. Phys. Solids* 1, 83.
Keyes, R. W. (1961). *IBM J. Res. Develop* 5, 266.
Kleinman, L., and Phillips, J. C. (1959). *Phys. Rev.* 116, 880.
Lin, P. J., and Kleinman, L. (1966). *Phys. Rev.*, 142, 478.
Loucks, T. L. (1965). *Phys. Rev.* 139, A1333.
Meyerhofer, D., and Braunstein, R. (1963). *Phys. Letters* 3, 171.
Paul, W. (1961). *J. Appl. Phys. Suppl.* 32, 2082.
Picus, G. E., and Bir, G. L. (1959). *Soviet Phys.-Solid-State* 1, 1502.
Pratt, Jr., G. W. (1963). *Rev. Mod. Phys.* 35, 502.
Pratt, Jr., G. W., and Ferreira, L. G. (1964). *Proc. Intern. Conf. Phys. Semicond.*
Pratt, Jr., G. W., and Ripper, J. E. (1965). *J. Appl. Phys.* 36, 1525.
Rabii, S. (1966). Ph.D. Thesis, M.I.T., unpublished.
Roth, L. M. (1960). *Phys. Rev.* 118, 1534.
Slater, J. C. (1937). *Phys. Rev.* 51, 846.

Quantum A Go Go

EARL CALLEN*

U.S. NAVAL ORDNANCE LABORATORY

WHITE OAK, SILVER SPRING, MARYLAND

Exploiting a suggestion by Aigrain (*1*), Bowers performed the following experiment: a very pure sample of sodium at liquid helium temperatures formed the core of a transformer, which was placed in a dc magnetic field. When a current in the primary was interrupted, eddy current decay in the sample induced a voltage in the secondary, which was displayed on an oscilloscope. Superimposed on the exponential was the oscillation predicted by Aigrain (*1*) and baptized by him, the "helicon." Bowers *et al.* (*2*) and Cotti *et al.* (*3*) pursued the oscillation. Helicons ("magnetoplasma oscillations" of plasma physics, "whistlers" of upper atmosphere physics) became a fashionable source of *Physical Review Letters* (*2–10*) and even a useful tool for the study of solids (*11–14*).

At first their physics was simple: From Maxwell's equations,

$$\omega^2 = \frac{c^2 q^2}{\mu(\omega, q)\, \varepsilon(\omega, q)}. \tag{1}$$

Consider first a nonmagnetic metal and ignore the small electronic susceptibility in the dc magnetic field, $H_0 \hat{z}$. Then $\mu(\omega, q) = 1$ and we desire the transverse components $\varepsilon^{\pm}(\omega, q)$ of the dielectric tensor. A transverse perturbation traveling in the $\hat{z}$ direction,

$$\mathbf{E}^{\pm} = E_0(\hat{x} \pm i\hat{y})e^{i(qz - \omega t)}, \tag{2}$$

induces a response of the same form:

$$\mathbf{P}^{\pm} = \left(\frac{\varepsilon^{\pm} - 1}{4\pi}\right)\mathbf{E}^{\pm} = -ne\mathbf{R}^{\pm}, \tag{3}$$

where $\mathbf{R}^{\pm}$ is a displacement wave. From Newton's laws, including the Lorentz force, one finds

$$\varepsilon^{\pm} = 1 - \frac{\omega_p^2}{\omega(\omega \pm \omega_c)}. \tag{4}$$

* *Present address:* Department of Physics, Faculty of Engineering Sciences, Osaka University, Toyonaka, Japan.

Right-hand circularly polarized light is reflected ($\varepsilon^+ < 0$) but for left-hand polarization there are two transmission bands ($\varepsilon^- > 0$ for $\omega < \omega_c$; $\omega > \omega_p$). Ignoring unity in Eq. (4), and for frequencies well below ω_c substitution of $\varepsilon^-(\omega, q)$ into Eq. (1) gives the quadratic helion dispersion relation (2,11,12,15,16)

$$\omega = \frac{c^2 \omega_c}{\omega_p^2} q^2. \tag{5}$$

At metallic densities the plasma frequency $\omega_p \cong 10^{16}$ sec^{-1} and in a field of 2×10^4 gauss the cyclotron frequency $\omega_c \cong 3.5 \times 10^{11}$ sec^{-1}. Sixty-cycle light then has a wavelength of approximately $\frac{1}{2}$ cm and a velocity of approximately 35 cm/sec in the metal.

Coupling of helicons and phonons is large only where their spectra cross (7,8):

$$\omega_x = \frac{v_s^2 \, \omega_p^2}{c^2 \, \omega_c}. \tag{6}$$

By knowledgable selection of a particular sound mode propagating in a special crystallographic direction in potassium with unusually low velocity v_s, Grimes and Buchsbaum (9) were able to observe this crossing.

Equation (4) gives only the real part of the complex dielectric function

$$\varepsilon^{\pm} = \varepsilon_1^{\pm} + i\varepsilon_2^{\pm}. \tag{7}$$

There is also an imaginary term, known in the context of magnetoacoustic absorption as the " Kjeldaas edge " (17,18), and in helicon lore as " doppler-shifted cyclotron resonance absorption " (4,15,19,20). An electron on the Fermi surface with velocity component $\pm v$ along the field direction experiences a doppler-shifted frequency. When this frequency coincides with ω_0 there is cyclotron excitation of the electron, and hence absorption of helicons within the cone

$$\omega = \omega_c \pm v_F q. \tag{8}$$

Stern (4) proposed that onset of this absorption be used to study Fermi surface topology.

The quantum theory of the dielectric tensor (21,22) differs importantly from the above. Helicon absorption occurs principally through electronic excitation between adjacent Landau levels, with the absorbing electron emerging from the Fermi sea. Thus $\varepsilon_2^-(\omega, q)$ is highly structured, with many shoulders and windows. The Kramers-Kronig relation shows that at each discontinuity in $\varepsilon_2^-(\omega, q)$ there is a logarithmic singularity in $\varepsilon_1^-(\omega, q)$ which greatly enriches the dispersion relation (10). Without displaying the complicated dielectric function we can none the less understand some of its important features. An electron on the nth Landau level, with initial $\hat{z}$ component of momentum $\hbar k_i$, has energy

$$E_n = \frac{\hbar^2 k_i^2}{2m} + \left(n + \frac{1}{2}\right)\hbar\omega_c. \tag{9}$$

In absorption of helicon energy $\hbar\omega$ and momentum $\hbar q$ the electron is excited to the $(n + 1)$st level. Conserving energy and momentum,

$$\omega = \omega_c + \frac{\hbar}{m}\left(k_i q + \frac{q^2}{2}\right), \tag{10}$$

but k_i and q are restricted by Pauli exclusion. To lie within the Fermi sphere on the nth Landau cylinder,

$$|k_i(n)| \leq [k_F^2 - (n + \tfrac{1}{2})k_c^2]^{1/2} \tag{11}$$

with

$$k_c \equiv (2m\omega_c/\hbar)^{1/2} \tag{12}$$

Transitions among low-lying levels (those in which $(n + \tfrac{1}{2})k_c^2 \ll k_F^2$) with $k_i \cong -k_F$ and $q \ll k_F$ produce the lower Kjeldaas edge of Eq. (8) and numerous fine absorption filaments and slits adjacent to it. This can be seen by expansion of Eq. (11) and substitution into Eq. (10). These slits should produce sharp oscillations in helicon attenuation (5,6), and absorption of transverse sound (23,24). They are quite similar in structure to the filaments along the Kjeldaas edge in $\varepsilon_2^z(\omega, q)$ due to $\Delta n = 0$ transitions, which are expected to cause "giant quantum oscillations" in longitudinal sound absorption (25). Small q transitions among inner levels, in which the electron has initial wave number $k_i \cong +k_F$, produce the upper Kjeldaas edge. There are also large momentum-transfer transitions among low-lying levels, those in which $k_i \cong -k_F$ and the electron traverses almost the entire Fermi diameter. These transitions produce absorption bands at $q \cong 2k_F$ with windows between of width $2\omega_c/v_F$.

Absorption by electrons on levels near the highest level beneath the Fermi surface display the usual $1/H$ oscillations. In Eq. (11) the highest level is

$$(n_{\max} + \tfrac{1}{2})k_c^2 \equiv k_F^2. \tag{13}$$

Depending upon the field strength the range of momentum on this highest inscribed cylinder is between

$$|k(n_{\max})| \leq k_c/\sqrt{2} \quad \text{and} \quad |k(n_{\max})| \leq k_c. \tag{14}$$

Transitions among high-lying levels produce absorption bands near $q \cong k_c$ separated by windows of the same width (10).

In summary, $\varepsilon_2^-(\omega, q)$ contains multitudes of fine streaks near $q = \omega_c/v_F \cong$ 10^4 cm^{-1}, broad bands and windows near $q = k_c \cong 10^6$ cm^{-1}, and absorption bands near $q = 2k_F \cong 10^8$ cm^{-1} separated by windows of width $2\omega_c/v_F \cong 10^4$ cm^{-1}.

The quantum mechanical $\varepsilon_2^-(\omega, q)$ is computed by equating the power absorbed from the wave to the rate of energy absorption by electrons in Landau states, calculated by the golden rule. From $\varepsilon_2^-(\omega, q)$ the real part of the dielectric function is found by the Kramers-Kronig relation. In contrast to the semiclassical picture of Eq. (8) there are now many windows within the doppler-shifted absorption cone. In contrast to Eq. (4) and its nonlocal extension, $\varepsilon_1^-(\omega, q)$ now displays wild oscillations near discontinuities in $\varepsilon_2^-(\omega, q)$. These oscillations grossly distort the dispersion relation within the absorption cone, decorating absorption filaments and bands with epiphora of semistable modes (10). For, in Eq. (1), suppose $\varepsilon_1^-(\omega, q)$ is less than c^2q^2/ω^2 at a frequency below an absorption band edge. The positive logarithmic singularity near the edge then enforces a solution of Eq. (1).

Now consider the situation in a ferromagnetic metal. To a good approximation the permeability, from the Landau-Lifshitz equation, is

$$\mu^-(\omega, q) = 1 + \frac{\gamma \cdot 4\pi M}{\omega_m - \omega} \qquad (15)$$

with M the saturation magnetization and ω_m the uncoupled magnon frequency:

$$\omega_m = \gamma H_m + \alpha q^2 \qquad (16)$$

Stern and Callen (20) show that the solution of Eq. (1), with $\varepsilon_1^-(\omega, q)$ from Eq. (4) and $\mu^-(\omega, q)$ from Eq. (15) is greatly different from the nonmagnetic case; there is strong magnon-helicon coupling at all q because of the high conductivity. Recall that in the semiclassical treatment $\varepsilon_1^-(\omega, q) < 0$ for $\omega_c < \omega < \omega_p$. The permeability of Eq. (15) also has a negative region: $\mu^-(\omega, q) < 0$ for $\omega_m < \omega < \omega_m + \gamma 4\pi M$. Suppose $\omega_m < \omega_c < \omega_m + \gamma 4\pi M < \omega_p$. Then the product $\mu\varepsilon > 0$ in three passbands:

$$0 < \omega < \omega_m; \qquad \omega_c < \omega < \omega_m + \gamma 4\pi M; \qquad \omega_p < \omega.$$

We have now re-examined this problem (10), employing the quantum-mechanical dielectric constant. We find coupled modes within the large windows in $\varepsilon_2^-(\omega, q)$. Their frequencies extend up to microwave and their wave numbers to $q \cong k_c$ far beyond the limit where any propagation could occur classically.

We have ignored line width and losses. Line width will damp out modes close to the edges of absorption bands, and appreciable losses, of either nonmagnetic or magnetic origin, will cause even "giant quantum oscillations" to be barely perceptible. For this reason the new modes are known everywhere as "Quantum Anomalous Greatly Obliterated Giant Oscillations"

REFERENCES

1. P. Aigrain, *Proc. Internat. Conf. Semicond. Phys.*, *Prague, 1960*, p. 224. Czech. Acad. Sci., Prague, 1961.
2. R. Bowers, C. Legendy, and F. Rose, *Phys. Rev. Letters* **7**, 339 (1961).
3. P. Cotti, P. Wyder, and A. Quattropani, *Phys. Letters* **1**, 50 (1962).
4. E. A. Stern, *Phys. Rev. Letters* **10**, 91 (1963).
5. J. J. Quinn, *Phys. Letters* **7**, 235 (1963).
6. P. B. Miller, *Phys. Rev. Letters* **11**, 537 (1963).
7. D. N. Langenberg and J. Bok, *Phys. Rev. Letters* **11**, 549 (1963).
8. J. J. Quinn and S. Rodriguez, *Phys. Rev. Letters* **11**, 552 (1963).
9. C. C. Grimes and S. J. Buchsbaum, *Phys. Rev. Letters* **12**, 357 (1964).
10. A. J. Glick, E. Callen, and G. Heiche, *Phys. Letters* **20**, 574 (1966).
11. F. Rose, M. Taylor, and R. Bowers, *Phys. Rev.* **127**, 1122 (1962).
12. R. G. Chambers and B. K. Jones, *Proc. Roy. Soc. (London)* **A270**, 417 (1962).
13. M. T. Taylor, J. R. Merrill, and R. Bowers, *Phys. Rev.* **129**, 2525 (1963).
14. For an excellent summary of recent research see *Proc. Intern. Conf. Semicond. Phys. 7th* **2**, Plasma Effects in Solids," Paris (1964) (Dunod, Paris 1965).
15. R. G. Chambers, *Phil. Mag.* **1**, 459 (1956).
16. M. H. Cohen, M. J. Harrison, and W. A. Harrison, *Phys. Rev.* **117**, 937 (1960).
17. T. Kjeldaas, Jr., *Phys. Rev.* **113**, 1473 (1959).
18. A. B. Pippard, *Rept. Progr. Phys.* **23**, 252–255 (1960).
19. P. B. Miller and K. K. Haering, *Phys. Rev.* **128**, 126 (1962).
20. E. A. Stern and E. R. Callen, *Phys. Rev.* **131**, 512 (1963).
21. J. J. Quinn and S. Rodriguez, *Phys. Rev.* **128**, 2487 (1962).
22. P. S. Zyrganov and V. P. Kalashikov, *Zh. Eksperim. i. Teor. Fiz.*, **41**, 1119 (1961) [*Soviet Phys. JETP (English Transl.)* **14**, 799 (1962)].
23. D. N. Langenburg, J. J. Quinn, and S. Rodriguez, *Phys. Rev. Letters* **12**, 104 (1964).
24. S. V. Gantsevich and V. L. Gurevich, *Zh. Eksperim. i Teor. Fiz.* **45**, 587 (1963) [*Soviet Phys. JETP (English Transl.)* **18**, 403 (1964)].
25. V. L. Gurevich, V. G. Skobov, and Yu. A. Firsov, *Zh. Eksperim. i Teor. Fiz.* **40**, 786 (1961). [*Soviet Phys. JETP (English Transl.)* **13**, 552 (1961)].

On the Use of Phase Shifts for Studying Impurity Effects in Narrow Bands
With Application to the Electronic Structure of Substitutional Alloys of Transitional Metals

J. FRIEDEL,* F. GAUTIER,† A. A. GOMÈS,* and P. LENGLART‡

I. Introduction

The purpose of this paper is to review recent advances made in the study of impurity effects in narrow bands. These are assumed to be described in a tight binding (LCAO) approximation, and the use of phase shifts for describing the perturbation is systematically developed.

The bulk of the paper is specifically centered on the electronic structure of substitutional impurities in the d-bands of transitional metals, in structures with one atom per cell (i.e., practically fcc and bcc structures); it assumes a

* Physique des Solides, Faculté des Sciences, Orsay, France.
† Institut de Physique, Faculté des Sciences, Strasbourg, France.
‡ Physique des Solides, Institut d'Electronique du Nord, Lille, France.

perturbation localized on the impurity atom and concentrates on effects related to the density of states. General conditions for the validity of the perturbation or rigid band approximation can then be set up; and the exact nature of the strong deviations from it due to various resonance effects can be defined. We shall show in particular that, strictly speaking, virtual bound d levels can only occur near a band edge, and under very restricted conditions.

As stressed at the end of this paper, the phase shift method can be applied in other cases. Extensions to less-localized perturbations and to wide bands are developed. The possible use in the study of interstitial impurities, of matrices with more than one atom per cell, phonons, or spin wave problems must be mentioned.

The model used for transitional metals is that originally used by Slater (1936) to discuss their magnetism; the work described here is a direct consequence of the type of analysis of perturbation in narrow bands first made by Koster and Slater (1954). However, in complex bands deduced from degenerate atomic states such as the d-bands of transitional metals, the treatment given here allows a simpler analysis, because it brings out more clearly the symmetry of the problem. The explicit use of phase shifts is of especial interest for a general discussion on the densities of states.

Section II of this paper describes the model used, introduces the general concepts, and studies the conditions of validity of the rigid band approximation. Section III is devoted to the strong deviations from this approximation due to resonance effects. Section IV reviews some possible extensions of this type of treatment.

II. The Impurity Problem for Localized Perturbations in Narrow Bands

A. THE MODEL

Having in mind a specific problem of transitional alloys, we shall make, in the main part of this paper, a number of simplifying assumptions. These will be analyzed and extended in the last part.

1. Band Structure. The band structure for the valence electrons of a transitional metal is made of d and s overlapping bands, on which the following is assumed: (a) The s-d mixing effects are neglected, in pure metals and in alloys. (b) The d-bands are described by a tight binding method which neglects all overlap integrals except those involving the lattice potential and atomic functions centered on neighboring sites. (c) Spin orbit coupling effects are neglected. (d) The lattice structure is assumed to have one atom per cell, and the d wave functions $|i\rangle$ $(i = 1, \ldots, 5)$ are chosen so that they are basis functions of the irreducible representations Γ of the point group of the lattice. In practice, applications will be made to cubic (fcc or bcc) crystals. The Γ representations are then Γ_{12} or Γ'_{25}.

2. *The Perturbing Potential.* We study highly diluted alloys, in which each impurity atom can be considered as acting independently. These impurity atoms are assumed to be substitutional, so that the symmetry of perturbed lattice is that of the (pure) lattice point group.

In the Hartree approximation, the perturbing potential $V_p(\mathbf{r})$ is due to (a) the impurity excess charge and (b) its screening charge, mostly by d-electrons. Owing to the screening, V_p has a finite range and, owing to the high density of d states, it is often well localized on the impurity cell. We shall assume for the moment this localization to be complete. Exchange effects, such as the possible apparition of localized magnetic moments, are not considered in this paper.

B. The $\overline{T}$-matrix and the phase shift operator

From each wave function $|\varphi^{(n)}\rangle$ of the pure metal describing a one-electron state of energy E, one can define an eigenfunction of the perturbed crystal by

$$|\psi^{(n)(+)}\rangle = \overline{T}^{(+)}(E)|\varphi^{(n)}\rangle, \tag{1}$$

where $\overline{T}^{(+)}(E)$ is the scattering operator defined by

$$\overline{T}^{(+)}(E) = 1 + \frac{1}{E-\mathscr{H}_0+i\eta} V_p \overline{T}^{(+)}(E); \qquad \eta = +0. \tag{2}$$

$\mathscr{H}_0$ is the one-electron Hamiltonian of the pure metal.

All the properties of the perturbed crystal can be deduced from a knowledge of $\overline{T}^{(+)}(E)$ and especially of the following:

(a) the perturbed wave functions [see Eq. (1)].

(b) the variation of the number $Z(E)$ of states of energy $E' \leqslant E$. It is easily shown (Blandin, 1961) that it is related to the phase shift operator $\delta(E)$ by

$$Z(E) = \frac{1}{\pi} \mathrm{Tr}_E \delta \tag{3}$$

where

$$\tan \delta(E) = -\pi\delta(E - \mathscr{H}_0)V_p\overline{K}(E) \tag{4}$$

The trace in (3) is taken over all the eigenfunctions of energy E and

$$\overline{K}(E) = \overline{T}(E)(1 - \pi i \delta(E - \mathscr{H}_0)V_p\overline{T}(E))^{-1}.$$

(c) The variation of the density of states: in the low concentration limit, the change in density of states per unit energy, volume, and spin for a concentration c is given by

$$\delta n(E) = c\frac{dZ(E)}{dE}, \tag{5}$$

All these equations are quite general. The perfect screening of the impurity thus requires exactly

$$Z(E_F) = Z,\tag{6}$$

where E_F is the Fermi level.

C. THE CHOICE OF A REPRESENTATION

The solution of Eq. (2) requires the choice of a representation. In the tight binding approximation, it is natural to choose a representation based on the complete set $|i\lambda\rangle$ of atomic d functions $|i\rangle$ centered on the crystalline sites $\mathbf{R}_\lambda$. This will be called the $\{i\lambda\}$ representation. It neglects the overlap integrals of atomic functions on different sites, and is especially useful if the perturbation potential V_p is well localized on the impurity cell. In the spirit of the tight binding approximation, one can then neglect all the matrix elements $(i\lambda|V_p|j\mu)$ except those $(i0|V_p|j0)$ involving the atomic functions on the impurity site. For a substitutional impurity in a lattice with one atom per cell, V_p has the symmetry properties of the point group of the lattice. The matric elements $(i0|V_p|j0)$ then vanish except if the i and j atomic states are identical. The corresponding integral $(i0|V_p|i0) = V_p(\Gamma)$ only depends on the nature of the corresponding class Γ in the irreducible representation of the point group of the lattice. Finally,

$$(i\lambda|V_p|j\mu) = \delta_{ij}\delta_{\lambda\mu}\delta_{\lambda 0} V(\Gamma).\tag{7}$$

In the cubic (fcc or bcc) lattices, there are only two values of $V(\Gamma)$, corresponding to $\Gamma = \Gamma_{12}$ and Γ'_{25}.

Introducing the Green functions

$$G_{ij}^{(+)}(E, \lambda\mu) = (i\lambda\left|\frac{1}{E - \mathcal{H}_0 + i\eta}\right|j\mu),\tag{8}$$

we have then from Eq. (2)

$$(i0|\bar{T}^+(E)|i0) = [1 - V(\Gamma)G_{ii}^{(+)}(E, 0, 0)]^{-1}\tag{9}$$

and the scattering operator is defined in the $\{i\lambda\}$ representation by

$$(i\lambda|\bar{T}^{(+)}(E)|j\mu) = \delta_{\lambda\mu}\delta_{\lambda 0}\frac{\delta ij}{1 - V(\Gamma_i)G_{ii}^{(+)}(E, 0, 0)}$$

$$+ (1 - \delta_{\lambda 0})\left\{(1 - \delta_{\lambda 0})\delta_{\lambda\mu}\delta_{ij} + \frac{\delta_{\mu 0}V(\Gamma_j)G_{ij}^{(+)}(E, \lambda, 0)}{1 - V(\Gamma_j)G_{ij}^{(+)}(E, 0, 0)}\right\}.\tag{10}$$

It should be stressed that the use of the $\{i\lambda\}$ representation would be strictly equivalent to that of the *Wannier representation* first developed by Koster and Slater (1954), if the narrow band considered were derived from nondegenerate atomic orbitals (Wolff, 1961; Clogston, 1962; Seeger and Staatzs 1962; Goodings and Moser, 1964). But, for narrow bands derived from degenerate atomic orbitals such as the d band of transitional metals, the use of the Wannier representation leads to much more complex equations than the $\{i\lambda\}$ representation. The physical reason is that each d subband does not, in general, possess, as a whole, the symmetry properties of the lattice, which therefore do not come out clearly from the equations. As a result, no simplification comparable to Eq. (7) occurs in the Wannier representation: the matrix elements of V_p between Wannier functions of different d subbands are usually different from zero; the Wannier functions of one subband are not well localized on an atomic cell, so that important matrix elements of V_p can involve Wannier functions centered on other sites than the impurity one, even when V_p is itself well localized on the impurity site (Gautier and Lenglart, 1965).

D. Main results in the $\{i\lambda\}$ representation

From the knowledge of $\bar{T}^{(+)}(E)$, Eq. (10), we can formally deduce the wave functions and the displaced charge. The corresponding changes in density of states will be discussed in full.

1. Wave Functions. The perturbed function $|\psi^{(n)(+)}(k)\rangle$ related by Eq. (1) to the Bloch function $|\varphi^{(n)}(k)\rangle$ of the nth subband with wave vector $\mathbf{k}$ is given by:

$$(i\lambda|\psi^{(n)(+)}(\mathbf{k})) = \sum_j \langle j|\varphi^{(n)}(\mathbf{k})\rangle \left[\delta_{ij} e^{ikR_\lambda} + \frac{V(\Gamma_j)G_{ij}^{(+)}(E,\lambda,0)}{1 - V(\Gamma_j)G_{ij}^{(+)}(E,0,0)} \right] \quad (11)$$

Note that there is a mixing of the various i components of the wave functions of the pure matrix: this is because each Bloch function is itself a mixing of orbitals of various symmetries. It will be seen below that the scattering amplitude in Eq. (11) is related to the phase shifts.

2. Displaced Charge $Z(E)$. From (3), the charge $Z(E)$ is given by

$$Z(E) = \frac{1}{\pi} \sum_\Gamma p\delta(E, \Gamma), \quad (12)$$

where p is the dimension of the irreducible representation Γ. Thus, for cubic lattices, $p = 2$ for Γ_{12} and 3 for Γ'_{25}. From Eqs. (4) and (9), we then have

$$\delta(E, \Gamma_i) = \tan^{-1} \left[\frac{-\pi V(\Gamma_i) n(E, \Gamma_i)}{1 - V(\Gamma_i) F(E, \Gamma_i)} \right], \quad (13)$$

where $-\pi n(E, \Gamma_i)$ and $F(E, \Gamma_i)$ are respectively the imaginary and real parts of $G_{ii}^+(E, 0, 0)$.

From definition (8), $n(E, \Gamma_i)$ is the density of occupation of one of the $|i\rangle$ orbitals of the Γ_i class at energy E and per unit of energy, spin, and atomic volume

$$n(E, \Gamma_i) = (i|\delta(E - \mathcal{H}_0)|i). \tag{14}$$

It is given, in the Bloch representation, by

$$n(E, \Gamma_i) = \frac{\Omega}{(2\pi)^3} \sum_n \int_{S_n(E)} \frac{dS_n}{|\nabla_\mathbf{k} E_n|} |(i|\varphi^{(n)}(\mathbf{k}))|^2. \tag{15}$$

Ω is the atomic volume, and the integration is taken over the surfaces $S_n(E)$ of constant energy $E = E_n(\mathbf{k})$. The orthonormalization of the Bloch functions $\varphi^{(n)}(\mathbf{k})$ leads to the sum rules

$$\int_{-\infty}^{+\infty} n(E, \Gamma_i)\, dE = 1, \tag{16}$$

$$\sum_\Gamma p n(E, \Gamma) = n(E), \tag{17}$$

where $n(E)$ is the ordinary density of states per unit energy, spin, and atomic volume of the unperturbed matrix.

From Eq. (8), the function $F(E, \Gamma_i)$ is similarly the Hilbert transform of $n(E, \Gamma_i)$:

$$F(E, \Gamma_i) = P \int \frac{n(E', \Gamma_i)\, dE'}{E - E'} \tag{18}$$

P is the Cauchy principal part.

We can note from Eqs. (12) and (15) that completely filled or empty sub-bands do not contribute directly to the total displaced charge, i.e., to the screening, although their presence affects contribution of the partially filled subbands through their contribution to $F(E, \Gamma_i)$. They also contribute directly to the spatial variation of the displaced charge through their action on the wave functions [Eq. (11)] and eventually through the occurrence of bound states extracted from them.

III. Change in the Density of States due to Alloying

A. GENERAL CONSIDERATIONS

This important aspect of the electronic perturbation due to impurities can be fairly directly related to changes in measurable properties (e.g., electronic specific heat, paramagnetism, Knight shift). These experimental results have been extensively discussed using either a "rigid band model" which assumes that the extra electrons of the impurities fill the d band of the matrix without otherwise changing its form (Mott and Jones, 1936), or the concept of "virtual bound state," which assumes that the d states of the impurity poorly mixes with the d band of the matrix (Clogston, 1962).

In this chapter, we want to discuss the conditions of validity of the rigid band model and the nature of the strong deviations from that model that can be due to resonant effects, leading eventually to the formation of virtual bound states. We shall show how the use of the phase shift concept helps in obtaining fairly general results without having to work out numerical results on a specific model.

In the low-concentration limit, the change in the density of states due to alloying is directly related to the energy variation of the displaced charge $Z(E)$, thus of the phase shifts $\delta(E, \Gamma)$. Equation (5) gives

$$\delta n(E) = c \frac{1}{\pi} \sum_{\Gamma} p \frac{d\delta(E, \Gamma)}{dE}. \tag{19}$$

The contributions $\delta n(E, \Gamma_i)$ of the various symmetry classes Γ are therefore additive, and can be discussed separately, using Eq. (13) for computing the phase shifts $\delta(E, \Gamma)$.

We can assume $n(E, \Gamma)$ and $dn(E, \Gamma)/dE$ to be continuous in E nearly everywhere in the band, from which we obtain the following properties, which will be useful in the discussion:

P1. $F(E, \Gamma)$ and $dF(E, \Gamma)/dE$ are continuous in the energy ranges of continuity of $n(E, \Gamma)$ and $dn(E, \Gamma)/dE$, respectively.

P2. When $n(E, \Gamma)$ has a first type of discontinuity for $E = E_1$, i.e., $n(E_1 + 0) \neq n(E_1 - 0)$, $F(E, \Gamma)$ has a logarithmic infinity for $E = E_1$. The same applies for dn/dE and dF/dE.

P3. For $E \geqslant E_t$, energy at the top of the band, $F(E, \Gamma)$ is positive and decreases with increasing energy E; in the same way, for $E \leqslant E_b$, energy at the bottom of the band, $F(E, \Gamma)$ is negative and decreases with increasing energy. Also, from *P1* there is necessarily an energy E_0 for which $F(E_0, \Gamma) = 0$. Finally $F(E, \Gamma)$ has generally a relative maximum of amplitude near the band edges.

P4. When the density of states $n(E, \Gamma)$ is zero at a band edge, we have for that energy $(E = E_b$ or $E_t)$

$$\frac{d\delta(E, \Gamma)}{dE} = - \frac{\pi V(\Gamma)}{1 - V(\Gamma)F(E, \Gamma)} \frac{dn(E, \Gamma)}{dE}. \tag{20}$$

Finally, for a solution E_i of the equation

$$1 - V(\Gamma)F(E, \Gamma) = 0 \tag{21}$$

we have

$$\frac{d\delta(E_i, \Gamma)}{dE} = - \frac{dF(E_i, \Gamma)/dE}{n(E_i, \Gamma)}. \tag{22}$$

P5. Expanding Eq. (15) in powers of $E_t - E$ gives

$$n(E, \Gamma) = \sum_n |(i|\varphi^{(n)}(\mathbf{k}_{tn})\rangle|^2 n^{(n)}(E)$$

$$+ \frac{\Omega}{2(2\pi)^3} \int_{S_n(E)} \frac{dS_n}{|\nabla_\mathbf{k} E|_n} (\mathbf{k} - \mathbf{k}_{tn}) \nabla_\mathbf{k} \cdot \nabla_{\mathbf{k}_{tn}} |(i|\varphi^{(n)}(\mathbf{k})\rangle|^2 (\mathbf{k} - \mathbf{k}_{tn}). \tag{23}$$

The vectors $\mathbf{k}_{tn}$ are at the top of the band structure, and the centrosymmetry of the surfaces S_n of constant energy has been used. From a theorem by Van Hove (1953), the first term is of order $(E_t - E)^0$ or $(E_t - E)^{1/2}$, the second of order $(E_t - E)^{3/2}$. The behavior of $n(E, \Gamma)$ near a band edge therefore depends on whether the integrals $(i|\varphi^{(n)}(\mathbf{k}_{tn})\rangle$ corresponding to all the atomic orbitals $|i)$ belonging to Γ vanish or not.

For instance, in fcc nickel or cobalt, the top of the d band occurs at the X points in k-space, and the wave functions at the top of the band have only Γ'_{25} components (Fletcher, 1952). In bcc iron, the top of the band seems to be at the H points, and only Γ_{12} components occur (Abate and Asdente, 1965).

B. CONDITIONS OF VALIDITY OF THE RIGID BAND MODEL

To first order in the perturbation $V(\Gamma)$, Eq. (13) gives

$$\delta(E, \Gamma) = -\pi V(\Gamma) n(E, \Gamma) + O_2(V). \tag{24}$$

The contribution of the Γ class to the change in density of states is thus:

$$\delta n(E, \Gamma) = -V(\Gamma) \frac{dn(E, \Gamma)}{dE} + O_2(V). \tag{25}$$

The perturbed density of states $n(E, c)$ for a concentration c of impurity can thus be written

$$\sum_\Gamma p n(E - cV(\Gamma), \Gamma). \tag{26}$$

Thus, to first order in $V(\Gamma)$ the contribution of the Γ class to the density of states is thus rigidly shifted by an amount $cV(\Gamma)$, without change of form. If the $V(\Gamma)$ are equal for all the classes, the whole density of states $n(E)$ is shifted by $cV(\Gamma)$ without change in form.*

The rigid band model is thus valid in the Born (first order) *approximation*, but only *if crystalline field effects are neglected*. In cubic lattices, the two

---

* The same result can of course be deduced from the change of energy, to first order in V, of a Bloch state:

$$E^{(n)}(\mathbf{k}) = \langle \varphi^{(n)}(\mathbf{k})|V_p|\varphi^{(n)}(\mathbf{k})\rangle = \sum_t V(\Gamma)|\langle \varphi^{(n)}(\mathbf{k})|i\rangle$$

is independent of n and $\mathbf{k}$ if all the $V(\Gamma)$ are equal.

$V(\Gamma)$'s would strictly be equal if V_p had spherical symmetry. Their difference is usually small compared with the bandwidth, and this explains the fair success of the rigid band model for substitutional impurities with small Z's, thus near to the matrix in the periodic table.

We wish now to discuss possible strong *deviations* from the Born approximation required by the rigid band model. These will occur whenever either of the two following conditions is *not* fulfilled:

$$|V(\Gamma)F(E, \Gamma)| \ll 1 \qquad (27)$$

or

$$|V(\Gamma)n(E, \Gamma)| \ll 1. \qquad (28)$$

Deviations are, of course, expected for large perturbations $V(\Gamma)$; for a given perturbation, they are expected mostly in the following zones of energy: (a) outside the band (bound states), (b) within the band, near the band edges [see *P3* and and (27)], (c) near peaks of the density of states: $n(E, \Gamma)$ or $F(E, \Gamma)$ take then large values [cf. (27) and (28)].

C. The Occurrence of Bound States

When $V(\Gamma) \geqslant [F(E_t, \Gamma)]^{-1}$, the scattering amplitudes of Eq. (11) are infinite for the energy $E_s \geqslant E_t$ of a bound state, solution of

$$F(E_s, \Gamma) = 1/V(\Gamma). \qquad (29)$$

From the monotonic variation of $F(E, \Gamma)$ outside the band, there is only *one* (possibly degenerate) solution for each class Γ at a given value of $V(\Gamma)$. Thus in the cubic lattices, two degenerate Γ_{12} and three degenerate Γ'_{25} bound states are separately extracted from the d band. Similar conclusions would apply for a strong enough attractive perturbation and bound states below the band. The bound state transforming like the orbital $|i\rangle$ has an amplitude on the central cell which is easily obtained:

$$|(i|\psi_i(E_s))|^2 = -\frac{F(E_s, \Gamma)^2}{dF(E_s, \Gamma)/dE}. \qquad (30)$$

We can note that the extension of the bound states, when just extracted from a band, are very different depending on the way $n(E, \Gamma)$ varies near the band edge.

Thus, when $n(E, \Gamma) = \alpha(E_t - E)^{1/2}$, the bound state has an infinite extension when it emerges from the band. When $n(E, \Gamma) = \alpha(E_t - E)^{3/2}$, it emerges with a finite extension.

D. The Occurrence of Virtual Bound States Near a Band Edge

As for free particles, a *virtual bound state* will be defined as a positive peak produced in the density of states by the perturbation. To be a proper virtual bound state, this peak must be narrow compared with the features of the density of states of the matrix; its area must also correspond, at least roughly, to the number of bound states that could occur in the same class. In other words, $\delta(E, \Gamma)$ must vary by an amount near π over a narrow range of energy.

The possible occurrence of such virtual bound states of a given class near a band edge is shown to depend on the behavior of the corresponding density of states $n(E, \Gamma)$ near that edge. We shall show that *a repulsive perturbation can only produce a virtual bound state of a given class near the top of the band if the wave functions at the top of the band do not contain atomic orbitals of the same class.* A similar result can be obtained for attractive perturbations and the bottom of the band.

We examine the deviations from the rigid band model produced by a repulsive potential V_p near the top E_t of the d band. V_p is thus too strong for conditions (27) or (28) to apply; but we assume it is not strong enough to extract a bound state. Thus, from (29), $V(\Gamma) < F(E_t, \Gamma)^{-1}$. From P2, this requires $n(E_t - 0, \Gamma) = 0$: virtual bound states of the Γ class cannot occur near an edge with a finite corresponding density of states. From P5, the only cases to discuss are therefore those where $n(E, \Gamma) = \alpha(E_t - E)^n$, with $n = \frac{1}{2}$ or $\frac{3}{2}$. $F(E, \Gamma)$ is then finite and continuous at $E = E_t$. If it has a negative slope just below E_t, Eq. (21) has at least two solutions E_i ($i = 1$ and 2) within the band: $E_1 \leqslant E_2 < E_t$. The scattering cross section which appears in Eq. (11) has a finite maximum for $E = E_2$. We shall show however that this "resonance" condition is *not* sufficient to produce proper virtual bound states, contrary to what has been sometimes stated (Wolff, 1961; Clogston, 1962).

(a) $n(E, \Gamma) = \alpha(E_t - E)^{1/2}$ (i.e., the Bloch states at the band edge have Γ components). The phase shift $\delta(E, \Gamma)$ decreases from 0 at the band edge with decreasing energies, with an initial infinite slope [P4, cf. Fig. 1].

When $n(E, \Gamma)$ is less than its parabolic development over all the d band, it can easily be shown that $F(E, \Gamma)$ has a positive slope just below E_t (Gautier and Gomès, 1965). $\delta(E, \Gamma)$ is then always less than $\pi/2$ [Fig. 1(a)], and no resonance occurs. This general case is similar to the behavior of the "s" phase shift in the scattering of particles by a spherical potential.

If $n(E, \Gamma)$ is greater than its parabolic development, $F(E, \Gamma)$ can have a negative slope just below E_t [Fig. 1(b)]; in that case, it has necessarily a maximum within the bandwidth. Equation (21) has then at least two solutions E_1 and E_2, between which $|\delta(E, \Gamma)| > \pi/2$. However the change in density of states due to the impurity, proportional to $d\delta/dE$, decreases continuously from $+\infty$ to negative values when the energy E decreases from E_t to E; there is usually no maximum of $d\delta/dE$ in this range of energy. Figure 2 shows, as an example, the various functions of interest for a localized potential acting on a non-degenerate band in the simple cubic structure. In fact a strong peak in the density of states near E_t is generally required to produce such a

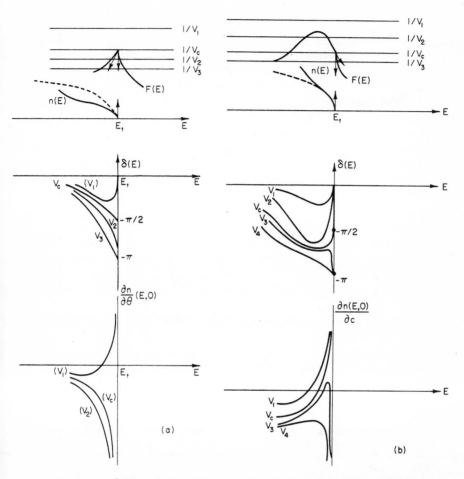

FIG. 1(a). $F(E)$, $\delta(E)$, and $\partial n(E, 0)/\partial c$ for $n(E)$ less than its parabolic development (schematic).

(b) $F(E)$, $\delta(E)$, and $\partial n(E, 0)/\partial c$ for $n(E)$ greater than its parabolic development (schematic).

maximum. The corresponding resonant state will be studied below (Section III, E); it is not a proper virtual bound state.

In conclusion, whatever the form of $F(E, \Gamma)$ near the top of the band, no virtual bound state can be produced if $n(E, \Gamma) = \alpha(E_t - E)^{1/2}$.

(b) $n(E, \Gamma) = \alpha(E_t - E)^{3/2}$ (i.e., the Bloch states at the band edge have no Γ component). From the continuity of $dn(E, \Gamma)/dE$ at the band edge and from *P2*, one deduces that $dF(E, \Gamma)/dE$ is continuous at the band edge, and therefore negative. Also, from *P4*, the phase shift has a vanishing slope at the

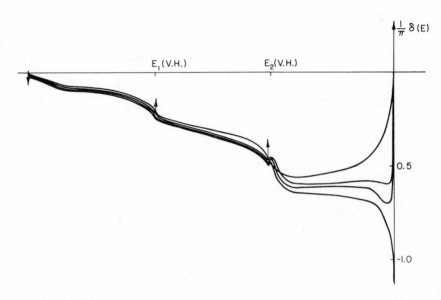

FIG. 2.   Phase shift curves for a nondegenerate band in the simple cubic structure.

band edge. It is then easily shown that a virtual bound state necessarily occurs near the band edge when the perturbation is not quite strong enough to produce the corresponding bound state. For, when $V(\Gamma) \to [F(E_t, \Gamma)]^{-1}$, the phase shift $|\delta(E, \Gamma)|$ which starts from E_t with zero slope, crosses the value $\pi/2$ and reaches values near to π in an energy range that tends toward E_t (Fig. 3). The variation is similar to that of the "p" phase shift for free electrons.

The virtual bound state produced has the following characteristics:

(i) The *top of the peak* in the density of states occurs at an energy E_c defined by $d^2\delta/dE_c^2 = 0$. It is usually distinct from the resonant energy E_2 such that $\delta = \pi/2$; but both energies tend towards E_t when $V(\Gamma) \to [F(E_t, \Gamma)]^{-1}$.

(ii) Its width is of the order of $-\pi/(d\delta/dE_2) = -\pi n/(dF/dE_2)$, and it decreases as $(E_t - E_2)^{3/2}$ when the state tends toward the edge.

(iii) The *number of supplementary states* per impurity atom, deduced from the area of the peak tends toward the number of atomic states of the Γ class when $E_2 \to E_t$.

(iv) These states are subtracted from an energy region centered around the other solution E_1 of Eq. (21). But it is usually subtracted from a large part of the band, so that there is no marked antiresonant peak in the density of states.

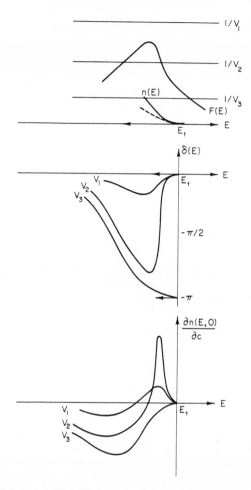

Fig. 3. $F(E)$, $\delta(E)$, and $\partial n(E, 0)/\partial c$ for a band such that $dn(E)/dE = 0$ (schematic).

E. Resonant and Antiresonant Effects Near to a Peak of Density of States

We shall now analyze briefly the possible effects of features of the density of states that occur within the band, away from the edges. We shall distinguish the possibilities of strong regular peaks of density and of Van Hove anomalies. We shall show that the resonant effects possible in these cases are not proper virtual bound states.

Let us assume that a high and sharp peak p, of density $n_p(E, \Gamma)$, is superimposed on a regular density of states $n_0(E, \Gamma)$.

For very small $V(\Gamma)$'s, when the rigid band model applies, the peak p produces in the same energy range a peak in the change of density of states due to alloying. The total number of states per impurity atom is proportional to $V(\Gamma)$ and to the total number of states in peak p.

We next consider $V(\Gamma)$ large enough for the condition (b) $|V(\Gamma)F_p(E, \Gamma)| \gg 1$ to apply near the energy E_t^p at the top of the peak p but with still (a) $V(\Gamma)n_0(E, \Gamma)$ and $V(\Gamma)|F_0(E,\ \Gamma| \ll 1$ over the whole range of energy of the band $(E_b < E < E_t)$.

The corresponding variation of $\delta(E,\ \Gamma)$ is shown in Fig. 4. From (a), it has

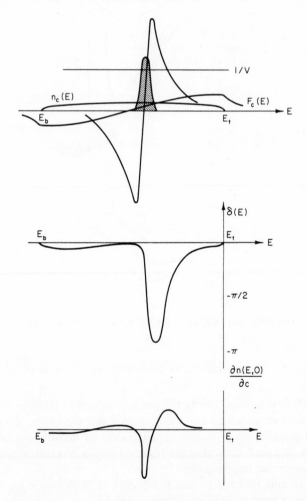

FIG. 4.   Effect of a sharp peak in $\delta(E)$ and $\partial n(E,\ 0)/\partial c$ (schematic).

very small values except near the peak. From (b), condition (21) is fulfilled for an energy $E_R > E_t^p$ as well as for an energy E_{AR} which falls within the peak. For decreasing energies, the phase shift $\delta(E, \Gamma)$ thus decreases sharply from small values to values near to $-\pi$ around E_R, then increases sharply from near to $-\pi$ to near to zero around E_{AR}. For energies below the peak, $\delta(E, \Gamma)$ is lower than the value $\delta_0(E, \Gamma)$ deduces from the action of $V(\Gamma)$ on $n_0(E, \Gamma)$ only.

The change in density of states due to the impurities has thus the following characteristic features in this special case (Fig. 4):

A sharp *antiresonant peak* within the peak p of the matrix. The width $\Delta_{AR} = E_t^p - E_{AR}$ of this peak is less than the width of the peak p and the high energy side of it for repulsive perturbations. The number of states per impurity atom contained in this antiresonant peak is nearly equal to the degeneracy of the Γ class in the limit of a large and narrow peak.

A *resonant peak* in the energy range above the peak ($E_t^p < E < E_t^p + \Delta_R$). Its width Δ_R is much larger than that of the peak p. It can be shown (Gautier and Gomès, 1965) that Δ_R increases with the number of states contained in peak p, so that the resonance peak is well marked only if this is a small fraction of the total number of Γ states in the d band. The number of states per impurity atom contained in the resonant peak is only near to the degeneracy of the Γ class if the phase shift $\delta_0(E, \Gamma)$ due to the broad part of the band is very small. This requires that $n_0(E)$ be small, in which case, as we have seen, the resonant peak is broad.

An *increase* in density below E_{AR}, with a large width, of order Δ_R. The corresponding number of states must of course be just equal to the difference between the antiresonant and the resonant peaks.

These results are preserved qualitatively for still larger perturbations, such that $V(\Gamma)|F_0(E, \Gamma)| \gg 1$, but with a smaller resonant peak and a more complex variation of the phase shift.

It can be said in a qualitative way that the resonant state described in this section is due to the d states of the matrix originally in the peak p and shifted in energy by the perturbation; in the same way, the antiresonant state describes the subtraction of those states from peak p. We have seen however that the resonant state is only well defined when its area is small. It should therefore not be confused with a proper virtual bound state.

F. Van Hove Singularities

Van Hove singularities (Van Hove, 1953) are expected in all bands, and in particular in the d band of transitional metals. Indeed most of the peaks in their density of states are probably nonregular and correspond to such singularities (cf. Wohlfarth and Cornwell, 1961).

At the energy E_s of such a singularity, the break in $dn(E, \Gamma)/dE$ produces an infinity in $dF(E, \Gamma)/dE$ (cf. *P2*). The phase shift $\delta(E, \Gamma)$ has thus an infinite slope; the change in density due to alloying has a very sharp peak with an infinite height.

Two points should be stressed: These phase shift singularities are localized in a narrow range of energy [Figs. 5(a) and 5(b)]. As an example, the singularities related to one nondegenerate band in the simple cubic structure are shown in Fig. 2. The infinity in the change $n(E, c) - n(E, 0)$ of density of states has no physical realty. It only means that the density of states $n(E, c)$ of the alloy varies more slowly than the concentration c near the Van Hove singularity $E = E_s$. A similar effect has been discussed by Lifshitz (1964).

IV. Extensions

It is now of some interest to discuss in what directions the preceding type of phase shift analysis can be extended. We develop the case of extended

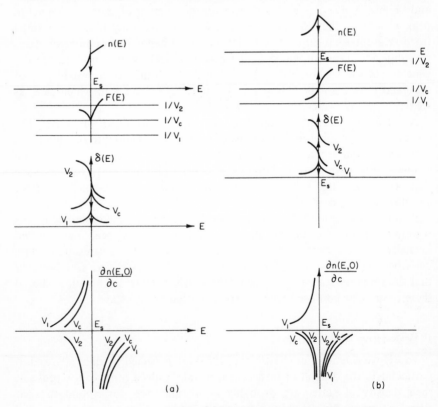

FIG. 5(a) and (b).   Effects of a Van Hove singularity (schematic).

perturbations (for narrow bands) and of broad bands, then list some other possible extensions.

A. EXTENDED PERTURBATIONS

We now assume that the perturbation potential V_p is no longer localized on an atomic site; we still assume, though, that it retains all the symmetries of the lattice point group. This type of extension is of interest in discussing substitutional impurities far from the matrix in the periodic table, such as Cr, V, Ti or Zn, Al, Si in nickel, where the perturbation is known to affect strongly the neighboring atoms in the matrix.

The use of the $\{i, \lambda\}$ representation defined in Section II,C would then lead to a more complex set of equations. But we can construct from it a new representation $\{\Gamma, \mathbf{u}\}$, which takes account of the extension and of the symmetries of the perturbation.*

Let us denote by λ the set of λ sites at an equal distance to the central site. With the corresponding atomic functions $|i\lambda\rangle$, we can build linear combinations which transform according to various symmetries of the lattice point group. The complete set of these combinations, which we shall denote $\{\Gamma\lambda\}$ forms a basis for the representations Γ of the lattice point group. However these representations are reducible; some of the combinations corresponding to different distances can have the same symmetry properties. We must then form linear combinations of these new functions with different distances to obtain a possible basis for all the irreducible representations Γ of the lattice point group. This set will be denoted $\{\Gamma\mathbf{u}\}$. Each linear combination obviously contains only atomic functions with a given symmetry: for d bands in the cubic lattices, d functions of the Γ_{12} or Γ_{25} class.

The advantages of this new representation are twofold:

(a) The scattering operator $\overline{T}^{(+)}(E)$ induces transitions only between atomic functions on perturbed sites. Thus only representations Γ with basis functions containing atomic functions on perturbed sites will be affected. The number of these representations is at most that of the lattice point group; it can be much lower if only a small number of neighbors is perturbed by the impurity. The corresponding number of basis functions is at most equal to the number of perturbed sites; it can be lower, if linear combinations at different distances λ have the same symmetry properties.

(b) The scattering operator is invariant under the operations of the lattice point group operator. It therefore is diagonal in the $\{\Gamma\mathbf{u}\}$ representation. For the representations Γ where $\{\Gamma\lambda\}$ is irreducible, $\overline{T}^{(+)}(E)$ thus is diagonal in

---

* The representation used here was introduced by Gautier and Lenglart, (1965). It is either simpler and more general that those used by Olszewski (1962), Kanamori (1965), Callaway (1964). and Clogston (1964).

$\{\Gamma\lambda\}$; for the representations Γ where $\{\Gamma\mathbf{u}\}$ is built up by linear combinations of $|\Gamma\lambda\rangle$ functions with p_μ different perturbed distances λ, the matrix elements of $\overline{T}^+(E)$ in $\{\Gamma\lambda\}$ are given by a set of difference equations of order p_μ^2. For perturbations with fairly close range, these number p_μ are very small, and the computation of the scattering operator thus very simple (cf. Gautier and Lenglart, 1965).

From Eq. (4), the phase shift operator has the same properties as the scattering operator. The change in the number of states of energy less than R, E due to an impurity, can then be written from Eq. (3) as

$$Z(E) = (1/\pi) \sum_\Gamma n_\Gamma \delta(E, \Gamma). \tag{31}$$

Here n_Γ is the dimension of the irreducible representation Γ and use has been made of the fact that the various $|\Gamma\mathbf{u}\rangle$ functions of the same representation Γ and with the same energy E must, by symmetry, have the same phase shift* $\delta(E, \Gamma) = \langle\Gamma\mathbf{u}|\delta|\Gamma\mathbf{u}\rangle$. Each irreducible representation Γ thus contributes separately to the change in density of states dZ/dE, and the discussion on the change in density due to alloying can proceed in much the same way as for localized potentials. Two complications are introduced however: (a) The impurity problem now depends on several parameters, corresponding to the action of the perturbation potential on the various types of neighbors to the impurity atom. The screening condition $Z(E_F) = Z$ is no longer sufficient to fix these parameters. (b) The relation between phase shift and perturbation potential can involve, for some representations Γ, the solution of a (simple) difference equation.

B. Broad bands. The generalized Wannier functions

Such an extension would be of great interest to treat the s band of normal or semimetals or indeed of transitional ones, or to compute transport effects in covalent or ionic insulators.

It is known (Des Cloizeaux, 1964a) that, in many cases, especially when the lattice has a center of inversion, it is possible to define *generalized* Wannier functions which (a) transform according to the various representations of the lattice point group, (b) decrease exponentially with distance. The preceding method can then be formally extended, replacing the atomic functions by these generalized Wannier functions. All the general results described in the preceding section on extended perturbations hold *exactly*, including the phase shift formula (31).

---

* The present formula (31) is identical to that obtained for free electrons scattered by a central potential well (Friedel, 1954). In the lattice case, the *finite* number of phase shifts is related to the finite order of the lattice point group; in the case of spherical symmetry, the infinite number of phase shifts is related to the infinite order of the rotation group.

For actual computations, this general method is probably not yet practical, because these Wannier functions are not known with enough accuracy. Although a general theorem concerning their spatial extension is lacking, it can be expected that, in broad bands, they extend too much over several sites for the simple approximation of localized perturbation to hold: the action of the perturbing potential on the Wannier functions of neighboring sites is probably never negligible in broad bands.

C. OTHER POSSIBLE EXTENSIONS

The phase shift method can of course be extended in various ways. For studies of electronic structures, other cases of interest for narrow bands would include bands with other than d symmetry. The method can be similarly applied to the perturbation by impurities of the *phonon* or the *spin wave* spectra. For electrons, phonons, or spin waves, cases of defects of lower symmetry could also be considered: substitutional *impurities* in lattices with more than one atom per cell, interstitial impurities, pairs of impurities, etc., *linear* or *planar defects* (dislocations; free surfaces, stacking faults, twin boundaries...).

The analysis should then be made in terms of the $\{\Gamma u\}$ representation corresponding to the irreducible representations Γ of the perturbed lattice. The choice of linear combinations of atomic functions $|\Gamma u\rangle$ is then less clear, except in cases of high symmetry, such as the interstitial impurities, the substitutional impurities in the NaCl or diamond structures, a free surface parallel to a close packed plane, etc. It is clear that, the lower the symmetry of the defect, the less interesting the phase shift method becomes.

REFERENCES

Abate, E., and Asdente, M. (1965). *Phys. Rev.* **140**, A1303.
Blandin, A., (1961). Thesis, Paris.
Callaway, J. (1964). *J. Math. Phys.* **5**, 783.
Clogston, A. M. (1962). *Phys. Rev.* **126**, 439.
Clogston, A. M. (1964). *Phys. Rev.* **136**, A1417.
Des Cloizeaux, J. (1964a) *Phys. Rev.* **135**, A685.
Des Cloizeaux, J. (1964b). *Phys. Rev.* **135**, A698.
Fletcher, G. C. (1952). *Proc. Phys. Soc. (London)* **65**, 192.
Friedel, J. (1954). *Advan. Phys.* **3**, 446.
Gautier, F., and Lenglart, P. (1965). *Phys. Rev.* **139**, A705.
Gautier, F., and Gomès, A. A. (1966). To be published.
Goodings, D. A., and Moser, B. (1964). *Phys. Rev.* **136**, A1093.
Kanamori, J. (1965). *J. Appl. Phys.* **36**, 929.
Koster, G. F., and Slater, J. C. (1954). *Phys. Rev.* **95**, 1167.
Lifshitz, I. M. (1964). *Advan. Phys.* **13**, 483.
Mott, N., and Jones, H. (1936). "The Theory of Properties of Metals and Alloys." Oxford Univ. Press, Oxford.

Olszewski, S. (1962). Thesis, Paris.
Seeger, A., and Staatzs, H. (1962). *Phys. Stat. Solidi* 2, 857.
Slater, J. C. (1936). *Phys. Rev.* 49, 537.
Van Hove, L. (1953). *Phys. Rev.* 89, 1189.
Wohlfarth, E. P., and Cornwell, T. F. (1961). *Phys. Rev. Letters* 7, 342.
Wolff, P. A. (1961). *Phys. Rev.* 124, 1030.

Limits of the Band Model and Transitions to the Metallic State

H. FRÖHLICH

DEPARTMENT OF THEORETICAL PHYSICS
UNIVERSITY OF LIVERPOOL, LIVERPOOL, ENGLAND

I. Introduction

The band theory of electrons in solids though usually highly successful becomes invalid in certain cases. There are two possibilities for this breakdown; the one first indicated by Mott (1949) refers to a simple crystal of one-electron centers (hydrogen atoms) which according to the band model has a half-filled band and is thus a metallic conductor. When the lattice distance is very large, however, an electron bound to one center overlaps very little with its neighbors. In the ground state each center should thus have an electron localized near it. A finite energy is then required to create a pair of free carriers; the model thus behaves as a semiconductor. The second possibility arises in cases of strong interaction of a single electron (in a nonmetal) with the ions of the lattice (cf. Fröhlich et al. 1963, where earlier literature is given). In some cases, this would lead to extremely narrow bands; if the energy broadening due to the interaction of an electron with the thermal vibrations of the lattice becomes larger than this bandwidth, the band model is no longer useful. Conduction then takes place by a jumping mechanism. From the uncertainty relation (Fröhlich and Sewell, 1959) it can be estimated that this situation is likely to occur when mobilities less than 0.1 cm^2/sec-V are found.

The two breakdowns of the band model are probably not unconnected. Thus many oxides, such as V_2O_3 which according to the band model should be metals, behave as semiconductors at low temperatures and, moreover, have very low mobility.

Mott has also predicted that, using the lattice distance as a parameter, a phase transition from the nonmetallic (large lattice distances) into the metallic state (small lattice distances, band model) should occur at a critical lattice distance. V_2O_3 and other oxides show a phase transition from a low-temperature nonmetallic state to a high-temperature metallic state which is probably not unconnected with Mott's prediction (cf. Mott, 1961).

Mott is largely concerned with the properties of the system in the immediate neighborhood of the ground state. It is quite feasible, however, that for given lattice distance the ground state of a system is nonmetallic but that it is metallic in higher excited states.

II. A Simple Model

It is instructive in this connection to illustrate the breakdown of the band model (first case) in terms of the number of levels in a narrow continuum above the ground state (Fröhlich, 1955). If the band model holds, then a total number of N electrons and N centers (N hydrogen atoms) provides a band with $2N$ one-electron states (two spin directions). For large lattice distances this band is very narrow. It hence leads to a narrow continuum of the whole system containing

$$Z_b = \binom{2N}{N} \simeq 2^{2N} \tag{1}$$

levels.

If, on the other hand, the ground state is described by electrons localized on the centers (one electron per center) then the spin degeneracy leads to a narrow continuum containing only

$$Z_l = 2^N \tag{2}$$

levels, i.e., a number which for large N is negligible compared with Z_b.

If in this localized model we would, however, permit each center to be occupied by up to two electrons (opposite spin) then the number of states would be Z_b as in the band model. These states form however a continuum only if the energy required to move an electron from one center to another (not a neighbor) vanishes—or is extremely small.

Assume now the ground state to be described in terms of localized electrons, i.e., that the band model is invalid. Let I_0 denote the minimum energy required to create a pair of carriers i.e., to remove one electron to a distant site. This energy involves long-range polarization effects. Now, if a number of such carriers has been created then they in turn will influence the energy I required to create a further pair of carriers. This influence will express itself through screening effects such that I is smaller than I_0. Let N_c be the number of negative (and positive) carriers and let

$$x = N_c/N. \tag{3}$$

We then assume I to depend on x only,

$$I = I_0 f(x). \tag{4}$$

A condition for a transition of the system into the metallic state is thus to assume that $f(x)$ becomes zero for $x \geq x_1$, with $x_1 \leq 1$, i.e.,

$$f(x) = 1 \quad \text{if} \quad x = 0; \qquad f(x) = 0 \quad \text{if} \quad x_1 \leq x \leq 1. \tag{5}$$

The screening effects leading to the decrease of $f(x)$ with x might be calculated with the help of approximations like the Debye-Hückel formula. A simple-minded treatment of this nature is of course objectionable. Nevertheless it seems instructive to show that it may lead to a first-order phase transition.

For this purpose we determine x from the thermal equilibrium condition (similar to ionization equilibrium) which at temperature T yields

$$\frac{x^2}{1-x} = \lambda(T)e^{-I/kT}. \tag{6}$$

Here $\lambda(T)$ increases with T; treatment of the carriers as free would require $\lambda(T) \propto T^3$. Thus x must satisfy the equation

$$\log \frac{(1-x)\lambda}{x^2} = \frac{I_0}{kT} f(x). \tag{7}$$

The left-hand side decreases from $+\infty$ at $x = 0$ to zero at $x = x_0$ and is negative for $1 \geq x > x_0$. Here,

$$x_0 = -\frac{\lambda}{2} + \left(\lambda + \frac{\lambda^2}{4}\right)^{1/2}, \tag{8}$$

i.e., $x_0 \simeq \lambda^{1/2}$ if $\lambda \ll 1$; $x_0 \simeq 1 - 1/\lambda$ if $\lambda \gg 1$. Note that $\lambda \to 0$ as $T \to 0$. Hence, for low temperatures, $x_0 < x_1$; Eq. (7) will then have one solution x_i with $x_i \ll 1$, the usual excitation of a few carriers $x_i \propto \exp(-\frac{1}{2}I_0/\kappa T)$. With increasing T, however, λ and hence x_0 increases and finally x_0 becomes larger than x_1. At high temperatures, therefore, there are at least two, possibly more, solutions of Eq. (7), depending on the detailed shape of $f(x)$. The system will choose the solution with the smallest free energy. We may then expect a transition from the semiconducting state with $x_i \ll 1$ to a state in which x is close to unity, i.e., a metallic state.

III. General Remarks

The approximations used in the treatment of phase transitions frequently break down just near the transition temperature. This also holds of the model suggested in Section II. Much work has been done on the theory of Coulomb interaction of electrons in the band model; one might, therefore, consider taking the band model as a starting point. For the band wave functions form a complete set of functions and are thus capable of describing states in which the band model is invalid. Taking the density (or lattice distance) as a parameter one should then expect for high densities a continuum of Z_b [cf. Eq. (1)] states above the ground state. At lower densities a number Z_l [Eq. (2)] of levels should be split off (to lower energies) from this continuum. Note that $Z_l/Z_b = 2^{-N}$ is negligibly small so that the number of states in the former continuum is hardly changed. Unfortunately, the work on Coulomb interaction of electrons in the band model has been justified for the high-density limit only. New methods should thus be devised to deal with the low-density case. It would not be surprising to find that the ordering influence of the Coulomb interaction may have serious repercussions on certain properties even at densities at which the Z_l ordered states are still within the continuum of the Z_b band states. This should apply in particular to metals with incomplete shells. It will be remembered that here the band model is in difficulties with regard to both superconductivity and ferromagnetism.

REFERENCES

Fröhlich, H. (1955). *Proc. 10th Solvay Conf.* p. 255.
Fröhlich, H., and Sewell, G. L. (1959). *Proc. Phys. Soc. (London)* **74**, 643.
Fröhlich, H., Machlup, S., and Mitra, K. T. (1963). *Phys. Kondens. Materie* **1**, 359.
Mott, N. F. (1949). *Proc. Phys. Soc. (London)* **A62**, 416.
Mott, N. F. (1961). *Phil. Mag.* **6**, 287.

Energy Bands in Periodic and Aperiodic Fields

H. JONES

DEPARTMENT OF MATHEMATICS, IMPERIAL COLLEGE
LONDON, ENGLAND

Certain aspects of the thermal and magnetic properties of metals, interpreted in accordance with the independent electron model, depend rather sensitively on the density of electronic states in the highest occupied energy band. For the periodic field of the perfect crystal, mathematical methods have been developed which lead to a determination of this density-of-states function. These methods depend primarily on Bloch's theorem which defines the wave vector in terms of which the individual electronic states are specified. Many determinations of energy-band structures of pure metals and semiconductors have now been made, notably by Slater and his colleagues.

In disordered alloys where the potential energy of an electron is an aperiodic function of position Bloch's theorem does not apply and the stationary states cannot be specified by points in wave-vector space. The determination of the individual eigenvalues, as a first step towards obtaining the density of states, is virtually impossible and other methods have to be sought. In recent years the properties of Green's functions of electrons in solids and liquids have been widely investigated [see for example Edwards (1962) and Jones (1964)] and this analysis has shed some light on the problem of the density of states in disordered alloys.

Let H denote the Hamiltonian of an electron in a space-periodic field which may include the special case of zero field, and let $V(\mathbf{r})$ denote a potential energy over the same range which has no periodic properties. The Green function G_0 corresponding to H is then defined by

$$(H - \varepsilon - i\eta)G_0(\mathbf{r}, \mathbf{r}'; \varepsilon) = -\delta(\mathbf{r} - \mathbf{r}'), \tag{1}$$

and the Green function G of the aperiodic field by

$$(H + V - \varepsilon - i\eta)G(\mathbf{r}, \mathbf{r}'; \varepsilon) = -\delta(\mathbf{r} - \mathbf{r}'), \tag{2}$$

where η is a real constant.

If $\Psi_{\mathbf{k}}(\mathbf{r})$ denotes the Bloch wave function of the periodic field and a diagonal element of G with respect to these functions is denoted by $G(\mathbf{k}, \varepsilon)$, then it

469

may be shown (Jones, 1965) that the density of states $N(\varepsilon)$ in the aperiodic field is given by

$$N(\varepsilon) = \frac{i}{8\pi^4} \mathcal{I} \int G(\mathbf{k}, \varepsilon) \, d^3k, \tag{3}$$

where $\mathcal{I}$ implies that the imaginary part of the integral is to be taken.

Two real functions $\Sigma(\mathbf{k}, \varepsilon)$ and $\Gamma(\mathbf{k}, \varepsilon)$ may be defined by the equation

$$G(\mathbf{k}, \varepsilon) = (\varepsilon - \varepsilon_\mathbf{k} - \Sigma + i\Gamma)^{-1}, \tag{4}$$

where $\varepsilon_\mathbf{k}$ is the eigenvalue belonging to $\Psi_\mathbf{k}(\mathbf{r})$. Hence Eq. (3) may be written

$$N(\varepsilon) = \frac{1}{8\pi^4} \int \frac{\Gamma(\mathbf{k}, \varepsilon) \, d^3k}{\{\varepsilon - \varepsilon_\mathbf{k} - \Sigma(\mathbf{k}, \varepsilon)\}^2 + \Gamma^2(\mathbf{k}, \varepsilon)}. \tag{5}$$

This relation is quite general but not, of course, useful until Σ and Γ can be determined. This is done by making use of the exact operator relation

$$G = G_0 + G_0 V G, \tag{6}$$

and by using the value of $G_0(\mathbf{k}, \varepsilon)$ in terms of the eigenvalue $\varepsilon_\mathbf{k}$, viz.

$$G_0(\mathbf{k}, \varepsilon) = (\varepsilon - \varepsilon_\mathbf{k} + i\eta)^{-1}. \tag{7}$$

The off-diagonal matrix elements of G with respect to the Bloch states $\Psi_\mathbf{k}(\mathbf{r})$ are given by

$$G(\mathbf{l}, \mathbf{k}) = \sum_\mathbf{m} G_0(\mathbf{l}, \mathbf{l}) V_{\mathbf{l}\mathbf{m}} G(\mathbf{m}, \mathbf{k}), \tag{8}$$

and the diagonal elements by

$$G(\mathbf{k}, \mathbf{k}) = G_0(\mathbf{k}, \mathbf{k}) + \sum_\mathbf{l} G_0(\mathbf{k}, \mathbf{k}) V_{\mathbf{k}\mathbf{l}} G(\mathbf{l}, \mathbf{k}). \tag{9}$$

Since (8) applies only for $\mathbf{l} \neq \mathbf{k}$ the diagonal element in the sum (9) must be removed before substituting for $G(\mathbf{l}, \mathbf{k})$ from (8). This gives

$$G(\mathbf{k}, \mathbf{k}) = G_0(\mathbf{k}, \mathbf{k}) + G_0(\mathbf{k}, \mathbf{k}) V_{\mathbf{k}\mathbf{k}} G(\mathbf{k}, \mathbf{k})$$
$$+ \sum_{\mathbf{l} \neq \mathbf{k}} G_0(\mathbf{k}, \mathbf{k}) V_{\mathbf{k}\mathbf{l}} \sum_\mathbf{m} G_0(\mathbf{l}, \mathbf{l}) V_{\mathbf{l}\mathbf{m}} G(\mathbf{m}, \mathbf{k}). \tag{10}$$

So far no approximation is involved, but from this stage onwards all off-diagonal elements of G in (10) will be neglected, on the grounds that according to (8) they would introduce higher than second powers of the off-diagonal elements of V. Hence to this approximation

$$G(\mathbf{k}, \mathbf{k})[1 - G_0(\mathbf{k}, \mathbf{k}) V_{\mathbf{k}\mathbf{k}} - G_0(\mathbf{k}, \mathbf{k}) \sum_{\mathbf{l} \neq \mathbf{k}} |V_{\mathbf{k}\mathbf{l}}|^2 G_0(\mathbf{l}, \mathbf{l})] = G_0(\mathbf{k}, \mathbf{k}) \tag{11}$$

which may be written

$$G^{-1}(\mathbf{k}, \mathbf{k}) = G_0^{-1}(\mathbf{k}, \mathbf{k}) - V_{\mathbf{k}\mathbf{k}} - \sum_{\mathbf{l} \neq \mathbf{k}} |V_{\mathbf{k}\mathbf{l}}|^2 G_0(\mathbf{l}, \mathbf{l}), \tag{12}$$

and thus by (4) and (7)

$$V_{\mathbf{kk}} + \lim_{\eta \to 0} \sum_{\mathbf{l} \neq \mathbf{k}} \frac{|V_{\mathbf{kl}}|^2}{\varepsilon - \varepsilon_{\mathbf{l}} + i\eta} = \Sigma\,(\mathbf{k}, \varepsilon) - i\Gamma(\mathbf{k}, \varepsilon), \tag{13}$$

which is the equation determining Σ and Γ the functions required to give $N(\varepsilon)$ according to Eq. (5).

Two widely different examples show the generality of (5) and (13). In the first example, H_0 is taken to be the field-free case of completely free electrons, and V a periodic potential. The matrix element $V_{\mathbf{kl}}$ are therefore the Fourier components of the potential V and vanish unless $\mathbf{l} = \mathbf{k} + \mathbf{K}$, where $\mathbf{K}$ is a reciprocal lattice vector of the periodic field. Since the denominator of the sum on the left of (13) does not vanish for any term in which $V_{\mathbf{k},\,\mathbf{k}+\mathbf{K}}$ is finite the sum is real and $\Gamma = 0$.

To evaluate (5) in this case let $\sigma = \varepsilon - \varepsilon_{\mathbf{k}} - \Sigma\,(\mathbf{k}, \varepsilon)$, and choose for the volume element d^3k the expression $dS/|\nabla\sigma|\,d\sigma$ where dS is an element of area on the surface $\sigma = $ const. As Γ tends to zero the expression $\Gamma/\pi(\sigma^2 + \Gamma^2)$ behaves like the delta function $\delta(\sigma)$ and consequently (5) reduces to

$$N(\varepsilon) = \frac{1}{(2\pi)^3} \int_{\sigma = 0} \frac{dS}{|\nabla\sigma|}, \tag{14}$$

where the integration is taken over the surface $\sigma = 0$, i.e.

$$\varepsilon - \varepsilon_{\mathbf{k}} - V_{\mathbf{kk}} - \sum_{\mathbf{K}} \frac{|V_{\mathbf{k},\mathbf{k}+\mathbf{K}}|^2}{\varepsilon - \varepsilon_{\mathbf{k}+\mathbf{K}}} = 0. \tag{15}$$

Equation (14) is the well-known expression for the density of states of energies given by (15). Equation (15) is the Wigner-Brillouin perturbation series which, unlike the Rayleigh-Schrödinger series, correctly describes the behavior of ε to second powers of the matrix elements of V, even in the neighborhood of the energy gaps.

In the second example, H_0 is taken to be the Hamiltonian of electrons in a periodic field, and V to be an aperiodic addition. The corresponding physical situation is that of electrons in a disordered alloy. The orthonormal functions used to transform the Green function are the Bloch wave functions $\Psi_{\mathbf{k}}$ of the periodic field, of which the eigenvalues are $\varepsilon_{\mathbf{k}}$.

Let $U(\mathbf{r} - \mathbf{R}_i)$ denote the difference in the potential energy of an electron when a solvent atom at $\mathbf{R}_i$ is replaced by a solute atom at the same lattice site. Then

$$V(\mathbf{r}) = \sum_i U(\mathbf{r} - \mathbf{R}_i), \tag{16}$$

where the summation is over n values of $\mathbf{R}_i$ corresponding to the n solute atoms in the lattice of unit volume which contains N lattice-sites. Hence

$$V_{kl} = \sum_i \int \Psi_l U(\mathbf{r} - \mathbf{R}_i) \Psi_k \, d^3r, \qquad (17)$$

and by making use of the property possessed by all Bloch functions, viz. $\Psi_k(\mathbf{r} + \mathbf{R}_i) = e^{i\mathbf{k} \cdot \mathbf{R}_i} \Psi_k(\mathbf{r})$, where $\mathbf{R}_i$ is a lattice vector, it follows that

$$V_k = \phi_{kl} \sum_i \exp[i(\mathbf{k} - \mathbf{l}) \cdot \mathbf{R}_i], \qquad (18)$$

where ϕ_{kl} is a matrix element independent of $\mathbf{R}_i$ which is equal to the integral in Eq. (17) when $\mathbf{R}_i$ is put equal to zero. Hence

$$|V_{kl}|^2 = |\phi_{kl}|^2 \sum_{i,j} \exp[i(\mathbf{k} - \mathbf{l}) \cdot (\mathbf{R}_i - \mathbf{R}_j)]. \qquad (19)$$

The sum may be evaluated by summing first over all $\mathbf{r}_j = \mathbf{R}_i - \mathbf{R}_j$ for given $\mathbf{R}_i$. It may be assumed that for different $\mathbf{R}_i$ these sums will be equal if the usual procedure is adopted of applying periodic boundary conditions. Hence, if $p(\mathbf{r}_j)$ denotes the probability of finding a solute atom at R_j, given that one exists at R_i, it follows that

$$|V_{kl}|^2 = |\phi_{kl}|^2 \left\{ n + n \sum_j p(\mathbf{r}_j) \exp[i(\mathbf{k} - \mathbf{l}) \cdot \mathbf{r}_j] \right\}, \qquad (20)$$

where

$$\sum_j p(\mathbf{r}_j) = n - 1. \qquad (21)$$

If the solute atoms formed a perfect superlattice $p(\mathbf{r}_j)$ would be unity for each superlattice vector $\mathbf{r}_j$ and zero otherwise. The sum in Eq. (20) would be over-all lattice vectors except 0, and therefore equal to -1 for arbitrary $\mathbf{k} - \mathbf{l}$ and hence for this case $V_{kl} = 0$. However, if $\mathbf{k} - \mathbf{l}$ were a reciprocal superlattice vector each exponential term would be unity and the sum equal to $n - 1$. Thus in this case $|V_{kl}|^2 = n^2 |\phi_{kl}|^2$. For given $\mathbf{k}$ the quantity $|V_{kl}|^2$ can be regarded as a function of position $\mathbf{l}$ in reciprocal lattice space. When a superlattice exists this function is zero everywhere except at a number of isolated points. When the solute atoms are randomly distributed over the solvent lattice $|V_{kl}|^2$ has quite a different form. The sum in Eq. (20) will be either zero (complete randomization) or of order unity when local order occurs. Thus the function of $\mathbf{l}$, $|V_{kl}|^2$, for each $\mathbf{k}$ will be finite over the whole reciprocal space, but may have maxima at points separated from $\mathbf{k}$ by small reciprocal superlattice distances.

It will now be shown how this difference is reflected in the band structure. When $|V_{kl}|^2$ is a continuous function of position the sum (13) may be transformed into an integral. For unit volume of the alloy the number of states in $d^3\mathbf{l}$ is $(2\pi)^{-3}d^3\mathbf{l}$, and thus if dS denotes an element of surface on the equi-energy surface $\varepsilon_\mathbf{l}$, Eq. (13) may be written

$$V_{\mathbf{kk}} + \lim_{\eta \to 0} \frac{1}{(2\pi)^3} \iint \frac{|V_{\mathbf{kl}}|^2}{\varepsilon - \varepsilon_\mathbf{l} + i\eta} \frac{dS}{|\nabla\varepsilon_\mathbf{l}|} d\varepsilon_\mathbf{l} = \Sigma - i\Gamma. \tag{22}$$

Let

$$F(\mathbf{k}, \varepsilon_\mathbf{l}) = \frac{1}{(2\pi)^3} \int_{\varepsilon_\mathbf{l}} |V_{\mathbf{kl}}|^2 \frac{dS}{|\nabla\varepsilon_\mathbf{l}|}, \tag{23}$$

thus (22) gives

$$\Sigma(\mathbf{k}, \varepsilon) = V_{\mathbf{kk}} + \mathscr{P} \int \frac{F(\mathbf{k}, \varepsilon_\mathbf{l})}{\varepsilon - \varepsilon_\mathbf{l}} d\varepsilon_\mathbf{l}, \tag{24}$$

and

$$\Gamma(\mathbf{k}, \varepsilon) = \pi F(\mathbf{k}, \varepsilon). \tag{25}$$

These two equations exhibit the well-known relationship between the real and imaginary parts of the Green function. When a superlattice exists $F(\mathbf{k}, \varepsilon_\mathbf{l})$ will, in general, be zero and hence also $\Gamma = 0$. In this case there is no line broadening and Σ is best determined directly by (13). In the disordered alloy $F(\mathbf{k}, \varepsilon_\mathbf{l})$ is finite and hence both Γ and Σ differ from zero. Σ may be regarded as determining the displacement of the energy levels and Γ their broadening.

To make further precise progress the detailed form of the functions $|V_{\mathbf{kl}}|^2$ and $\varepsilon_\mathbf{l}$ must be known, but certain general properties can be inferred without this knowledge.

Consider an isolated energy band for which $N_0(\varepsilon) = 0$ if $\varepsilon_0 > \varepsilon > \varepsilon_1$. Since the integration in (23) is taken over the equi-energy surfaces of the pure metal it is clear that when $\varepsilon < \varepsilon_0$, or $\varepsilon > \varepsilon_1$, $F(\mathbf{k}, \varepsilon) = 0$. Consequently for the regions just beyond the band limits of the pure metal, the density of states in the alloy is given by

$$N(\varepsilon) = \frac{1}{(2\pi)^3} \int_{\varepsilon_\mathbf{k}} \delta(\varepsilon - \varepsilon_\mathbf{k} - \Sigma(\mathbf{k}, \varepsilon)) \frac{dS}{|\nabla\varepsilon_\mathbf{k}|}. \tag{26}$$

If $\Sigma(\mathbf{k}, \varepsilon)$ depends on $\mathbf{k}$ only through $\varepsilon_\mathbf{k}$, as is the case for the scattering of free electrons by screened charges, then for $\varepsilon < \varepsilon_0$ or $\varepsilon > \varepsilon_1$,

$$N(\varepsilon) = N_0(\varepsilon_\mathbf{k}), \tag{27}$$

where $\varepsilon_\mathbf{k}$ is the root of the equation

$$\varepsilon - \varepsilon_\mathbf{k} - \Sigma(\varepsilon_\mathbf{k}, \varepsilon) = 0. \tag{28}$$

From this it follows that the lowest and greatest energies in the alloy band are given by the roots of

$$\varepsilon - \varepsilon_0 - \Sigma(\varepsilon_0, \varepsilon) = 0, \tag{29}$$

and

$$\varepsilon - \varepsilon_1 - \Sigma(\varepsilon_1, \varepsilon) = 0. \tag{30}$$

If the potentials $U(\mathbf{r} - \mathbf{R}_i)$ are so chosen that the diagonal elements of V are zero Eq. (24) may be written

$$\Sigma = \mathscr{P} \int_{\varepsilon_0}^{\varepsilon_1} \frac{\langle |V_{kl}|^2 \rangle_{\varepsilon_1} N_0(\varepsilon)}{\varepsilon - \varepsilon_1} d\varepsilon_1, \tag{31}$$

where $\langle |V_{kl}|^2 \rangle_{\varepsilon_1}$ is an average taken over the surface ε_1. An estimate of Σ for values of $\varepsilon < \varepsilon_0$ is therefore given by

$$\Sigma = -\langle |V_{kl}|^2 \rangle \mathscr{N}/\bar{\varepsilon}, \tag{32}$$

where $\mathscr{N}$ is the number of states in the band and $\bar{\varepsilon}$ an energy of order of the bandwidth. According to (29) it will be seen that the bottom of the band is depressed by an amount given by (32). From (23) it may be anticipated that the value of F and therefore Γ will be largest at the center of the band and from (24) that Σ is likely to be small in this neighborhood.

The following conclusions may be drawn from the foregoing analysis: (a) An energy band is broadened in a dilute disordered alloy by a finite amount, i.e., the line broadening is not constant. (b) The maximum line width and the minimum displacement occur near the center of the band. These results have also been obtained by Sergeeva (1965). (c) Depending on the position of the Fermi limit in relation to the center of the band (or peak) the density of states may be increased or decreased by scattering. Clearly if the Fermi limit is at the center of the band, line broadening will reduce $N(\varepsilon_F)$, whereas if the Fermi limit is near the band edge, line broadening will increase $N(\varepsilon_F)$. (d) Order (either short-range or long-range) affects both the energy displacement Σ and the line width Γ, and therefore the effect on the density of states may not be strictly parallel with the residual resistivity. (e) The present theory which depends upon a series development of the Green function terminated at second powers of the perturbation matrix elements does not lead to the appearance of singularities in $N(\varepsilon)$ either within or below the pure metal band.

REFERENCES

Edwards, S. F. (1962). *Proc. Roy. Soc.* **A267**, 139.
Jones, H. (1964). *Proc. Roy. Soc.* **A285**, 461.
Sergeeva, G. C. (1965). *Soviet Phys. JETP* **21**, 108.

Some Elementary Thoughts on the Slater Intra-Atomic Exchange Model for Ferromagnetism

J. H. VAN VLECK

DEPARTMENT OF PHYSICS
HARVARD UNIVERSITY
CAMBRIDGE, MASSACHUSETTS

I. Introduction

When Heisenberg took the mystery out of the Weiss molecular field in 1927 by showing that exchange effects can couple atomic magnets, it was supposed for a while that direct interatomic exchange would give the desired interaction. As time went on, it became clear that this is not the case, and physicists are still debating the details of the exchange mechanism in the iron group. Here the situation is much less clear than in the rare earths where the coupling between the f electrons is generally conceded to be of the Kasuya-Yosida-Ruderman-Kittel indirect type via conduction electrons. Thirty years ago, Slater (1936, 1937) suggested that in nickel the requisite interaction could be found in the intra-atomic exchange integral connecting d electrons. Such an explanation of ferromagnetism is commonly called one based on "Hund's rule coupling." This is the origin of ferromagnetism which I personally consider the most likely in the iron group. So it seems appropriate in a volume honoring Slater to give some of my reasons.

In recent years, a number of papers (Kanamori, 1963; Gutzwiller, 1963, 1964, 1965; Hubbard, 1963, 1964, 1965) have presented calculations which suggest that in the tight binding approximation ferromagnetism can be obtained even without invoking Hund's rule. It should, however, be mentioned that all of these authors have some misgivings whether this is really so, as a

475

rather strange band shape or density of states must be assumed. Also, Lieb and Mattis (1962) have shown unequivocally that with a particular model of a somewhat special character, wherein a three-dimensional potential factors into three one-dimensional ones, ferromagnetism cannot be obtained without invoking Hund's rule. Mattis (1963, 1964) has amplified this argument further in two subsequent articles. The present paper may seem somewhat lacking in rigor, or oversimplified, in view of the very detailed work in the various papers we have cited, and especially in view of the very scholarly and complete review and discussion of the whole situation by Herring (1966) in a forthcoming volume of the Rado-Suhl series. However, the various articles usually involve considerable mathematical analysis. So it is perhaps not entirely amiss if in the present paper we aim to present some elementary considerations which make it highly probable that the Hund's rule effect is usually a necessary ingredient to get ferromagnetism out of the tight binding approximation.

II. The U, T Model

Until the final section VI, we shall be concerned entirely with the tight binding approximation for a system in which there is only one orbital state per atom. We suppose that there is a one-electron transfer integral T associated with the passage of an electron from one atom to another neighboring one, and that there is a promotion or Coulomb energy U if two electrons are on the same atom. We can take T to be negative if the wave functions are appropriately and similarly phased on all atoms. This is the sign behavior basic to all molecular theory based on the linear combination of atomic orbitals, and follows from the general lemma that the lowest wave function is nodeless. We neglect such refinements as corrections for nonorthogonality, and since our model involves only two parameters, we call it the U, T model. The Hamiltonian function, more or less self-explanatory, is thus

$$\mathscr{H} = T \sum_{\sigma} \sum_{\text{neighbors}} a_{k\sigma}^{+} a_{l\sigma} + \tfrac{1}{2} U \sum_{k,\sigma} n_{k\sigma} n_{k-\sigma}, \tag{1}$$

where $a_{k\sigma}^{+}, a_{k\sigma}$ are creation and destruction operators for an electron being on atom k, and where the index $\sigma (= \pm \tfrac{1}{2})$ designates the sign of the spin in some given direction. The number $n_{k\sigma} = a_{k\sigma}^{+} a_{k\sigma}$ of electrons of given spin direction on a given atom can only be 0 or 1. The total number of electrons is $n = \sum_{k,\sigma} n_{k\sigma}$. The factor $\tfrac{1}{2}$ appears in the second member of Eq. (1) because each polar state is counted twice in the summation.

The superficial argument which appears to extract ferromagnetism from (1) if U is sufficiently large runs as follows: Assume that the first $\tfrac{1}{2} n$ orbital states are doubly occupied, with compensating spins. Ferromagnetism is supposed to ensue if the system is unstable with respect to spin reversal, i.e., if the decrease in polar energy more than offsets the increase in orbital energy associated with the T terms when we let there be more up than down spins. If $\rho(E)$ be the density of orbital states (relative to energy) at the assumed Fermi surface with complete spin compensation, the increase in the interatomic orbital energy when a number Δn of electrons are promoted to singly occupied states is

$$(\Delta n)^2/\rho(E)$$

while with the molecular field approximation the change in polar energy is

$$[U(\tfrac{1}{2}n - \Delta n)(\tfrac{1}{2}n + \Delta n) - U(\tfrac{1}{2}n)^a]/N = - U(\Delta n)^2/N,$$

where N is the total number of sites among which the n electrons are distributed. The total energy is lowered or, in other words, the system is unstable if

$$U\rho(E)/N > 1. \qquad (2)$$

It is generally recognized that the condition (2) for ferromagnetism is too lenient. Kanamori (1963), using essentially a Brueckner-Goldstone type of approximation, and Hubbard (1963), using Green's functions, find that the condition (2) for ferromagnetism should instead be replaced by one of the form

$$U_{\text{eff}}\rho(E)/N > 1, \qquad (3)$$

where U_{eff} is much smaller than U, because of the effect of screening. In particular, U_{eff} is of the order T rather than U in the limit $U \to \infty$. So ferromagnetic instability is no longer automatically achieved simply by allowing U to be large. As U_{eff} and N/ρ both are then of the order T, orders of magnitude arguments can no longer be used to discover whether (3) is satisfied. It does appear from (3) that there is ferromagnetism if the density $\rho(E)$ at the top of the Fermi surface is sufficiently large compared to the average bandwidth. Kanamori and Hubbard both show that certain admittedly ad hoc and artificial band shapes will cause (3) to be fulfilled. The flaw in this type of argument is that the band shape is not something which can be adjusted in an arbitary fashion, but instead it is a consequence of the Hamiltonian (1). It is the author's belief that were it possible to make an accurate calculation, ferromagnetism would never, or practically never,* ensue from the simple Hamiltonian (1). In simple physical terms, the reason for my conviction is that the lower the total spin, the more polar states (i.e., states with two electrons on the same atom) can be intermixed into the wave function, and the energy consequently lowered, as compared with a situation where doubling up on the atom is impossible. This is simply a manifestation of the truism that when

---

* It should, however, be noted that for a face centered cubic lattice Gutzwiller (1963) finds that the Hamiltonian (1) with $U = 0$ gives a logarithmic singularity in ρ if the band is nearly full, and then (3) is automatically satisfied. This is a rather special situation, but it makes one hesitate to say categorically that ferromagnetism can never occur for the U,T model.

low-lying nonpolar levels are allowed to interact with higher levels, they are depressed further. The fallacy involved in the naive use of (2) arises from the fact that without corrections for polarization or interconfiguration interaction, completely uncorrelated or itinerant wave functions, in general, mix together polar and nonpolar terms and so possess increased energy just because the energy of two electrons is raised when they climb on the same atom. Then the completely ferromagnetic state, where no such climbing is possible with our U,T model, would have the lowest energy of all if $|U/T|$ is large. Inclusion of the corrections, however, completely changes the situation.

III. Analogy to the Case of Only Two Atoms

The importance of interconfiguration interaction and the inadequacy of the Hartree or molecular field approximation underlying (2) is simply illustrated by the familiar case of two electrons exposed to equal attracting centers A, B, i..e, the hydrogen molecule. We start with one-electron wave functions which are linear combinations,

$$\psi_g = (\psi_A + \psi_B)/\sqrt{2}, \qquad \psi_u = (\psi_A - \psi_B)/\sqrt{2},$$

of atomic orbitals. We shall neglect nonorthogonality and direct (i.e., interatomic) exchange. If one uses a molecular field or orbital procedure analogous to that used in obtaining (2), one finds that the two-electron wave functions and their corresponding energies are

$$\begin{aligned}
\Psi(^3\Sigma_u) &= [\psi_u(1)\psi_g(2) - \psi_u(2)\psi_g(1)]/\sqrt{2}, & E &= 0, \\
\Psi(^1\Sigma_u) &= [\psi_u(1)\psi_g(2) + \psi_u(2)\psi_g(1)]/\sqrt{2}, & E &= U, \\
\Psi(^1\Sigma_g) &= \psi_g(1)\psi_g(2), & E &= \tfrac{1}{2}U + 2T, \\
\Psi(^1\Sigma_g) &= \psi_u(1)\psi_u(2), & E &= \tfrac{1}{2}U - 2T.
\end{aligned} \tag{4}$$

From cursory examination of these equations it would appear that the triplet would be lowest if U is large. This situation would be the two-center analog of ferromagnetism. The flaw in this calculation is that it has neglected matrix elements connecting the two $^1\Sigma_g$ states, which makes them have energies given by

$$E(^1\Sigma_g) = \tfrac{1}{2}U \pm (\tfrac{1}{4}U^2 + 4T^2)^{1/2} \tag{5}$$

and the lowest member of the pair is deeper than the triplet regardless of the values of T and U.

In my opinion, as long as one sticks to the Hamiltonian (1), essentially this state of affairs persists, i.e., interaction makes the state of minimum spin lowest, even when there is a large number of sites, which can in general exceed the number of electrons (or alternatively of holes) in the band. Of course it is dangerous to make such a broad, and rather intuitive, generalization from a rather trivial example; Herring even says that the evidence is only "fragmentary" that ferromagnetism can never be extracted from (1). It should, however, be mentioned that the mere fact that alkali or other metals characterized by nondegenerate bands are never found experimentally to be ferromagnetic is evidence of a sort. From the theoretical standpoint, the following line of consideration seems to me to give some assurance that, at least ordinarily, ferromagnetism does not flow out of the Hamiltonian (1).*

IV. The Case $n = N$ of One Electron per Atom

When there are a large number of atoms, the simplest case to consider is where there is just one electron per atom, so that $n = N$. We start now with the completely non-polar configuration, and regard the polar configurations where two electrons double up on the same atom as perturbations. The non-polar configuration has zero transfer energy, as there is no possibility of an electron jumping from one atom to another without introducing polarity. Furthermore, this zero energy configuration is completely independent of spin, as there is no interaction of any sort. Now introduce the interaction with excited states as a perturbation, and consider only terms of the order T^2/U. An electron on one atom can slide over and double up with another electron on an adjacent atom, at the expense of introducing a polar energy U, only if their spins are antiparallel or, more exactly, only if, regarded as a two-electron system, the pair is in a singlet rather than a triplet state. Since the triplet and singlet states have respectively $\mathbf{s}_i \cdot \mathbf{s}_j = \frac{1}{4}, -\frac{3}{4}$, this restriction can be expressed by saying that the operative nondiagonal transfer term taking a given electron on atom A to a neighbor atom B already occupied by one electron is

$$\langle AB|\mathcal{H}|B^2\rangle = T(\tfrac{1}{4} - \mathbf{s}_i \cdot \mathbf{s}_j)\sqrt{2}.$$

The factor $\sqrt{2}$ comes from using wave functions of the proper symmetry as regards permutation between A and B. The second-order effect of a perturbation by upper states j which lifts the degeneracy of a family of originally consident energy levels is to introduce an effective Hamiltonian[†]

$$\langle i|\mathcal{H}_{\text{eff}}|i'\rangle = -\sum_j [\langle i|\mathcal{H}|j\rangle\langle j|\mathcal{H}|i'\rangle/h\nu_{ji}]. \tag{6}$$

* The procedure which is to be presented in Sections IV and VI, whereby perturbation theory is used to take account of the repercussions of the states of higher polarity and to generate an effective Hamiltonain for the states of minimum polarity, was briefly explained by the writer in two earlier review articles (Van Vleck, 1953, 1957). In particular, Eq. (8) of the 1953 article is the same as the Eq. (8) of the present paper. This line of attack is seldom noticed, perhaps because it was previously presented only rather incidentally in the discussion of other magnetic problems, and so is now elaborated in more detail.

† For proof of the relation (6) see, for instance, Kemble (1937).

As $hv_{ji} = U$, we thus see that the effective Hamiltonian introduced by the creeping in of polarity is, to lowest order in T^2/U,

$$\mathcal{H}_{eff} = -2(2T^2)U^{-1} \sum_{neighbors} (\tfrac{1}{4} - \mathbf{s}_k \cdot \mathbf{s}_l)^2.$$

The extra factor 2 appears because an electron can jump from A onto B or from B onto A. Since $(\mathbf{s}_k \cdot \mathbf{s}_l + \tfrac{1}{4})^2 = \tfrac{1}{4}$, this relation can be written

$$\mathcal{H}_{eff} = (4T^2/U) \sum_{neighbors} (\mathbf{s}_k \cdot \mathbf{s}_l - \tfrac{1}{4}). \tag{7}$$

The important thing is that the coefficient $4T^2/U$ of $\mathbf{s}_k \cdot \mathbf{s}_l$ is positive, and so (7) represents an antiferromagnetic rather than a ferromagnetic situation. Consequently the lowest state will be that of zero or minimum spin. This can also be seen qualitatively from the fact that there are more different orientation possibilities, and so more depression of the ground state by interaction with the polar upper states, the lower the resultant spin. The state of maximum spin, in particular, cannot interact with any polar states at all.

V. The Case $n \neq N$ of Unequal Numbers of Electrons and Sites

In the more general case* where the number of electrons is less than or greater than the number of sites, we have not been able to construct with any degree of rigor a proof that the lowest state for our U,T model is that of minimum spin. If one tries to construct a proof along the lines of that for the special case $n = N$, one notes, first of all, that the manifold of non-polar states (or of minimum polarity if $n > N$) has a band structure, since the n electrons can redistribute themselves among the N various sites without introducing any polarity if $n < N$, or more than the minimum unavoidable amount $U(n - N)$ if $n > N$. Furthermore, this band structure will show some dependence on spin. This fact seems rather surprising at first, as the only constant entering in the problem is the one-electron transfer integral T. The reason is that by successive one-electron jumps one can pass from one configuration to another differing from it only by a permutation, and as a

---

* An important difference should be noted in the physics of the situations discussed in Section V as compared with Section IV. In the ideally non-polar configuration for $n = N$, no electrical conductivity or specific heat is possible, as no redistribution is possible. On the other hand, when $n \neq N$ there can be conductivity and specific heat even in the manifold of minimum polarity, since electrons can redistribute themselves among the sites without changing the number of unoccupied ones if $n < N$, or of doubly inhabited ones if $n > N$. When $n = N$, conductivity and specific heat can begin to appear as soon as U is no longer treated as extremely large compared to T. That appreciable conductivity sets in rather suddenly when T/U exceeds a certain critical value has been stressed by Hubbard (1964). This corresponds to the physical fact that the distinction between insulators and conductors is usually a rather sharp one.

result the energy is correlated with the symmetry types of the orbital permutation group, and hence, because of the exclusion principle, with spin alignment. As a simple example consider two electrons distributed in a lattice consisting only of three equivalent sites situated at the vertices of an equilateral triangle (ABC). If (120), for instance, denotes an unsymmetrized state where electrons 1,2 are respectively on sites A,B, then by one-electron jumps one can go through the sequence $(120) \rightarrow (102) \rightarrow (012) \rightarrow (210)$. When one introduces the proper symmetric or antisymmetric combinations, it turns out that the state of lowest energy is that of zero spin. For the more general problem of a ring containing two electrons and n sites, one finds that the singlet is usually deepest, but that for certain values of n, the deepest singlet and triplet may coincide. For a quadrilateral $(ABCD)$ with three electrons, one of the states with $S = \frac{1}{2}$ has a lower energy than any with $S = \frac{3}{2}$. We omit details of the secular equations that lead to these results, as the calculations are elementary.

When we come to a real lattice with three dimensions and a large number of atoms, the dependence on spin of the states of minimum polarity appears to be a complicated topological problem involving the various types of links which can be constructed, analogous to Feynman diagrams, and we are unable to make any definite statements. However, we believe that the dependence on spin is usually a rather minor part of the band structure, since only a small fraction of the various successive transfers lead to configurations differing from the original one only by a permutation.* Probably a state of minimum spin is lowest, as low spin states are the most numerous and give the most possibility of being pried apart by the permutation effect. In any case we can invoke the perturbing influence of the states of less than minimum polarity to give antiferromagnetism. The large number of terms of order T^2/U presumably outweighs the small fraction of those of order T that are spin dependent. One can still include the second-order effect of the excited states by introducing the effective Hamiltonian (7) with, of course, the understanding that the sum goes only over the pairs of adjacent sites that are both occupied in some

---

* For a linear lattice, there can be no permutations of the type we are discussing in the state of minimum polarity, since one electron cannot pass another without raising the polarity while passing. Hence, there can be no dependence on spin until one considers the perturbing effect of upper states of the lattice, and it is this effect which makes the system behave in accordance with the Lieb-Mattis theorem, as of course it must, since the problem is one-dimensional. This situation is reflected in the fact that Slater *et al.* (1953) find that for a U,T system with only two electrons free to redistribute themselves along a linear chain, the singlet separates from and falls below the triplet only one when one includes terms of the order T^2/U. On the other hand, for the two-dimensional 3×3 problem which they treat and which we discuss later, the excess of energy of the triplet over the singlet is of the order T, a manifestation of the fact that there is the permutation effect, and interaction with upper configurations need not be invoked to pry apart the states of minimum polarity differing in spin.

configuration of minimum polarity (zero polarity if $n \lessgtr N$). In addition there is another effect not found in the special case $n = N$. Namely, if sites A and B are originally singly occupied and C is empty, and if A and C are both neighbors of B, then an electron can pass from A to C by going through an intermediate state in which two electrons are on B. This will lead to effective transfer terms of the order $-T^2/U$ whereby an electron can make double jumps. These terms are negative, and therefore presumably bonding. Also, they are present only if the spins of A and B are oppositely directed. So presumably these new transfer terms tend to strengthen the antiferromagnetic tendency. It seems, however, somewhat questionable to consider them at all, since we are neglecting all interactions except those between nearest neighbors.

We have discussed primarily the case that U is large compared to T. In the other limit that U is very small compared to T, the nonmagnetic state is clearly lowest, as the total energy is minimized if the deepest states in the band are doubly occupied. If the transfer effect is finally widened in scope to give free electrons (i.e., $U/T = 0$, and the T terms finally flow over into the kinetic energy terms, one gets the Pauli feeble paramagnetism, as long as true exchange is neglected. The antiferromagnetism which we obtain with the U,T model for large U can therefore be regarded as the counterpart for tight binding of the Pauli feeble paramagnetism for loose or no binding.

If ferromagnetism does not ensue from the U,T model if $U/T \gg 1$ or $U/T \ll 1$, one suspects that this is also the case for intermediate ranges of T/U, but of course this is no rigorous proof. In this connection, there are two further papers that can be mentioned which cover the intermediate range with certain approximations. Slater *et al.* (1953) have shown that for a two-dimensional model of a 3×3 lattice containing 9 sites in all, the singlet is lower than the triplet. This is some indication that in slightly filled bands (or slightly empty ones, using holes instead of electrons), there is no ferromagnetism with a U,T model, inasmuch as the simple pair effects presumably dominate the cooperative behavior, if only a relatively small number of sites are occupied. Unfortunately, comparable calculations for a three-dimensional lattice are wanting. Kikuchi (1953) has treated an arbitrary lattice of similar sites by a procedure which is closely allied to the constant coupling approximation of Kasteleijn and van Kranendonk (1956) and Nakamura (1953). The difference is that he allows migration within the pair which is taken as the fundamental cluster. He finds that the U,T model cannot give ferromagnetism with his approximations.

VI. Effect of Degeneracy and Hund's Rule Coupling

How do we get ferromagnetism if it is not provided by the U,T model, and if direct interatomic exchange is negligible? It can creep in when we remove the restriction that there is only one orbital state per atom, and allow the polar states of high multiplicity to be considerably lower than those of lower multiplicity. The non-polar states with parallel spins then can be more depressed by perturbation from polar states than those with antiparallel ones simply because the denominators in the formula for the perturbed energy are smaller, even though the "line-strength" associated with the perturbation is greater if the alignment is antiparallel. This can be seen by looking at a rather schematic model with, say, five orbital states per atom, as in the d-shell, and with the orbital magnetism quenched by the crystalline field, so that we need consider only the magnetic effects of spin. We will assume that there is one electron per site, so that one has the simplest case $n = N$. We also add the rather naive assumption that the transfer integral T is independent of which of the five states the electron lands up on when jumping from one atom to another. One can easily convince oneself that the perturbing line strength is $\frac{6}{4}$ as great in the singlet as in the triplet case, since the Pauli principle does not allow a given electron to land in an already occupied state, so that, so to speak, for $\frac{1}{5}$ of the transitions the line strength is taken out of the triplet and put in the singlet. If we further assume that all the triplet states of a doubly occupied atom have an energy lower than that of the singlets by an amount $2 J_0$, the formula for the effective Hamiltonian analogous to (7) is

$$\mathscr{H}_{\text{eff}} = 2\left(\frac{6T^2}{U + J_0} - \frac{4T^2}{U - J_0}\right)\mathbf{s}_i \cdot \mathbf{s}_j + \text{constant} \tag{8}$$

and ferromagnetism can ensue if $J_0 > U/5$. We have used the notation J_0 for the intra-atomic exchange integral in order to distinguish it from the inter-atomic exchange integral, which is so commonly denoted by J.

According to this view, ferromagnetism can arise only if the intra-atomic exchange integral J_0 is not too small compared with the mean polar energy U. Estimates of U seem to be steadily diminishing with time. The question of the size of U has been reviewed and considered very carefully by Herring (1966), who concludes that U may be only a matter of a volt or so. Among other things a polar lattice has a favorable Madelung energy, and there can be screening of the intra-atomic interaction by penetration by s or p conduction electrons. This screening effect will, incidentally, diminish J_0 as well as U. When one gets to a situation where U, J_0, and T are of the same order of magnitude, one is in a difficult region, for neither an uncorrelated band model nor the localized one such as we have employed is a good starting point for a perturbation calculation. Unfortunately, one seems to be in just this state of affairs in the iron group, and everything that I have said should be regarded as more schematic than realistic. It is simply my feeling that the Hund's rule coupling as originally proposed by Slater is usually an essential ingredient. It may well be (a possibility suggested by Herring, 1966) that there is a near cancellation of many terms, and that the Hund's rule coupling parameter i.e., the intra-atomic exchange integral, even when diminished by screening, is what tips the scales in favor of ferromagnetism. Whether this coupling is also necessary to get localized magnetic states in an otherwise nonmagnetic conductor is a somewhat different question, but the presumption is that if it is responsible for the ferromagnetism of d electrons, then it is also probably needed for them to produce localized states.

ACKNOWLEDGMENTS

The writer is indebted to Professor Henry Ehrenreich for informative discussions, and to Dr. Conyers Herring for the opportunity of seeing the manuscript of his monograph in advance of publication.

REFERENCES

Gutzwiller, M. C. (1963). *Phys. Rev. Letters* **10**, 159.
Gutzwiller, M. C. (1964). *Phys. Rev.* **134**, A923.
Gutzwiller, M. C. (1965). *Phys. Rev.* **137**, A1726.
Herring, C. (1966). "Exchange Interaction among Itinerant Electrons," *In* "Magnetism, A Treatise on Modern Theory and Materials" (G. T. Rado and H. Suhl, eds.), Vol. IV. Academic Press, New York.
Hubbard, J. (1963). *Proc. Roy. Soc. (London)* **A276**, 238.
Hubbard, J. (1964). *Proc. Roy. Soc. (London)* **A277**, 237; **A281**, 401.
Hubbard, J. (1965). *Proc. Roy. Soc. (London)* **A285**, 542.
Kanamori, J. (1963). *Progr. Theoret. Phys. (Kyoto)* **30**, 275.
Kasteleijn, P. W., and van Kranendonk, J. (1956). *Physica* **22**, 317.
Kemble, E. C. (1937). "The Principles of Quantum Mechanics," Sect. 48C. McGraw-Hill, New York. (Reprinted by Dover, New York, 1958.)
Kitkuchi, R. (1953). Progress Report, Solid State and Molecular Theory Group, M.I.T., Jan. 15, April 15.
Lieb, E., and Mattis D. (1962). *Phys. Rev.* **125**, 164.
Mattis, D. (1963). *Phys. Rev.* **132**, 2521.
Mattis, D. (1964). *Physics* **1**, 183.
Nakamura, Y. (1953). *Busseiron Kenkyo* **63**, 12.
Slater, J. C. (1936). *Phys. Rev.* **49**, 537, 931.
Slater, J. C. (1937). *Phys. Rev.* **52**, 198.
Slater, J. C., Statz H., and Koster, G. F. (1953). *Phys. Rev.* **91**, 1323.
Van Vleck, J. H. (1953). *Rev. Mod. Phys.* **25**, 226.
Van Vleck, J. H. (1957). *Nuovo Cimento Suppl.* **6**, 885.

Some Aspects of the Theory of Spin Waves in Metals and Alloys

E. P. WOHLFARTH

DEPARTMENT OF MATHEMATICS, IMPERIAL COLLEGE, LONDON, ENGLAND

I. Introduction

Slater (1937) was the first to describe the properties of spin waves on the basis of energy band theory. His discussion was applicable to ferromagnetic insulators and, under some approximations, leads, among others, to the following result:

If the energy $\hbar\omega_q$ of spin waves with wave vector $\mathbf{q}$ is expanded in even powers of q, then the leading term, corresponding to long wave lengths, is essentially of the form

$$\hbar\omega_q = Dq^2, \tag{1}$$

where

$$D = \tfrac{1}{6}za^2(J - 2W_r^2/I). \tag{2}$$

Here a is the interatomic distance, z the number of nearest neighbors, J the Heisenberg exchange integral for nearest neighbors, W_r the interatomic hopping integral determining the bandwidth and I an energy whose major contribution is the intraatomic Coulomb interaction. The second term in Eq. (2) is in the nature of a superexchange interaction energy, and Slater's analysis thus predates Anderson's discussion (1950, 1959) of the importance of superexchange in magnetic insulators.

Since 1937 there have been several important developments in the theory of spin waves, and it seems appropriate on this occasion to summarize some of these, with particular reference to metallic ferromagnets.

485

The first development to be noted is the establishment of the itinerant electron model of ferromagnetism in metals. Some of the basic ideas of this model had, in fact, also been proposed by Slater (1936a,b), but it was left to Stoner (1938, 1939) to put these ideas on a more systematic basis. Briefly, the model combines the use of Fermi statistics, the concept of single particle excitations in energy bands, and the use of a molecular field to represent the interactions between the single particles. The theoretical status of this model was discussed by Wohlfarth (1953) and more recently in great detail by Herring (1966). Among several relevant results of this work is the condition for ferromagnetism of the single particles, the so-called Stoner criterion,

$$IN(E_F) > 1, \tag{3}$$

where $N(\varepsilon)$ is the density of single particle states per atom and E_F the paramagnetic Fermi energy. It has, however, been shown (Wohlfarth and Rhodes, 1962; Shimizu and Katsuki, 1964; Shimizu, 1964) that a more searching analysis than hitherto, leading in particular to a more reliable criterion for ferromagnetism, is obtainable by considering the total course of curves relating the total energy E as a function of the relative magnetization ζ at $0°K$. This type of analysis shows that ferromagnetism may set in even where (3) is not obeyed. A discussion of E, ζ curves is given in Section II which includes an example of the insufficiency of (3).

Another development is the theoretical discussion of the properties of spin waves in metals. Their very existence in metals was at one time taken to obviate the itinerant electron model, but such is no longer the case. First Herring (1952a,b) and later many others showed quite clearly that the two types of excitations (single particle and spin wave) are fully capable of peaceful coexistence, and that a dispersion relation between spin wave energy and wave vector can be established for particular assumptions. For a particular set of assumptions [(1) a single band of itinerant electrons, (2) the only interaction is the short range, intraatomic interaction which is reduced from I to I_{eff} by correlation and/or conduction electron screening, (3) the interaction entering the expression for the spin wave energy is the same as that determining the properties of the single particles] the dispersion relation is of the form (1) but with D containing, apart from the superexchange term in (2), a kinetic energy term corresponding to the motion of the single particles and zero only in the insulating limit. The first term in (2) does not occur for this set of assumptions.

A brief discussion of spin waves in metals and the derivation of D (see, for example, Izuyama and Kubo, 1964; Englert and Antonoff, 1964) is given in Section III. The resulting formula is, however, unwieldy as complicated summations over the single particle $\mathbf{k}$-space are involved. Hence work is now in progress to calculate D and to assess its properties for some simple forms of the single particle energy and for limiting values of the relative magnetization ζ. Some of the results already obtained are discussed in Section IV. It is found that in some cases D is positive if (3) or a more relevant criterion is obeyed and that in some of these cases D vanishes together with ζ. Elsewhere, D may be negative under these circumstances so that, in line with the discussion of Mattis (1965) and others, the ferromagnetic ground state must be unstable compared with one corresponding, presumably, to antiferromagnetic ordering or a spiral spin configuration. In one case discussed in Section IV both the criterion for ferromagnetism of the single particles and the sign of D indicate a stable ferromagnetic ground state although this seems to be forbidden here by the Lieb-Mattis theorem (1962). Hence even more searching methods are needed to test the ground state for stability. (See Penn (1966) and Katsuki and Wohlfarth (1966) for more recent work.)

A third development since 1937 has been the introduction of various experimental measurements of D. One of the most fruitful of these involves the small angle neutron scattering technique (Hatherly *et al.*, 1964; Shirane *et al.*, 1965); this has been applied to a wide range of ferromagnetic metals and alloys and published and unpublished data are reproduced in Section V (by courtesy of Lowde, Stringfellow, and their colleagues). The question arises how these data are to be interpreted in the absence of reliable calculated values of D corresponding to the band structure of these alloys. As discussed semi-quantitatively in Section IV, for want of a more reliable comparison it seems not unreasonable to correlate D roughly with the Curie temperature T_c. This correlation is shown in Section V to be as good as can be expected.

II. Itinerant Electron Ferromagnetism at 0°K

On the basis of the premises listed in Section I it is possible (Wohlfarth and Rhodes, 1962) to obtain the total energy of a ferromagnetic metal as a function of the relative magnetization ζ at 0°K in the form

$$E(\zeta) = \int_{E_F}^{E_F^+} \varepsilon N(\varepsilon)\, d\varepsilon - \int_{E_F^-}^{E_F} \varepsilon N(\varepsilon)\, d\varepsilon - \tfrac{1}{2} n k_B \theta' \zeta^2, \tag{4}$$

where

$$\tfrac{1}{2} n \zeta = \int_{E_F}^{E_F^+} N(\varepsilon)\, d\varepsilon = \int_{E_F^-}^{E_F} N(\varepsilon)\, d\varepsilon. \tag{4a}$$

Here n is the number of particles per atom, $E_F^\pm$ are the Fermi energies for the $\pm$ spins, and

$$k_B \theta' = \tfrac{1}{2} n I_{\text{eff}}. \tag{5}$$

Minimizing $E(\zeta)$ gives

$$E_F^+ - E_F^- = \Delta E = 2 k_B \theta' \zeta, \tag{5a}$$

this being the so-called exchange or molecular field splitting (Wohlfarth, 1965). Ferromagnetism then occurs if $E(\zeta)$ has a maximum at $\zeta = 0$ and a minimum or extremum at a finite value of ζ. Since

$$\frac{d^2E(\zeta)}{d\zeta^2} = \frac{1}{4} n^2 \left\{ \frac{1}{N(E_F^+)} + \frac{1}{N(E_F^-)} \right\} - nk_B\theta', \qquad (6)$$

this is the case if (3) is satisfied ($I \rightarrow I_{\text{eff}}$). However (Shimizu and Katsuki, 1964; Shimizu, 1964) the function $E(\zeta)$ may well have a *minimum* at $\zeta = 0$, so that (3) is not satisfied, but reach a further minimum or extremum at a finite value of ζ where

$$E(\zeta) < E(0). \qquad (7)$$

Apart from the question whether (7) really implies that this second equilibrium state is indeed invariably attained, the possibility thus exists that the Stoner criterion is not always a reliable guide to the occurrence of ferromagnetism.

The above authors show that this situation is likely to occur if E_F lies near a minimum of the $N(\varepsilon)$ curve, and it is thus of interest to consider as an example the unrealistic case of a linear metal in the tight binding approximation as here the single particle energy $\varepsilon(\mathbf{k})$ used in the calculation of D in Section IV is known and the $N(\varepsilon)$ curve has a positive curvature. Here

$$\varepsilon(k) = W\sin^2 \tfrac{1}{2}ak, \qquad N(\varepsilon) = \{\pi\varepsilon(W - \varepsilon)\}^{-1/2}, \qquad (8)$$

where W is the bandwidth. If $\beta = \tfrac{1}{2}n\pi$, then

$$E(\zeta) = \frac{1}{\pi} W\sin\beta\{1 - \cos(\beta\zeta) - (j\beta^2/\pi\sin\beta)\zeta^2\}, \qquad (9)$$

where $j = I_{\text{eff}}/W$. The Stoner criterion is thus $j > j_S$, where

$$j_S = \tfrac{1}{2}\pi\sin\beta, \qquad (10)$$

while ferromagnetism actually occurs when $j > j_c$, where

$$j_c = j_S\{2\sin(\tfrac{1}{2}\beta)/\beta\}^2 \leq j_S. \qquad (11)$$

For other forms of $\varepsilon(\mathbf{k})$ and $N(\varepsilon)$, such as a band where the curvature of $N(\varepsilon)$ is predominantly negative, the Stoner criterion is, however, relevant.

III. Summary of the Theory of Spin Waves in Metals

For the set of assumptions listed in Section I the Hamiltonian may be expressed in terms of destruction and creation operators c, c^* in the form

(Herring, 1966; Izuyama and Kubo, 1964; Englert and Antonoff, 1964; and others)

$$\mathscr{H} = \sum_{k,\sigma} \varepsilon(k)c_{k\sigma}^* c_{k\sigma} + \frac{1}{2} \sum_{qkk'\sigma\sigma'} V(q)c_{k+q\sigma}^* c_{k'-q\sigma'}^* c_{k'\sigma'} c_{k\sigma}. \tag{12}$$

Here $\varepsilon(k)$ is the single particle energy, σ, σ' are spin operators and $V(q)$ is the Fourier transform of the interaction energy. In later applications this will be taken to be determined only by the intraatomic interaction I_{eff}, when $V(q)$ is independent of q. The equation of motion for the operator $S_q(k)$, which corresponds to the removal of a particle with $+$ spin in a state k to a state $k + q$ and a reversal of the spin to $-$, and which is thus given by

$$S_q(k) = c_{k+q-}^* c_{k+}, \tag{13}$$

is

$$i\hbar \dot{S}_q(k) = [S_q(k), \mathscr{H}]; \tag{14}$$

this may be solved by using the random phase approximation. In terms of unknown coefficients $\alpha_q(k, \omega)$, which define the spin wave operator $\eta_q(\omega)$ associated with a frequency ω and are given by

$$\eta_q(\omega) = \sum_k \alpha_q(k, \omega)S_q(k), \tag{15}$$

the equation of motion is transformed to

$$[\hbar\omega_q - \varepsilon(k + q) + \varepsilon(k) - 2V(0)\zeta]\alpha_q(k, \omega)$$

$$+ \frac{2}{n}\sum_{k'} (f_{k'}^+ - f_{k'+q}^-)V(q)\alpha_q(k',\omega) = 0, \tag{16}$$

so that

$$1 + \frac{2}{n}V(q)\sum_k \frac{f_k^+ - f_{k+q}^-}{\hbar\omega_q - \varepsilon(k + q) + \varepsilon(k) - 2V(0)\zeta} = 0, \tag{17}$$

where the $f^{\pm}$ are Fermi functions and ζ is the relative magnetization. By considering the behavior of (17) in the complex $\omega-$ plane it may be shown that (17) has two types of solutions: (1) Excitations of the single particles in the energy band,

$$\hbar\omega_q = \varepsilon(k + q) - \varepsilon(k) + 2V(0)\zeta; \tag{18}$$

these commence at $q = 0$ at an energy equal to the exchange splitting

$$\Delta E = 2V(0)\zeta = 2k_B\theta'\zeta = nI_{eff}\zeta \tag{19}$$

above the ground state. (2) Spin waves which are low lying and have an energy which vanishes at $q = 0$ and which departs from the origin for small q

according to (1), with D now given (for a cubic metal) by

$$D = \mathop{L}_{q \to 0} \frac{2[V(0) - V(\mathbf{q})]\zeta}{q^2} + \frac{1}{3}\sum_{\mathbf{k}}\left[\frac{f_{\mathbf{k}}^+ + f_{\mathbf{k}}^-}{2}\nabla_{\mathbf{k}}^2\varepsilon(\mathbf{k})\right.$$

$$\left. - \frac{f_{\mathbf{k}}^+ - f_{\mathbf{k}}^-}{\Delta E}(\nabla_{\mathbf{k}}(\varepsilon(\mathbf{k}))^2\right]\bigg/\sum_{\mathbf{k}}(f_{\mathbf{k}}^+ - f_{\mathbf{k}}^-). \qquad (20)$$

The first term in (20) is equivalent to the first term in (2) and involves inter-actions of the Heisenberg type which will no longer be considered in the fol-lowing. The second term is the kinetic energy term which vanishes in the insulating limit and thus does not occur in (2). The last, superexchange, term in (20) does occur in (2), in rudimentary form.

In order to calculate the complete spin wave spectrum, (17) must be considered as it stands. In this way higher order terms in $\hbar\omega_{\mathbf{q}}$ (recently observ-ed by Shirane et al., 1965; Weber and Tannenwald, 1965) could be calculated. Eventually the two solutions of (17) will merge when $q = q_{max}$, say; for $q > q_{max}$ the spin waves are damped with a short life time.

IV. Theoretical Calculations of D

Equation (20) for D, with the first term excluded in the present approxima-tions, is a complicated expression involving, as it does, intricate summations in $\mathbf{k}$-space. Thus, though these approximations are rather restrictive, it is even then not easy to obtain reliable values of D for any specific ferromagnetic metal or alloy since $\varepsilon(\mathbf{k})$ curves and their derivatives are not generally known with sufficient accuracy and since interband effects must in any case be very important. The attack on D has therefore had to be two-pronged: (1) Calculate D for some simple forms of $\varepsilon(\mathbf{k})$ in order to gain some feeling for the proper-ties of this function; (2) attempt, on the basis of such calculations, to obtain some other property of real materials with which D may be expected to have some degree of correlation.

The first type of energy band used in calculating D corresponded to the effective mass approximation (Herring, 1952b; Thompson, 1963, Mattis, 1963). It is found that at $0°K$, and with $\zeta < 1$,

$$D = \frac{\hbar^2}{2m^*}\frac{1}{\zeta}\{1 - g(\zeta)\},$$

where

$$g(x) = \tfrac{2}{5}[(1 + x)^{5/3} - (1 - x)^{5/3}]/[(1 + x)^{2/3} - (1 - x)^{2/3}], \qquad (21)$$

while if $\zeta = 1$, i.e., $\Delta E > 2^{2/3}E_F$,

$$D = \frac{\hbar^2}{2m^*}\{1 - 2^{8/3}E_F/5\Delta E\}. \qquad (21)^*$$

If ζ is small, expansion of (21) gives

$$D = \hbar^2\zeta/18m^* + O(\zeta^3), \tag{22}$$

so that here D vanishes exactly where ζ vanishes, i.e., where $I_{eff}N(E_F) = 1$. It may be shown (Doniach and Wohlfarth, 1965) that the proportionality of D with ζ in this limit is a general consequence of the form of (20) and is not just a consequence of the effective mass approximation. If the Stoner criterion is not relevant, however (see Section II), the situation is more complicated, as discussed below. Where this difficulty does not arise it has been found by Thompson *et al.* (1964) that the Curie temperature T_c and the value of ζ at $0°K$ are proportional in this limit. Hence

$$D \sim k_B T_c a^2 f(n) + O(T_c^3), \tag{23}$$

where a is the lattice constant and n the number of electrons per atom. For the effective mass approximation

$$D = (\pi/6\sqrt{2})(k_B T_c/k_F^2) + O(T_c^3), \tag{23*}$$

where k_F is the Fermi momentum, so that here $f(n) \sim n^{-2/3}$. Since for most ferromagnetic alloys T_c varies more rapidly with composition than does n it appears that some degree of correlation is to be expected between D and T_c, even where this is not small. This correlation, derived here as a rough guide from a preliminary consideration of the form of the spin wave spectrum in the weakly magnetic metallic limit, is also found in what may be regarded as the opposite limit, that where the Heisenberg model alone is applicable. Here (Hatherly *et al.*, 1964)

$$D \sim k_B T_c a^2/(S + 1), \tag{24}$$

where S is the localized spin. The degree of correlation between D and T_c actually found is shown in Section V.

Further calculations of D are needed for other types of energy band so as to see how general are the results for the parabolic band quoted above. As a first attempt D was calculated for the unrealistic case of a linear metal where $\varepsilon(k)$ and $N(\varepsilon)$ are given by (8). It is found that at $0°K$,

$$\frac{D}{Wa^2} = \frac{1}{8\beta}\left\{\sin 2\beta - \frac{\pi}{8j\beta}(4\beta - \sin 4\beta)\right\}, \tag{25}$$

where W is the bandwidth, $j = I_{eff}/W$, and $\beta = \frac{1}{2}n\pi$; it is assumed that $j > j_c$, where j_c is given by (11), when $\zeta = 1$. The first term in (25) gives the kinetic energy contribution which is seen to vanish correctly when $n = 1$, i.e. in the insulating limit. The second term gives the superexchange contribution analogous to that in (2); when the zone is full ($n = 1$, $\zeta = 1$)

$$D = -W^2 a^2/8I_{eff}. \tag{26}$$

On the other hand, if n is small the superexchange term also becomes small and D is determined mainly by the kinetic energy term; if $n \to 0$ ($\zeta = 1$),

$$D = \tfrac{1}{4}Wa^2. \tag{27}$$

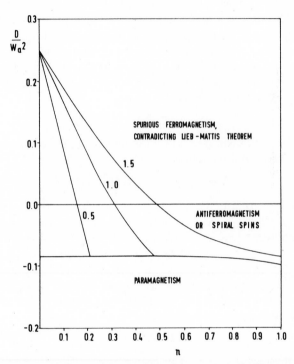

FIG. 1. Variation of coefficient D with electron/atom ratio n of a linear metal. Numbers on curves $j = I_{eff}/W$; I_{eff}, effective interaction; W, bandwidth; a, interatomic distance.

Fig. 1 shows the relation between D/Wa^2 and n for a range of values of j; for each of these there is an *upper* limit to n determined by the condition $j > j_c$ (this effect results from the form of the $N(\varepsilon)$ curve). Beyond this range the metal is paramagnetic ($\zeta = 0$). For another range of n, as shown, D is negative so that the ferromagnetic ground state is unstable; here the metal is presumably antiferromagnetic or has a spiral spin configuration. Finally, for small values of n, as already implied by (27), D is positive and $j > j_c$, so that on the basis of these two criteria alone the metal should have a ferromagnetic ground state. Since the Lieb-Mattis theorem (1962) forbids this in the present case, however, it seems that further criteria for ferromagnetism must be sought, both here and possibly also in more realistic cases. It may be, for example, that, although D is positive, the whole spin wave spectrum

$\hbar\omega_q$ reaches negative values at some larger values of q. On the other hand, the Lieb-Mattis Theorem does not apply in the presence of Heisenberg exchange. It is thus of interest that the exchange integral J needed to stabilize the ferromagnetic ground state for the above calculation is small for all three values of I_{eff} shown in Fig. 1, where the largest negative value of D is only about $-0.1\ Wa^2$.

Calculations of D are now in progress (Katsuki and Wohlfarth, 1966) for three-dimensional models of a metal, and diagrams of the type shown in Fig. 1 are being obtained. The problems treated are not unrelated to those discussed by Penn (1966) regarding the stability of magnetic metals.

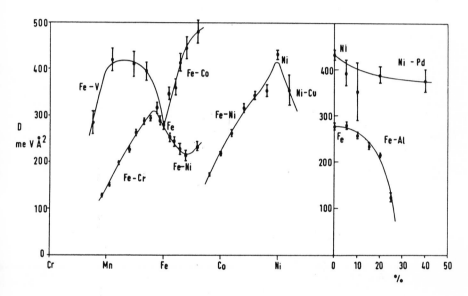

FIG. 2.   (a) Experimental values of D for ferromagnetic alloys (for references, see text).

V. Experimental Values of D of Ferromagnetic Alloys

Measurements of D using the small-angle neutron scattering technique were made as follows: B.C.C. Fe—Ni, Fe—Co, Fe—Cr, Fe—V (Lowde *et al.*, 1965), Fe—Al (Antonini *et al.*, 1966), F.C.C. Fe—Ni (Hatherly *et al.*, 1964), Ni—Pd (Stringfellow and Torrie, 1964), Ni—Cu (Stringfellow, 1965). Values of the Curie temperature T_c are given in the normal literature and have been collected for the present purpose by Stringfellow. The variation of D and T_c is shown in Figs. 2(a) and 2(b), respectively. Apart from some obvious

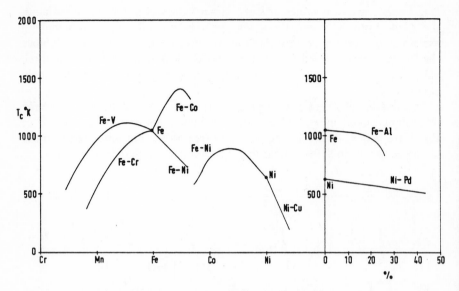

FIG. 2.   (b) Experimental values of Curie temperature T_c.

deviations between the two sets of curves the over-all qualitative correlation is
reasonable, but not sufficiently so that the theoretical discussion of this paper
can be said to be entirely vindicated. Clearly, further experimental and theoretical work in this rewarding field is necessary.

ACKNOWLEDGMENTS

It gives me great pleasure to acknowledge the helpful discussions and assistance from
R. D. Lowde, M. W. Stringfellow, S. Doniach, D. M. Edwards, and A. Katsuki.

REFERENCES

Anderson, P. W. (1950). *Phys. Rev.* **79**, 350.
Anderson, P. W. (1959). *Phys. Rev.* **115**, 2.
Antonini, B., Lowde, R. D., and Stringfellow, M. W. (1966). To be published.
Doniach, S., and Wohlfarth, E. P. (1965). *Phys. Letters* **18**, 209.
Englert, F., and Antonoff, M. M. (1964). *Physica* **30**, 429.
Hatherly, M., Hirakawa, K., Lowde, R. D., Mallett, J. F., Stringfellow, M. W., and Torrie,
    B. H. (1964). *Proc. Phys. Soc.* **84**, 55.
Herring, C. (1952a). *Phys. Rev.* **85**, 1003.
Herring, C. (1952b). *Phys. Rev.* **87**, 60.
Herring, C. (1966). *In* "Magnetism" (G. T. Rado and H. Suhl, eds.), Vol. IV. Academic,
    New York.

Izuyama, T., and Kubo, R. (1964). *J. Appl. Phys.* **35**, 1074.
Katsuki, A., and Wohlfarth, E. P. (1966). *Proc. Roy. Soc.* To be published.
Lieb, E., and Mattis, D. C. (1962). *Phys. Rev.* **125**, 164.
Lowde, R. D., Shimizu, M., Stringfellow, M. W., and Torrie, B. H. (1965). *Phys. Rev. Letters* **14**, 698.
Mattis, D. C. (1963). *Phys. Rev.* **132**, 2521.
Mattis, D. C. (1965). "Theory of Magnetism." Harper, New York.
Penn, D. R. (1966). *Phys. Rev.* **142**, 350.
Shimizu, M. (1964). *Proc. Phys. Soc.* **84**, 397.
Shimizu, M., and Katsuki, A. (1964). *Phys. Letters* **8**, 7.
Shirane, G., Nathans, R., Steinsvoll, O., Alperin, H. A., and Pickart, S. J. (1965). *Phys. Rev. Letters* **15**, 146.
Slater, J. C. (1936a). *Phys. Rev.* **49**, 537.
Slater, J. C. (1936b). *Phys. Rev.* **49**, 931.
Slater, J. C. (1937). *Phys. Rev.* **52**, 198.
Stoner, E. C. (1938). *Proc. Roy. Soc.* **A165**, 372.
Stoner, E. C. (1939). *Proc. Roy. Soc.* **A169**, 339.
Stringfellow, M. W. (1965). Unpublished.
Stringfellow, M. W., and Torrie, B. H. (1964). Unpublished.
Thompson, E. D. (1963). *Ann. Phys. (N.Y.)* **22**, 309.
Thompson, E. D., Wohlfarth, E. P., and Bryan, A. C. (1964). *Proc. Phys. Soc.* **83**, 59.
Weber, R., and Tannenwald, P. E. (1965). *Phys. Rev.* **140**, A498.
Wohlfarth, E. P. (1963). *Rev. Mod. Phys.* **25**, 211.
Wohlfarth, E. P. (1965). *Proc. Intern. Conf. Magnetism, Nottingham*, p. 51.
Wohlfarth, E. P., and Rhodes, P. (1962). *Phil. Mag.* **7**, 1817.

Band Structure of Transition Metals Calculated by the Green's Function Method

J. YAMASHITA, S. WAKOH, and S. ASANO

THE INSTITUTE FOR SOLID STATE PHYSICS
THE UNIVERSITY OF TOKYO, TOKYO, JAPAN

I. Introduction

It has become apparent that the understanding of metallic ferromagnetism and antiferromagnetism is a central problem at present in solid state physics. In the study of metallic ferromagnetism two extreme models, the itinerant model and the localized model, are usually adopted. Since neither of them seems to be adequate for accurate description of d-electrons in transition metals, a number of investigators are making an effort to find a way in the middle of these two extremes.

It must be noticed, however, that the one-electron band theory still seems to be important, because it allows qualitative, sometimes semiquantitative, descriptions of many properties of transition metals. Further, it is hoped that the one-electron band model is useful as a starting point to more sophisticated treatments. Therefore, it seems to be adequate to work out the band structure of transition metals, especially in the ferromagnetic and antiferromagnetic states, with a detailed examination of the basic assumptions on which the band structure is derived.

Recently, the shape of the Fermi surface of some transition metals has been elucidated experimentally by several investigators using various powerful

497

methods, so that it becomes possible to examine whether or not the band theory
is able to produce the shape of the Fermi surface determined by experiments.

It is a somewhat complicated problem to calculate the band structure of
transition metals. Both the augmented plane wave method (Slater, 1937) and
the Green's function method (Kohn and Rostoker, 1954), however, have
proved to be sufficiently accurate ones. The extensive study on the band
structure of transition metals by the APW method has been done by Slater's
group (Slater, 1965). On the other hand, the GFM was applied to copper by
Segall (1962) and to transition metals by the authors of this article (Yamashita
et al., 1963). Although the wave equation is accurately solved in a given
potential, it remains a difficult problem to choose a suitable crystal potential.
Unfortunately, we have not yet found a practical method to derive the best
one-electron potential from the first principle. The determination of the
crystal potential will be the main subject in Section III.

In this paper, we shall mention the band structure of ferromagnetic iron
and nickel, and the antiferromagnetic chromiun putting special emphasis on
the shape of the Fermi surface.

Another important problem is to elucidate the electronic structure of
transition-metal alloys. In general, the problem is a very difficult one, because
the mathematical difficulties inherent to a disordered system prevent the
proper development of the theory. The electronic structure of a simple
superlattice of transition elements is, however, easily evaluated by the APW
method or by the GFM. Here, we shall mention the results of calculation on
the electronic structure of the ferromagnetic superlattice CoFe.

II. Methods of Computation

The computational procedure used here is the Green's function method.
The wave function is expanded within an inscribed sphere, and the $l = 0, 1$,
and 2 components are considered. The energy values are evaluated at the
points of high symmetry in the Brillouin zone. The evaluation of the energy
at general points takes too much time, so the interpolation method developed
by Slater and Koster (1954) is adopted to calculate the energy value at general
points. The density-of-states is evaluated from the energy values thus calculated at many points in the Brillouin zone, and then the Fermi surface is
calculated as a function of the wave number vector by the GFM. The wave
function is also calculated by the GFM. The perturbation method is used to
obtain the wave function outside the inscribed sphere.

Besides the GFM the APW method is also used to calculate the energy
values and the wave functions of the superlattice CoFe at points of high
symmetry. The APW method is quite suitable for the calculation of the wave
function outside the inscribed sphere.

III. The Determination of the Potential

The periodic potential which we use for determination of energy bands must be in some sense a self-consistent potential. The construction of the Hartree-Fock potential, however, is out of question owing to computational difficulties. Further, it is not at all obvious that the HF potential is the best effective potential, because the correlation effect may be very important in the study of d-electrons in transition metals. Therefore, we must have some simple procedure by which the crystal potential is determined from the knowledge of the Bloch functions below the Fermi surface. Here, such potential will be called "effective potential." In general, the effective potential will depend upon the wave number vector as well as upon the quantum number l, but it is much easier to choose an effective potential—that is a function of position only. At the present stage of development of the theory, the effective potential is justified only when it leads to results in agreement with experiment, so that the band theory is not completely free from the phenomenological character.

As the first approximation the crystal potential is assumed to be

$$V_0(\text{metal}) = V(\text{free ion}) + V(\text{single OPW}),$$

where $V(\text{free ion})$ is the Chodorow potential for the 3d HF function of the free $(\text{metal})^+$ ion, and $V(\text{single OPW})$ is the potential due to conduction electrons whose wave function is assumed to be the single OPW function. In the next approximation the potential is assumed to be given by

$$V(\text{metal}) = V(\text{free ion}) + V_c(\text{metal}) - V_c(\text{atom}) + V_{ex}(\text{metal}) - V_{ex}(\text{atom}).$$

Here, $V_c(\text{atom})$ is the Coulomb potential due to the atomic 3d electrons, and $V_{ex}(\text{atom})$ is the exchange potential in the configuration of the free atom, which is calculated by the Hartree-Fock-Slater free-electron approximation. The Coulomb potential, $V_c(\text{metal})$, is determined from the charge distribution of all electrons in the 3d and the conduction bands. The potential due to the conduction electron is evaluated from the knowledge of the wave function at the energy of $E(\Gamma_1) + \frac{3}{5}E_F$ and a number of the conduction electrons. The charge distribution of d-like electrons is calculated at seven energy values in the 3d bands. After the 3d wave function is evaluated, and is averaged through angle variables and is normalized in the Wigner-Seitz cell, the charge distribution is determined as a function of position for each of seven energy parameters. By multiplying a weight, which is obtained from the density-of-states of the d-bands, to each of seven functions of the charge distribution, and summing them up, we obtain the total charge distribution of the 3d electrons. The exchange potential of the metal, $V_{ex}(\text{metal})$, is evaluated again by the method of HFS free electron approximation. Since the crystal potential and the wave functions are thus interrelated, they must be determined self-consistently.

The energy band of copper is computed to test the potential mentioned previously. The results are in good agreement with those obtained by Segall with the Chodorow potential. For the purpose of illustration, the relative energy values obtained by the self-consistent potential are listed in Table 1, together with those obtained in earlier calculations (Wakoh, 1965).

TABLE 1

Some Band Energies[a] of Copper Obtained by Various Potentials'

Potential	$\Gamma_{25'} - \Gamma_1$	$X_5 - \Gamma_1$	$X_5 - X_1$
Segall	0.331	0.470	0.300
Chodorow	0.399	0.516	0.249
Mattheiss	0.468	0.572	0.250
Present	0.386	0.499	0.245

[a] In rydberg units.

IV. Results

A. FERROMAGNETIC IRON

In a ferromagnetic state the up-spin electrons and the down-spin electrons move in the different self-consistent potential. The difference in the potential is taken into account through the exchange potential:

$$\lambda\{V_{ex}(\text{metal}) - V_{ex}(\text{atom})\},$$

where λ is an adjustable parameter, which is determined so as to make the number of the down-spin electrons 5.1, and that of the up-spin electrons 2.9 per atom. As the result of calculation the value of λ is determined as 0.5. The $E(k)$ curves thus obtained are illustrated in Fig. 1. The Fermi energy is calculated as -0.142 Ry, and the temperature coefficient of the electronic specific heat, γ, is evaluated as 9.4×10^{-4} cal/mole deg^2, while the observed value is 12×10^{-4} cal/mole deg^2. The bandwidth $(H_{25'} - H_{12})$ is also evaluated as 0.395 Ry for the up-spin band, and 0.352 Ry for the down-spin band. The exchange splitting energy is not a constant, but depends on the state, for example, 1.78 eV at Γ_{12} and 0.46 eV at Γ_1.

Next, let us discuss the shape of the Fermi surface derived from the magneto-resistance observed by Reed and Fawcett (1964, 1965). Experimental data are consistent with the behavior of a compensated metal. From the band structure obtained here, it can be seen easily, that the numbers of electrons on the electron sheets and holes on the hole sheets are equal. The result of the observation is illustrated in Fig. 2. On the other hand, the Fermi surface

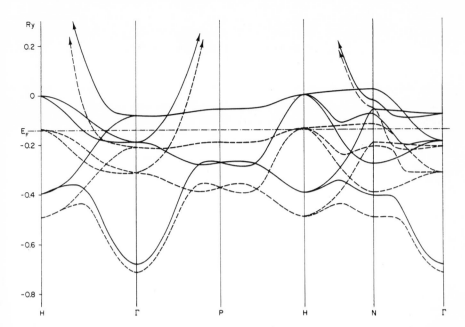

FIG. 1. The calculated bands for ferromagnetic iron along the various symmetric axes in the Brillouin zone. Solid curves represent the spin-up bands and dashed curves represent the spin-down bands. E_F denotes the Fermi energy.

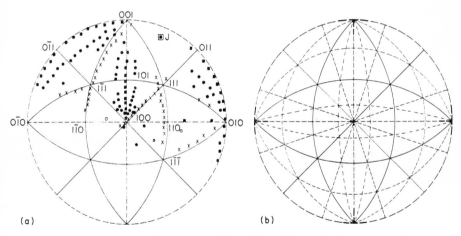

(a)

(b)

FIG. 2. (a) Stereogram showing the position of the minimum in the magnetoresistance rotation curves for an iron whisker. The current direction J is indicated by a double square, the minima near the dashed-line (100) planes by ■ and □ (the latter corresponding to the back of the stereogram), the minima near the continuous-line (110) planes by X, and the shallow minima in non-symmetry direction by ●. (After Reed and Fawcett, 1965.)

(b) Stereogram which corresponds to Fig. 2(a), obtained by the theory. The full line shows the position of the minima due to the open orbit in the [110] direction, the heavy broken line due to that in the [001] direction on the hole-like surface, the light broken line due to that in the [001] direction on the electron-like surface, and the dotted line due to that in the [130] direction. It corresponds to the black circle in (a).

obtained by the present calculation is shown in Fig. 3 (the up-spin band), and in Fig. 4 (the down-spin band). As seen from Fig. 4, there appear an electron Fermi surface around the Γ point and two small hole pockets around the H point. The holelike multiply connected surface exists in the [1, 1, 0]

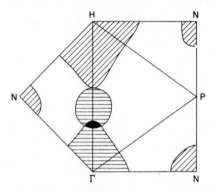

FIG. 3. Intersection of (110) and (100) up-spin planes with the Fermi energy for ferromagnetic iron.

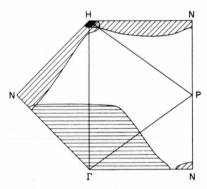

FIG. 4. Intersection of (110) and (100) down-spin planes with the Fermi energy for ferromagnetic iron.

direction, which connects the H points. Therefore, the open orbit is observable, whenever the magnetic field exists in the {1, 1, 0} plane. [It corresponds to the full line in Fig. 2(b).] According to the theory, the open orbit in the [0, 0, 1] direction is observable, only when the magnetic field exists in the {0, 0, 1} plane within an angle of 8° from the [1, 0, 0] axis. [It is shown by the heavy broken line in Fig. 2(b).] According to the experiment, however, the open orbit exists when the angle is beyond 8°. This may be interpreted by the occurrence of the magnetic breakdown phenomenon at the Δ_5 axis on the Fermi surface of the up-spin bands (Fig. 3). Further, the open orbit in the [1, 3, 0] direction seems to be observed by Fawcett and Reed.

The de Haas-van Alphen studies were carried out by Anderson and Gold (1963). They observed the oscillations of the period $(2.16 \pm 0.15) \times 10^{-7} \, G^{-1}$ in a [100] whisker, and the period $(2.71 \pm 0.16) \times 10^{-7} \, G^{-1}$ in a [110] whisker. The observed period will be ascribed to the lense in the up-spin Fermi surface. The period is anisotropic, and it is estimated to be $2–5 \times 10^{-7} \, G^{-1}$, but it is rather sensitive to the choice of the potential. The effective mass is also determined as $0.25 \, m_0$ by the experiment. The corresponding value is estimated as $0.26 \, m_0$ by the detailed calculation of the energy values near the lense surface.

The wave function of both spin states are evaluated. The wave function of the down-spin electrons is a little contracted as compared with that of the up-spin electrons because of the difference in the exchange potential. As a result, it is expected that the direction of the spin polarization is reversed at the boundary region of the Wigner-Seitz cell, where the density of the up-spin electrons is beyond the density of the down-spin electrons in spite of the minority of the former. Of course, the polarization of s-electrons must be considered in order to discuss the experimental result.

B. Ferromagnetic Nickel

The band structure of both paramagnetic and ferromagnetic nickel was worked out by the tightbinding approximation (Flecher and Wohlfarth, 1951), by the APW method (Hanus, 1962; Mattheiss, 1964), and by the GFM (Yamashita *et al.*, 1963; Wakoh and Yamashita, 1964). From these works it becomes apparent that the band theory is able to produce the main observed character of the Fermi surface in ferromagnetic nickel. The self-consistent potential mentioned previously is also applicable to this problem. If we assume that $\lambda = 1$, the self-consistent potential gives the following results (Wakoh, 1965). The number of up-spin electrons is estimated as 4.67 and that of down-spin electrons as 5.33, so that the Bohr magneton number is evaluated as 0.66, while the experimental value is 0.6. The s-band of down-spin electrons has a neck around the L point. The calculated value of the radius of the neck is about 1.25 times of the observed value. The density-of-states curve has a high peak near the Fermi energy. The value of γ of the electronic specific heat is estimated from the theory as $14 \times 10^{-4} \, cal/mole \, deg^2$, while the observed value is $17 \times 10^{-4} \, cal/mole \, deg^2$. The mixing ratio of the γ-components and the ε-components of the unbalanced d-electron numbers is determined by the theory as 27.4% and 72.6%, respectively. The corresponding experimental values are 27% and 73%, respectively. In the case of iron, we have also obtained good agreement; that is, the theoretical values are 53.7% and 46.3% respectively, while the experimental values are 53% and 47%, respectively.

C. ANTIFERROMAGNETIC CHROMIUM

It is not at all obvious that the one-electron band theory is able to explain why chromium exhibits metallic antiferromagnetism. It is expected, however, that many experimental facts on antiferromagnetic chromium are derived from the band theory, if once the antiferromagnetic state is assumed to be realized in Cr. Some results of a preliminary calculation follow.

First, we consider a metallic chromium in a complete antiferromagnetic state. Then, the problem is to calculate the band structure of a CsCl-type superlattice, where spin-dependence of the potential is taken into account self-consistently by the HFS free-electron approximation (Slater and Koster, 1954). Here, the number difference between the up-spin electrons and the down-spin electron on each atom is assumed to be 0.6. Then, the spin dependent potential is given by

$$V_\uparrow(\text{Cr} \uparrow) = V_\downarrow(\text{Cr} \downarrow) = V_{sc} - \Delta V_{ex}$$

and

$$V_\uparrow(\text{Cr} \downarrow) = V_\downarrow(\text{Cr} \uparrow) = V_{sc} + \Delta V_{ex},$$

where $V_\uparrow$ means the potential for up-spin electrons, $V_\downarrow$ for down-spin electrons, $\text{Cr} \uparrow$ means the lattice site which is normally occupied by up-spin electrons and $\text{Cr} \downarrow$ the lattice site normally occupied by down-spin electrons, and V_{sc} is the potential in the paramagnetic state, which is determined self-consistently by the method mentioned in Section III. The exchange potential ΔV_{ex} is expressed as:

$$\Delta V_{ex} = \lambda \times 6\{(3\rho/4\pi)^{1/3} - (3\rho_0/4\pi)^{1/3}\}$$

Here,

$$\rho = \rho_0 + \delta\rho,$$

where $2\rho_0$ is the total charge density, and $\delta\rho$ is calculated from the d-wave functions of the states being situated in a part of the k-space just below the Fermi surface, which contains 0.3 electrons per atom. The two values, 0.5 and 1, are assigned to the parameter λ. The $E(k)$ curves thus obtained are illustrated in Fig. 5. As seen from the figure, the energy gap appears near the Fermi surface on the Σ and Λ axes. It is important to note that this gap is widely extended in the k-space and appears mostly near the Fermi surface. In fact, there is an electron Fermi surface around Γ and a hole Fermi surface around H in the paramagnetic chromium. (The Fermi surface is almost identical to that illustrated in Fig. 3.) In the antiferromagnetic chromium, however, two surfaces are overlapped in the Brillouin zone of a simple cubic type, so as to bring about the energy gap. It is a remarkable fact that the energy gap appears on almost whole areas where the electron surface around Γ and the hole surface around H contact each other. Only the small regions around the Δ axes are exceptional. Let us look at the lower boundary surface of the energy gap that separates the allowed region from the forbidden one. The energy value at a point on this surface is a function of the direction of a k-vector. There are local maximums on this surface, and the holes exist near these maximum points. It is another remarkable fact that the energy values of all local maximum points are nearly equal, that is, the difference is at most 0.005 Ry.

By comparing the band energy of the antiferromagnetic state $E_A(k)$ with that of the paramagnetic state, $E_P(k)$ we see that the following relations are satisfied:

$$E_A(k) < E_P(k), \quad \text{when} \quad E_P(k) < E_F,$$

and

$$E_A(k) > E_P(k), \quad \text{when} \quad E_P(k) > E_F$$

with a few exceptions near the Fermi surface. In general, the amount of the energy difference is quite small, (the order of 0.001 Ry), but it becomes larger near the boundary surface of the energy gap, (the order of 0.01 Ry). On the other hand, the width of the gap on the surface of the Brillouin zone is at variance. At some points, it amounts to more than 0.03 Ry, while at other points it is much smaller.

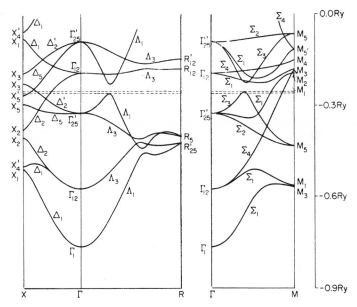

FIG. 5. Energy bands in antiferromagnetic chromium. The upper and the lower dotted horizontal line show the Fermi energy in the paramagnetic state and the antiferromagnetic state, respectively ($\lambda = 0.5$).

In order to confirm self-consistency of the exchange potential we have calculated the wave function at 64 points in the Brillouin zone, and estimated the spin density at the up-spin lattice site. The result is shown in Table 2. As seen from the table, the d-electrons only contribute to the spin polarization.

TABLE 2

THE CONTRIBUTION FROM S-, P-, AND D-COMPONENTS OF THE WAVE
FUNCTIONS TO THE MAGNETON NUMBER AT THE CHROMIUM SITE

| | Outside | At up-spin site | | | At down-spin site | | | Net |
		s	p	d	s	p	d	spin
$\lambda = 1$	1.02	0.18	0.18	2.56	0.18	0.18	1.70	0.86
$\lambda = 0.5$	1.02	0.18	0.18	2.35	0.18	0.18	1.91	0.44

The amount of the spin polarization is about $0.86\mu_B$ and $0.44\mu_B$, when $\lambda = 1$ and $\lambda = 0.5$, respectively. Thus, we see that the self-consistent exchange potential is attainable, if the value of λ is assumed to be a little larger than 0.5. It is quite important that the observed magnetic moment is derived from the band model with a reasonable assumption to the potential. In the anti-ferromagnetic state, the wave function is completely polarized on the boundary surface of the gap, and the boundary surface above the gap has the polarization of an opposite direction relative to the surface below the gap. Therefore, the most favorable condition for the antiferromagnetic state is that the greater part of the Fermi surface is situated within the energy gap. As mentioned previously, the energy gap appears mostly near the Fermi surface, and it is widely extended, so that it is quite certain that the formation of the anti-ferromagnetic sublattice is favorable to the band energy. Further, existence of the gap near the boundary of the Brillouin zone may contribute to the energy gain in the antiferromagnetic state. Thus, the band theory seems to produce some evidences for metallic antiferromagnetism in chromium. It is not at all obvious, however, that the antiferromagnetic state is really a stable one, because the correlation energy is not considered in these discussions.

From a point of view of the spin density wave theory (Overhauser, 1962) the model mentioned previously is regarded as a special case of the spin density wave model with the wave vectors

$$Q = (2\pi/a) (100).$$

According to the experiment the antiferromagnetic lattice structure is slightly modulated by the spin density wave with a long period which is equivalent to the length of 20.8 unit cells. Therefore, the simple antiferromagnetic model is not applicable to pure chromium. Lomer (1962) was the first to apply Overhauser's idea to chromium. He suggested that a more favorable state was the one in which the spin density wave with a wave vector

$$Q_1 = (2\pi/a)(0.95, 0, 0)$$

exists, because the size of the electron Fermi surface around Γ is slightly smaller than the size of the hole Fermi surface around H, so that they are most effectively coupled by having the largest contact area, when the hole surface is displaced by Q_1. It is rather hard to derive a definite number of Q_1 from the band theory, because it depends upon the relative position of the s- and d-bands sensitively. As is well known, this relative position is quite sensitive to the potential. It is almost certain, however, that the value of Q_1 lies between 0.9 and 1, according to the present calculation. At present, however, we are not able to make a further step. It is very hard to derive any other quantitative conclusions for the spin-density-wave state from the band theory.

It is observed that the period of the spin density wave is quite sensitive to a small amount of impurities. For example, the period is decreased by addition of a small amount of vanadium, while it is increased by addition of a small amount of Mn. It is not hard for the Lomer model to give a qualitative explanation to those phenomena. When a small amount of Mn is added as an impurity, the total number of electrons is increased, so as to make the size of the electron Fermi surface larger, and the hole Fermi surface smaller. Thus, the value of Q_1 is increased and the difference $(Q - Q_1)$ becomes smaller. It makes the period longer. When a certain amount of Mn is added, both the electron and the hole Fermi surface have the same size, and the complete antiferromagnetic structure is expected to be realized. The decrease of the period in the case of vanadium impurities is also interpretable by a similar argument. On the other hand, a more detailed study is necessary, in order to develop a quantitative theory of the impurity effect. According to experiment a complete antiferromagnetic state is realized, when the Mn impurity of about 2 at. % is added to chromium. At present, it is not certain whether the electron- and hole-Fermi surface have really the same size at this impurity content, or the spin density wave can not be stable at this impurity content owing to the impurity scattering.

D. FERROMAGNETIC SUPERLATTICE CoFe (50 ATOMIC PERCENT EACH)

As the crystal potential we use V_0 (Fe metal) and V_0 (Co metal) in the respective inscribed atomic sphere. In this case, the self-consistent approach has not yet been carried out. The number of s-electrons is assumed to be one for each atom. In a ferromagnetic state all d-bands of down-spin states are assumed to be filled up with electrons. Then, $6n$ up-spin electrons occupy the s- and d-bands up to the Fermi energy. Here, n is the number of the atomic

pair in the unit volume. The band structure of the superlattice CoFe is determined by the GFM at the points of high symmetry. For the purpose of comparison, the band structures of bcc Fe and Co with the same lattice constant
($a = 5.3873$ au) are calculated. Except for the appearance of the energy gaps
the $E(k)$ curves of the superlattice CoFe are quite similar to those of iron and
cobalt in the bcc structure. The density-of-states in CoFe is found to be nearly
equal to the simple average of those in Co and Fe. Therefore, the general
character of the density-of-states is quite similar to that of the metallic iron
in the bcc structure. It has two peaks, and a minimum between them.
The Fermi surface is situated at the energy slightly larger than the minimum point. These theoretical results are in good agreement with the general prediction given by Mott on the basis of the rigid band model (Mott,
1964).

It is needless to say that appearance of the energy gaps is the most important
character of the superlattice. The general character of $E(k)$ curves in CoFe
is quite similar to that in Cr mentioned previously. The Fermi surface is
situated at the energy region between $E(\Gamma_{12})$ and $E(\Gamma_{25'})$, so that the formation
of the superlattice will reduce the band energy and the superlattice structure
seems to be stabilized.

The neutron diffraction experiment reveals that the iron cell has a magnetic
moment of about $3\mu_B$ and the cobalt cell has a moment of about $2\mu_B$. It means
that there are about seven d-electrons in the iron cell and about eight
d-electrons in the cobalt cell. In the band picture, it means that the wave function is more concentrated to the cobalt cell at the lower part of the d-bands,
while it is more concentrated to the iron cell at the upper part of the d-bands,
so as to make the charge distribution more concentrated to the cobalt cell.
Detailed investigation on the nature of the wave function in CoFe confirms
that the prediction mentioned previously is approximately correct within
the accuracy of the present calculation.

Thus, we find that the average character of the compound lattice is revealed
in the band structure and in the density-of-states, while the individual character of each component is manifested in the nature of the crystal wave
functions. These rather opposite characters are well harmonized in CoFe,
because the crystal has a full translational symmetry in the superlattice
structure.

Next, let us make some speculations about the electronic structure of the
disordered lattice of CoFe. According to the neutron diffraction experiment
the magnetic moment of the iron cell and the cobalt cell in the disordered
lattice are nearly equal to those in the ordered lattice. Moreover, the magnetic
moment is practically constant through the wide range of the component
ratio. Thus, each component in CoFe seems to retain its individual character.
On the other hand, the electronic specific heat of the disordered 50–50 at. %

CoFe is again nearly equal to that of the superlattice. Further, variation of the electronic specific heat with component ratio is well interpreted by the rigid band model, that is, the density-of-states obtained by the computation agrees fairly well with that determined by the experiment. Therefore, the band theory seems to be well applicable to the disordered lattice. The individual character and the itinerant character, however, do not seem to be compatible except for the superlattice. Let us consider the lower part of the d-band, where the wave function has a large amplitude only at the position of Co. Since the cobalt is not orderly arranged, the wave function must be distorted considerably from the Bloch function. The wave function near the Fermi surface, however, may have a different character. It may have nearly equal amplitude at both atomic cells and it would be connected almost smoothly from a cobalt cell to the next iron cell, so that the density-of-states near the Fermi surface is expected to be given by the density-of-states obtained from the average potential model.

REFERENCES

Anderson, J. R., and Gold, A. V. (1963). *Phys. Rev. Letters* **10**, 227.
Flecher, G. C., and Wohlfarth, E. P. (1951). *Phil. Mag.* **42**, 106.
Hanus, J. G. (1962). *M.I.T. Solid State and Molecular Theory Group Quarterly Progress Report No. 44*, 29.
Kohn, W., and Rostoker, N. (1954). *Phys. Rev.* **94**, 111.
Lomer, W. M. (1962). *Proc. Phys. Soc. (London)* **80**, 489.
Mattheiss, L. F. (1964). *Phys. Rev.* **A134, A970**.
Mott, N. F. (1964). *Advan. Phys.* **13**, 325.
Overhauser, A. W. (1962). *Phys. Rev.* **128**, 1437.
Reed, W. A., and Fawcett, E. (1964). *Phys. Rev.* **136**, A422.
Reed, W. A., and Fawcett, E. (1965). Private communication.
Segall, B. (1962). *Phys. Rev.* **125**, 109.
Slater, J. C. (1937). *Phys. Rev.* **51**, 846.
Slater, J. C. (1965). "Quantum Theory of Molecules and Solids," Vol. 2. McGraw-Hill, New York.
Slater, J. C., and Koster, G. F. (1954). *Phys. Rev.* **94**, 1498.
Wakoh, S. (1965). *J. Phys. Soc. Japan* **20**, 1894.
Wakoh, S., and Yamashita, J. (1964). *J. Phys. Soc. Japan* **19**, 1342.
Yamashita, J., Fukuchi, M., and Wakoh, S. (1963). *J. Phys. Soc. Japan* **18**, 999.

Superconductors and Superfluids

JOHN BARDEEN

DEPARTMENT OF PHYSICS AND MATERIALS RESEARCH LABORATORY
UNIVERSITY OF ILLINOIS, URBANA, ILLINOIS

I. Introduction

As pointed out by London (1935, 1950), superfluid He II and superconductors are quantum systems on a macroscopic scale. In recent years, many beautiful experiments have been done which illustrate in striking ways the quantum aspects. These include demonstrations of quantization of circulation in He II and of flux in superconductors. Remarkable quantum interference effects in superfluid flow analogous to single and double-slit diffraction in optics have been observed with use of Josephson tunnel junctions. While the original descriptions of superfluids were phenomenological, it is now possible to see how the characteristic properties may be derived from basic microscopic theory and to see more clearly what are the essential features. As we shall see, an important concept is a macroscopic condensate wave function with amplitude and phase.

In order to keep the mathematics as simple as possible, we shall for the most part suppose that space variations are sufficiently slow so that a local theory can be used. This should be true under almost all conditions in He II, but in superconductors, except near the transition temperature T_c, a nonlocal theory is generally required. Even though our local theory may not give a correct quantitative description of superconductors, it does give a satisfactory

511

qualitative picture. We shall not be concerned very much with electromagnetic properties of superconductors, so that most of what we have to say will be equally valid for superfluid He. Further, we shall be concerned mainly with quasistatic flow and assume that time variations are sufficiently slow so that quasiparticle excitations are in local equilibrium.

A basic property of a superfluid is macroscopic occupation of a given quantum state. In He II it is the momentum state of the Bose condensate; in superconductors, where the electrons are fermions, it is the common momentum of the ground-state pairs. In He II at rest, even in the presence of interactions between the particles, a finite fraction of the atoms are in the momentum state $\mathbf{p}_s = 0$. The momentum distribution of the ground-state wave function has a δ-function peak at $\mathbf{p} = 0$, estimated (McMillan, 1965) to contain about 11% of the particles at $T = 0$, the fraction decreasing to zero at the λ-point. Although there is as yet no adequate theory of the λ-transition, it is generally assumed that it corresponds with onset of macroscopic occupation of the ground state. If there is flow in the ground state, the state of macroscopic occupation, $\mathbf{p} = \mathbf{p}_s$, is different from zero. The flow may vary slowly from point to point, so that $\mathbf{p}_s$ may be a function of position. Often the ground-state flow is specified by the velocity, $\mathbf{v}_s = \mathbf{p}_s/m$, where m is the actual mass of a helium atom.

The ground-state wave function of a superconductor with no current flow is made up of configurations in which the electron states are occupied in pairs of opposite spin and momentum $(\mathbf{p}\uparrow, -\mathbf{p}\downarrow)$ such that if one of the pair is occupied in any configuration, the other is also (Bardeen et al., 1957). When there is persistent current flow, the pairs $(\mathbf{p} + \frac{1}{2}\mathbf{p}_s\uparrow, -\mathbf{p} + \frac{1}{2}\mathbf{p}_s\downarrow)$ each have exactly the same momentum $\mathbf{p}_s$. Thus $\mathbf{p}_s = 2m\mathbf{v}_s$ defines the common momentum per pair in the ground state and $\mathbf{v}_s$ the velocity of flow. The definition of $\mathbf{v}_s$ is somewhat arbitrary. For our purpose it is most convenient to take for m the true mass, not an effective mass for the Bloch electrons.

In the two-fluid model (Tisza, 1938; Landau, 1941), the density of superfluid matter flow is $\mathbf{j}_s = \rho_s\mathbf{v}_s$. This is the equilibrium flow associated with a given small velocity $\mathbf{v}_s$ in the ground state. If starting from rest the whole system were displaced by velocity $\mathbf{v}_s$, the matter flow would be $\rho\mathbf{v}_s$, where ρ is the total density. If we now let the excitations come into local equilibrium, keeping $\mathbf{v}_s$ fixed, the flow will decrease. For a normal system, the local equilibrium would correspond to $\mathbf{j}_s = \rho_s = 0$. However, for a superfluid a net flow $\rho_s\mathbf{v}_s$ remains; this defines the superfluid density ρ_s. The normal component of flow is that associated with a nonequilibrium distribution of excitations of the system. In He II, such excitations can come into equilibrium with each other; the equilibrium may correspond to that which would exist in a reference frame moving with velocity $\mathbf{v}_n$. The total flow relative to the rest frame is then $\mathbf{j} = \rho_n\mathbf{v}_n + \rho_s\mathbf{v}_s$. In a superconductor, the excitations generally come into equilibrium with the lattice rather than with each other, so that $\mathbf{v}_n = 0$ in the absence of applied fields.

A macroscopic variable important for describing superfluid flow is the phase $\chi(\mathbf{r})$ of the superconducting wave function. It has the property that if $\chi(\mathbf{r})$ varies slowly in space, $\mathbf{p}_s(\mathbf{r}) = \hbar \, \nabla\chi(\mathbf{r})$. The concept of an effective wave function was introduced in some of the early phenomenological or semi-phenomenological theories of superfluid flow in helium and in superconductors. Its importance has received added emphasis in connection with Josephson tunneling in superconductors and related experiments in He II.

Some recent discussions of the theory from this point of view are those of Anderson (1964) and of Josephson (1964, 1966) for superconductors and of Anderson (1966), Martin (1965), and Hohenberg and Martin (1964) for superfluid helium. The author [see Bardeen (1965)] has given a brief introduction to the subject. A symposium on quantum fluids was held at the University of Sussex in 1965. The proceedings (D. F. Brewer, editor, 1966) contain both review articles and short accounts of original research.

The phase may be defined in terms of microscopic theory by use of an appropriate Green's function formalism. However, if the space variations are sufficiently slow so that a local theory is appropriate, simple quite general considerations can be used. Following a brief review of some of the earlier theories, we give a general formulation valid in the local limit. Basic definitions in terms of Green's functions follow. We conclude by discussing several examples that illustrate the use of the phase in describing quantum aspects of superfluids on a macroscopic scale.

II. Phase and Condensate Wave Functions

Superfluids have the features of a single macroscopic quantum state extending throughout the entire body. This is true even at finite temperatures in the presence of thermal excitations and also when there is impurity scattering. Several approaches have been used to define a condensate wave function to describe superfluid flow.

Ginzburg and Landau (1950) introduced on phenomenological grounds the concept of an effective wave function $\Psi(\mathbf{r}) = a(\mathbf{r})e^{i\chi(\mathbf{r})}$ to describe superfluid flow in superconductors. The amplitude and phase are related to ρ_s and $\mathbf{p}_s$:

$$a^2 = \rho_s/\rho, \tag{1}$$

$$\mathbf{p}_s = -\frac{i\hbar}{2}\frac{(\psi^* \, \nabla\psi - \psi \, \nabla\psi^*)}{\psi^*\psi}. \tag{2}$$

The latter gives

$$\mathbf{p}_s = \hbar\nabla\chi. \tag{3}$$

As so defined, p_s is the canonical momentum; in the presence of a vector potential $A(r)$ the kinetic momentum is

$$m^* v_s = p_s - (e^*/c)A = \hbar \nabla \chi - (e^*/c)A. \tag{4}$$

In the modern version of the theory (Gor'kov, 1959) $m^* = 2m$ and $e^* = 2e$ are the mass and charge of a pair. When v_s is replaced by the corresponding density of flow $\rho_s v_s$, Eq. (4) is essentially the first London equation that accounts for the Meissner effect.

The phase χ plays the same sort of a role in determining superfluid flow in superconductors that the voltage does in ordinary ohmic flow in normal metals. If there is no supercurrent flow, χ must be the same everywhere in a superconductor, even over "miles of dirty lead wire," just as the voltage is the same everywhere in a normal metal in the absence of a current. The long-range coherence of phase is intimately connected with the superfluid properties.

Not long after Ginzburg and Landau proposed their theory of super-conductivity, Penrose and Onsager (1956) gave a more microscopic approach to define an effective wave function for He II. They suggested that the density matrix of the superfluid is of the form:

$$\rho(r, r') \equiv \int \Psi^*(r, r_2, r_3, \ldots, r_N)\Psi(r', r_2, r_3, \ldots, r_N) \, d\tau_2 \cdots d\tau_N$$

$$= \Psi^*(r)\Psi(r') + \text{incoherent terms}. \tag{5}$$

The incoherent terms vanish for $r - r'$ large. The first term is the coherent contribution which remains finite as $r - r' \to \infty$; it corresponds to what Yang (1962) calls off-diagonal long-range order (ODLRO). If n_0 is the density of particles in the condensate,

$$\psi(r) = [n_0(r)]^{1/2}e^{i\chi(r)}. \tag{6}$$

As we shall discuss in Section VI, a two-particle density matrix is required for superconductors.

The phase was introduced by London (1950) and by Feynman (1955) by considering the displacement in momentum space of the many-particle wave function $\Psi_0(r_1, r_2, \ldots, r_N)$ describing the state with no current flow. If the momentum $p_s(r) = \hbar \nabla \chi(r)$ varies slowly in space, the appropriate function is

$$\Psi = \exp\left[i \sum_j \chi(r_j)\right]\Psi_0(r_1, r_2, \ldots, r_N). \tag{7}$$

The quasiparticle excitations of the system may take up a new equilibrium after the displacement. If so, the wave function will be modified from Eq. (7) and the current flow will decrease from ρv_s to $\rho_s v_s$ as discussed above. However, the momentum of the ground-state particles or pairs is still given by $p_s = \hbar \nabla \chi$.

III. General Statistical Relations

To determine the average of any quantity Q over a system in thermal equilibrium we average over a grand canonical ensemble:

$$\langle Q \rangle_{\text{av}} = \frac{\sum_{\alpha} \langle \alpha, p_s | Q e^{-\beta(\mathcal{H} - \mu N)} | \alpha, p_s \rangle}{\sum_{\alpha} \langle \alpha, p_s | e^{-\beta(\mathcal{H} - \mu N)} | \alpha, p_s \rangle}, \tag{8}$$

where $\mathcal{H}$ is the Hamiltonian, N is the number operator, and α represents a state of the system. In a homogeneous superfluid, one must specify in addition the momentum p_s of macroscopic occupation of the ground state and restrict the sum to states with a given p_s. Specifying p_s represents a "broken symmetry" similar to specifying the direction of magnetization in a ferromagnet. The matter flow is obtained by taking $Q = \sum_j p_j$, where p_j is the momentum operator for particle j. For $p_s = m^* v_s$ sufficiently small, the flow j_s is proportional to v_s; the coefficient of proportionality defines ρ_s:

$$j_s = \langle \sum_j p_j \rangle_{\text{av}} = \rho_s v_s. \tag{9}$$

This definition of ρ_s is a general one, not dependent on a quasiparticle model for the excitation spectrum. As T increases from 0 to T_c (or T_λ), ρ_s decreases from the total density ρ to zero.

A superfluid is characterized by a value of ρ_s different from zero; in a normal system, $\rho_s = 0$. Suppose that the equilibrium current is initially zero in some rest frame. Then displace the entire system in velocity space by v, giving a flow ρv. In a normal system equilibrium is reestablished by scattering of quasiparticles and the flow drops to zero. The totality of states summed over to get the new equilibrium current is exactly the same as the initial set. This is not true of a superfluid where a unique frame corresponding to that of macroscopic occupation exists.

These considerations account for the persistence of currents in superfluids. Scattering of quasiparticles does not change the common momentum p_s of pairs in the ground state. Only a force which acts on all or a large fraction of the particles can do so. Superfluid flow is the equilibrium flow corresponding to the given p_s.

That it is p_s (or v_s) which remains unchanged is shown very strikingly in experiments of Reppy and Depatie (1964) on persistent current flow in He II. They initiate circulation in the helium by first rotating the container above the critical velocity and then bringing it to rest. In their first experiments, the amount of angular momentum in the resulting persistent current flow was determined by releasing the container so that it is free to rotate and then destroying the persistent current by a heat pulse. The angular momentum initially in the liquid is then shared with the container, so that the container starts to rotate

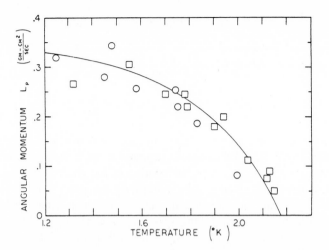

FIG. 1.   Observed angular momentum of persistent currents in He II as a function of termperature to which container is cooled. Squares indicate values obtained when the container was cooled directly to the temperature of measurement and circles when it was first cooled to a higher temperature and then cooled further while held at rest. The solid curve is proportional to ρ_s/ρ. (After Reppy and Depatie, 1964.)

with an angular velocity ω. If I is the total moment of inertia of the container and liquid, the angular momentum, initially in the persistent current of the liquid, is $L = I\omega$. The observed values of L are independent of the time the container is held at rest, even for periods as long as a day. They find that L varies with temperature in the same way as ρ_s/ρ (see Fig. 1). If the temperature is just below T_λ, so that ρ_s is small, L is correspondingly small. In later experiments (Reppy, 1965) the angular momentum of the persistent current was measured directly by gyroscopic effects. This nondestructive method permits repeated measurements of the same circulation pattern as the temperature is varied. In this way, measurements could be made very close to the λ point (Clow and Reppy, 1966).

If one stops the container at a temperature T_1 just below T_λ and then cools the system to a lower temperature T_2 while it is being held at rest, the measured angular momentum is about the same as it would be if the container were initially brought to rest at T_2. Thus it is $\mathbf{v}_s$ and not the angular momentum of the fluid that remains fixed as the container is cooled. The angular momentum increases in proportion to ρ_s as the temperature is lowered from T_1 to T_2. Since the container is fixed, the fluid can take up angular momentum from the walls. Somewhat similar experiments have been done with persistent currents in thin superconducting films.

The linear relation, $\mathbf{j}_s = \rho_s \mathbf{v}_s$ is generally valid for He II, but is valid for superconductors only when $\mathbf{v}_s$ is sufficiently small. Further, in the presence of a

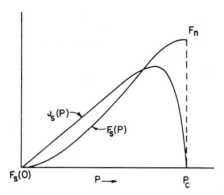

FIG. 2. Supercurrent density $\mathbf{j}_s$ and free energy F_s versus kinetic momentum $\mathbf{P} = m^*\mathbf{v}_s = \mathbf{p}_s - (e^*/c)\mathbf{A}$ (schematic).

magnetic field defined by a vector potential $\mathbf{A}$, the free energy and current densities are functions of $m^*\mathbf{v}_s$ as defined by Eq. (4) rather than $\mathbf{p}_s$ alone. More generally, after the initial linear increase, $\mathbf{j}_s(\mathbf{v}_s)$ goes over a maximum with increasing $\mathbf{v}_s$ and then decreases to zero when $\mathbf{v}_s$ reaches a critical value $\mathbf{v}_c$, as shown schematically in Fig. 2. Also shown in Fig. 2 is the way the free energy $F_s(\mathbf{v}_s)$ depends on $\mathbf{v}_s$. The flow density is given by the derivative of the free energy:

$$\mathbf{j}_s(\mathbf{v}_s) = dF_s(\mathbf{v}_s)/d\mathbf{v}_s. \tag{10}$$

At the critical velocity, the free energy in the superconducting state is equal to that of the normal state:

$$F_s(\mathbf{v}_c) = F_n. \tag{11}$$

Note that the change in F_s between $\mathbf{v}_s = 0$ and $\mathbf{v}_s = \mathbf{v}_c$ is equal to the free-energy difference between normal and superconducting states in the absence of current flow:

$$F_s(\mathbf{v}_c) - F_s(0) = F_n - F_s(0) = \mathscr{H}_c^2/8\pi. \tag{12}$$

Presumably similar relations hold for He II, but practically it is not possible to reach velocities (or values of $\mathbf{v}_s - \mathbf{v}_n$) sufficiently large to get appreciable depletion of the ground state and thus deviations from the linear relation.

As an example, let us consider the case of an ideal superconductor at $T = 0$ in the quasiparticle approximation (Rogers, 1960; Bardeen, 1962). In the frame for which $\mathbf{p}_s = 0$, the quasiparticle energies are given by $E(\mathbf{p}) = (\varepsilon_p^2 + \Delta^2)^{1/2}$, where ε_p is the energy of the corresponding state in the normal metal. If the system is displaced so as to move with a velocity $\mathbf{v}_s$, the quasiparticle energy becomes $E(\mathbf{p}) + \mathbf{p} \cdot \mathbf{v}_s$. If $\mathbf{v}_s$ is sufficiently large it is favorable to form a pair of excitations corresponding to displacing a particle from one side of the Fermi surface to the opposite. The energy required is

$$2(\Delta - p_F v_s), \tag{13}$$

which becomes negative for $v_s > \Delta/p_F$. This corresponds to the Landau criterion, $\mathbf{p} \cdot \mathbf{v}_s > E(\mathbf{p})$ for which the displaced ground state becomes unstable against formation of quasiparticles. When v_s becomes larger than Δ/p_F, depairing sets in rapidly and the gap parameter Δ decreases. The current density reaches a maximum for $v_s = 1.03\ \Delta/p_F$ and goes to zero for $v_s = v_c = 1.359\ \Delta/p_F$. The region between $v_s = \Delta/p_F$ and $v_s = v_c$ is one of gapless superconductivity in that pairs of excitations can be formed with no expenditure of energy, thus absorption can take place at arbitrarily low frequency.

In general the Landau criterion $\mathbf{p} \cdot \mathbf{v}_s > E(\mathbf{p})$ does not give the critical velocity for destruction of the superfluid state, but is that for the onset of gapless superconductivity (or superfluidity). The superfluid state persists until a somewhat higher critical velocity is reached corresponding to $\Delta \to 0$ or, in the case of He II, depletion of the ground state, $n_0 \to 0$.

While there is an equilibrium mass flow when $\mathbf{p}_s$ is different from zero, there is no corresponding heat flow. The heat flow is defined by

$$\mathbf{j}_h = \mathbf{j}_\varepsilon - \mathbf{j}_p \mu, \tag{14}$$

where $\mathbf{j}_\varepsilon$ is the energy flow, $\mathbf{j}_p = \mathbf{j}_s/m$ is the particle flow and μ is the chemical potential. In the reference frame in which the excitations come to equilibrium there is no heat flow, $\mathbf{j}_h = 0$. Another way of expressing this result is that the entropy flows with the normal component of the two-fluid model. While the absence of heat flow in the equilibrium frame follows from general considerations, it is difficult to give an explicit general proof from microscopic theory. Most proofs that have been given make use of the quasiparticle approximation. Ambegaokar and Rickayzen (1966) have derived general expressions for the accelerated currents of energy and matter induced in a superconductor by a long wavelength electric field and have shown that the induced heat current is indeed equal to zero. To prove this result it is necessary to introduce some sort of scattering in order to bring about an equilibrium distribution.

IV. Quantization of Circulation and Vortex Lines

Quantization of circulation follows from the expression relating the ground-state momentum $\mathbf{p}_s$ with the gradient of the phase. The relation $\mathbf{p}_s = \hbar\ \mathrm{grad}\ \chi$ implies curl $\mathbf{p}_s = 0$, or potential flow. From the fact that χ must be single valued it follows that

$$\oint \mathbf{p}_s \cdot d\mathbf{l} = nh, \tag{15}$$

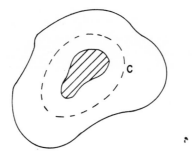

FIG. 3.   Contour about a hole in a multiply connected superfluid.

where the integration is around a closed contour and n is an integer. In liquid He II this implies quantization of circulation, as first observed by Vinen (1961), and in superconductors of flux, as we shall discuss below. Vinen, by an ingenious method, measured the circulation of He II about the axis of a cylindrical tube after it was cooled below the λ point. He generally found one unit of circulation, and was able to measure h/m with an accuracy of about 3%.

Consider, as illustrated in Fig. 3, a contour around a hole in a multiply connected superconductor through which flux is threading. Suppose that the contour is outside of the penetration depth of the flux, so that everywhere along the contour $v_s = 0$. From Eq. (4), this implies that $p_s = e^*/c\mathbf{A}$. Thus making use of the quantization condition (London, 1950):

$$\Phi = \text{flux enclosed} = \oint \mathbf{A} \cdot d\mathbf{l} = (c/e^*) \oint \mathbf{p}_s \cdot d\mathbf{l} = nhc/e^*. \qquad (16)$$

With $e^* = 2e$, the flux unit is $hc/2e = 2 \times 10^{-7}$ G-cm^2, half the value predicted by London, who took $e^* = e$. The first measurements of flux quantization in small superconducting cylinders by Deaver and Fairbank (1961) and by Doll and Näbauer (1961) as well as subsequent experiments give values corresponding to $e^* = 2e$. They measured the flux frozen in small cylindrical tubes with superconducting walls when cooled into the superconducting state in the presence of an external field H parallel to the axis of the tube. If there were no quantization effects, one would expect to find $\Phi = aH$, where a is the area of the inside of the cylinder (including the penetration region of the super-conductor). However, the measurements indicate that Φ remains zero until H reaches a value greater than half that required for a single flux quantum, $\Phi_0 = hc/2e$, when Φ jumps to a full quantum. With further increase in H, Φ remains constant until H reaches a value corresponding to $\frac{3}{2}\Phi_0$, when Φ jumps to $2\Phi_0$, etc.

The value $e^* = 2e$ was subsequently explained (Byers and Yang, 1961) in terms of the pairing of electrons in the ground state. From the viewpoint of London, there is not just one, but two independent ground states, one of which, Ψ_0, yields even multiples, the other $\Psi_{1/2}$ odd multiples of $hc/2e$. Effects of pairing may be taken into account by taking for $\mathbf{p}_s$ in Eq. (15) the momentum of a pair, as we have done.

As pointed out by Onsager (1949) and by Feynman (1955) for superfluid helium and by Abrikosov (1957) for superconductors, it is possible to have circulation in simply connected systems in the form of quantized vortex lines. The amplitude of the effective wave function defining the motion of the superfluid goes to zero at the core of the vortex line. The solution corresponding to a straight vortex line along the z-axis of cylindrical coordinates (r, z, φ) is of the form:

$$\psi(r, \varphi) = a(r)e^{in\varphi}, \tag{17}$$

where $a(r) \to 0$ for $r \to 0$ and n is an integer giving the number of quanta of circulation. It can be shown that for a given total vorticity it is energetically favorable to have it split up into vortex lines of single rather than multiple quanta, so that normally $n = 1$. When He II is in rotation with an angular velocity ω, there is a uniform density of vortex lines; the number per unit area is $2m\omega/h$. Many experiments have been done which demonstrate clearly the presence of such quantized vortex lines in rotating helium. Abrikosov (1957) showed that in certain types of superconductors, called type II, it is favorable to have flux enter in the form of quantized vortex lines when the applied field exceeds a lower critical field H_{c1}, the metal remaining superconducting until the field reaches an upper critical field H_{c2}. His theory forms the basis for our understanding of the properties of type II superconductors.

Measurements of quantization of circulation or of flux allow one to determine h/m (for helium) or of h/e (for superconductors) by purely macroscopic measurements. These are very striking illustrations of quantum effects on a macroscopic scale.

V. Phase as a Quantum Variable

So far we have shown how supercurrents are related to gradients of phase, but we have not shown how the phase, χ, itself may be defined as a quantum variable. As we shall see, it may be regarded as the variable conjugate to the particle number N, so that if one is specified, there is an uncertainty in the other, with an uncertainty relation $\Delta N \Delta \chi \sim 1$. Let us first consider an isolated body with no current flow, so that $\chi(\mathbf{r})$ is a constant independent of $\mathbf{r}$. To introduce the phase, one must deal with states in which the number of particles is not specified exactly. Thus if Φ_N is a state with exactly N particles, one considers linear combinations of functions of the form

$$\Psi = \sum_N a_N \Phi_N, \tag{18}$$

where the Φ_N differ only in the number of particles in the ground state. Such functions were introduced for mathematical convenience by Cooper, Schrieffer, and the author (see Bardeen *et al.*, 1957) in their first papers on the theory of superconductivity. It has turned out that use of such functions is not only convenient for mathematical reasons, but also makes good physical sense, in that it allows one to define the phase. There are no matrix elements of the Hamiltonian connecting states with different N, so that if the a_N are sharply peaked about a given N, calculations made with Ψ are substantially equal to those made with Φ_N. In superconductors, only even numbers of particles need occur and N may be regarded as the number of pairs. As pointed out by Anderson (1958, 1964, 1966), Josephson (1962, 1964), Ferrell and Prange (1963), and others, a state with a precise phase χ may be defined as the function

$$\Psi_\chi = \sum_N e^{iN\chi} \, \Phi_N. \tag{19}$$

Thus N may be regarded as the operator $-i\partial/\partial\chi$ conjugate to N. Normally N is a very large number, so that χ may be specified with little uncertainty even though $\Delta N/N \ll 1$.

Because of the uncertainty relation $\Delta N \, \Delta\chi \sim 1$, a measurement of χ requires an experiment in which the particle number N can change in an unspecified way. For a superconductor, this means that it must be possible for electrons to flow in or out of the body during the measurement, so that it cannot be electrically isolated.

One way the phase difference between two superconductors can be measured is by Josephson tunneling. Prior to experimental verification, Josephson (1962) made the remarkable prediction that a supercurrent can flow between two superconductors separated by a thin insulating barrier through which electrons can tunnel. He showed that for a junction of area sufficiently small so that magnetic effects are unimportant, the supercurrent flow is proportional to the sine of the phase difference between the two metals:

$$J = J_1 \sin(\chi_1 - \chi_2), \tag{20}$$

where J_1 is the maximum current density which occurs for $\chi_1 - \chi_2 = \pi/2$. Many of the most beautiful experiments illustrating the quantum aspects of superfluids make use of Josephson tunneling.

Anderson (1962) has pointed out that the Josephson current is related to the coupling energy between the two superconductors that arises from the possibility that ground-state pairs can tunnel back and forth between them. In the coupled system, the numbers of electrons on each side of the barrier is not specified exactly. The free energy associated with this coupling is:

$$W_{12} = -\frac{\hbar}{2e} J_1 \cos(\chi_1 - \chi_2), \tag{21}$$

JOHN BARDEEN

where J_1 is now an electrical current rather than a mass flow. Thus

$$J = \frac{2e}{\hbar} \frac{\partial W_{12}}{\partial(\chi_1 - \chi_2)}. \tag{22}$$

This is the analog of the Eq. (10) for flow due to a gradient in phase in a bulk superfluid.

Let us now consider a general formulation of superfluid flow in which the phase $\chi(\mathbf{r})$ and the number density $n(\mathbf{r})$ are considered to be canonical conjugate field variables both of which can be specified with reasonable accuracy. The free-energy density $F(\mathbf{p}_s, n)$ is assumed to depend on $\mathbf{p}_s(\mathbf{r}) = \hbar\nabla\chi$ and on $n(\mathbf{r})$, implying a local theory. The total free energy may be taken as the Hamiltonian for the system.

$$\mathcal{H} = \int F(\hbar\nabla\chi, n(\mathbf{r}))\, d\mathbf{r}. \tag{23}$$

The Hamiltonian equations of motion with $\hbar\chi$ and n as conjugate variables are:

$$\frac{\partial n}{\partial t} = -\operatorname{div}\frac{\partial F}{\partial \mathbf{p}_s} = -\operatorname{div}\mathbf{j}_p, \tag{24}$$

where j_p is the particle current density, and

$$\hbar\frac{\partial \chi}{\partial t} = -\frac{\partial F}{\partial n} = -\mu, \tag{25}$$

where μ is the chemical potential. The gradient of the latter equation is

$$\frac{\partial \mathbf{p}_s}{\partial t} = -\operatorname{grad}\mu. \tag{26}$$

Equation (24) is the continuity equation and Eq. (26) the acceleration equation for the superfluid. In a superconductor, $\mathbf{p}_s$, n and μ all refer to pairs.

More general equations for superconductors can be obtained by including magnetic fields through the vector potential. The free energy and current density then depend on the kinetic momentum $m^*\mathbf{v}_s$ as defined in Eq. (4), the equation of motion for which is

$$m^*\frac{\partial \mathbf{v}_s}{\partial t} = -\operatorname{grad}\mu - \frac{e^*}{c}\frac{\partial A}{\partial t}. \tag{27}$$

It should be emphasized that these equations apply to impure as well as pure superconductors, even when the mean free path is less than the coherence distance. Equation (27) is the second London equation; the first is that corresponding to Eq. (4).

Conservation of free energy follows from Eqs. (25) and (26). If we multiply (26) on the left by $\partial F/\partial \mathbf{p}_s$ and on the right by the equivalent $\mathbf{j}_p$, we get

$$\frac{\partial F}{\partial \mathbf{p}_s} \cdot \frac{\partial \mathbf{p}_s}{\partial t} = \frac{\partial F}{\partial t} = -\mathbf{j}_p \cdot \text{grad } \mu. \tag{28}$$

The right-hand side is the rate at which work is done on the system.

VI. Definitions in Terms of Green's Functions

The condensate wave function can be defined more precisely in terms of exact states by use of many particle functions with varying numbers of particles in the ground state, as in Eq. (18). The functions Ψ_N refer to the entire system and differ only in the number of particles in the condensate; the excitations are assumed to be the same, at least to terms of $O(1/N)$. The sum for a given state α of the system

$$\Psi_\alpha = \frac{1}{(\Delta N)^{1/2}} \sum_{m=-j}^{i} \Psi_{\alpha, N+m}, \tag{29}$$

is over a range $\Delta N = 2j + 1$ in the vicinity of $\langle N \rangle_{av}$, where ΔN is a large number, but such that $\Delta N/N$ is small. Averages over the ground state or over a thermal ensemble are made with use of the functions Ψ_α.

For the Bose system, superfluid He, the condensate wave function is defined by (Beliaev, 1958):

$$\psi_c(\mathbf{r}, t) = \langle \psi(\mathbf{r}, t) \rangle, \tag{30}$$

where $\psi(\mathbf{r}, t)$ is the wave field operator, $\sum e^{i\mathbf{p} \cdot \mathbf{r}} c_p(t)$, in the Heisenberg representation. Typical matrix elements which contribute to the thermal average are of the form

$$\langle N - 1, \alpha | \psi(\mathbf{r}, t) | N, \alpha \rangle. \tag{31}$$

The wave function $\psi_c(\mathbf{r}, t)$ has amplitude and phase, and is of the form

$$\psi_c(\mathbf{r}, t) = a(\mathbf{r}, t) e^{i\chi(\mathbf{r}, t)} \tag{32}$$

where $a(\mathbf{r}, t)$ may be interpreted as $[n_0(\mathbf{r}, t)]^{1/2}$ as in Eq. (6). Hydrodynamical equations for superfluid flow can be derived from the equation of motion for $\psi_c(\mathbf{r}, t)$; a rather complete discussion has been given by Hohenberg and Martin (1964).

In a superconductor, one must deal in general with an effective wave function for a pair of particles. The appropriate function is the anomalous Green's function introduced by Gor'kov (1958) and defined by

$$e^{-2i\mu t_1} F_{\alpha\beta}(\mathbf{r}_1, t_1; \mathbf{r}_2, t_2) = \langle \psi_\alpha(\mathbf{r}_1, t_1) \psi_\beta(\mathbf{r}_2, t_2) \rangle \tag{33}$$

where α and β are opposite spin coordinates. The time factor associated with removing a pair of particles with Fermi energy μ has been separated out. Averages are again over states of the form (29); in typical matrix elements the particle number differs by two on the two sides:

$$\langle N - 2, m | \psi_\alpha(\mathbf{r}_1, t_1) \psi_\beta(\mathbf{r}_2, t_2) | N, m \rangle. \tag{34}$$

It is the two-particle rather than the one-particle density matrix which has a factorizable part:

$$\rho_2(\mathbf{r}_1, \mathbf{r}_2, \mathbf{r}'_1, \mathbf{r}'_2) = F(\mathbf{r}_1, \mathbf{r}_2) F^+(\mathbf{r}'_1, \mathbf{r}'_2) + \text{incoherent terms.} \tag{35}$$

For a homogeneous system with no current flow, F depends only on the difference coordinates:

$$F_{\alpha\beta}(\mathbf{r}_1 - \mathbf{r}_2, t_1 - t_2). \tag{36}$$

Slow changes with position or time can be taken into account by the additional variables $\mathbf{R} = \frac{1}{2}(\mathbf{r}_1 + \mathbf{r}_2)$ and $T = \frac{1}{2}(t_1 + t_2)$. The range $\mathbf{r}_1 - \mathbf{r}_2$ over which $F_{\alpha\beta}$ has appreciable magnitude defines the size of the pair wave function, it is of the order of the Pippard coherent distance ξ_0.

A local theory of the sort we have used earlier applies only when changes with $\mathbf{R}$ occur slowly over a coherence distance. When this is not true, the structure of the pair wave function becomes important and the dependence of $F_{\alpha\beta}$ on $\mathbf{r}_1$ and $\mathbf{r}_2$ should include effects of the space and time variations. The resulting equations give time-dependent generalizations of the Ginzburg-Landau equations. They are difficult to apply when nonlocal effects are important. A uniform current flow is described by an $F_{\alpha\beta}$ of the form:

$$F_{\alpha\beta} = \exp(i\mathbf{p}_s \cdot \mathbf{R}) F(\mathbf{r}_1 - \mathbf{r}_2), \tag{37}$$

where $\mathbf{p}_s$ is the momentum of a pair.

Also important in the Green's function formulation is the usual single-particle Green's function, which for a homogeneous system is defined by

$$G(\mathbf{r}, t) = -i\langle T\psi_\alpha(\mathbf{r}, t)\psi_\alpha^*(0, 0)\rangle. \tag{38}$$

Here T represents time ordering. The Fourier transform may be expressed in terms of the spectral function $A(p, \omega)$. As defined by Kadanoff and Baym (1962), $G(\mathbf{r}, t) = G^>(\mathbf{r}, t)$ for $t > 0$ and $G = G^<$ for $t < 0$, where

$$\begin{aligned} G^>(\mathbf{p}, \omega) &= (1 - f(\omega))A(\mathbf{p}, \omega) \\ G^<(\mathbf{p}, \omega) &= f(\omega)A(\mathbf{p}, \omega) \end{aligned} \tag{39}$$

and where $f(\omega)$ is the Fermi function $1/(1 + e^{\beta(\omega - \mu)})$. One may regard $G^<$ as the density of particles of momentum $\mathbf{p}$ and energy ω and $G^>$ as the density of holes. The general expressions for matter and heat currents are

$$\mathbf{j}_{si} = \iint \frac{d^3\mathbf{p}}{(2\pi)^3} \frac{d\omega}{2\pi} \mathbf{p}_i A(\mathbf{p}, \omega; \mathbf{p}_s) f(\omega) \tag{40}$$

$$\mathbf{j}_{hi} = \frac{1}{m} \iint \frac{d^3\mathbf{p}}{(2\pi)^3} \frac{d\omega}{2\pi} \mathbf{p}_i(\omega - \mu) A(\mathbf{p}, \omega; \mathbf{p}_s) f(\omega). \tag{41}$$

Here we have specified $\mathbf{p}_s$ as the momentum state of macroscopic occupation. For a superfluid, $\mathbf{j}_s(\mathbf{p}_s)$ differs from zero when $\mathbf{p}_s > 0$, but $\mathbf{j}_h$ should always be zero in the equilibrium frame. As we mentioned earlier, it seems to be difficult to give a general proof of the latter without making use of the quasiparticle approximation.

VII. Interference Effects with Josephson Tunnel Junctions

Following Josephson's prediction that superfluid flow could occur between two superconductors separated by a thin tunneling barrier, and that the current flow depends on the difference in phase of the superconducting wave functions on the two sides, many experiments have been done to confirm the theory and to exhibit wave interference phenomena. We shall discuss two of these, one involving flow through a single junction and the other two junctions in parallel. What is measured is the maximum supercurrent $I_{\max}$ as a function of magnetic field H applied parallel to the plane of the junction and transverse to the direction of current flow. The effect of the magnetic field is to give a shift in phase difference along the barrier in a direction perpendicular to the field. This results in oscillations in $I_{\max}$ as a function of H as currents from various parts of the barrier add in and out of phase. A single barrier gives a pattern analogous to a single-slit diffraction pattern in optics, the two junctions in parallel give a pattern similar to double-slit diffraction.

A single tunnel junction in a transverse magnetic field is illustrated schematically in Fig. 4. The barrier is generally an oxide layer with a thickness t of the order of 10–20 Å. We shall suppose that the width of the junction is sufficiently small so that magnetic fields produced by the tunnel current itself can be neglected. The applied field is assumed to be in a direction perpendicular to the plane of the paper; it extends into the superconductors on each side of the junction a distance of the order of the penetration depth λ, typically $\sim 5 \times 10^{-6}$ cm. The junction extends for a width w, from $x = -w/2$ to $x = +w/2$ with the center at $x = 0$. Let $\Phi \approx Hw(t + 2\lambda)$ be the total flux penetrating the junction; the flux per unit length is Φ/w.

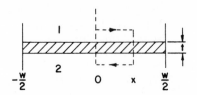

Let us consider how the phase difference varies with x. Consider a contour just outside of the penetration region so that $\mathbf{v}_s = 0$ and $\mathbf{p}_s = \hbar \nabla \chi = (2e/c)\mathbf{A}$. Thus

$$\chi_1(x) = \chi_1(0) + \frac{2e}{\hbar c} \int_0^x \mathbf{A} \cdot d\mathbf{l} \qquad (42a)$$

$$\chi_2(x) = \chi_2(0) + \frac{2e}{\hbar c} \int_0^x \mathbf{A} \cdot d\mathbf{l}. \qquad (42b)$$

The difference may be expressed in the form

$$\chi_1(x) - \chi_2(x) = \chi_1(0) - \chi_2(0) + \frac{2e}{\hbar c} \oint \mathbf{A} \cdot d\mathbf{l}, \qquad (43)$$

where the contour extends between 0 and x along the dotted lines indicated in Fig. 4. The contour integral is just the enclosed flux $x\Phi/w$. Defining $\Phi_0 = hc/2e$ as one flux unit, we have

$$\chi_1(x) - \chi_2(x) = \chi_1(0) - \chi_2(0) + 2\pi x \Phi/w\Phi_0. \qquad (44)$$

The maximum supercurrent occurs for $\chi_1(0) - \chi_2(0) = \pi/2$. Using this value, and Eq. (20) for the current density, we have per unit length of junction:

$$I_{\max} = J_1 \int_{-w/2}^{w/2} \sin\left(\frac{\pi}{2} + \frac{2\pi x \Phi}{w\Phi}\right) dx = J_1 w \left| \frac{\sin(\pi\Phi/\Phi_0)}{\pi\Phi/\Phi_0} \right|. \qquad (45)$$

This expression is identical with that of the amplitude of a Fraunhofer pattern for optical diffraction by a slit, with Φ or magnetic field replacing position on the screen. Note that $I_{\max}$ vanishes when Φ is an integral multiple of a flux quantum Φ_0.

Such a diffraction pattern was first observed by Rowell (1963). Figure 5 is a plot from data of Langenberg et al. (1966) for a Sn—SnO$_2$—Sn junction at 1.2°K with a width of 0.25 mm. Only one sign of the magnetic field is shown; the pattern is symmetric for the opposite sign. The period of the Fraunhofer pattern is 1.25 G.

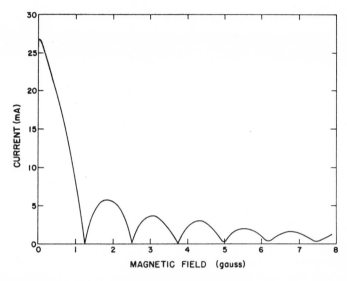

FIG. 5. Maximum supercurrent versus magnetic field for a Sn—SnO$_2$—Sn junction at 1.2°K. The plot should be symmetric for fields in the opposite direction. (After Langenberg *et al.*, 1966.)

Jaklevic and co-workers (1964, 1965) have observed interference phenomena for a configuration of two Josephson tunnel junctions in parallel, as illustrated schematically in Fig. 6. In a transverse magnetic field, flux in the insulating region A separating the upper and lower conductors 1 and 2 gives a difference in phase between the junctions a and b. Oscillations in total current flow between 1 and 2 occur as the currents in a and b come in and out of phase with varying magnetic field. If Φ_A is the total flux enclosed in the circuit, the phase difference between a and b from Φ_A is $2\pi\Phi_A/\Phi_0$. Including the diffraction

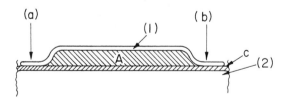

FIG. 6. Configuration for two Josephson tunnel junctions a and b in parallel. The region A is insulating. The maximum supercurrent between superconductors 1 and 2 is observed as a function of a magnetic field applied normal to the cross section indicated. A very thin insulating layer C, separates the two metals at the junctions. (After Jaklevic *et al.*, 1964, 1965.)

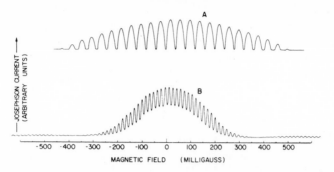

FIG. 7.   Maximum supercurrent versus magnetic field for configuration similar to that of Fig. 6 with junctions of Sn—SnO$_2$—Sn. For A the field periodicity is 39.5 mG, for B 16 mG. Approximate maximum currents are 1 mA(A) and 0.5 mA(B). (After Jaklevic *et al.*, 1965.)

effects at each junction as given by Eq. (45), the maximum current per unit length of junction is

$$I_{max} = 2\,J_1 w \left| \frac{\sin\,(\pi\Phi_J/\Phi_0)}{\pi\Phi_J/\Phi_0}\,\cos(\pi\Phi_A/\Phi_0) \right|. \qquad (46)$$

Since the flux Φ_A is much larger than the flux Φ_J going through each junction, one observes with varying field a rapid oscillation with period given by Φ_A superimposed on an envelope given by Φ_J. Typical plots of I_{max} versus H for two different specimens are shown in curves A and B of Fig. 7.

Some experiments have been done by introducing flux in the circuit by means of a solenoid confined to the insulating region A so that while there is a vector potential there is no magnetic field within the superconductors. Similar results are observed. Since the junction regions are in zero or a small constant stray field, there is no variation of Φ_J as Φ_A is changed and the oscillations have uniform amplitude. There is, of course, an emf in the superconducting circuit when the field in the solenoid is changed. However, they find similar results if the specimen is warmed up to the normal state while the flux is changed and then cooled. The experiments demonstrate the importance of the vector potential in determining flow even when no electric or magnetic fields exist in the metals while in the superconducting state.

Values of the flux quantum deduced from such experiments are found to be within a few percent of the theoretical values, $hc/2e$. The main source of error is usually the measurement of the effective area through which the field penetrates.

Zimmerman and Mercereau (1965) have rotated a circular interferometer with two junctions in parallel to measure h/m of the superconducting electrons. Rotation at an angular velocity ω is equivalent in first order to a magnetic field along the axis of rotation, $H = (2mc/e)\omega$. Oscillations in I_{max} are observed as ω is varied. From the period of the oscillation and the effective area of the circuit, they find a value for the Compton wavelength $h/mc = (2.4 \pm 0.1) \times 10^{-10}$ cm, very close to the accepted value, 2.43×10^{-10} cm.

VIII. The ac Josephson Effect

Another prediction of Josephson (1962) is that if a steady voltage V is applied to a tunnel junction one should find an alternating supercurrent with an angular frequency $\omega = 2\,eV/\hbar$. The voltage implies a difference in chemical potential per pair on the two sides of $2\,eV$. Thus, from Eq. (25), the phase difference increases linearly with time:

$$\chi_1(t) - \chi_2(t) = \chi_1(0) - \chi_2(0) - 2\,eVt/\hbar. \qquad (47)$$

The supercurrent should then vary with frequency as

$$J = J_1 \sin[\chi_1(0) - \chi_2(0) - \omega t] \qquad (48)$$

with ω as given above. One might expect that the current would decrease rapidly as the frequency approaches that required to excite a pair of quasi-particles, corresponding to $eV \sim \Delta(T)$. This would limit V to the millivolt range and the frequencies at low temperatures to ~ 350 GHz for Sn and ~ 650 GHz for Pb. However, Shapiro steps, as discussed below, are observed to much higher frequencies (e.g., up to 900 GHz).

The microwave power generated directly in this way is small and difficult to observe because of the poor impedance match between the junction volume and the space outside. Langenberg *et al.* (1965, 1966) have obtained a power of $\sim 10^{-11}$ W in the X band external to a Sn—SnO$_2$—Sn junction. By using one junction as a generator and a second junction closely coupled to the first as a detector, Giaever (1965) was able to observe a power in the detector junction of the order of 10^{-7} W.

Another way of observing the ac Josephson current indirectly is to beat it against an applied microwave field. When the frequency of the Josephson current, $2\,eV/\hbar$, is coincident with or an integral multiple of that of the applied field, a direct supercurrent should be observed. In experiments that have been done to verify this prediction, first by Shapiro (1963), a fixed microwave field is applied and the voltage across the junction is measured as the current passing through the junction is varied. Steps where voltage is constant for a considerable range of current are observed (Fig. 8) when $V = nh\nu/2e$. Anderson and Dayem (1964) have done similar experiments in which the tunnel junction is replaced by a narrow thin-film bridge separating the two superconductors.

An analog of the ac Josephson effect in superconductors has been observed

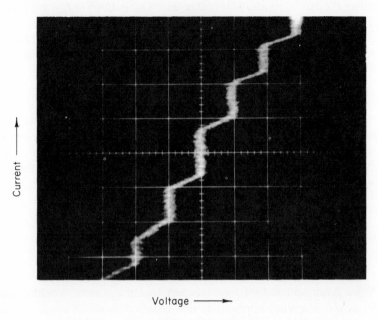

Voltage ———➤

FIG. 8.   Current-voltage characteristic of a Nb-oxide-Pb tunnel junction at 4.2°K with microwave power at a frequency of 9.75 Gc applied. Current scale (vertical) is 0.20 mA per large division; voltage scale (horizontal) is 0.020 mV per large division. Steps of constant voltage are at intervals $hv/2e = 0.0197$ mV. (After Shapiro, private communication.)

by Richards and Anderson (1965) in helium. Two baths of superfluid helium are separated by a small orifice which provides a weak coupling between the two containers. The equivalent of the microwave field is provided by an ultrasonic transducer which gives a sound wave field of frequency v impinging on the orifice. A difference z in head between the two baths gives a difference in chemical potential across the orifice of mgz, where g is the gravitational acceleration. The head difference z is measured as a function of time. Small steps of approximately constant head were observed at values of $z = nhv/mg$. Some subharmonics, especially half-steps, were observed as well.

IX. Vortex Motion in Superconductors

Quantized vortexes occur in both helium and superconductors and have been studied in great detail. We shall confine the discussion here to vortexes in superconductors and their motion, a problem important for understanding the properties of type II superconductors. As first predicted by Abrikosov (1957), in the mixed state between the lower and upper critical fields, H_{c1} and H_{c2}, flux penetrates in the form of a closely packed array of parallel vortexes,

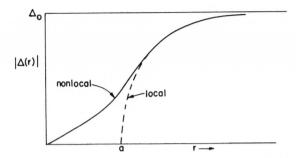

FIG. 9. Schematic plot of magnitude of the gap parameter $|\Delta(r)|$ versus the radial distance r from the center of a vortex line for nonlocal and local theories. (After Bardeen and Stephen, 1965.)

each containing a single flux quantum $hc/2e$. Thus for $B \sim 10^3$ G/cm^2, there are $\sim 10^3/(2 \times 10^{-7}) = 5 \times 10^9$ lines/cm^2.

A detailed theory requires a knowledge of the structure of a vortex and of the quasiparticle excitation spectrum in the vicinity of the core. The gap parameter $\Delta(r)$ may be taken as the effective wave function of Eq. (17). As illustrated by the solid line in Fig. 9, the amplitude $|\Delta(r)|$ goes to zero as $r \to 0$ and approaches a constant value Δ_0 for large r. The size of the core as determined by the radius corresponding to the point of inflection is of the order of the coherence distance ξ_0. Caroli *et al.* (1964) have calculated the excitation spectrum for a pure superconductor near $T = 0°$K. They find that it is about the same as that of a model consisting of a normal core of radius $a \cong \xi_0$ about which the supercurrents circulate. The region $r < d$ is one of gapless superconductivity.

The nonlocal theory is difficult, requiring solutions of coupled nonlinear differential equations. However, a good qualitative and even semiquantitative description can be obtained with use of a local model of the sort we have discussed in previous sections. In this model it is assumed that the local superfluid current density depends only on the local kinetic momentum, $m^* \mathbf{v}_s = \mathbf{p}_s - (e^*/c)\mathbf{A}$. In a gauge for which $\mathbf{A}$ has only a φ-component $A_\varphi(r)$, $\mathbf{p}_s$ also has only a φ-component, given by

$$\mathbf{p}_{s\varphi}(r) = \hbar/r. \tag{49}$$

As r decreases, $\mathbf{p}_{s\varphi}$ increases until at some radius $r = a$, v_s reaches the critical value v_c for destruction of superconductivity. In the local model, $\Delta(r)$ decreases as one approaches the core and goes to zero at $r = a$, as indicated in the dotted line of Fig. 9. For $r < a$, the metal is normal. If the vector potential can be neglected, the core radius for a pure metal near $T = 0$ is

$$a = \hbar/(2mv_c) \cong 1.16\xi_0, \tag{50}$$

about equal to that of the model suggested by Caroli *et al.* (1964).

It is possible to express the core radius in terms of the upper critical field H_{c2}, which also depends on the coherence distance. Gor'kov's (1959) expression for H_{c2} at $T = 0°K$ is

$$H_{c2} \cong 1.5\, \hbar c/(4e\xi^2) \cong \hbar c/2ea^2. \qquad (51)$$

This relation between H_{c2} and a also appears to be valid at finite temperatures and in the presence of impurity scattering. The only restriction is that A_φ can be neglected, which implies $H \ll H_{c2}$. For fields near H_{c2} the corresponding relation is $H_{c2} \cong \hbar c/ea^2$.

Several groups (Bardeen and Stephen, 1965; Volger *et al.*, 1964; van Vijfeijkes and Niessea, 1965; Nozieres and Vinen, 1966) have used a local model to discuss the theory of vortex motion in type II superconductors. Experimentally, what is observed is the resistivity and Hall effect in the mixed state when a transport current flows perpendicular to the direction of the magnetic field and thus to the vortex lines, as illustrated in Fig. 10. Each vortex is subject to a force per unit length $(\mathbf{J}_T \times \mathbf{\Phi}_0)c$, where $\mathbf{J}_T$ is the transport current density and $\mathbf{\Phi}_0$ is a vector representing one quantum of flux directed along the vortex lines. The vortex lines thus tend to move in a direction perpendicular to $\mathbf{J}_T$. Ordinarily the lines are pinned and do not move until $\mathbf{J}_T$

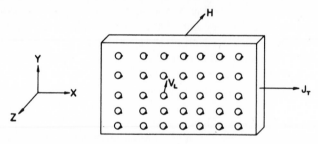

FIG. 10.   Schematic diagram illustrating flux flow in type II superconductors. Vortex lines are produced by a transverse magnetic field. They are driven across the slab by a transport current along the length.

is sufficiently large to overcome the pinning forces. When this is the case, voltages are observed. The electric field in the specimen is just what one would calculate as being generated by the moving flux lines by induction. If $\mathbf{v}_L$ is the velocity with which they move and $\mathbf{B} \cong \mathbf{H}$ is the total flux density from the vortex lines, $\mathbf{E} = -(1/c)(\mathbf{v}_L \times \mathbf{B})$.

Under steady-state conditions, vortexes are created on one side of the specimen and destroyed on the opposite, so there is no net change of flux. For this reason, objections have been raised to calling the electric field an induction field, but the result is nevertheless correct (Josephson, 1965; Casimir, 1965). A direction of $\mathbf{v}_L$ perpendicular to $\mathbf{v}_T$ gives a normal resistive voltage, motion parallel to $\mathbf{v}_T$ gives a Hall voltage.

From measurements on several specimens of varying composition and at various temperatures, Kim *et al.* (1965) found an approximate law of corresponding states for the flux flow resistivity ρ_f. Their observations could be fitted by a law of the form

$$\rho_f/\rho_n = (H/H_{c2})f \tag{52}$$

where ρ_n is the resistivity in the normal state, $H \cong B$ is the applied field, H_{c2} is the upper critical field, and f is a factor of the order of one, actually nearly equal to one at $T = 0°K$. A Hall voltage of the same order as that in the normal state is also observed, as will be discussed later. Kim *et al.* pointed out that the dissipation could be accounted for approximately if in the flux flow state the transport current flows directly through the essentially normal cores of the vortex lines. Rosenblum and Cardona (1964) had earlier proposed such a picture in their interpretation of data on the microwave surface resistance of type II superconductors.

The theory based on the local model gives just this result. Electric fields generated by the motion of the vortex lines lead to normal current flow in the vicinity of the cores and thus to dissipation and viscous drag. The motion of a vortex is essentially adiabatic, so that if $J_0(\mathbf{r})$ is the circulation about a stationary vortex, the current distribution of a moving vortex is $\mathbf{J}_0(\mathbf{r} - \mathbf{v}_L t)$. Similarly, $\mathbf{p}_s$ and $\mathbf{A}_\varphi$ are functions of $\mathbf{r} - \mathbf{v}_L t$. The electric field $\mathbf{E}$ (or, more properly, voltage gradient) is then given by

$$\partial \mathbf{p}_s/\partial t = -\mathbf{v}_L \cdot \nabla \mathbf{p}_s = -\nabla \mu = e^* \mathbf{E}, \qquad r > a \tag{53}$$

with $\mathbf{p}_s = \mathbf{p}_{s\varphi} = \hbar/r$ as in Eq. (49). For $r < a$, $\mathbf{E}$ is constant and perpendicular to $\mathbf{v}_L$; the field pattern is illustrated in Fig. 11.

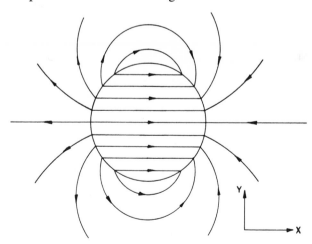

Fig. 11. Electric field pattern generated by motion of a vortex line according to the local theory.

When the motion v_L is produced by the force due to a transport current, the field is just that required to drive the transport current through the normal core. The total current is

$$\mathbf{J}_T + \mathbf{J}_0(\mathbf{r} - \mathbf{v}_L t)$$

where $\mathbf{J}_T$ is in part a super and in part a normal current. The model accounts for the empirical law of Kim [Eq. (51)] for the flux flow resistivity. If the vortex were pinned, the transport current would flow around the normal core and there would be no dissipation.

According to the model, the Hall angle in the mixed state should be the same as that of the normal state for a field equal to that within the core of the vortex line. When the Hall effect is taken into account, there is an angle α between the current density $\mathbf{J}_c$ and the electric field $\mathbf{E}_c$, as illustrated in Fig. 12.

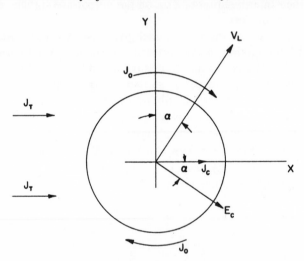

FIG. 12. Origin of Hall voltage in flux flow according to the local theory. When in motion from a force due a transport current density $\mathbf{J}_T$, the current flows directly through the normal core so that the density inside the core $\mathbf{J}_c = \mathbf{J}_T$. The electric field $\mathbf{E}_c$ is at a Hall angle α relative to $\mathbf{J}_c$. Motion of the vortex is perpendicular to $\mathbf{E}_c$, so that $v_{Lx}/v_{Ly} = \tan \alpha$. (After Bardeen and Stephen, 1965.)

The transport current still flows directly through the normal core, so that the current density within the core, $\mathbf{J}_c$, is equal to and parallel to $\mathbf{J}_T$. The velocity v_L is normal to the electric field, and so makes an angle α with the vertical direction, that normal to $\mathbf{J}_T$. The Hall angle in the mixed state given by $\tan \alpha = v_{Lx\varphi}/v_{Ly}$ is therefore also equal to α. This result appears to be consistent with experimental measurements on very pure niobium (Reed et al., 1965), but not with those on alloys (Niessen et al., 1965). For the latter, the Hall angle increases as H drops below H_{c2}, a result not yet accounted for by theory.

X. Summary

We have reviewed here just a few of the many experiments that have been done which relate to macroscopic quantum aspects of superfluids. Superfluid flow can be described by a condensate wave function with amplitude and phase. While a correct description of a superconductor is nonlocal, requiring a pair wave function, a good qualitative and even semiquantitative picture can be obtained from a local model. We have seen how the superfluid properties are related to the macroscopic occupation of a quantum state, from Bose condensation in He II and from pairing in superconductors. The momentum state of macroscopic occupation is related to the gradient of phase of the condensate wave function. The phase may be regarded as a quantum field variable conjugate to particle number. The Hamiltonian is the total free energy of the system and the equations of motion are the continuity equation and the equation giving acceleration of the superfluid. Applications of the theory to experiments on quantization of circulation and of flux, on various phenomena involving Josephson tunneling and on vortex motion in type II superconductors illustrate some of the aspects of macroscopic quantization that have been observed.

REFERENCES

Abrikosov, A. A. (1957). *Zh. Eksperim. i Teor. Fiz.* **32**, 1442 (*English Transl.; Soviet Phys. JETP* **5**, 1174).

Ambegaokar, V., and Rickayzen, G. (1966). *Phys. Rev.* **142**, 146.

Anderson, P. W. (1958). *Phys. Rev.* **112**, 1900.

Anderson, P. W. (1962). *Phys. Rev. Letters* **9**, 309.

Anderson, P. W. (1964). *In* "Lectures on the Many Body Problem" (E. R. Caianello, ed.), Vol. 2, p. 113. Academic Press, New York.

Anderson, P. W. (1966). *Rev. Mod. Phys.* **38**, 298.

Anderson, P. W., and Dayem, A. H. (1964). *Phys. Rev. Letters* **13**, 195.

Bardeen. J. (1962). *Rev. Mod. Phys.* **24**, 667.

Bardeen, J. (1965). *In* "Low Temperature Physics, LT9" (J. G. Daunt, D. O. Edwards, F. J. Milford, and M. Yaqub, eds.), Part A, pp. 3–7. Plenum Press, New York.

Bardeen, J., and Stephen, M. J. (1965). *Phys. Rev.* **140**, A1197. (Note that there are some differences in notation, e.g., p_s is the momentum per particle rather than per pair.)

Bardeen, J., Cooper, L. N., and Schrieffer, J. R. (1957). *Phys. Rev.* **108**, 1175.

Beliaev, S. (1958). *Zh. Eksperim. i Teor. Fiz.* **34**, 443 (*English Transl.; Soviet Phys. JETP* **7**, 299).

Brewer, D. F. (1966). Editor, *Proc. Symp. Quantum Fluids, 1966.* North-Holland Publ., Amsterdam.

Byers, N., and Yang, C. N. (1961). *Phys. Rev. Letters* **7**, 46.

Caroli, C., de Gennes, P. G., and Matricon, J. (1964). *Phys. Letters* **9**, 307.

Casimir, H. G. B. (1965). *Phys. Letters* **17**, 177.

Clow, J. R., and Reppy, J. D. (1966). *Phys. Rev. Letters* **16**, 887.

Deaver, Jr., B. S., and Fairbank, W. M. (1961). *Phys. Rev. Letters* **7**, 43.

Doll, R., and Näbauer, M. (1961). *Phys. Rev. Letters* **7**, 51.

Ferrell, R. A., and Prange, R. E. (1963). *Phys. Rev. Letters* **10**, 479.
Feynman, R. P. (1955). *Progr. Low Temp. Phys.* **I**, 17.
Giaever, I. (1965)l *Phys. Rev. Letters* **14**, 904.
Ginzburg, V. L., and Landau, L. D. (1950). *Zh. Eksperim. i Teor. Fiz.* **20**, 1064.
Gor'kov, L. P. (1958). *Zh. Eksperim. i Teor. Fiz.* **34**, 735 (*English Transl.; Soviet Phys. JETP* **1**, 505).
Gor'kov, L. P. (1959a). *Zh. Eksperim. i Teor. Fiz.* **36**, 1918 (*English Transl.; Soviet Phys. JETP* **9**, 1364).
Gor'kov, L. P. (1959b). *Zh. Eksperim. i Teor. Fiz.* **37**, 1407 (*English Transl.; Soviet Phys. JETP* **10**, 998).
Hohenberg, P. C., and Martin, P. C. (1964). *Ann. Phys.* (*N.Y.*) **34**, 291.
Jaklevic, R. C., Lambe, J., Silver, A. H., and Mercereau, J. E. (1964). *Phys. Rev. Letters* **12**, 159, 274.
Jaklevic, R. C., Lambe, J., Mercereau, J. E., and Silver, A. H. (1965). *Phys. Rev.* **140**, A1628.
Josephson, B. D. (1962). *Phys. Letters* **1**, 251.
Josephson, B. D. (1964). *Rev. Mod. Phys.* **36**, 216.
Josephson, B. D. (1965). *Phys. Letters* **16**, 242.
Josephson, B. D. (1966). *Advan. Phys.*
Kadanoff, L. P., and Baym, G. (1962). *In* "Quantum Statistical Mechanics." Benjamin, New York.
Kim, Y. B., Hemstead, C. A., and Strnad, A. R. (1965). *Phys. Rev.* **139**, A1163.
Landau, L. D. (1941). *J. Phys.* (*U.S.S.R.*) **5**, 71.
Langenberg, D. N., Scalipino, D. J., Taylor, B. N., and Eck, R. E. (1965). *Phys. Rev. Letters* **15**, 294.
Langenberg, D. N., Scalipino, D. J., and Taylor, N. B. (1966). *Phys. Rev.*
London, F. (1935). *Proc. Roy. Soc.* (*London*) **A152**, 24.
London, F. (1950). *In* "Superfluids," Vol. I. Wiley, New York.
Martin, P. C. (1965). *In* "Low Temperature Physics, LT 9" (J. G. Daunt, D. O. Edwards, F. J. Milford, and M. Yaqub, eds.), Part A, pp. 9–18. Plenum Press, New York.
McMillan, W. L. (1965). *Phys. Rev.* **138**, A442.
Niessen, A. K., and Staas, F. A. (1965). *Phys. Letters* **15**, 26.
Nozieres, P., and Vinen, W. F. Private communication.
Onsager, L. (1949). *Nuovo Cimento* Suppl. **6**, 2, 249.
Penrose, O., and Onsager, L. (1956). *Phys. Rev.* **104**, 576.
Reed, W. A., Fawcett, E., and Kim, Y. B. (1965). *Phys. Rev. Letters* **14**, 790.
Reppy, J. D. (1965). *Phys. Rev. Letters* **14**, 733.
Reppy, J. D., and Depatie, D. (1964). *Phys. Rev. Letters* **12**, 187.
Richards, P. L., and Anderson, P. W. (1965). *Phys. Rev. Letters* **14**, 540.
Rogers, K. T. (1960). Superconductivity in small systems, Ph.D. Thesis, University of Illinois.
Rosenblum, B., and Cardona, M. (1964). *Phys. Rev. Letters* **12**, 657.
Rowell, J. M. (1963). *Phys. Rev. Letters* **11**, 200.
Shapiro, S. (1963). *Phys. Rev. Letters.* **11**, 80.
Tisza, L. (1938). *Nature* **141**, 913.
van Veijfeijken, A. G., and Niessen, A. K. (1965). *Phys. Letters* **16**, 23; Philips Res. Repts **20**, 205.
Vinen, W. F. (1961). *Proc. Roy. Soc.* (*London*) **A2460**, 218.
Volger, J., Staas, F. A., and van Vijfeijken, A. G. (1964). *Phys. Letters* **9**, 303.
Yang, C. N. (1962). *Rev. Mod. Phys.* **34**, 694.
Zimmerman, J. E., and Mercereau, J. E. (1965). *Phys. Rev. Letters* **14**, 887.

The Impedance Field Method of Noise Calculation in Active Semiconductor Devices

W. SHOCKLEY

STANFORD UNIVERSITY, STANFORD, CALIFORNIA, AND
BELL TELEPHONE LABORATORIES, INCORPORATED, MURRAY HILL, NEW JERSEY

JOHN A. COPELAND

BELL TELEPHONE LABORATORIES, INCORPORATED, MURRAY HILL, NEW JERSEY

R. P. JAMES

STANFORD UNIVERSITY, STANFORD, CALIFORNIA

I. Introduction and Remarks about Professor Slater

This article is a consequence of two aspects of Professor Slater's existence. He is noted for the simplicity and soundness of his presentations of difficult subjects, and his coming birthday has led to an invitation for contributions. The material presented in this contribution has resulted as a by-product of an investigation of the theory of noise for active two terminal transit time devices, particularly those involving the negative differential mobility known as the Gunn effect. The connection between the circuit properties of such

537

devices and basic noise generation required the development of new theoretical approaches. These in turn led the authors progressively further back to some of the foundations of the theory of noise for steady-state nonequilibrium conditions.

Since a major objective was to understand the undesirably high noise figures of experimental devices, the attitude of the research had a practical aspect. Furthermore, the expression of the results should be readily accessible for application by semiconductor device engineers.

These considerations called for a presentation quite different from the basic reference for this subject: " Fluctuations from the Nonequilibrium Steady State " by Lax (1). In this treatment Lax investigates the postulates necessary to arrive at various general formulas (such as our additivity theorem for spectral densities and the expression of spectral densities in terms of diffusion constants). He also surveys the literature and comments on relevant aspects of many contributions. In this article we have put the emphasis on exposition, and the interested reader is referred to Lax for references related to earlier work.

Some comments on the sequence of the research may be of interest. A starting point was the idea that "straggle diffusion," resulting from inter-valley scattering might be an important source of additional noise. This led rather quickly to the recognition of the importance of the $4q^2Dn = 4kT\sigma$ relationship between noise source density and Johnson noise discussed in VII. This noise source density was then used to derive the noise appearing at the device terminals. In this way the macroscopic fluctuations were expressed in terms of the microscopic fluctuations of the charge carriers. A very puzzling period of confusion occurred in this development. When the formula we now call the "diffusion-impedance field noise formula" was first derived, the impedance field was thought of only as a "localized transfer impedance." What this quantity had to do with the lumped constant R for Johnson noise for the equilibrium case was frustratingly obscure until the "distributed power theorem" was discovered. This then led to the impedance field concept which now makes the relationship relatively obvious.

Other conceptual difficulties involved thinking about separate disturbances of holes and electrons and here the method of imrefs (2,3) was found applicable, and a reciprocity theorem for a four-terminal imref situation was derived. [The reader may be interested in knowing that the "most appropriate authority" (3) who reduced by a factor of three the number of syllables required to describe "quasi-Fermi level" was Fermi himself, half-facetiously, in response to a request for suggestions.]

The preparation of the article reflects the senior author's training under Slater. One of the most helpful thinking aids has been the "movie film" visualization of the principle of detailed balance. This movie film thinking tool is used in Section II as a replacement for mathematically sophisticated tools such as Fourier integral theorems. In fact an attempt has been made to keep the mathematical requirements for the reader at the level ordinarily in use for elementary circuit theory analysis, diffusion equations, and semiconductor device theory.

Some results representing in effect work in progress at the time the manuscript was transmitted are included as appendices. For these the level of exposition has been aimed more at the professional specialist in the field.

Except for these appendices an attempt has been made to produce a contribution that would, hopefully, get a passing grade in a Slater course on science textbook writing.

II. The Fluctuation Model

The motions of electrons of interest in semiconductors are those in which they move as conduction electrons in the conduction band or as holes in the valence band. They may also be captured on traps and may tunnel through the energy gap in abrupt junctions. For all such cases whether active or passive, it is possible to conceive of idealized noiseless steady-state conditions having the same dc values as the actual conditions. The noise which we shall analyze arises from deviations from this ideal noiseless steady state.

As an example of a configuration corresponding to a noiseless steady state we visualize a semiconductor device carrying constant average currents. Under these conditions we imagine that in the conducting regions the current is carried by electrons or holes moving monatonically without scattering with a fictitious microscopic velocity equal to the macroscopic drift velocity, as suggested in Fig. 1. We can imagine the electrons to be moving in uniformly spaced arrays, perhaps ideally on a flowing lattice which changes one of its lattice constants as the electrons proceed from regions of higher density to lower density. (We shall not here consider trapping or carrier generations.

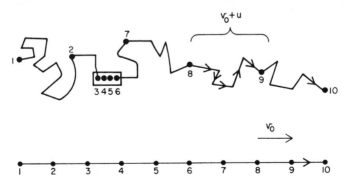

FIG. 1. Actual motion and idealized noiseless motion.

For such cases electrons generated through recombination centers could probably be regarded as produced by each center in a perfectly regular way at a fixed frequency for each center with the phases of various centers of the same frequency uniformly distributed.) The idealized noiseless situation will produce negligible ac signals or noise at the device terminals. Differences between the behavior in an actual case and this idealized case are the fluctuations that we shall consider in calculating noise.

In order to seek the simplest possible level in the presentation of this material we shall avoid the use of Fourier integral methods and shall instead make use of a fictitious temporal periodicity for our conceptual model of the device. This enables the treatment to proceed in terms of a Fourier series with periodicity T_p. The physical justification is that if we arbitrarily select the fictitious period as being long compared to the time of measurement for some noise measuring instrument, then the average value read by the instrument will be the same whether the system repeats from $t = T_p$ to $2T_p$ just what it did from $t = 0$ to T_p or undergoes independent random processes.

For purposes of exposition we shall consider the movie film method used by Slater and assume that we have a photographic record of the motion of each particle in the actual circumstances. We replace the actual behavior of the system by taking a section of duration T_p and running it repetitively. In order to avoid discontinuities we imagine that just before the completion of the desired time period T_p, we look at the picture at zero time and then beginning at some short time before T_p we deliberately introduce some forces from the outside so that just as the time T_p is reached we have succeeded in placing electrons and holes in the specimen so as to duplicate precisely the conditions that prevailed at $t = 0$. The disturbance we produce by this adjustment operation can be made as insignificant a part of the history as we like by making T_p longer.

Accordingly any of the processes we consider are periodic with the important features displayed in equations (1) to (3):

$$T_p = \text{fictitious period.} \tag{1}$$

The phenomena can then be expanded in Fourier series with frequencies ω:

$$\omega = \text{multiples of } \frac{2\pi}{T_p}. \tag{2}$$

The allowed frequencies are evenly spaced with the minimum interval between frequencies being

$$\Delta f_{min} = \frac{1}{T_p} = \text{minimum frequency interval.}$$

The fluctuating quantity of chief interest in this article is the velocity of a carrier. To be specific we consider a hole which advantageously has a positive charge; we write its velocity as

$$v(t) = v_0(t) + \delta v(t) \equiv v_0(t) + u(t). \tag{3}$$

This represents a hole which is moving in the structure considered in approximately the location in which an ideal hole in the noiseless reference state would move with a velocity $v_0(t)$. For this purpose $v_0(t)$ is the steady motion with the macroscopic drift or diffusion velocity. Consequently $\delta v(t)$, or $u(t)$ for brevity, will contain the random or Brownian motion that for the thermal equilibrium case gives Johnson noise.

In developing the noise phenomena in Fourier series, we shall focus attention on certain elements of volume in the device denoted by $\Delta(\text{vol})_\alpha$, $\Delta(\text{vol})_\beta$, etc. These are supposed to be many mean free paths in size, so that the random velocity of a hole in one volume is not significantly correlated with its random velocity in another volume. [One of the major steps in the development will consist of showing in Eq. (56) that the sum of the effects of these elements of volume may be replaced by a volume integral.]

At any given instant in a volume

$$(\text{vol})_\alpha = \Delta x \, \Delta y \, \Delta z \tag{4}$$

There is a *vector dipole current* defined by

$$\delta \dot{\mathbf{P}}_\alpha = q \sum_j \mathbf{u}_j(t) \tag{5}$$

(in some cases we shall imply a vector relationship by such an equation; in other cases it will apply to say the x-component only; it is intended that the context make this clear). If we consider the effect during a time from t_1 to t_2, then the disturbance from the ideal steady state is as if hole "j" were displaced by

$$\Delta \mathbf{r}_j = \int_{t_1}^{t_2} \mathbf{u}_j(t) \, dt \tag{6}$$

compared to how it would have moved for the ideal noiseless condition. The effect is thus as if at the end of the interval $t_1 \rightarrow t_2$ a charge q had been removed from where the hole would have gone from t_1 to t_2 in the noiseless condition and replaced with a displacement of $\Delta \mathbf{r}_j$. This is like setting up a current generator between two points $\Delta \mathbf{r}_j$ apart and passing an average current $q/(t_2 - t_1)$ between them during interval $t_1 \rightarrow t_2$. This corresponds to building up a dipole at a rate $q\mathbf{u}_j$.

Another way of visualizing this situation is to consider the displacement current reaching two grounded parallel planes Δx apart. The current due to a moving charge in vacuum is δI_{jx} where well-known electrostatic theory (4) gives

$$\delta I_{jx} = \frac{q_j u_{jx}}{\Delta x} \tag{7}$$

and the dipole charge builds up on the plates at a rate

$$\delta \dot{P}_{jx} = \Delta x \, \delta I_{jx} = q_j u_{jx}. \tag{8}$$

If the space between the plates is filled with a uniform semiconducting dielectric, it can be seen that the same division of charge occurs. (This can be established by noting that the point charge will have the same influence as it would have if spread uniformly over a plane; and a plane charge if inserted from infinity will induce charges in direct proportion to the admittances on both sides.) However, it is not necessary to consider these details since their effects are automatically accounted for in the impedance field treatment of the next section.

Each element $\Delta(\text{vol})_\alpha$ is thus taken to contain a fluctuation of $\delta \mathbf{P}_\alpha$ that has a component in the direction of interest [this direction is identified in connection with Eq. (27)] given by

$$\delta \dot{P}_\alpha = q \sum u_j(t) \quad \text{in} \quad \Delta(\text{vol})_\alpha$$
$$= q \sum a_\omega e^{i\omega t} \equiv q U_\alpha, \tag{9}$$

where α_ω is a Fourier coefficient of the period T_p. The $u_j(t)$ contribution from a given electron persists only while it is in $\Delta(\text{vol})_\alpha$. After it moves out of $\Delta(\text{vol})_\alpha$, its fluctuations are accounted for in another element of volume. The symbol U_α will be used to represent the sum over the holes in the volume.

III. The Impedance Field

In order to determine the effects of the $\delta \dot{P}_\alpha$ fluctuations on measurable noise, we shall next consider some purely macroscopic small-signal aspects of a general semiconductor device. For this purpose we consider two physical contacts (for example the two terminals of a diode). We ground one of them and measure an ac component of voltage denoted by δV_N in respect to ground on the other (δV_N will become noise voltage in Sections IV and V). We shall refer to this other terminal as "N."

We now imagine, as represented in Fig. 2, a third imaginary point contact at a position interior to the body at a vector position $\mathbf{r}_\alpha$ in respect to some fixed origin. If the semiconductor is n-type, we imagine that at this "contact" we furnish an inward current δI_α which means we extract electrons from that point at a rate $\delta I_\alpha / |q|$ electrons per second. The return circuit is provided to the grounded terminal.

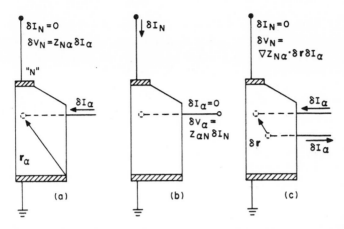

FIG. 2. The impedance field: (a) Current δI_α into fictitious terminal "α" produces δV_N. (b) Current δI_N produces δV_α. (c) Dipole current $\delta\mathbf{r}\,\delta I_\alpha$ produces δV_N.

This disturbance in carrier distribution may alter charge distributions far from the point at $\mathbf{r}_\alpha$, especially if the structure is an active device with large electric fields. It will alter the voltage at "N." In keeping with small-signal theory we may write

$$\delta V_N = Z_{N\alpha}\,\delta I_\alpha, \tag{10}$$

where δI_α is now thought of as a complex current vector $\delta I_{\alpha 0}\exp(i\omega t)$ of which the real part represents the current. The impedance factor $Z_{N\alpha}$ is also a complex function of ω and $\mathbf{r}_\alpha$.

Next consider what occurs if a current is put in at $\mathbf{r}_\alpha$ (by removing $\delta I_\alpha/|q|$ electrons/sec at $\mathbf{r}_\alpha$) and removed at a point $\mathbf{r}'_{\alpha 2}$ (by injecting the electrons back at that point). By linear superposition the resulting δV_N is

$$\delta V_N = [Z_{N\alpha}(\mathbf{r}_\alpha) - Z_{N\alpha}(\mathbf{r}'_\alpha)]\,\delta I_\alpha$$
$$= \nabla Z_{N\mathbf{r}}\cdot\delta\mathbf{r}\,\delta I_\alpha = \nabla Z_{N\mathbf{r}}\cdot\delta\dot{\mathbf{P}}_\alpha, \tag{11}$$

where $Z_{N\mathbf{r}}$ is understood to be a function of ω corresponding to voltage produced at the left subscript by current in at the right subscript and where $\delta\mathbf{r}$ is the (nearly) infinitesimal separation

$$\delta\mathbf{r} = \mathbf{r}_\alpha - \mathbf{r}'_\alpha$$

and the *dipole current vector* $\dot{\mathbf{P}}_\alpha$ is defined as

$$\delta\dot{\mathbf{P}}_\alpha \equiv \delta\mathbf{r}\,\delta I_\alpha. \tag{12}$$

Evidently the dipole current vector $\delta\dot{\mathbf{P}}_\alpha$ is just the rate at which an electric dipole vector would increase in strength in free space by a transfer of plus charge at rate I_α from point $\mathbf{r}'_\alpha$ to point $\mathbf{r}_\alpha$.

The relationship to the fluctuation considerations of Section II should now be apparent. Since $\delta\dot{P}_{\alpha x}$ of that section represents a ratio of transfer of charge over a distance Δx it can produce an output voltage calculated from the x-component of $\nabla Z_{N_{\mathbf{r}}}$ times the x-component of $\delta\dot{\mathbf{P}}_\alpha$.

The *impedance field vector* $\nabla Z_{N_{\mathbf{r}}}$, defined for small signals as discussed in the development of Eq. (11), is an essential concept in the treatment of noise in this article. It has the dimensions of electric field divided by current or ohms/cm. The quantity $\nabla Z_{N_{\mathbf{r}}} \cdot \delta\mathbf{r}$ = transfer impedance for current between $\mathbf{r}_\alpha$ and $\mathbf{r}'_\alpha$ in producing voltage between ground and "N."

We shall also use the reciprocal transfer impedance $\nabla Z_{\mathbf{r}N} \cdot \delta\mathbf{r}$ = transfer impedance N to the $\mathbf{r}_\alpha$-$\mathbf{r}'_\alpha$ pair. This gives the voltage developed at $\mathbf{r}_{\alpha 1}$ minus that at $\mathbf{r}_{\alpha 2}$ per unit current into N flowing to ground. We shall use this in connection with the distributed power theorem of Eq. (16).

Similarly $Z_{N_{\mathbf{r}}}$ and $Z_{\mathbf{r}N}$ represent voltages above ground produced per unit current into α and out at ground for $Z_{N_{\mathbf{r}}}$ and into N and out at ground for $Z_{\mathbf{r}N}$. When $\mathbf{r}_\alpha$ terminates at "N," then $Z_{N_{\mathbf{r}}}$ and $Z_{\mathbf{r}N}$ are identical and become the impedance Z of the diode:

$$\text{For \quad "}\mathbf{r}\text{''} \to \text{"}N\text{'':} \qquad Z_{N_{\mathbf{r}}} = Z_{\mathbf{r}N} = Z = R + iX, \tag{13}$$

where R and X are the real and imaginary parts.

For the purpose of later comparison with Johnson noise, we shall next derive the distributed power theorem which shows a relationship between a certain volume integral of the impedance field and R, the real part of the impedance between "N" and ground. For this purpose we consider that the specimen can be described by a complex conductance scalar (extensions to conductance tensors and to separate hole and electron conductances will not be considered here), which may be a function of position so that the total current density, including displacement current, is J amp/cm^2 given by

$$J = \sigma E = (\sigma_r + i\sigma_i)E \tag{14}$$

where E is the electric field. If a current $I_0 \exp(i\omega t)$ flows into "N," then the real electric field E is

$$E = Re\, \nabla Z_{\mathbf{r}N} I_0 e^{i\omega t}$$

$$E_x = \left| \frac{\partial}{\partial x} Z_{\mathbf{r}N} \right| I_0 \cos(\omega t) \qquad \text{etc. for } y \text{ and } z \tag{15}$$

This electric field produces an in-phase current density component that is σ_r times as large as each component of E.

The average power dissipation (watts/cm^3) is thus $\frac{1}{2}|\Delta Z_{\mathbf{r}N}|^2 \sigma_r I_0^2$; the $\frac{1}{2}$ comes from $\langle\cos^2\rangle$ and the absolute value squared of a complex vector is the sum of the absolute values squared for its three components.

If the real part of the impedance between "N" and ground is R, then the total power circuit is $\frac{1}{2}RI_0^2$. Equating this power to the integral of the power density gives

$$R = \int |\nabla Z_{rN}|^2 \sigma_r \, d(\text{vol}) \tag{16}$$

This relationship may be referred to as the *distributed power theorem*.

If the specimen is reciprocal so that

$$Z_{rN} = Z_{Nr} \text{ for thermal equilibrium and } B = 0 \tag{17}$$

as is the case for thermal equilibrium and no magnetic field, then the reciprocal power theorem applies to Z_{Nr} as well as to Z_{rN} and we have

$$R = \int |\nabla Z_{Nr}|^2 \sigma_r \, d(\text{vol}). \tag{18}$$

This last expression involves the impedance field appropriate for the distributed noise sources that replace σ_r in nonequilibrium conditions. Equations (16–18) cause the new noise formula of Section VIII to reduce correctly to Johnson-Nyquist noise (5,6) for thermal equilibrium.

IV. The Principle of Linearity for Significant Deviations

The types of noise considered in this article are regarded as caused by microscopic fluctuations from a noiseless steady state by deviations represented in general by $\delta F(t)$. Evidently as defined $\delta F(t)$ has a long time average value of zero. Examples of δF already discussed are $\delta \dot{P}$ and u. Significant resulting noise values, denoted in general by $\delta N(t)$, are produced at an output terminal when a sufficient number of independent microscopic events produce a sufficiently large combined effect $\delta F(t)$. For such significantly large deviations from steady state, a microscopic linear modulation occurs in the sense that the output noise is given by a frequency dependent factor M times δF. This microscopic linear modulation corresponds to transfer impedance coefficients like those discussed in the impedance field treatment.

The principle of significant linearity is the foundation upon which expressions like $\delta V_N = Z_{Nr}\delta I_\alpha$ depend, i.e., resulting noise is obtained by multiplying the elementary fluctuations by a linear modulating factor which in general is a frequency-dependent complex number.

This principle of linear modulation of significant deviations is particularly relevant for the case of space-charge limited shot noise in vacuum tubes. This can be seen by considering the insignificant effect of one electron. Obviously one extra electron crossing the potential energy maximum cannot modulate the current of the other electrons by, for example, 0.983 other electrons. However, the noise due to one extra electron would be negligible, i.e., not significant. A significant deviation, occurring by chance of course, of 10,000 electrons would be a macroscopic disturbance in the linear range and could quite reasonably be expected to prevent on the average the passage of 9830 other electrons. In this case of a significant deviation it is appropriate to say that the random current δ corresponding to 10,000 electrons is modulated by a reduction factor $m = 1 - 0.983 = 0.017$ to produce a final current that might be read as δN which corresponds to $M\delta F$. This is the *principle of linearity for significant deviations.**

V. Spectral Densities

In this section we shall assume that the fluctuations in an element of volume $\Delta(\text{vol})_\alpha$ produce a dipole current $\delta\dot{\mathbf{P}}_\alpha$ which in turn produces an output noise voltage δV_N. We shall assume that the $\Delta(\text{vol})_\alpha$ are sufficiently large so that no elementary fluctuation, such as a mean free path, overlaps significantly from one to another. Consequently, $\delta\dot{\mathbf{P}}_\alpha$ and $\delta\dot{\mathbf{P}}_\beta$ from two regions are uncorrelated.

On the other hand a disturbance in $\Delta(\text{vol})_\alpha$ caused by $\delta\dot{\mathbf{P}}_\alpha$ can propagate in an active device and produce disturbances in $\Delta(\text{vol})_\beta$. The effect of these disturbances on the output, however, are already included in $\nabla Z_{Nr} \cdot \delta\dot{\mathbf{P}}_\alpha$. What is deliberately neglected is any influence that $\delta\dot{\mathbf{P}}_\alpha$ may have on the fluctuations $\delta\dot{\mathbf{P}}_\beta$ themselves. This is legitimate in semiconductors where the basic fluctuations are collisions, capture, emission, etc., which are not significantly affected by noise disturbances from other regions.

We shall first define spectral density of a fluctuating quantity and prove an additivity theorem. For brevity and generality we shall first not treat

$$\delta V_N = \sum_\alpha \nabla Z_{Nr} \cdot \delta\dot{\mathbf{P}}_\alpha \tag{19}$$

but instead a generic form

$$\delta N = \sum M_j \, \delta F_j = \sum b_\omega e^{i\omega t} \tag{20}$$

where δN and δF_j represent fluctuations in general, all of course with the fictitious periodicity T_p. The equation is symbolic and $\sum M_j \delta F_j$ means that $M_j(\omega)$ is a complex impedancelike quantity so the equation has significance in keeping with linear circuit theory conventions. For calculating a real physical case we must then have $b_\omega = b^*_{-\omega}$ so that δF will be a real function of time. This equality that assures reality will automatically occur since the δF_j are

---

* We have tested these ideas on a distinguished author of review articles on noise. His reaction does not suggest that they are either banal or unsound; however, his reaction does suggest that their significance may not be obvious from the brief discussion of this section.

themselves real quantities and consequently the Fourier coefficients $a_{j\omega}$ satisfy $a^*_{j\omega} = a_{j-\omega}$ and, furthermore, the impedancelike quantities M satisfy

$$M_j(\omega) = M^*_j(-\omega) \qquad (21)$$

for any real physical situations. (We exclude possible influences of magnetic fields.) Since the value of b_ω is

$$b_\omega = \sum_j M_j(\omega)a_{j\omega}, \qquad (22)$$

the relationship $b_\omega = b^*_{-\omega}$ follows at once.

The spectral density $S(\delta N, \omega)$ is defined like an average power over the period T_p (denoted by $\langle \ \rangle_{T_p}$) per unit frequency as follows:

$$S(\delta N, \omega) \equiv \frac{\langle (\delta N \text{ in } \Delta f \text{ at } \omega)^2 \rangle_{T_p}}{\Delta f}$$

$$= \frac{\langle (\sum 2|b_\omega|\cos(\omega t + \text{const}))^2 \rangle}{\Delta f}$$

$$= \frac{\sum 2|b_\omega|^2}{\Delta f} = 2\langle |b_\omega|^2 \rangle T_p. \qquad (23)$$

[The identity is a definition that the average is over one period T_p; the first equal sign follows from the reality of δN; the second from the fact that the average over the period T_p eliminates cross terms between different ω values and gives a factor $\frac{1}{2}$ from $\cos^2$; and the third equality follows from the fact that $n(\Delta f)$, the number of frequencies in Δf, is $T_p \Delta f$ so that $1/\Delta f = T_p/n(\Delta f)$ and $\sum |b_\omega|^2/n(\Delta f) \equiv \langle |b_\omega|^2 \rangle_\omega$.] In this expression $\langle |b_\omega|^2 \rangle_\omega$ is an average over a narrow frequency band ω, which contains many frequencies if T_p is large enough. (The individual $|b_\omega|^2$ in this range will fluctuate because of effects like the off-diagonal terms in Fig. 3 discussed below.)

The well-known Johnson-Nyquist noise formula (5,6), $\langle \delta V^2 \rangle = 4kTR\Delta f$ leads to a spectral distribution of

$$S(\delta V, \omega) = 4kTR. \qquad (24)$$

We shall show that the general formulation developed in this article leads correctly to this expression for the case of thermal equilibrium; the proof depends on $Z_{Nr} = Z_{rN}$ which appropriately applies.

An additivity theorem for independent spectral densities holds for the δF_i of Eq. (35) provided the individual δF_i are independent of each other, as we shall show is true for the $\delta \dot{P}_\alpha$ terms. Then in $\langle |b_\omega|^2 \rangle_\omega$ averaged over many frequencies, contributions of terms from $\delta F_j \delta F_k$ of the form $2Re[M_j(\omega)a_{j\omega}M^*_k(\omega)a^*_{k\omega}]$ average to zero leaving only

$$\langle |b_\omega|^2 \rangle_\omega = \sum_j |M_j(\omega)|^2 \langle |a_{j\omega}|^2 \rangle_\omega, \qquad (25)$$

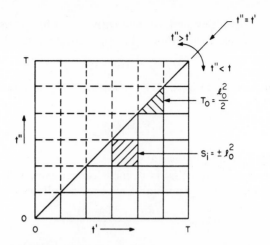

FIG. 3. The double integral for x_j^2 considered as a lower large triangle having $t'' < t'$ with subdivision into triangles and squares.

so that since $S(\delta F_j, \omega) = 2\langle |a_{j\omega}|^2 \rangle_\omega T_p$

$$S(\delta N, \omega) = \sum_j |M_j(\omega)|^2 S(\delta F_j, \omega), \qquad (26)$$

a relationship which may be called *the additivity theorem for spectral densities.*

This additivity theorem of Eq. (26) can be applied to $S(\delta V, \omega)$ in terms of $S(\delta \dot{P}_\alpha, \omega)$. We shall for simplicity assume that ∇Z_{Nr} is parallel to $\delta \dot{P}_\alpha$. (For example, if the surfaces of constant Z_{Nr} are perpendicular to lines of current flow in a " one-dimensional " structure, then the relevant $\delta \dot{P}_\alpha$ is the component parallel to current flow.) We shall, furthermore, argue that, because of the size of the $\Delta(\text{vol})_\alpha$ regions compared to a mean free path of a carrier, there is no correlation between the $\delta \dot{P}_\alpha$ of one region and $\delta \dot{P}_\beta$ of another. Consequently from

$$\delta V_N = \sum_\alpha \nabla Z_{Nr} \, \delta \dot{P}_\alpha \qquad (27)$$

we can conclude from the additivity theorem that

$$S(\delta V_N, \omega) = \sum_\alpha |Z_{Nr}|^2 S(\delta \dot{P}_\alpha, \omega). \qquad (28)$$

This reduces the noise calculation problem to finding a systematic way of calculating $S(\delta \dot{P}_\alpha, \omega)$ and carrying out the sum over the $\Delta(\text{vol})_\alpha$.

In keeping with δF_j above, we consider the expansion of $\delta \dot{P}_\alpha$ in a Fourier series with period T_p:

$$\delta \dot{P}_\alpha = q \sum a_\omega e^{i\omega t} = q U_\alpha(t), \qquad (29)$$

where $U_\alpha(t)$ is introduced for convenience in writing equations:

$$U_\alpha(t) \equiv \sum u_j(t) \qquad \text{for} \quad \Delta(\text{vol})_\alpha. \tag{30}$$

The spectral density of the dipole current is thus

$$S(\delta \dot{P}_\alpha, \omega) = 2q^2 \langle |a_\omega|^2 \rangle_\omega T_p. \tag{31}$$

The problem is to evaluate $\langle |a_\omega|^2 \rangle_\omega$ from known properties of the $u_j(t)$ as they are summed in U_α. Since the U_α is real, a_ω and $a_{-\omega}$ are complex conjugates and as Fourier coefficients are determined by

$$T_p a_\omega = T_p a^*_{-\omega} = \int_0^{T_p} e^{-i\omega t} U_\alpha(t) \, dt. \tag{32}$$

The desired quantity $|a_\omega|^2$ is given by

$$T_p^2 |a_\omega|^2 = \int_0^{T_p} \int_0^{T_p} e^{i\omega(t'-t'')} U_\alpha(t') U_\alpha(t'') \, dt' \, dt''. \tag{33}$$

This double integral expression is the subject of the next section.

VI. Autocorrelation, Diffusion, and Noise

A. The Autocorrelation Function

The autocorrelation function is the basic concept used in evaluating the double integral of Section V for $T_p^2 |a_\omega|^2$. We shall discuss the autocorrelation function first not for the case of $U_\alpha(t)$ but instead for $u_j(t)$ for one carrier. The autocorrelation function for $u_j(t)$ as we shall use it is an average over all the carriers (either holes or electrons, not both) that are in $\Delta(\text{vol})_\alpha$ during one period T_p. We denote the function as u_c^2 where the subscript c indicates "correlation":

$$u_c^2(t' - t'') = \langle u_j(t') u_j(t'') \rangle_j = u_c^2(t'' - t'). \tag{34}$$

This average over many carriers "j" may be replaced by an average over one carrier for a long time provided the carrier stays in a similar environment. In calculating $S(\delta \dot{P}_\alpha, \omega)$ the average must in principle be over the many "j" carriers that spend varying times T_j in $\Delta(\text{vol})_\alpha$. In an active semiconductor device, the behavior of any one carrier may be quite different in $\Delta(\text{vol})_\beta$ than it was in $\Delta(\text{vol})_\alpha$; for example, it may be in a higher electric field and become hot so that $u_c^2(t)$ may change substantially.

As we shall show below, the important attribute for calculating noise is what we shall call the *diffusion of u at frequency* ω:

$$D(u, \omega) = Re \int_0^\infty e^{i\omega t} u_c^2(t) \, dt. \tag{35}$$

For the simple case in which u represents the x-component of random velocity of Brownian movement for which the ideal noiseless state is the particle at rest, $D(u, 0)$ reduces to the diffusion constant.

A *correlation time* τ_c can be defined in terms of the diffusion constant $D(u, 0)$ and the mean squared random velocity:

$$D(u, 0) = \int_0^\infty u_c^2(s) \, ds = u_c^2(0)\tau_c = \langle u_j^2 \rangle_j \tau_c, \tag{36}$$

where the definition of the mean square follows from (34). For many cases of interest $u_c^2(s)$ is $\langle u_j^2 \rangle_j$, or $\langle u^2 \rangle$ for short, times an exponential decay factor $\exp(-t/\tau_{\text{mft}})$ where τ_{mft} is the mean free time. For this case τ_c defined by (36) equals τ_{mft} and $\langle u^2 \rangle = \langle v_x^2 \rangle = \langle v^2 \rangle / 3$ where v is the speed of the particle. These relationships lead to the familiar result $D = \langle v^2 \rangle \tau_{\text{mft}}/3$.

In calculating noise we shall be concerned with more general cases such as "intervalley" scattering in multivalley semiconductors and trapping; for these, $u_j(t)$ will represent deviations from the uniform, orderly, average, noiseless $v_0(t)$. Many aspects of these cases are so closely related to the simple case of diffusion that we shall treat the latter in detail.

B. Diffusion

Accordingly we consider how a group of particles having velocities $u_j(t)$ along the x-axis are spread out at a time $t = T$ having all been at $x = 0$ at $t = 0$. Evidently

$$x_j = \int_0^T u_j(t) \, dt \tag{37}$$

and

$$x_j^2 = \int_0^T \int_0^T u_j(t')u_j(t'') \, dt' \, dt'', \tag{38}$$

and, if this is averaged over many particles,

$$\langle x_j^2 \rangle_j = \int_0^T \int_0^T u_c^2(t' - t'') \, dt' \, dt'' \tag{39}$$

since the order of integration and averaging can be interchanged. Before considering the last autocorrelation integral, we shall consider the $u_j(t')u_j(t'')$ integral of Eq. (38) in detail for a very simple case:

Suppose $T = n\tau_0$ and u is constant throughout each subinterval τ_0 with a value which is either $+u_0$ or $-u_0$ determined by chance. (This is suggestive of a mean free time τ_0 and mean free path $l_0 = u_0\tau_0$. As we show below the correlation time τ_c is $\tau_0/2$.) Then the integral for x_j becomes

$$x_j = \int_0^T u_j(t) \, dt = l_0 \sum_{s=1}^n a_{js}, \tag{40}$$

where $a_{js} = \pm 1$. [The relationship of this to the binomial distribution is discussed following Eq. (45).] The double integral then can be divided into a checkerboard as shown in Fig. 3. Furthermore, since $u(t')u(t'')$ is symmetrical about the diagonal $t'' = t'$ only the lower triangle $t'' < t'$ of the large $T \times T$ square need be considered. This contains n little triangles each of area $\tau_0^2/2$ and of contribution $+ l_0^2/2 \equiv T_0$ to the integral and $(n^2 - n)/2$ little squares each giving $\pm l_0^2 \equiv S_i$. The value of x_j^2 is then twice the lower big triangle:

$$x_j^2 = 2\left[nT_0 + \sum_i S_i \right]. \tag{41}$$

If this is averaged over many carriers, the S_i terms average to zero so that the entire contribution comes from the diagonal strip of little triangles giving

$$\langle x_j^2 \rangle_j = 2nT_0 = 2\left(\frac{T}{\tau_0}\right)\left(\frac{l_0^2}{2}\right) = 2T\left(\frac{u_0^2 \tau_0}{2}\right) = 2TD, \tag{42}$$

the last forms being written for aid in identifying the diffusion constant.

The relationship $\langle x^2 \rangle = 2DT$ is well known and readily established for particle diffusion in an unbounded medium with diffusion constant D. The proof is as follows: If the concentration is $c(x, t)$, and $\int c(x, t)\, dx = 1$, then integration by parts readily establishes

$$\frac{d\langle x^2 \rangle}{dt} = \left(\frac{d}{dt}\right) \int x^2 c(x,t)\, dx = \int x^2 \left[\frac{\partial c(x, t)}{dt} \right] dx = D \int x^2 \left(\frac{\partial^2 c}{\partial x^2}\right) dx$$

$$= 2D \int c\, dx = 2D, \tag{43}$$

so that in Eq. (42) it is evident that $u_0^2 \tau_0/2$ must represent the diffusion constant due to u. [A trivial pedagogical extension is to consider a uniform concentration gradient and show that for the $\tau_0 u_0 = l_0$ model the flux is $(u_0^2 \tau_0/2) dc/dx$.]

For this case the autocorrelation function is easily seen to be $[(\tau_0 - t)/\tau_0] u_0^2$ for $t < \tau_0$ so that $D(u, 0)$ is $u_0^2 \tau_0/2$ and the correlation time $\tau_c = \tau_0/2$. This agrees with Eq. (42).

The value of x_j^2 for any one particle may, of course, differ greatly from the average $\langle x_j^2 \rangle_j$. The spread in x_j^2 can be found from $\langle x_j^4 \rangle_j$ compared to $\langle x_j^2 \rangle_j^2$; squaring Eq. (41) gives

$$x_j^4 = 4\left[n^2 T_0^2 + 2n_0 T_0 \sum_i S_i + \sum_i \sum_k S_i S_k \right]. \tag{44}$$

Averaging over all carriers leaves the first constant term unchanged, eliminates the second sum, and in the double sum leaves only the $S_i^2 = l_0^4 = 4T_0^2$

terms for the $(n^2-n)/2$ squares of Fig. 3. Consequently we obtain

$$\langle x_j^4 \rangle_j = 4[n^2 T_0^2 + 2(n^2 - n)T_0^2]$$

$$= 3\langle x_j^2 \rangle_j^2 - \left(\frac{2}{n}\right) \langle x_j^2 \rangle_j^2. \tag{45}$$

Thus the mean square deviation of x^2 for large n becomes

$$\langle x_j^4 \rangle_j - \langle x_j^2 \rangle_j^2 = 2\langle x_j^2 \rangle_j^2, \tag{46}$$

showing that the off-diagonal terms account for a large spread in x_j^2 although they do not contribute to $\langle x_j^2 \rangle_j$. This large spread in x_j^2, which gives a *rms* spread of $\sqrt{2}\langle x_j^2 \rangle$, is exactly that given by a Gaussian distribution. [This result is expected because our simplest model gives a final distribution of particles that is simply the binomial coefficient $\binom{n}{r}$ where $r = (-nl_0 + x)/n$ since at $t = T = n\tau_0$ the particles are at integral multiples of l_0 and the extreme positions are $\pm nl_0$.]

With Eq. (46) and its interpretation we conclude our use of the $\tau_0 u_0 = l_0$ model. The important features related to the roles of diagonal and nondiagonal terms will be seen to have significance for the more general cases considered next.

The result that $D(u, 0)$ of Eq. (35) is the diffusion constant applies in general to any $u(t)$ that has zero average value and corresponds to a disturbance with a finite correlation time so that $u_c^2(t)$ vanishes rapidly for large t. This can be seen by integrating Eq. (39) over the lower triangle $t'' < t'$ of Fig. 3. If the integration is carried out first over dt, the result is

$$\langle x_j^2 \rangle_j = 2 \int_0^T \left(\int_{t''}^T u_c^2(t' - t'') \, dt' \right) dt'' = 2 \int_0^T D(u, 0) \, dt'' = 2TD(u, 0), \tag{47}$$

which shows the diffusion relationship in general.

(The factor 3 in $3\langle x_j^2 \rangle^2$ in Eq. (45) for x_j^4 also follows in general by expressing x_j^4 as a four-dimensional integral from 0 to T for each of four t's, say t_1, t_2, t_3, t_4, the integrand being the products of the four corresponding u_j's. When the average over "j" is carried out, significant values for the intergrand result only if pairs of the t's differ by $\sim \tau_c$; this leads to three pairings: $[(t_1 t_2)(t_3 t_4)]$, $[(t_1 t_3)(t_2 t_4)]$, and $[(t_1 t_4)(t_2 t_3)]$, and for each the integration gives $4D^2(u, 0)T^2$ which leads to Eq. (45).)

For completeness we shall compare expression Eq. (47) for D with the familiar case of carriers having an isotropic effective mass m and a mean free time τ that is a function of energy only. For this case if the velocity at one time has x component u_x, then at a time t later it will on the average have $u_x e^{-t/\tau}$ so that

$$u_{xc}^2(t) = \langle u_x^2 e^{-t/\tau} \rangle_{all}, \tag{48}$$

where the average is over all carriers. The diffusion constant along the x-axis is then obtained by interchanging the order of integration and averaging:

$$D(v_x, 0) = \int_0^\infty \langle v_x^2 e^{-t/\tau} \rangle \, dt = \langle v_x^2 \tau \rangle_{\text{all}} = \left(\frac{kT}{q} \right) \mu. \tag{49}$$

That this does fit the Einstein relation is seen from the fact that the mobility μ for this model is given by the well-known formula with averaged mean free time weighted by v^2

$$\mu = \frac{q \langle v^2 \tau \rangle}{\langle v^2 \rangle m}, \tag{50}$$

and $\langle v^2 \rangle = 3 \langle v_x^2 \rangle$ so that $3kT = \langle v^2 \rangle m = 3 \langle v_x^2 \rangle m$ from which the result readily follows.

An important difference between the case of the ordinary diffusion constant and the $D(u, \omega)$ of this paper is that the correlation times of trapped carriers or intervalley scattering may be long enough that the dependence of $D(u, \omega)$ upon ω may be significant in an experimentally accessible range.

C. APPLICATION TO NOISE

Returning to $T_p^2 |a_\omega|^2$ needed for $S(\delta \dot{P}_\alpha, \omega)$, we note that the integral over $U_\alpha(t') U_\alpha(t'')$ is of the form already considered for $u_j(t') u_j(t'')$. We can thus conclude that, for the averages needed to calculate noise, only the diagonal strip, corresponding to the triangles of Fig. 3 need be considered. In terms of the $u_j(t)$ the expression of Eq. (33) for $T_p^2 |a_\omega|^2$ is

$$T_p^2 |a_\omega|^2 = \sum_j \sum_k \int_0^{T_p} \int_0^{T_p} e^{i\omega(t'-t'')} u_j(t') u_k(t'') \, dt' \, dt''. \tag{51}$$

In this double sum uncorrelated terms involving u_j and u_k products, although they may contribute significantly to any particular $|a_\omega|^2$, will average to zero for calculating noise. Hence the double sum reduces to a single sum of $u_j(t') u_j(t'')$, and since these are summed over all the electrons the integrand $e^{i\omega(t'-t'')} u_j(t') u_j(t'')$ can be replaced by its average value $e^{i\omega(t'-t'')} u_c^2(t'-t'')$. Since this integrand changes to its complex conjugate when t' and t'' are interchanged, we can by reasoning like that used for Fig. (3) and Eq. (45) take twice the real part of the integral over the big triangle $t'' < t'$. This procedure leads to terms like Eq. (45) for each "j" with T_j the time each carrier stays in $\Delta(\text{vol})_\alpha$ replacing T so that

$$T_p |a_\omega|^2 = \sum_j T_j 2Re \int_0^\infty e^{i\omega s} u_c^2(s) \, ds$$

$$= 2D_\alpha(u, \omega) \sum_j T_j. \tag{52}$$

Noting that if the density of carriers in $\Delta(\text{vol})_\alpha$ is n_α the sum of times T_j must be $T_p n_\alpha \Delta(\text{vol})_\alpha$, we can evaluate as follows

$$T_p^2 |a_\omega|^2 = 2D_\alpha(u, \omega) \sum T_j$$
$$= 2D_\alpha(u, \omega) n_\alpha \Delta(\text{vol})_\alpha T_p,$$
$$S(\delta \dot{P}, \omega) = q^2 2 T_p |a_\omega|^2 = 4q^2 D_\alpha(u, \omega) n_\alpha \Delta(\text{vol})_\alpha. \tag{53}$$

The last form indicates that spectral density $S(\delta \dot{P}, \omega)$ for $\Delta(\text{vol})_\alpha$ can be taken to be a spectral density per unit volume

$$S_V(\delta \dot{P}_\alpha, \omega) = 4q^2 D_\alpha(u, \omega) n_\alpha \tag{54}$$

times the volume.

This establishment of a volume density for the spectral density permits us to discard the $\Delta(\text{vol})_\alpha$ set and replace the sum of $S(\delta \dot{P}_\alpha, \omega)$ in $S(\delta V_N, \omega)$ by an integral of S_V. To be consistent we shall drop the subscript α and change notation as follows:

$$S_v(\delta \dot{P}_\alpha, \omega) \to S_v; \qquad D_\alpha(u, \omega) \to D; \qquad n_\alpha \to n, \tag{55}$$

where the dependence of the new symbols upon $\mathbf{r}$ and ω is implicitly understood.

The sum for $S(\delta V_N, \omega)$ can then be written as

$$S(\delta V_N, \omega) = \int |\nabla Z_{N\mathbf{r}}|^2 S_v \, d(\text{vol})$$
$$= \int |\nabla Z_{N\mathbf{r}}|^2 4q^2 Dn \, d(\text{vol}). \tag{56}$$

This expression formally reduces the problem of calculating noise in a semiconductor device into two problems: (a) calculation of the impedance field $\nabla Z_{N\mathbf{r}}$ corresponding to introducing dipole current sources as discussed in Section III and (b) calculating the spectral density of the elementary fluctuations as $\delta \dot{P}$ terms as S_v spatial densities.

In the next section we give the formulation as a basic test by verifying that it leads to the Johnson-Nyquist result for thermal equilibrium conditions.

VII. The Diffusion-Impedance Field Noise Formula

The integral derived in the last section attributes the cause of the noise to the diffusion sources $S(\delta \dot{P}_\alpha, \omega) = 4q^2 D_\alpha(u, \omega) n_\alpha$ modulated through the impedance field to give the output voltage. We shall refer to it as the *diffusion-impedance field noise formula*:

$$S(\delta V_N, \omega) = \int |\nabla Z_{N\mathbf{r}}|^2 4q^2 Dn \, d(\text{vol}). \tag{57}$$

One test of the diffusion-impedance field noise formula consists of applying it to obtain the Johnson-Nyquist result $S(\delta V_N, \omega) = 4kTR$. This result is established by using the Einstein relationship to obtain

$$q^2 Dn = q^2 \left(\frac{kT}{q}\right)\mu n = kT\sigma_r,$$
(58)

where σ_r is the ohmic conductivity of Eq. (14).

For the thermal equilibrium case $Z_{Nr} = Z_{rN}$. This permits rewriting the noise formula to obtain

$$S(\delta V_N, \omega) = \int |\nabla Z_{Nr}|^2 4q^2 Dn \, d(\text{vol})$$

$$= 4kT \int |\nabla Z_{rN}|\sigma_r \, d(\text{vol})$$

$$= 4kTR,$$
(59)

in keeping with the distributed power theorem of Eqs. (17) and (19).

VIII. Trapping and Intervalley Scattering

We shall next evaluate the spectral density of a noise source for carriers drifting under an electric field E along the x-axis in a volume $\Delta(\text{vol}) = \Delta x \, \Delta y \, \Delta z$. We shall suppose that the carrier density is n and that the carriers may be in either of two conditions; on the average a fraction α of the carriers are in an "a" condition and β are in a "b" condition. These conditions may be $a = $ mobile, $b = $ trapped for one example or $a = $ fast valley, $b = $ slow valley for another. We shall also denote the numbers of the carriers by a and b.

$$a = \alpha n \, \Delta(\text{vol}),$$
(60)

$$b = \beta n \, \Delta(\text{vol}).$$
(61)

We shall suppose that the carriers in condition a have a microscopic drift velocity along the x axis of v_a and fluctuations u_a about this and similarly define v_b and u_b. The average drift velocity is

$$\bar{v} = \alpha v_a + \beta v_b,$$
(62)

and the value of u is

$$u = \beta\Delta + u_a = v_a - \bar{v} + u_a \text{ for "} a \text{" carriers}$$

$$u = -\alpha\Delta + u_b = v_b - \bar{v} + u_b \text{ for "} b \text{" carriers,}$$

where

$$\Delta = v_a - v_b.$$
(63)

We suppose that a carrier makes many transitions between the two conditions while passing through $\Delta(\text{vol})$.

We shall first assume no interference effects, such as limited availability of traps, and take v_a as the probability of transition from a to b and v_b for b to a. Then if the number of carriers are not at their steady-state values

$$\dot{a} = -v_a a + v_b b, \tag{64}$$

$$\dot{b} = v_a a - v_b b. \tag{65}$$

Multiplying the equations by v_a and v_b and subtracting gives

$$\frac{d}{dt}(v_a a - v_b b) = -v(v_a a - v_b b), \tag{66}$$

where v

$$v = v_a + v_b \equiv \frac{1}{\tau} \tag{67}$$

is obviously the decay constant for any disturbance from the steady-state condition with $v_a a - v_b b = 0$. Evidently

$$\alpha = \frac{v_b}{(v_a + v_b)} ; \qquad \beta = \frac{v_a}{(v_a + v_b)} . \tag{68}$$

In terms of this model we shall show that if v is much less than 1

$$u_c^2(s) = \alpha\beta\Delta^2 e^{-vs} + \alpha u_{ca}^2(s) = \beta u_{ca}^2(s). \tag{69}$$

To prove this we note that $u(t')u(t' + s)$ includes four cases classified according to whether the carrier is in condition "a" or "b" at t' and whether the carrier is in condition "a" or "b" at $t' + s$.

In order to calculate $u_c^2(s)$ for this model we assume that the relaxation times τ_{ca} and τ_{cb} for u_a and u_b are much less than the decay time $1/v$ for transition. Hence in $u(t')u(t' + s)$ the contribution from $u_a(t')u_a(t' + s)$ is found a fraction α of the time and $u_b(t')u_b(t' + s)$ a fraction β.

If s is comparable to τ_{ca} or τ_{cb} the chance that $u(t')$ and $u(t'')$ correspond to different conditions is $\tau_{ca}v$ or $\tau_{cb}v$, and this is assumed negligible. Hence u_a and u_b contribute $\alpha u_{ca}^2(s)$ and $\beta u_{cb}^2(s)$ to $u_c^2(s)$.

The effect of the Δ term may be seen simply. Suppose we consider a sample of many carriers all in condition a with $u = \beta\Delta$ at $t = 0$. Their average value of u decays to zero as $\beta\Delta \exp(-vt)$. Hence for them $\langle u(0)u(t)\rangle = \beta^2\Delta^2 \exp(-vt)$. The chance of finding a carrier in state a is α however, so the contribution that these carriers make to $u_c^2(s)$ is $\alpha\beta^2\Delta^2 \exp(-vs)$. A similar contribution comes from carriers initially in condition b.

Combining all these contributions leads to

$$u_c^2(s) = \alpha\beta\Delta^2 \, e^{-vs} + \alpha u_{ca}^2(s) + \beta u_{cb}^2(s). \tag{70}$$

The resulting value for $D(u, \omega)$ is

$$D(u, \omega) = \frac{\alpha\beta\Delta^2\tau}{1 + (\omega\tau)^2} + \alpha D(u_a, \omega) + \beta D(u_b, \omega). \tag{71}$$

This expression for D may be used in the diffusion-impedance field formula.

Appendix A. The Reciprocity Theorem for Imrefs

The results of the previous sections can be extended to cases where holes and electrons are not in equilibrium with each other or with traps or recombination centers by making use of the imref of quasi-Fermi level. The method used here introduces a set of imrefs: φ_p for holes, φ_n for electrons, φ_t for a trap. For the situation shown in Fig. 4 all of these φ's represent small disturbances

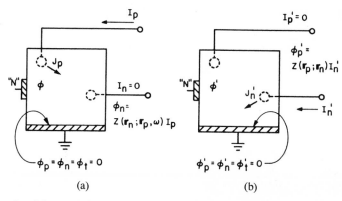

Fig. 4. Conditions considered in proof of reciprocity theorem for imrefs: (a) Hole current I_p at $\mathbf{r}_p$ results in imref φ_n at $\mathbf{r}_n$. (b) Electron current I_n' at $\mathbf{r}_n$ results in imref φ_p' at $\mathbf{r}_p$.

from $\varphi = 0$, the thermal equilibrium level. The free hole charge density ρ_p for small disturbances from the equilibrium (subscript 0) condition is

$$\rho_p = qn_i \exp[(\varphi_p - V_i)/V_\theta] = \rho_{p0} \exp[(\varphi_p - \varphi_e)/V_\theta]$$

$$= \rho_{p0} + \frac{\rho_{p0}}{V_\theta}(\varphi_p - \varphi_e), \qquad |\varphi_p - \varphi_e| \ll V_\theta, \tag{A1}$$

where φ_e is the small signal disturbance in the intrinsic level V_i where

$$V_i = V_{i0} + \varphi_e. \tag{A2}$$

The free electron charge density is similarly

$$\rho_n = -qn_i \exp[(V_i - \varphi_n)/V_\theta] = \rho_{n0} \exp[(\varphi_e - \varphi_n)/V_\theta]$$

$$= \rho_{n0} + \frac{\rho_{n0}}{V_\theta}(\varphi_e - \varphi_n), \qquad |\varphi_e - \varphi_n| \ll V_\theta. \tag{A3}$$

The imrefs lead to current densities of the form

$$\mathbf{J}_p = -\mu_p \rho_p \nabla \varphi_p = -\sigma_p \nabla \varphi_p \equiv \sigma_p \mathbf{E}_p, \tag{A4}$$

$$\mathbf{J}_n = +\mu_n \rho_n \nabla \varphi_n = -\sigma_n \nabla \varphi_n \equiv \sigma_n \mathbf{E}_n, \tag{A5}$$

where the $\mathbf{E}$'s are effectively electric fields that would be measured using pairs of $p+$ and $n+$ probes.

The dielectric displacement current density $\mathbf{J}_e$ due to rate of changes of $\mathbf{E}_e \equiv -\nabla\varphi_e$, the small signal electric field, is

$$\mathbf{J}_e = i\omega K E_e = -i\omega K V \dot{\varphi}_e \equiv \sigma_e \mathbf{E}_e, \tag{A6}$$

where K is the permittivity in farads/cm. This notation enables us usefully to write for the total current density

$$\mathbf{J} = \mathbf{J}_p + \mathbf{J}_n + \mathbf{J}_e = \sum_\alpha \mathbf{J}_\alpha \tag{A7}$$

where, of course

$$\nabla \cdot \mathbf{J} = 0. \tag{A8}$$

The concepts just discussed for currents and imrefs are used in deriving a reciprocity theorem for imrefs for situations like that represented in Fig. 4. Here two conditions are represented:

1. *Unprimed.* A hole current I_p is injected at a vector position $\mathbf{r}_p$ and flows out at ground producing an imref φ_n for electrons at position $\mathbf{r}_n$. Evidently for small signals φ_n must be proportional to I_p times a function of the two position vectors:

$$\phi_n = Z(\mathbf{r}_n; \mathbf{r}_p)I_p, \tag{A9}$$

where the semicolon separates the position and type of the output voltage, to the left, from that of the input, to the right.

2. *Primed.* An electron current I_n' is introduced at $\mathbf{r}_n$ producing an imref φ_p' at $\mathbf{r}_p$, For this condition:

$$\varphi_p' = Z(\mathbf{r}_p; \mathbf{r}_n)I_n'. \tag{A10}$$

Our problem is to prove from the same equations used for semiconductor device analysis that these two Z's are equal. [This result also follows, of course, from much more general considerations—Onsager's principle of microscopic reversibility (7). However, we wish to check the imref methodology for future use in noise calculations.]

If the "two-vector" Z's are reciprocal, the same will be true for two pairs of circuits. Thus if $Z(\mathbf{r}_1, \mathbf{r}_2; \mathbf{r}_3, \mathbf{r}_4)$ or more compactly $Z(12, 34)$, is the voltage developed between $\mathbf{r}_1$ and $\mathbf{r}_2$ per unit current into $\mathbf{r}_3$ and out of $\mathbf{r}_4$, then we can prove $Z(12, 34) = Z(34, 12)$ as follows:

$$Z(12, 34) = Z(1, 3) - Z(2, 3) - Z(1, 4) + Z(2, 4)$$

$$= Z(3, 1) - Z(3, 2) - Z(4, 1) + Z(4, 2)$$

$$= Z(34, 12). \tag{A11}$$

In order to prove this theorem we introduce a vector $\mathbf{H}$

$$\mathbf{H} = \sum_\alpha (\varphi_\alpha \mathbf{J}'_\alpha - \varphi'_\alpha \mathbf{J}_\alpha) \tag{A12}$$

where the three φ's and $\mathbf{J}$'s are functions of position in the specimen, and apply Gauss' theorem to Fig. 4 taking as the surface the outer surface of the specimen (for this purpose imagine all surface recombination centres and traps are moved 18 Å inside so that the $\mathbf{J}$'s are tangential), a surface just inside "N", a surface just inside the ground contact, and two small spheres around $\mathbf{r}_n$ and $\mathbf{r}_p$. The integral of $\mathbf{H} \cdot d\mathbf{S}$ (outward normal) gives zero on all but the small spheres at $\mathbf{r}_n$ and $\mathbf{r}_p$; either because all φ's are zero, or all φ's are equal (at "N") and $\int \mathbf{J} \cdot d\mathbf{S}$ gives zero, or $\mathbf{J}_n \cdot d\mathbf{S} = \mathbf{J}_p \cdot d\mathbf{S} = \mathbf{J}_e \cdot d\mathbf{S} = 0$ on the free surface. From the spheres at $\mathbf{r}_n$ and $\mathbf{r}_p$ we get the only contributions and these are found to give

$$\int \mathbf{H} \cdot d\mathbf{S} = -\varphi_n(\mathbf{r}_n) I'_n + \varphi'_p(\mathbf{r}_p) I_p = -Z(\mathbf{r}_n; \mathbf{r}_p) I_p I'_n + Z(\mathbf{r}_p; \mathbf{r}_n) I'_n I_p$$

$$= \int \nabla \cdot \mathbf{H} \, d(\text{vol}), \tag{A13}$$

the last equality being Gauss' theorem.

For a linear disturbance to a semiconductor in thermal equilibrium with no field the divergence in (A13) vanishes (as we shall show below) so that the two-point reciprocity is established. To show that $\nabla \cdot \mathbf{H} = 0$ we make use of symmetry relationships in the elementary process. First we note that $\nabla \cdot \mathbf{H}$ has one part of the form $\nabla \varphi \cdot \mathbf{J}$ and another of the form $\varphi \nabla \cdot \mathbf{J}$. The first part can be rewritten as

$$\sum_\alpha (E_\alpha \sigma_\alpha E'_\alpha - E'_\alpha \sigma_\alpha E_\alpha). \tag{A14}$$

This is clearly zero if σ_α is a scalar and even if σ_α is a symmetrical tensor, as it should be in the absence of a magnetic field.

The $\varphi \nabla \cdot \mathbf{J}$ terms are more complicated. The proof they give zero depends on showing that the $\nabla \cdot \mathbf{J}$'s are related to the φ's by an admittance matrix with coefficients $A_{\alpha\beta}$ having dimensions of mho/cm^3:

$$\nabla \cdot J_\alpha = \sum_\beta A_{\alpha\beta} \varphi_\beta \qquad (A15)$$

and that $A_{\alpha\beta} = A_{\beta\alpha}$ from which it follows that the $+\varphi \nabla \cdot \mathbf{J}$ and $-\varphi \nabla \cdot \mathbf{J}$ terms in $\nabla \cdot \mathbf{H}$ cancel so that $\nabla \cdot \mathbf{H} = 0$.

The proof of the reciprocity theorem for the Z's can thus be completed by showing that the six nondiagonal matrix elements satisfy $A_{pn} = A_{np}$, $A_{pe} = A_{ep}$, and $A_{ne} = A_{en}$. We shall prove these equalities for a simplified model having one acceptor trap and a direct recombination mechanism (or one so fast that storage in the centers is negligible). For this model we must consider three varying charge densities; in addition to ρ_n and ρ_p, the charge density of holes on traps varies from its thermal equilibrium value ρ_{pto} by an ac component $\delta\rho_{pt}$ (8):

$$\delta\rho_{pt} = [\rho_{pto}(1 - f_{pto})/V_\theta] (\varphi_t - \varphi_e) \equiv C_t(\varphi_t - \varphi_e), \qquad (A16)$$

where f_{pto} is the fraction of traps that have holes on them at thermal equilibrium. C_t is defined by the identity and has the dimensions of farads/cm^3. If the thermal equilibrium rate of emission of the charge density of holes from traps is $e_p \rho_{pto}$, then the net rate of capture of hole charge on traps is

$$\delta\dot\rho_{pt} = i\omega\delta\rho_{pt} = (qe_p\rho_{pto}/V_\theta) (\varphi_p - \varphi_t)$$
$$\equiv A_t(\varphi_p - \varphi_t), \qquad (A17)$$

where the admittance A_t in mho/cm^3 is defined by the identity. Eliminating φ_t, we obtain

$$\delta\rho_{pt} = [C_t/(1 + i\omega\tau_t)] (\varphi_p - \varphi_e) \equiv C_t(\omega) (\varphi_p - \varphi_e), \qquad (A18)$$

where C_t is defined by the identity and

$$\tau_t = C_t/A_t. \qquad (A19)$$

The rate of generation of hole charge density through recombination centers may be written for a fast recombination model as $A_g(\varphi_n - \varphi_p)$ so that the equation of continuity for hole charge becomes

$$\nabla \cdot \mathbf{J}_p = -\dot\rho_p - \delta\dot\rho_{pt} + A_g(\varphi_n - \varphi_p)$$
$$= -i\omega[(\rho_{p0}/V_\theta) + C_t] (\varphi_p - \varphi_e) + A_g(\varphi_n - \varphi_p), \qquad (A20)$$

in which the ρ_{p0} term comes directly from (A1). This equation gives A_{pe} and A_{pn}; for example $A_{pn} = A_g$. Similarly

$$\nabla \cdot J_n = -i\omega(-\rho_{n0}/V_\theta) (\varphi_n - \varphi_e) + A_g(\varphi_p - \varphi_n), \qquad (A21)$$

which gives A_{ne} and A_{np}; A_{np} satisfies the symmetry condition $A_{np} = A_g = A_{pn}$. The A_{en} and A_{ep} matrix elements are obtained from (A8):

$$\nabla \cdot \mathbf{J}_e = -\nabla \cdot \mathbf{J}_p - \nabla \cdot \mathbf{J}_n$$
$$= i\omega[(\rho_{po}/V_\theta) + C_t(\omega)](\varphi_p - \varphi_e) + i\omega(-\rho_{no}/V_\theta)(\varphi_n - \varphi_e). \quad \text{(A22)}$$

Inspection shows that the necessary symmetry is preserved through the appearance of the differences of φ's always in the form $A_{\alpha\beta}(\varphi_\alpha - \varphi_\beta)$ in $\nabla \cdot \mathbf{J}_\alpha$ and minus the same form in $\nabla \cdot \mathbf{J}_\beta$ so that $-A_{\alpha\beta}(\varphi_\alpha - \varphi_\beta) = A_{\beta\alpha}(\varphi_\beta - \varphi_\alpha)$ and $A_{\alpha\beta} = A_{\beta\alpha}$. It is intuitively clear that generalization of the model considered here will still preserve the symmetry necessary to establish the reciprocity of the Z's.

Appendix B. Field of a One-Dimensional Sample with Carrier Drift

The following model can be applied to the GaAs transit time diode. Consider a rod of semiconductor with a uniform majority carrier current flowing in the x direction with drift velocity $v(x)$ where the x coordinate varies from 0 to L. The sample is assumed uniform in the y and z coordinates.

If at time t a quantity of charge δQ is removed from the drifting carrier stream at point x and replaced at point $x + \delta x$, the effect is that of creating a dipole layer which initially affects the electric field only at points between x and $x + \delta x$ (see Fig. 5). As time passes two things happen: (a) the dipole layer drifts toward the drain contact ($x = L$), and (b) the voltage step created by the dipole layer δV changes according to

$$\frac{d}{dt} \delta V = -v\delta V, \quad \text{(B1)}$$

$$v = \frac{\rho_f \mu^*}{K}, \quad \text{(B2)}$$

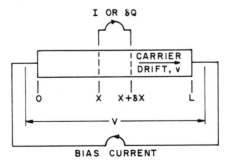

FIG. 5.   Drifting dipole layer interpretation of disturbance in stream of drifting carriers.

where ρ_f is the fixed charge, μ^* is the differential mobility, and K is the dielectric permittivity. Equation (B2) can be derived from Eq. (4.16) of Ref. (9) by considering the effect of space charge on the length of the drifting dipole. Because of the carrier drift, the dipole layer may drift into regions where the dielectric relaxation constant v is significantly different. In the GaAs transit time diode, v may change sign as the electric field varies along x.

To discuss the development of a disturbance in the drifting carrier stream, it is convenient to associate with each point, x, a timelike variable, s, which is the time required for a point fixed on the carrier stream to drift from the source contact ($x = 0$) to the point x.

$$s(x) = \int_0^x \frac{1}{v(x')} \, dx'.$$

The transit time T is equal to $s(L)$. Since s for this case is a monotonic function of x, any function of x can also be expressed as a function of s. The relative change in voltage of drifting dipole layer is described by a dimensionless function $\varphi(s)$ defined by

$$\varphi(0) = 1,$$

$$\frac{d}{ds} \varphi(s) = -v(s)\varphi(s). \tag{B3}$$

In terms of $\varphi(s)$ an expression for the voltage, δV, across the whole sample resulting from the displacement of charge δQ across the segment x to $x + \delta x$ as a function of time can be easily found. The initial voltage is the same as would be produced by putting charge δQ on a parallel plate capacitor with capacity $KA/\delta x$. The relative change in voltage with time is given by $\varphi(s(x) + t)/\varphi(s(x))$. The voltage is then given by

$$\delta V(t) = \frac{\delta Q \, \delta x}{KA} \frac{\varphi(s(x) + t)}{\varphi(s(x))}, \qquad 0 \leq t \leq T - s(x)$$

$$= 0, \qquad\qquad\qquad t > T - s(x) \tag{B4}$$

The impedance field gradient $Z_x(x, \omega)$ is defined as the ratio of voltage produced at the end terminals to the alternating current inserted through the vanishingly small segment between x and $x + \delta x$ divided by δx. This differential transfer impedance can be found as a function of frequency by Fourier analysis of the current pulse $\delta Q \delta(t)$, where $\delta(t)$ is the Dirac impulse function, and the resulting voltage $\delta V(t)$ just considered

$$\delta Q \delta(t) = \frac{1}{2\pi} \int_{-\infty}^{\infty} e^{i\omega t} I(\omega) \, d\omega, \tag{B5}$$

$$I(\omega) = \delta Q \tag{B6}$$

and

$$\delta V(t) = \frac{1}{2\pi} \int_{-\infty}^{\infty} e^{i\omega t} V(\omega) \, d\omega, \tag{B7}$$

$$V(\omega) = \int_{-\infty}^{\infty} e^{-i\omega t} V(t) \, dt$$

$$= \frac{\delta Q \, \delta x}{KA} \int_{0}^{T-s(x)} \frac{e^{-i\omega t} \varphi(s(x) + t)}{\varphi(s(x))} \, dt$$

$$= \frac{\delta Q \, \delta x \, e^{i\omega s}(x)}{KA\varphi(s(x))} \int_{s(x)}^{T} e^{-i\omega t} \varphi(t) \, dt. \tag{B8}$$

Now the differential transfer impedance or impedance field gradient is

$$\frac{\partial}{\partial x} Z(x, \omega) = \frac{V(\omega)}{I(\omega) \, \delta x} = \frac{e^{i\omega s}(x)}{KA\varphi(s(x))} \int_{s(x)}^{T} e^{-i\omega t} \varphi(t) \, dt. \tag{B9}$$

The impedance of the whole device may be found by considering the voltage produced at the contacts when the same current is flowing through all segments of the sample. The result is

$$Z(\omega) = \int_{0}^{L} \frac{\partial}{\partial x} Z(x, \omega) \, dx$$

$$= \frac{1}{KA} \int_{0}^{L} \frac{e^{i\omega s}(x)}{\varphi(s(x))} \int_{s(x)}^{T} e^{i\omega t} \varphi(t) \, dt \, dx. \tag{B10}$$

Equation (B9) gives the impedance field gradient which is used in Eq. (53) to calculate the open circuit output noise voltage. The short circuit noise current can then be calculated by using the impedance given by Eq. (B10).

REFERENCES

1. M. Lax, *Rev. Mod. Phys.* **32**, 25 (1960).
2. W. Shockley, *Bell System Tech. J.* **28**, 435 (1949).
3. W. Shockley, M. Sparks, and G. K. Teal, *Phys. Rev.* **83**, 151 (1951).
4. W. Shockley, *J. Appl. Phys.* **9**, 635 (1938).
5. J. B. Johnson, *Phys. Rev.* **32**, 97 (1928).
6. H. Nyquist, *Phys. Rev.* **32**, 110 (1928).
7. H. B. G. Casimir, *Rev. Mod. Phys.* **17**, 343 (1945).
8. W. Shockley, *Proc. I.R.E.* **46**, 973 (1958).
9. W. Shockley, *Bell System Tech. J.* **33**, 799 (1954).

The Size of an Exciton in a Molecular Crystal

G. G. HALL

MATHEMATICS DEPARTMENT, UNIVERSITY OF NOTTINGHAM, ENGLAND

I. Introduction

The literature on the theory of excitons in molecular crystals can be divided into two classes according to whether the exciton is assumed to be of infinite extent or about the size of one molecule. The first assumption is usual when treating spectral properties, e.g., Silbey *et al.* (1965), and the second when treating conductivity properties, e.g., Northrop and Simpson (1956). The difference between these assumptions is not just the trivial one of the volume disturbed since the long-range contributions to the excitation energies, which are substantial, are present on the first assumption but absent on the second. The principal object of this paper is to indicate how this question may be resolved. It begins with a summary of the application to excitons of the long-wave theory which has been developed in order to deal effectively with long-range effects and shows how the introduction of a finite lifetime into the theory modifies it. In particular, the form of the exciton created during light absorption is contrasted with the form of the excitons involved in subsequent effects.

II. The Long-Wave Theory

The basic difficulty in calculating the excited states of a molecular crystal is that of evaluating the conditionally convergent sums of the dipolar interactions between excited molecules. The same difficulty arises in considering the vibrations of an ionic crystal. One solution of this problem is the long-wave theory described in detail by Born and Huang (1954) and summarized elegantly by Slater (1960). This theory uses the approximation that the wavelength of the waves is much greater than the separation between nearest dipoles and this is certainly valid in the molecular crystal problem. The application of the theory to the molecular exciton problem has been given by Hall (1958, 1962) and Amos (1963) and will be described here as the limit of a sequence of theories of gradually increasing complexity.

The first attempts to account for the spectra of molecular crystals in terms of the excited states of the free molecules were made by Davydov (1962) and are summarized in his book. In these, the interaction between a molecule and its immediate neighbors is the only one included in the theory. These interactions produce wide bands of excited states, but only a few of these states are involved in light absorption because of the conservation of crystal momentum between the photon and the exciton so that the spectrum of the crystal consists of sharp lines. If the excitation energy of a free molecule is U then the interaction energy between one molecule and all of its neighbors inside a sphere can be expressed in the form of an additional term which is the scalar product of the dipolar transition moment T and an effective electric field I due to the remaining molecules inside the sphere. The very short range forces between nearest neighbors can also be included by modifying U.

The excitation energy is then

$$W = U - \mathbf{T} \cdot \mathbf{I}, \tag{1}$$

and in the calculations of Craig and Hobbins (1955) and Craig and Walsh (1958) all molecules within a sphere of radius 20 Å contribute to the effective field I. The apparent convergence of the lattice sums for I is misleading, however, since this is a property of the sphere and not of the infinite sums. When the sums are extended to the infinite limit there is an additional polarization contribution of Lorenz-Lorentz type which, for transverse excitons, gives

$$W = U - \mathbf{T} \cdot \mathbf{I} - (4\pi/3v)T^2, \tag{2}$$

where v is the volume associated with each molecule. The calculations of Silbey, Jortner, and Rice show that this extra term can sometimes become very large.

The use of the electric field formalism in this classical way as a method of calculating the intermolecular forces suggests that another effect needs to be introduced into the theory. This is the polarization of the medium between the dipoles which is described by a dielectric constant or, alternatively, by the polarizability α. This effect can be evaluated electrostatically and changes the excitation energy to

$$W = U - \mathbf{T} \cdot \mathbf{I} - V(1 - \tfrac{4}{3}\pi\alpha)^{-1}, \tag{3}$$

where

$$V = \tfrac{4}{3}\pi(\mathbf{T}^2/v + \alpha\mathbf{T}\cdot\mathbf{I}). \tag{4}$$

In all these refinements the electric field is treated as an electrostatic field distinct from the electromagnetic field of the photon. This is an acceptable approximation so long as the two are far from resonance, but when considering photon absorption we are concerned precisely with resonance since the fields must be given wave vectors $\mathbf{k}$ and angular frequencies ω which are the same. The full electromagnetic theory then has a composite solution in which the energy quantum is present partly in the form of an exciton and partly in the electromagnetic field. This electromagnetic exciton is similar in conception to the polariton described by Fano (1956, 1960) and Hopfield (1958) and differs primarily in that it retains the use of the classical electromagnetic field whereas polariton theory uses second quantization both for the exciton field and the electromagnetic field. Although the polariton formalism can ultimately be extended to include all the effects listed above it is rather more difficult to do so because of self-energy terms. The equation for the excitation energy that embodies the effect of this electromagnetic coupling of the exciton with the photon is given by Amos (1963) as

$$W = U - \mathbf{T}\cdot\mathbf{I} + V\left(2 + \frac{c^2k^2}{\omega^2}\right)\left\{\left(1 + \frac{8}{3}\pi\alpha\right) - \frac{c^2k^2}{\omega^2}\left(1 - \frac{4}{3}\pi\alpha\right)\right\}^{-1}, \tag{5}$$

but this is inaccurate since negative frequency terms are omitted. These terms are important theoretically, as has been pointed out by Fowler (1964) and Ball and McLachlan (1964), because they lead to a dispersion relation which satisfies the causality principle but, in practice, their quantitative effect is small. The corrected formula becomes

$$W^2 = (U - \mathbf{T}\cdot\mathbf{I})^2$$
$$+ 2V(U - \mathbf{T}\cdot\mathbf{I})\left(2 + \frac{c^2k^2}{\omega^2}\right)\left\{\left(1 + \frac{8}{3}\pi\alpha\right) - \frac{c^2k^2}{\omega^2}\left(1 - \frac{4}{3}\pi\alpha\right)\right\}^{-1} \tag{6}$$

Although the theory now incorporates most of the significant effects related to the electromagnetic field it has still to be modified to allow for the finite lifetime of the excited state. This is not a classical effect but it can be brought into the classical theory by making the energy complex with a negative imaginary part. Thus U is replaced by $U - \tfrac{1}{2}i\gamma$, where γ is the width of the band or $\hbar/\gamma$ the lifetime of the excited state, and this leads to the same formulas as those of the Weisskopf-Wigner theory (1930). In the region of anomalous dispersion, which is also the region of light absorption, this modification makes the theory very much more realistic. Thus, the dielectric constant at the resonant frequency becomes finite and the reflexion coefficient ceases to be unity.

The theory requires some modification, particularly to the definition of the transition moment **T**, when there are several molecules of the same species per unit cell. Amos (1963) has made these changes and applied the theory to the naphthalene band around 2200 Å and the anthracene band around 2500 Å, but experimental results are not sufficient to provide an adequate test of the theory. It is especially difficult to obtain independent estimates of α and γ.

III. The Exciton Lifetime

The device, adopted above, of introducing the exciton lifetime into the theory by means of a complex energy is an approximation to the true situation in which the exciton is also coupled to the phonon degrees of freedom. In normal circumstances, this coupling means that individual vibronic transitions have to be considered and the width of these is very small. Nevertheless, the observed absorption is a superposition of many vibrational peaks, and it may be argued that it is their envelope and its width which are important. In his study of hypochromism, Nesbet (1964) has shown that if the band shape is rectangular this result follows so that the value of γ is the full Franck-Condon width. Nesbet uses a width of 0.74 eV for ethylene, and this is a typical value for all conjugated systems. It corresponds to a lifetime of 10^{-15} sec.

An immediate consequence of this large effective value of γ can be seen in Figure 2 of Amos' paper which is drawn to illustrate the absorption when γ is large. The absorption is centered on an excitation energy which is now identical with that obtained in the original theory which included only the interactions from neighbors lying inside a sphere of definite radius. Thus, in this indirect way, the calculations by Craig *et al.* using a sphere can be justified for those transitions having large values of γ.

IV. Exciton Size

Another consequence of the short exciton lifetime is a short extinction length. For a γ of 0.74 eV the extinction length is about 10^{-5} cm. Following the interpretation of the width γ, this length must be interpreted as the result of superimposing a large number of bands each of which has a much longer extinction length. The exciton is therefore limited in extent and is created at the surface since the photon cannot penetrate the material to produce excitons in the interior. This finite size of the exciton explains why the long range terms vanish from the excitation energy leaving only the local effects and the spherical sum. In principle the exciton could have infinite extent in planes normal to the wave vector but in practice this is limited by the coherence of the external radiation which creates the exciton. The coherence diameter (Born and Wolf, 1959) will usually include many molecules but is small in comparison with the specimen sizes. Thus the exciton can be pictured as finite in extent and so with an energy independent of specimen size or shape.

Another aspect of this attenuation is that the movement of these excitons is so very heavily damped that they cannot contribute to the transport of energy. Furthermore, an elaborate investigation would be needed to determine how excitons in a region of anomalous dispersion can carry energy since even a classical discussion (Stratton, 1941) shows that neither the phase velocity nor the group velocity is appropriate though possibly the signal velocity could be used. It becomes necessary, therefore, to find alternative explanations of the phenomena usually attributed to the movement of the exciton.

One of the most important of these observations is the dependence of the fluorescence spectrum on the concentration of impurities (Bowen *et al.*, 1949; Northrop and Simpson, 1956). This is easily explained in terms of the chance of an impurity lying inside the finite size of the exciton and the chance of the impurity trapping the energy by accepting the exciton's energy and losing part of it irreversibly to the lattice.

The other major consideration involved in the discussion of mobility is of the fate of the original exciton. Since the lifetime is very much shorter than the natural lifetime of a band it is clear that the exciton is not decaying by emission of a photon but is being transformed internally by a phonon collision. The result of such a collision will usually be to leave an exciton having approximately the same energy but a different crystal momentum. Such an exciton is no longer in the region of anomalous dispersion and so has more normal properties. It is these excitons with their much longer lifetime and no attenuation which will contribute to collision processes in the body of the crystal. Thus, the original problem of the discrepancy between the properties of the excitons as assumed in describing different phenomena is resolved by distinguishing sharply between the originally formed excitons which are finite in extent and immobile, and the excitons to which these decay which are not extinguished and will be involved in collisions.

REFERENCES

Amos, A. T. (1963). *Mol. Phys.* **6**, 393.
Ball, M. A., and McLachlan, A. D. (1964). *Proc. Roy. Soc.* **A285**, 435.
Born, M. and Huang, K. (1954). "Dynamical Theory of Crystal Lattices." Oxford Univ. Press, London and New York.
Born, M., and Wolf, E. (1959). "Principles of Optics," p. 315. Pergamon, Oxford.
Bowen, E. J., Mikiewicz, E., and Smith, F. W. (1949). *Proc. Phys. Soc.* **A62**, **26**.
Craig, D. P., and Hobbins, P. O. (1955). *J. Chem. Soc.* **539**, 2309.

Craig, D. P., and Walsh, J. R. (1958). *J. Chem. Soc.* 1613.

Davydov, A. S. (1962). "Theory of Molecular Excitons." McGraw-Hill, New York.

Fano, U. (1956). *Phys. Rev.* **103**, 1202.

Fano, U. (1960). *Phys. Rev.* **118**, 451.

Fowler, G. N. (1964). *Mol. Phys.* **8**, 375.

Hall, G. G. (1958). *Technical Report No. 15*, Quantum Chemistry Group, University of Uppsala.

Hall, G. G. (1962). *Proc. Roy. Soc.* **A270**, 285.

Hopfield, J. J. (1958). *Phys. Rev.* **112**, 1955.

Nesbet, R. K. (1964). *Mol. Phys.* **7**, 211.

Northrop, D. C., and Simpson, O. (1956). *Proc. Roy. Soc.* **A234**, 136.

Silbey, R., Jortner, J., and Rice, S. A. (1965). *J. Chem. Phys.* **42**, 1515.

Slater, J. C. (1960). *Quarterly Progress Report No. 38*, Solid State Group, M.I.T.

Stratton, J. A. (1941). "Electromagnetic Theory," p. 339. McGraw-Hill, New York.

Weisskopf, V., and Wigner, E. (1930). *Z. Physik* **63**, 54.

Finite Rotation Groups and Crystal Classes in Four Dimension

II. Revised Tables and Projection of Groups of Antisymmetry in Three Dimensions

A. C. HURLEY

DIVISION OF CHEMICAL PHYSICS
C.S.I.R.O., CHEMICAL RESEARCH LABORATORIES
MELBOURNE, AUSTRALIA

I. Introduction

Some years ago (Hurley, 1951, Part I)* the author used Goursat's (1889) analysis of finite rotation groups in four dimensions ([4]) to enumerate the four-dimensional crystal classes. At that time no physical application of these groups was envisaged. Since then, however, generalized groups of symmetry in [3] introduced by Shubnikov (1964) and others have found extensive applications in crystallography (Niggli, 1964). One method for obtaining these generalized symmetry groups is to project the ordinary symmetry groups from a space of higher dimensionality. Indeed Shubnikov's original derivation of the polar, gray and black-white groups of finite plane figures was by projection from the point groups in [3].

When this projection method was applied to the [4] crystal classes listed in Part I it was found that not all of the known polar, gray and black-white groups in [3] were obtained. This indicates that the list given in Part I is incomplete, as has been suggested by others (Niggli, 1964; Wondratschek and Neubüser, 1965). The enumeration of the crystal classes in [4] has been repeated using the same methods as before. Two errors, which led to the omission of several classes, were detected as well as several misprints. Now, 227 crystal classes are found in [4] (previously 222) or which 45 are irreducible

---

* Hereafter referred to as Part I.

(previously 45). Applying the projection method to this revised list we obtain 32 polar, 32 gray, and 58 black-white groups in [3] in agreement with results by other methods (Niggli, 1964).

II. Revised Tables of Crystal Classes in [4]

The revised list of crystal classes in [4] is given in Tables 1a, 1b, 2a, and 2b. As in Part I each crystal class is specified both in Goursat's notation and by the number of elements with given values of the invariants χ, σ and d. These invariants are the coefficients in the characteristic equation

$$\det (\lambda I - A) \equiv \lambda^4 - \chi(A)\lambda^3 + \sigma (A)\lambda^2 - \chi(A)\lambda + d(A) = 0 \qquad (1)$$

for the 4×4 orthogonal matrix A.

The sets of values of (χ, σ, d) which occur are labelled as follows:

$$I = (4, 6, 1);$$

$$A = (0, 0, 1), \quad B = (0, 1, 1), \quad C = (0, -1, 1), \quad D = (0, 2, 1),$$

$$E = (0, -2, 1), \quad F = (0, 0, -1);$$

$$K = (1, 0, 1), \quad L = (1, 1, 1), \quad M = (1, 2, 1), \quad N = (1, 0, -1); \qquad (2)$$

$$R = (2, 2, 1), \quad S = (2, 3, 1), \quad T = (2, 0, -1);$$

$$Z = (3, 4, 1);$$

together with I' $(= -I)$, K', L', M', N'; R', S', T'; Z' formed from the above by changing the sign of the trace χ.

For the crystal classes containing $-I$ (Tables 1a, 1b) we tabulate half the number of types A, B, $--$ F and omit the dashed types; an asterisk (*) denotes an irreducible class. Entries which differ from those of Part I are indicated by boldface type or in footnotes to the tables.

The three groups X.$m = 3, n = 2$; XIII'.$m = 4, n = 6$ and XIV.$m = 3$ shown in Table 1a' are of some interest. Although these groups contain only elements with integral invariants, it was shown in Part I that they are not crystal classes. Thus, although any element of one of these groups appears as an integral 4×4 matrix in a suitable coordinate system, it is impossible to choose a coordinate system such that all the elements of one of these groups appear in integral form simultaneously. Such groups do not exist for a space of dimensionality less than 4. These groups may be considered as pseudo crystal classes. If these three groups are included with the 227 crystal classes in [4], a total of 230 groups is obtained, equal in number to the space groups in [3]. This seems to be just a numerical coincidence.

TABLE 1a

PROPER CRYSTAL CLASSES IN [4] CONTAINING $-I^a$

Goursat Group	Order	*	I	A	B	C	D	E	K	L	M	R	S	Z	Projected groups
I $\mu = \nu = 1, D = 1$	2		1											·	$1'(1)$
$D = 2, q = 1$	4		1					1						·	$2/m'(2)$
$D = 3, q = 1$	6		1						2					·	$3'(3)$
$D = 4, q = 1$	8		1					1		4		2		·	$4/m'(4)$
$D = 5, q = 2$	10		1						2					·	
$D = 6, q = 1$	12		1					1	2		4	2		2	$6/m'(6)$
$D = 12, q = 5$	24		1					1	2					2	
$\mu = 1, \nu = 2, D = 1$	4		1	2			1							·	
$D = 2, q = 1$	8		1				1						2	·	
$\mu = 1, \nu = 3, D = 1,$	6		1		2									·	
$D = 2, q = 1$	12		1			2		1					2	·	
$\mu = 2, \nu = 2, D = 1$	8		1				2						2	·	
$D = 2, q = 1$	16		1			2	2	1				4	4	·	
$\mu = 2, \nu = 3, D = 1$	12		1				1						4	·	
$\mu = 3, \nu = 3, D = 1$	18		1			2			4				4	·	
$D = 2, q = 1$	36		1		4	2		1	4				4	4	
II $m = 1, n = 2$	8		1										·	·	
$m = 1, n = 3$	12		1				3						2	·	
$m = 2, n = 2$	16		1			2	3						2	·	
$m = 2, n = 3$	24		1			6	4					4	4	·	
$m = 3, n = 2$	24		1			6	3	3	4				4	·	
$m = 3, n = 3$	36		1				3	3						4	
III $m = 2, n = 2$	8		1				1	2					·	·	
$m = 2, n = 3$	12		1			2	2	3				4	2	·	
$m = 4, n = 2$	16		1	4			1	1					·	·	
$m = 4, n = 3$	24		1	6		2	1	·					2	·	

TABLE 1a—*continued*

PROPER CRYSTAL CLASSES IN [4] CONTAINING $-I^a$

Goursat Group	Order	*	I	A	B	C	D	E	K	L	M	R	S	Z	Projected groups
$m=6, n=2$	24		1	.	4	2	1	2	.	.	.	.	2	.	
$m=6, n=3$	36		1	.	6	.	.	3	4	.	.	.	4	.	
IV $\mu=1, \nu=2$	16		1	2	.	.	3	2	.	.	.	.	2	.	
$\mu=1, \nu=3$	24		1	.	2	.	3	4	.	.	.	.	.	.	
$\mu=2, \nu=2$	32		1	4	.	.	4	3	.	.	.	4	.	4	
$\mu=3, \nu=3$	72		1	.	10	6	3	4	4	.	.	.	4	4	
V $m=1$	24		1	.	.	.	3	.	.	.	.	.	8	.	
$m=2$	48		1	.	.	8	4	3	.	.	.	.	8	.	
$m=3$	72		1	.	.	6	3	.	16	.	.	.	10	.	
VI $m=3$	24		1	.	.	.	3	.	8	.	.	.	.	.	
VIII $\mu=1$	48		1	6	.	.	3	6	.	.	.	.	8	.	
$\mu=2$	96		1	12	.	8	4	3	.	.	.	12	8	.	
X $m=2, n=2$	32	*	1	.	.	.	.	9	4	.	.	.	4	.	
$m=3, n=3$	72	*	1	.	.	12	6	9	4	.	.	.	4	.	
XI $\mu=1, \nu=1, D=2, q=1$	8		1	.	.	.	.	3	3	.	.	.	.	.	$m'm'm'(222)$
$D=3, q=1$	12		1	.	.	.	.	3	2	.	.	.	.	.	$\bar{3}'m'(32)$
$D=4, q=1$	16		1	.	.	.	.	5	.	.	.	2	.	.	$4/m'm'm'(422)$
$D=5, q=2$	20		1	.	.	.	.	5	.	4	.	.	.	.	
$D=6, q=1$	24		1	.	.	.	.	7	2	.	.	.	.	2	$6/m'm'm'(622)$
$D=12, q=5$	48		1	.	.	.	.	13	2	.	4	2	.	2	
$\mu=1, \nu=2, D=2, q=1$	16		1	2	.	.	1	4	2	.	.	2	.	.	
$\mu=1, \nu=3, D=2, q=1$	24		1	.	2	.	.	7	2	.	.	.	2	.	
$\mu=2, \nu=2, D=1$	16		1	.	.	.	2	5	.	.	.	.	.	.	
$D=2, q=1$	32		1	.	.	2	2	9	.	.	.	4	.	.	
$\mu=2, \nu=3, D=1$	24		1	.	.	2	1	6	2	.	.	.	2	.	
$\mu=3, \nu=3, D=1$	36		1	.	.	.	.	9	4	.	.	.	4	.	
$D=2, q=1$	72		1	.	4	.	.	19	4	.	.	4	4	4	

Goursat Group	Order	*	I	A	B	C	D	E	K	L	M	R	S	Z	Class
XII $m=2, n=4$	32	*	1	4	·	·	4	7	·	·	·	·	·	·	
$m=2, n=6$	48	*	1	·	4	2	4	11	·	·	·	·	·	·	
$m=3, n=4$	48	*	1	6	·	6	3	6	4	·	·	·	2	2	
$m=3, n=6$	72	*	1	·	6	6	3	12	·	·	·	·	2	4	
XIII $m=4, n=4$	64	*	1	8	16	·	6	13	4	·	·	4	·	4	
$m=6, n=6$	144	*	1	·	·	12	6	25	·	·	·	·	·	4	
XIII' $m=4, n=4$	32	*	1	8	12	·	2	5	4	·	·	·	·	·	
$m=6, n=6$	72	*	1	·	·	·	·	15	·	·	·	·	·	4	
XIV $m=2$	96	*	1	·	·	24	6	9	·	·	·	·	·	8	
XVI $m=2$	96	*	1	12	·	8	4	15	16	·	·	·	·	8	
$m=3$	144	*	1	18	·	6	3	18	·	·	·	12	·	10	
XVII $\mu=2$	192	*	1	24	·	24	6	21	16	·	·	·	·	8	$m'3(23)$
XVIII $\mu=1$	48	*	1	6	·	·	3	6	8	·	·	·	·	16	
XX	288	*	1	·	·	48	6	9	64	·	·	·	·	·	$m'3m'(432)$
XXI	24	·	1	·	·	·	·	3	8	·	·	·	·	·	
XXII	96	*	1	·	·	·	6	9	32	·	·	6	·	·	
XXVI	48	·	1	·	·	·	·	9	8	·	·	·	·	·	
XXVII	192	*	1	24	·	·	6	21	32	·	·	12	·	·	
XXVIII	576	*	1	72	·	48	6	45	64	·	·	36	16	·	
XXXII	120	·	1	·	·	·	·	15	20	24	·	·	·	·	

 a In all 73 crystal classes 20 of which are irreducible. Projection gives 11 black-white groups in [3].

TABLE 1a'

PROPER [4] ROTATION GROUPS, WITH INTEGRAL INVARIANTS, CONTAINING −I, WHICH ARE NOT CRYSTAL CLASSES

Goursat Group	Order	*	I	A	B	C	D	E	K	L	M	R	S	Z
X $m=3, n=2$	48	*	1	6	4	6	6	9	·	·	·	·	2	·
XIII' $m=4, n=6$	48	*	1	·	4	2	1	8	·	·	·	·	2	·
XIV $m=3$	144	*	1	·	·	30	6	9	16	·	·	·	10	·

TABLE 1b

IMPROPER CRYSTAL CLASSES IN [4] CONTAINING —Iᵃ

Goursat Group	Order	*	I	A	B	C	D	E	F	K	L	M	N	R	S	T	Z	P_{max}	Projected groups
XXXIII $\mu = \nu = 1$, $D = 1$	4		1													1		2	$\bar{1}1'$; $2'/m(m)$
$D = 2$, $q = 1$, $1 = 0$	8		1					1								2	2	3	$2/m1'$; $mmm'(mm2)$
$1 = 1$	8		1					1	2									2	$4'/m(\bar{4})$
$D = 3$, $q = 1$, $1 = 0$	12		1						2				2			3		2	$\bar{3}1'$; $6'/m(\bar{6})$
$q = 2$, $1 = 0$	12		1						2							2		1	$3m(3m)$
$D = 4$, $q = 1$, $1 = 0$	16		1					1	2			4				2	2	2	$4/m1'$
$q = 3$, $1 = 0$	16		1					1								4	4	1	$4/mmm(4mm)$
$1 = 2$	16		1					1	4		4	4		2		4	4	0	
$D = 6$, $q = 1$, $1 = 0$	24		1					1	2	2			4	2		2	2	2	$6/m1'$
$q = 5$, $1 = 0$	24		1					1	6	2				2		6	2	1	$6/mmm(6mm)$
$1 = 3$	24		1					1	6	2						2	2	0	
$D = 12$, $q = 5$, $1 = 0$	48		1					1		2		4		2	4	6	2		
$q = 7$, $1 = 0$	48		1					1		2		4	8	2	4	4	2		
$\mu = \nu = 2$, $D = 1$	16		1			2		1	2	2					2	2			
$D = 2$, $q = 1$, $1 = 0$	32		1			2	2	1	4	4			6	4	4	4			
$\mu = \nu = 3$, $D = 1$	36		1		4			1		4			6	4		3			
$D = 2$, $q = 1$, $1 = 0$	72		1		4		2	1	4	4			12	4	4	6	4		
XXIV $m = n = 2$	64	*	1		4		6	9	12							4			
$m = n = 3$	144	*	1		12		6	9	18				12			6			
XXXV $\mu = \nu = 1$, $D = 2$, $q = 1$, $1 = 0$	16		1					3	2							4		4	$mmm1'$
$1 = 1$	16		1					3	2	2						2		2	$4'/m'm'm(\bar{4}2m)$
$D = 3$, $q = 1$, $1 = 0$	24		1					3	2	2				2		4		2	$\bar{3}m1'$; $6'/mmm'(\bar{6}m2)$
$D = 4$, $q = 1$, $1 = 0$	32		1					5	2	4			2	2		6		2	$4/mmm1'$
$q = 3$, $1 = 2$	32		1					5	6	2				2		2		1	

																	Group
$D = 6, q = 1, 1 = r = 0$	48	1				7	·	2	·	4	·	4	·	8	2	2	6/mmm 1'
$q = 5, 1 = r = 3$	48	1				7	6	2	·	4	·	4	·	8	2	2	1
$D = 12$	96	1				13	6	2	4	8	2	·	2	10	2		
$\mu = \nu = 2, D = 1$	32[b]	1			2	5	4	·	·	·	·	·	·	4			
$D = 2, q = 1, 1 = r = 0$	64	1			2	9	8	·	·	·	4	·	4	8	6		
$\mu = \nu = 3, D = 1$	72	1				9	·	4	·	12	·	·	·	12			
$D = 2, \mathbf{q} = \mathbf{1}, \mathbf{1} = r = 0$	144	1		4	2	19	·	4	·	24	·	4	4	4			
From XIII' $m = n = \mathbf{4}$	64	*	1		2	5	12	·	·	12	·	4	·	4	6		
$m = n = \mathbf{6}$	144	*	1	8		15	18	4	·	12	·	4	·	6			
XXXVI $\mu = \nu = 1, D = 2$	16	1				3	4	·	·	·	·	·	·	·			1
$D = 5$	40	*	1			5	10	4	·	·	·	·	·	·			
$\mu = \nu = 2, D = 1$	32	*	1		2	5	8	·	·	·	4	·	·	·			
$D = 2$	64	*	1		2	9	16	4	·	·	·	·	·	4			
$\mu = \nu = 3, D = 1$	72	*	1			9	18	4	·	·	·	4	·	4			
$D = 2$	144	*	1	4		19	36	4	·	·	4	4	4	4			
XXXVII $m = 2$	128	*	1	8	6	13	24	4	24	·	4	·	8	8			
$m = 3$	288	*	1	16	12	6	25	36	4	8	4	4	12	4	12	4	
XXXIX	48	1				3	3	8	8	·	·	4	6	4			1 m31'
XL	48	1			6	3	6	8	8	·	32	·	6	6			1 m'3m($\overline{4}3m$)
XLI	192	*	1		6	9	12	32	32	·	32	·	4	4			
XLII	192	*	1		6	9	36	32	·	·	·	·	12	12			
XLIII	576	*	1	**48**	6	9	36	64	·	96	16	16	12	12			
XLIV	96	1	·		6	9	6	8	·	**8**	6	6	·	**10**			1 m3m1'
XLV	1152	*	1	72	48	6	45	72	64	·	192	36	36	16	24		
XLVII	384	*	1	24		6	21	48	32	·	32	12	·	16			
LI	240	1	·			15	30	20	24	·	20	·	·	10			

[a] In all 50 crystal classes 17 of which are irreducible. Projection gives 11 gray and 10 black-white groups in [3].

[b] In Part I this group was listed again as Goursat's XXXVII. $m = \mu = \nu = 1$. The two groups are equivalent.

TABLE 2a

PROPER CRYSTAL CLASSES IN [4] NOT CONTAINING $-I$[a]

Order	*	I	B	E	K	L'	M	M'	R	R'	S'	Z	Z'	P_{max}	Projected groups
1		1	.	.	.	.	.	.	.	.	.	.	.	1	1
2		1	.	1	.	.	.	.	.	.	.	.	.	2	2; $m'(1)$
3		1	.	.	2	.	.	.	.	.	.	.	.	1	3
4		1	.	1	.	.	.	2	.	.	.	.	.	1	4
4		1	.	1	.	.	.	.	2	.	.	.	.	1	$\bar{4}'(2)$
5		1	.	.	.	4	.	.	.	.	.	.	.		
6		1	.	1	2	.	.	.	.	.	.	2	.	1	6
6		1	.	1	2	.	.	.	.	.	.	.	2	1	$\bar{6}'(3)$
12		1	.	1	2	.	4	.	.	2	.	.	2		
12		1	.	1	2	.	.	4	2	.	.	.	2		
3		1	.	.	.	.	.	.	.	.	2	.	.		
6		1	2	1	.	.	.	.	.	.	2	.	.		
9		1	.	.	4	.	.	.	.	.	4	.	.		
18		1	4	1	4	.	.	.	.	.	4	2	2		
6		1	.	3	.	.	.	.	.	.	2	.	.		
18		1	6	3	4	.	.	.	.	.	4	.	.		
4		1	.	3	.	.	.	.	.	.	.	.	.	4	222; $m'm'2(2)$
6		1	.	3	2	.	.	.	.	.	.	.	.	2	32; $3m'(3)$
8		1	.	5	.	.	.	2	.	.	.	.	.	2	422; $4m'm'(4)$
8		1	.	5	.	.	.	.	2	.	.	.	.	2	$\bar{4}'2m'(222)$
10		1	.	5	.	4	.	.	.	.	.	.	.		
12		1	.	7	2	.	.	.	.	.	.	.	2	2	$\bar{6}'m'2(32)$
12		1	.	7	2	.	.	.	.	.	.	2	.	2	622; $6m'm'(6)$
24		1	.	13	2	.	4	.	.	2	.	.	2		
24		1	.	13	2	.	.	4	2	.	.	.	2		
12		1	2	7	.	.	.	.	.	.	2	.	.		
18		1	.	9	4	.	.	.	.	.	4	.	.		
36		1	4	19	4	.	.	.	.	.	4	2	2		
36	*	1	12	15	4	.	.	.	.	.	4	.	.		
12		1	.	3	8	.	.	.	.	.	.	.	.	1	23
24		1	.	9	8	.	.	6	.	.	.	.	.	1	432
24	*	**1**	.	9	8	.	.	.	**6**	.	.	.	.	1	$\bar{4}'3m'(23)$
60	*	1	.	15	20	24	.	.	.	.	.	.	.		

[a] In all 33 crystal classes, 2 of which are irreducible. Projection gives 11 polar and 10 black-white groups in [3].

TABLE 2b

IMPROPER CRYSTAL CLASSES IN [4] NOT CONTAINING −I[a]

Order	*	I	B	E	F	K	L'	M	M'	N	N'	R	R'	S'	T	T'	Z	Z'	$P_{\max}$	Projected groups
2		1													1				2	m; $1'$
2		1														1			2	$\bar{1}$; $2'(1)$
4		1		1											1	2			3	$2'/m'(\bar{1})$; $22'2'(2)$
4		1		1											2	1			3	$2/m$; $21'$; $mm'2'(m)$
4		1								2	2								3	$mm2$; $m1'$
4		1			2										1	1			2	$\bar{4}$; $4'(2)$
6		1				2					2								2	$\bar{3}$; $6'(3)$
6		1				2				2						3			2	$\bar{6}$; $31'$
6		1				2									3	3			1	$32'(3)$
6		1		1		2									3				1	$3m$
8		1		1	2							2	2	2	1	1			2	$4/m$; $41'$
8		1		1								2	2	2					1	$\bar{4}2'2'(4)$
8		1		1								2							1	$4mm$
8		1		1	2	2				4	4				1	1			2	$\bar{4}1'$; $4'/m(2/m)$
8		1		1		2									2	2			2	$\bar{4}2'm(mm2)$
12		1		1		2				2	2					6	2		1	$6/m$; $61'$
12		1		1		2				2	2	2					2		1	$62'2'(6)$
12		1		1		2				4					6		2		1	$6mm$
12		1		1		2							2	2	2	3		2	2	$6'/m'(3)$
12		1		1	6	2				4	4		2	2	3	3		2	2	$\bar{6}1'$
12		1		1	6	2									3	3		2	1	$\bar{6}m2'(3m)$
24		1		1	6	2	4	4		4	4	2			3	3		2		
24		1		1	6	2	4	4		4	4	2			2	2		2		
24		1		1	6	2			4			2			3	3		2	0	

TABLE 2b—continued

Improper Crystal Classes in [4] Not Containing $-I^a$

Order	*	I	B	E	F	K	L'	M	M'	N	N'	R	R'	S'	T	T'	Z	Z'	P_{max}	Projected groups
24		1	.	1	.	2	.	4	4	.	8	2	.	.	.	.	.	2	4	
24		1	.	1	.	2	.	4	4	8	.	2	.	.	.	.	.	2	4	
18		1	.	.	.	4	.	.	.	.	6	.	.	4	.	3	.	.	.	
18		1	.	.	.	4	.	.	.	6	.	.	.	4	3	.	.	.	.	
36		1	4	1	.	4	.	.	.	.	12	.	.	4	6	.	2	2	.	
36		1	4	1	.	4	.	.	.	12	.	.	.	4	.	6	2	2	.	
36		1	4	1	.	4	.	.	.	6	6	.	.	4	3	3	2	2	.	
8		1	.	3	.	.	.	.	.	.	.	.	.	.	1	3	.	.	4	$2221'$; $mm'm'(2/m)$
8		1	.	3	.	.	.	.	.	.	.	.	.	.	3	1	.	.	4	mmm; $mm21'$
8		1	.	3	2	.	.	.	.	.	.	.	.	.	.	2	.	.	2	$4'22(222)$; $\bar{4}2'm'(\bar{4})$
8		1	.	3	2	.	.	.	.	.	.	.	.	.	2	.	.	.	2	$\bar{4}2m$; $4'mm'(mm2)$
12		1	.	3	.	2	.	.	.	.	.	.	.	.	3	3	.	.	2	$3m'(\bar{3})$; $6'22'(32)$
12		1	.	3	.	2	.	.	.	2	.	.	.	.	1	3	.	.	2	$\bar{6}m2$; $3m1'$
12		1	.	3	.	2	.	.	.	2	.	.	.	.	3	1	.	.	2	$\bar{3}m$; $6'mm'(3m)$
12		1	.	3	.	2	.	.	.	.	.	.	.	.	3	3	.	.	2	$321'$; $\bar{6}m'2'(\bar{6})$
16		1	.	5	2	.	.	.	.	.	.	.	2	.	3	3	.	.	2	$\bar{4}2m1'$; $4'/mmm'(mmm)$
16		1	.	5	2	.	.	.	.	.	.	2	.	.	5	1	.	.	2	$4/mmm$; $4mm1'$
16		1	.	5	2	.	4	.	.	.	.	2	.	.	1	5	.	.	2	$4221'$; $4/mm'm'(4/m)$
20	*	1	.	5	10	.	4	.	.	.	.	.	.	.	.	.	.	.	.	
24		1	.	7	.	2	.	.	.	4	.	.	.	.	3	5	.	2	2	$6'/m'mm'(\bar{3}m)$
24		1	.	7	.	2	.	.	.	.	4	.	.	.	5	3	.	2	2	$\bar{6}m21'$
24		1	.	7	6	2	.	.	.	4	.	.	.	.	.	2	.	2	1	

Order	*																	Class
24		1	7	6	2	·	4	·	·	·	·	·	2	2	·	·	1	6/mmm; 6mm1'
24		1	7	·	2	2	2	2	·	·	7	1	·	·	·	2	2	6221'; 6/mm'm'(6/m)
24		1	7	·	2	2	2	2	·	·	1	7	·	·	2	2	2	
48		1	13	6	2	4	4	4	·	·	5	5	·	·	·	·		
48		1	13	6	2	8	8	·	·	·	7	3	·	·	·	·		
48		1	13	6	2	·	·	8	·	·	3	7	·	·	2	2		
36		1	9	·	4	12	12	12	·	·	6	·	·	·	·	·		
36		1	9	·	4	·	·	6	·	·	3	6	·	·	·	·		
36	*	1	9	18	4	6	6	18	·	·	3	3	·	·	·	·		
36		1	9	·	4	·	6	6	·	·	·	1	·	·	·	·		
72		1	19	18	4	6	12	12	·	·	3	6	·	·	2	2		
72		1	19	18	4	18	·	·	·	·	9	3	·	·	2	2		
72	*	1	15	·	4	·	·	8	·	·	·	6	·	·	·	·		
72	*	1	15	·	·	12	8	8	·	·	3	3	·	·	·	·		
24		1	3	6	8	8	·	·	·	·	6	3	·	·	·	·		231'
24		1	3	6	8	·	·	·	·	·	1	1	·	·	·	·		m3
24	*	1	3	6	8	·	·	8	·	·	3	6	·	·	·	·		4'32'(23)
24	*	1	3	6	8	·	8	·	·	·	·	·	·	·	·	·		43m
48	*	1	9	6	8	·	·	·	6	·	6	7	·	·	·	·		m3m'(m3)
48	*	1	9	6	8	8	8	·	6	·	3	3	·	·	·	·		43m1'
48		1	9	6	8	8	8	8	·	·	7	9	·	·	·	·		
48		1	9	6	8	8	·	8	·	·	1	1	·	·	·	·		
120	*	1	15	30	20	24	20	20	·	·	9	·	·	·	·	·		4321'
120	*	1	15	30	20	24	20	·	·	·	·	10	·	·	·	·		m3m

---

[a] In all 71 crystal classes 6 of which are irreducible. Projection gives 21 polar, 21 gray and 27 black-white groups in [3]. From Tables 1a,b and 2a,b we have a grand total of 227 crystal classes 45 of which are irreducible. Projection gives a total of 32 polar, 32 gray and 58 black-white groups in [3] in agreement with enumerations by other methods (Niggli 1964).

III. Projected Groups

The [4] crystal classes which are reducible to the form

$$\begin{bmatrix} X & 0 \\ 0 & \pm 1 \end{bmatrix}, \tag{3}$$

with X a set of 3×3 integral matrixes, yield generalized symmetries in [3] when projected along the fourth coordinate (Shubnikov, 1964; Niggli, 1964). The following three cases arise:

(1) Only positive signs occur in the reduced form (3). Projection leads to a polar group in [3]. The set X forms one of the ordinary crystal classes in [3]. The elements which occur in X are, in international notation:

n: rotation through angle $2\pi/n$ $(n = 1, 2, 3, 4, 6)$

$\bar{n}$: rotatory-inversion through angle $2\pi/n$ $(n = 1, 2, 3, 4, 6)$, $\bar{2} = m$.

(2) Each three-dimensional symmetry element (n or $\bar{n}$) occurs twice in the reduced form (3), once associated with $+1$ and once with -1. Projection gives a gray group in [3] in which each symmetry element occurs both in uncolored form (n or $\bar{n}$) and in colored form (n' or $\bar{n}'$). A gray group is denoted by adding $1'$ to the symbol for the ordinary [3] crystal class, e.g. $\bar{4}3m1'$.

(3) The elements (say Y) associated with $+1$ in the reduced form (3) from a subgroup of index 2 of the whole set X. Both X and Y are ordinary [3] crystal classes. On projection one obtains a black-white group in which the symmetry elements of Y are uncolored and the remaining symmetry elements of X are colored (i.e., dashed). Following Niggli (1964) we refer to Y as the kernel of the black-white group X and write Y in parenthesis after the international symbol for X, e.g., $32'(3)$.

The invariants χ, σ, and d of elements in the reduced form (3) are calculated using the diagonal forms of the [3] symmetry elements:

$$n = \text{diag}\,(\varepsilon_n, \varepsilon_n^*, 1), \quad \bar{n} = \text{diag}\,(-\varepsilon_n, -\varepsilon_n^*, -1),$$

where

$$\varepsilon_n = e^{2\pi i/n}.$$

Comparing the results of this calculation with the list (2), we obtain Table 3 which shows the [3] symmetry elements which can result from projection of a given [4] symmetry element.

From Table 3 we deduce:

(a) No crystal class in [4] containing any element A, B, C, D, L, M, S, L', M', S' can be reduced to the form (3) appropriate for projection. This is immediately clear from the characteristic equation (1), since neither $+1$ nor -1 is a root of this equation for these elements.

TABLE 3

PROJECTION IN [3] OF SYMMETRY ELEMENTS IN [4]

I → 1	I′ → 1̄′	N → 3̄,6′	N′ → 6̄,3′
E → 2,2̄′		R → 4	R′ → 4̄′
F → 4̄,4′		T → 2̄,1′	T′ → 1̄,2′
K → 3̄	K′ → 3′	Z → 6	Z′ → 6̄′

A, B, C, D, L, M, S, L′, M′, S′ cannot be projected to [3].

(b) A gray group in [3], which always contains the symmetry element 1′, can only arise by projection from a crystal class in [4] which contains at least one element of type T.

(c) Since the element I′ (= −I) in [4] always gives 1̄′ in [3], we have the following relations for the [3] groups projected from a [4] class of Table 1a and 1b.

$$N(n) = N(\bar{n}') \qquad N(n') = N(\bar{n}), \qquad n = 1, 2, 3, 4, 6$$

Here $N(\cdots)$ denotes the number of symmetry elements of the indicated type.

The projected groups given in the final column of Table 1a follow immediately from the results (a) and (c); each entry in Table 1a which does not contain A, B, C, D, L, M, or S yields just one black-white group. The kernel H of this group G is a proper crystal class in [3], and the remaining elements of G are obtained from H on multiplication by the symmetry element 1̄′ (the colored inversion).

The derivation of the projected groups from the [4] crystal classes of Tables 1b, 2a and 2b is not quite so simple. We see from Table 3 that a given symmetry type in [4] may lead on projection to two distinct symmetry types in [3]. For this reason, a crystal class in [4] may yield several distinct groups on projection. The complications arising from this situation may be analyzed in terms of the invariant sums $g^{-1}\Sigma\chi^2$ and $g^{-1}\Sigma\sigma$, where the summations are over all elements of a [4] crystal class D_4 or order g. From the values of these sums inferences may be drawn concerning the reducibility of D_4 considered as a representation of itself. These inferences, which are shown in Table 4, follow from the character and reality conditions for irreducible representations (Wigner, 1959) and the relation

$$\chi(A^2) = \chi^2(A) - 2\sigma(A), \tag{4}$$

which is a direct consequence of the definition of σ (Eq. (1)).

In Table 4, Γ_n denotes a real irreducible representation of dimension n, $(\Gamma_n + \Gamma_n^*)$ denotes a pair of complex conjugate representations and dashes are used to distinguish inequivalent representations of the same dimension.

The maximum number of [3] groups obtained on projection, P_{max}, is given by the number of inequivalent, real, one-dimensional representations contained in D_4.

TABLE 4

REDUCED FORMS OF A [4] CRYSTAL CLASS D_4

$g^{-1}\Sigma\chi^2$	$g^{-1}\Sigma\sigma$	Inference	P_{max}
1		$D_4 = \Gamma_4$	0
2	0	$\begin{cases} D_4 = \Gamma_3 + \Gamma_1 \\ D_4 = \Gamma_2 + \Gamma_2' \end{cases}$	1 0
3	0	$D_4 = \Gamma_2 + \Gamma_1 + \Gamma_1'$	2
3	1	$D_4 = \Gamma_2 + (\Gamma_1 + \Gamma_1^*)$	0
4	0	$D_4 = \Gamma_1 + \Gamma_1' + \Gamma_1'' + \Gamma_1'''$	4
4	1	$\begin{cases} D_4 = 2\Gamma_2 \\ D_4 = (\Gamma_1 + \Gamma_1^*) + \Gamma_1' + \Gamma_1'' \end{cases}$	0 2
4	2	$D_4 = (\Gamma_1 + \Gamma_1^*) + (\Gamma_1' + \Gamma_1'^*)$	0
5		$D_4 = \Gamma_2 + 2\Gamma_1$	1
6	1	$D_4 = 2\Gamma_1 + \Gamma_1' + \Gamma_1''$	3
6	2	$D_4 = 2\Gamma_1 + (\Gamma_1' + \Gamma_1'^*)$	1
8	2	$D_4 = 2\Gamma_1 + 2\Gamma_1'$	2
8	4	$D_4 = 2(\Gamma_1 + \Gamma_1^*)$	0
10		$D_4 = 3\Gamma_1 + \Gamma_1'$	2
16		$D_4 = 4\Gamma_1$	1

We see from Table 4 that, except for the two cases (2, 0) and (4, 1) the values of the invariant sums specify the reduced form of D_4, and hence P_{max}, uniquely. However, even in cases where P_{max} is uniquely specified, the actual number of distinct [3] groups obtained by projection may fall short of P_{max}. Consider, for example, the [4] crystal class

$$I + E + 2T \tag{5}$$

appearing in Table 2b. Here $g^{-1}\Sigma\chi^2 = 6$, $g^{-1}\Sigma\sigma = 1$ so that, from Table 4, $D_4 = 2\Gamma_1 + \Gamma_1' + \Gamma_1''$, $P_{max} = 3$. From the expressions given in Part I and Goursat (1889) the explicit form of the matrixes of the group (5) are as follows:

$$I = \text{diag}(1, 1, 1, 1); \quad E = \text{diag}(1, 1, -1, -1);$$
$$T = \text{diag}(1, 1, -1, 1); \quad T = \text{diag}(1, 1, 1, -1). \tag{6}$$

Equation (6) shows four real one-dimensional representations, two of which are equivalent in agreement with Table 4. However, upon projection along each of the coordinate axes we obtain the [3] groups (all matrixes diagonal).

$$(1, 1, 1), \qquad (1, -1, -1), \qquad (1, -1, 1), \qquad (1, 1, -1) \text{ i.e., } mm2 \qquad (7)$$

$$(1, 1, 1), \qquad (1, -1, -1), \qquad (1, -1, 1), \qquad (1, 1, -1) \text{ i.e., } mm2 \qquad (8)$$

$$(1, 1, 1), \qquad (1, 1, -1)', \qquad (1, 1, 1)', \qquad (1, 1, -1) \text{ i.e., } m1' \qquad (9)$$

$$(1, 1, 1), \qquad (1, 1, -1)', \qquad (1, 1, -1), \qquad (1, 1, 1)' \text{ i.e., } m1' \qquad (10)$$

The identity of the projected groups (7) and (8) is, of course, to be expected since they are obtained by projecting equivalent representations. However, the projected groups (9) and (10) are also identical, the inequivalence of the projected representations being reflected merely in a permutation of the symmetry elements.

Fortunately, nearly all the cases in which the actual number of projected groups falls short of $P_{\max}$ are equally simple, since they involve fully reducible groups, which may be considered in diagonal form.

Most of the [3] projected groups shown in the final columns of Tables 1b, 2a and 2b may be written down immediately using the results of Tables 3 and 4. The remaining [3] groups were obtained from the explicit forms of the elements of the [4] crystal classes (Part I, Eq. (5) and Goursat (1889)). The final list of 32 polar, 32 gray and 58 black-white groups agrees with that obtained by other methods (Niggli, 1964); all the [4] crystal classes omitted from the lists of Part I (1 from Table 2a, 5 from table 2b) are checked by the projection of [3] groups.

Note added in proof. An independent derivation of the [4] crystal classes has been completed by H. Wondratschek and J. Neubüser (private communication by J. Neubüser). Their derivation starts from the four maximal crystal groups obtained by Hermann (1949, 1951). These maximal groups are entries XLV; LI; XXXVII, $m = \mu = \nu = 3$; XXXV, $\mu = 1$, $\nu = 1$, $D = 12$ of Table 1b. Wondratschek and Neubüser have used a computer to find all subgroups of these four groups, eliminating equivalent groups at each step. Their final results agree exactly with the 227 crystal classes given here. Since Hermann makes no use of Goursat's (1889) work the two derivations are completely independent and their agreement provides a most valuable check on the accuracy and completeness of Tables 1a, 1b, 2a and 2b. A preliminary account of the two calculations has been submitted for publication in *Acta Crystallographica*.

ACKNOWLEDGMENT

The author is much indebted to Professor Wondratschek and Dr. Neubüser for pointing out errors and omissions in the lists of Part I.

REFERENCES

Goursat, M. E. (1889). *Ann. Sci. École Norm. Super.* **6** (3) 9.

Hermann, C. (1949). *Acta Cryst.* **2**, 139.

Hermann, C. (1951). " Struktur und Materie der Festkörper." Springer, Berlin.

Hurley, A. C. (1951). *Proc. Cambridge Phil. Soc.* **47**, 650 (Part I).

Niggli, A. (1964). "Advances in Structure Research by Diffraction Methods," Vol. 1, p. 199 (R. Brill, ed.). Wiley (Interscience), New York.

Shubnikov, A. V., Belov, N. V., and others, (1964). " Coloured Symmetry." Pergamon, New York.

Wigner, E. P. (1959). "Group Theory." Academic Press, New York.

Wondratschek, H., and Neubüser, J. (1965). Private communication.

Quantum Noise VIII: Harmonic Oscillator Relaxation from Definite Quantum States

HUNG CHENG* and MELVIN LAX

BELL TELEPHONE LABORATORIES

MURRAY HILL, NEW JERSEY

I. Introduction

Appreciable progress has been made in the study of noise in classical and quantum systems in the Markoffian limit. For recent progress and a summary of the literature see the author's series of papers (Lax, QI–QV). For slightly non-Markoffian systems, in other words, systems in interaction with a reservoir whose correlation times are short but not zero, there has also been recent progress. See, for example, Lax (QIII) and Argyres (1963). However, aside from the quasi-static approximation, there has been no practical success with the long correlation time situation, the case in which the reservoir correlation times are comparable to the relaxation times in the system.

A useful way in which to study the long correlation time problem would be to find an example for which exact solutions are available and to study the nature of these solutions in various limiting cases. Louisell and Walker (1965) appear to provide us with such an example, a system harmonic oscillator

* *Present address:* Physics Department, Massachusetts Institute of Technology, Cambridge, Massachusetts.

interacting harmonically with a reservoir consisting of a continuum of independent harmonic oscillators. Louisell and Walker calculate the density matrix of the system only for an initial condition of displaced Gaussian form. They then show that the future of the system continues to have a displaced Gaussian form determined by the mean motion of the system harmonic oscillator and the energy of the system harmonic oscillator as a function of time. The equation for the mean motion of such a harmonic oscillator is easy to write down and to solve exactly. While the equation for the mean excitation of such a harmonic oscillator can also be written down fairly simply, it is not an equation that can be solved directly in any simple way. Louisell and Walker demonstrate that in the appropriate short correlation time limit the results typical of Markoffian systems (see Lax, QIV) are obeyed.

In this paper we shall extend the Louisell-Walker work in two ways: (1) we shall obtain a solution for the future of the density matrix for the case in which the system is initially in a definite state. (2) We shall be concerned not so much with approximate solutions for the equations obeyed by the mean excitation, but rather with exact expressions for this mean excitation either at a general time or as t approaches infinity. Our principal contribution of the first kind is an exact expression for $P(mt|n0)$, the probability of a system oscillator being found in state m at time t if it was initially in state n at time 0. Our principal contribution of the second kind is a proof that if the reservoir possesses no density of states at the perturbed frequency Ω_0 of the system, the system does not come to equilibrium. We shall interpret this conclusion to mean that in such cases a transport equation does not exist, and if state n cannot be reached from state m in first-order perturbation theory (in other words using one reservoir phonon) then no time proportional transitions occur from state n to state m using an arbitrary number of reservoir phonons. This conclusion is not entirely a trivial one, since matrix elements for multiphonon processes exist. What happens, although we have not the space to demonstrate it here, is that such multiphonon processes can happen in many ways and the coherent sum of all transition amplitudes add to zero. See Fig. 1 for an example of such a multiphonon process.

II. The Reduced Density Matrix

To shorten the length of our equations we have adopted the Louisell-Walker Hamiltonian in the rotating wave approximation

$$\mathcal{H} = \omega_0 a^\dagger a + \sum_{j=1}^{N} [\omega_j b_j^\dagger b_j + \kappa_j a^\dagger b_j + \kappa_j^* a b_j^\dagger] + e(t)\, a^\dagger + e^*(t)a \qquad (1)$$

This approximation is discussed in QIV, especially Appendix C. It should not have any qualitative effects on our conclusions. The variables a and $a^\dagger$ are

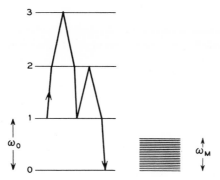

FIG. 1. We display the ladder of system harmonic oscillator states, in the case in which the system frequency ω_0 exceeds the maximum reservoir frequency ω_M. A multiphonon transition from the first excited state to the ground state can, in principle, take place by the path shown. If each step involves the emission of large reservoir phonons, or the absorption of small reservoir phonons, energy conservation is possible after enough steps. Nevertheless, we show in the text, that such transitions do not occur.

the usual destruction and creation operators of our system harmonic oscillator. The variables b_j, $b_j^\dagger$ are corresponding destruction and creation operators for reservoir oscillator j. The c-number function $e(t)$ is an external driving force that acts on the system oscillator. We have adoped units in which $\hbar = 1$. The Heisenberg equations for the mean motion of these oscillators in the presence of the driving force can be written down easily and solved. A canonical transformation can then be performed in which each oscillator is shifted by its mean motion. The new Hamiltonian then has the same form as Eq. (1) with the driving terms omitted. We shall therefore omit the driving forces from Eq. (1) and assume that the variables a, b_j are already taken relative to their mean values.

The Louisell-Walker starting density matrix for the system can then be written in the form

$$\sigma_\lambda(0) = (1 - e^{-\lambda})\exp(-\lambda a^\dagger a) = [n(0)]^{a^\dagger a}/[n(0) + 1]^{a^\dagger a + 1} \qquad (2)$$

where

$$\lambda = \hbar\omega_0/kT_s, \qquad (3)$$

and

$$n(0) \equiv \langle a^\dagger(0)\, a(0)\rangle \equiv (\exp \lambda - 1)^{-1} \equiv n(\lambda, 0) \qquad (4)$$

represents the *mean* excitation number in the initial state. Louisell and Walker choose the density matrix of the reservoir at the initial time to be in a Gaussian state so as to maximize the entropy. Since the equations of motion are linear the density matrix of system plus reservoir must remain a Gaussian for all time. Thus the complete density matrix of system plus reservoir is completely characterized by a knowledge of all the second moments as a function of time. These second moments obey equations discussed in some detail in Section V. In any case the density matrix of the system itself remains in Gaussian form and can therefore be written

$$\sigma_\lambda(t) = [n(t)]^{a^\dagger a}/[n(t) + 1]^{a^\dagger a + 1}, \tag{5}$$

where

$$n(t) = \langle a^\dagger(t) \, a(t) \rangle \equiv n(\lambda, t) = f(t) \, n(\lambda, 0) + g(t) \tag{6}$$

is the mean excitation of the system oscillator as a function of time. The positive numerical functions of time $f(t)$ and $g(t)$ are discussed in detail in Sections V–VII. Their initial values are obviously given by

$$f(0) = 1, \qquad g(0) = 0. \tag{7}$$

The occupancy of the state with excitation number m is given by the particular matrix element

$$\sigma_\lambda(t)_{mm} = [f n(\lambda, 0) + g]^m/[f n(\lambda, 0) + g + 1]^{m+1}. \tag{8}$$

III. Density Matrix for a Given Initial State

Our initial condition

$$\sigma^{(n)}(0) = \delta(a^\dagger a, n)$$

$$= (1/2\pi) \int_0^{2\pi} e^{in\theta} e^{-i\theta a^\dagger a} \, d\theta$$

$$= (1/2\pi) \int_0^{2\pi} e^{in\theta} \, [\sigma_\lambda(0)/(1 - e^{-\lambda})]_{\lambda = i\theta} \, d\theta \tag{9}$$

can be written as a linear superposition of Gaussian density matrixes. We can therefore write our general solution at time t as the corresponding linear superposition of the Louisell-Walker solutions:

$$\sigma^{(n)}(t) = 1/2\pi \int_0^{2\pi} e^{in\theta} \, [\sigma_{i\theta}(t)/(1 - e^{-i\theta})] \, d\theta. \tag{10}$$

The transition probability from initial state n to m is therefore given by

$$P(mt|n0) = \sigma^{(n)}(t)_{mm}$$

$$= \frac{1}{2\pi} \int_0^{2\pi} \frac{e^{in\theta} \, d\theta}{1 - e^{-i\theta}} \frac{[f n(i\theta, 0) + g]^m,}{[f n(i\theta, 0) + g + 1]^{m+1}}, \tag{11}$$

where

$$n(i\theta, 0) = [\exp(i\theta) - 1]^{-1}. \tag{12}$$

Using the abbreviation $u = \exp(-i\theta)$ we can rewrite (11) in the form

$$P(mt|n0) = \frac{1}{2\pi i} \oint \frac{du}{u^{n+1}} \frac{[g + (f - g) u]^m}{[1 + g + (f - g - 1)u]^{m+1}}. \tag{13}$$

The further transformation

$$u = v(1 + g)/(1 + g - f) \tag{14}$$

leads to an even simpler form

$$P(mt|n0) = \frac{(1 + g - f)^{n-m}(f - g)^m}{(1 + g)^{n+1}} H\left(n, m, \frac{g(1 + g - f)}{(1 + g)(f - g)}\right) \tag{15}$$

$$H(n, m, z) = \frac{1}{2\pi i} \oint \frac{dv}{v^{n+1}} \frac{(z + v)^m}{(1 - v)^{m+1}}$$

$$= \text{coefficient of } v^n \text{ in } (z + v)^m (1 - v)^{-m-1}$$

$$= z^m F(-m, -n; -m-n; -1/z)(m + n)!/[m!n!] \tag{16}$$

where $F(a, b; c; z)$ is the hypergeometric function.

A. CHARACTERISTIC FUNCTION

Using the abbreviation $w = e^{i\alpha}$, we can write the characteristic function in the form

$$\langle e^{i\alpha a^\dagger a} \rangle \equiv \langle w^{a^\dagger a} \rangle = \sum_m w^m P(mt|n0). \tag{17}$$

Using Eq. (15) and performing the sum, we obtain as our characteristic function

$$\langle e^{i\alpha a^\dagger a} \rangle \equiv \langle e^{i\alpha m} \rangle = \frac{[1 + (1 - w)(g - f)]^n}{[1 + (1 - w)g]^{n+1}}. \tag{18}$$

From this characteristic function we immediately obtain the first and second moments

$$\langle m \rangle = -i\partial \langle e^{i\alpha m} \rangle / \partial \alpha|_{\alpha=0} = f(t)n + g \tag{19}$$

$$\langle m^2 \rangle - \langle m \rangle^2 = (fn + g)(1 + fn + g) - f^2 n(1 + n). \tag{20}$$

By comparing Eqs. (17) and (18) we obtain a new expression for the transition probability:

$$P(mt|n0) = \text{coefficient of } w^m \text{ in } [1 + (1 - w)(g - f)]^n/[1 + (1 - w)g]^{n+1}. \tag{21}$$

B. Special Cases

Using Eqs. (16) and (21) we shall write down a number of special cases for the transition probability:

$$P(mt|o0) = g^m/(1 + g)^{m+1} \tag{22}$$

$$P(mt|10) = [mf + g(1 + g - f)]g^{m-1}/(1 + g)^{m+2} \tag{23}$$

$$P(ot|n0) = (1 + g - f)^n/(1 + g)^{n+1} \tag{24}$$

$$P(1t|n0) = [g(1 + g - f) + nf](1 + g - f)^{n-1}/(1 + g)^{n+2} \tag{25}$$

$$P(ot|o0) = (1 + g)^{-1} \tag{26}$$

$$P(1t|o0) = g/(1 + g)^2 \tag{27}$$

$$P(ot|10) = (1 + g - f)/(1 + g)^2 \tag{28}$$

$$P(1t|10) = [g(1 + g - f) + f]/(1 + g)^2. \tag{29}$$

We shall see later that when the reservoir temperature is at absolute zero the function g can be set equal to zero. In this case the transition probability vanishes for $m > n$ and reduces for $m \leq n$ to

$$P(mt|n0) = f^m (1 - f)^{n-m} \frac{n!}{m!(n - m)!} \quad \text{if} \quad g = 0. \tag{30}$$

IV. Approach to Equilibrium

In the Markoffian limit we have shown in Lax (QIV, 3.8) that the mean excitation of the harmonic oscillator obeys

$$d\langle a^\dagger a\rangle/dt = \gamma\bar{n} - \gamma\langle a^\dagger a\rangle, \tag{31}$$

which has the solution

$$\langle a^\dagger(t)\, a(t)\rangle = e^{-\gamma t}\langle a^\dagger(0)a(0)\rangle + \bar{n}(1 - e^{-\gamma t}), \tag{32}$$

so that

$$f(t) = e^{-\gamma t}; \qquad g(t) = \bar{n}(1 - e^{-\gamma t}). \tag{33}$$

These results have also been found by Louisell and Walker after the use of a Weisskopf-Wigner approximation. We note the particular result

$$f(\infty) = 0, \tag{34}$$

which tells us that the mean excitation of the oscillator eventually forgets what the initial excitation does. We expect therefore that $f(\infty) = 0$ is the general condition for approach to equilibrium. We note that in this limit

$$z = g(1 + g - f)/[(1 + g)(f - g)] \to -1 \tag{35}$$

so that

$$H(n, m, -1) = (-1)^m, \tag{36}$$

from which we obtain the transition probability at infinite time in the form

$$P(m\infty|n0) = [g(\infty)]^m/[1 + g(\infty)]^{m+1}, \tag{37}$$

a result which is independent of the starting state n. Equation (37) describes the usual "Gaussian" equilibrium state appropriate to a mean quantum number

$$\bar{n} = g(\infty), \tag{38}$$

independent of the initial excitation.

V. Equations of Motion for the Second Moments

For simplicity of notation we treat the system oscillator as oscillator zero among the complete set of oscillators and thus write a Hamiltonian in the form of

$$\mathcal{H} = \Sigma\, b_r^\dagger b_s \mathcal{H}_{sr}; \qquad b_0 = a,\, b_0^\dagger = a^\dagger \tag{39}$$

$$\mathcal{H}_{00} = \omega_0,\, \mathcal{H}_{j0} = \kappa_j,\, \mathcal{H}_{0j} = \kappa_j^* \tag{40}$$

$$\mathcal{H}_{ij} = \omega_i \delta_{ij} \qquad i, j \neq 0. \tag{41}$$

The Heisenberg equation of motion for the set of second moments is then given in the form

$$id b_i^\dagger b_j/dt = \sum_s [b_i^\dagger b_s \mathcal{H}_{sj} - \mathcal{H}_{is} b_s^\dagger b_j] \tag{42}$$

or

$$idy_{ij}/dt = [y, \mathcal{H}]_{ij} \qquad \text{all} \quad i, j, \tag{43}$$

where

$$y_{ij}(t) \equiv \langle b_i^\dagger(t) b_j(t) \rangle; \qquad y_{00}(t) = \langle a^\dagger(t) a(t) \rangle = n(t), \tag{44}$$

$$y_{ij}(0) = \langle b_i^\dagger(0) b_j(0) \rangle = \delta_{ij} n_i. \tag{45}$$

The n_i represent the initial excitations of the oscillators i. We also obtain the second-moment equations

$$idb_i b_j/d_a = \sum_s [b_i b_s \mathcal{H}_{sj} + b_s b_j \mathcal{H}_{si}], \tag{46}$$

from which we can conclude

$$\langle b_i(t) b_j(t) \rangle = 0 \qquad \text{if} \quad \langle b_i(0) b_j(0) \rangle = 0. \tag{47}$$

Thus we need only concern ourselves with the set of equations (43). We can treat these equations by making the Laplace transformation

$$Y_{ij}(p) \equiv \int_0^\infty e^{-pt} y_{ij}(t) \, dt. \tag{48}$$

This leads us to the set of algebraic equations

$$p Y_{00}(p) = n_0 + i \sum_{j \neq 0} [\kappa_j^* Y_{j0}(p) - Y_{0j}(p)\kappa_j] \tag{49}$$

$$(i\omega_{0j} + p)Y_{j0}(p) = i\kappa_j Y_{00}(p) - i \sum_{k \neq 0} Y_{jk}(p)\kappa_k \tag{50}$$

$$(i\omega_{ji} + p)Y_{ij}(p) = i[\kappa_i Y_{0j}(p) - Y_{i0}(p)\kappa_j^*] + n_i \delta_{ij}. \tag{51}$$

We then introduce the definition

$$i \sum_{j \neq 0} [\kappa_j^* Y_{j0} - Y_{0j}\kappa_j] \equiv - S(p)Y_{00}(p) + R(p), \tag{52}$$

from which we can solve for the motion of our special oscillator in the form

$$Y_{00}(p) = \frac{n_0}{p + S(p)} + \frac{R(p)}{p + S(p)}, \tag{53}$$

which leads to a time-dependent excitation for that oscillator in the form

$$n(t) = f(t)n_0 + g(t), \tag{54}$$

where the time-dependent functions $f(t)$ and $g(t)$ are given by the inverse Laplace transforms

$$f(t) = \frac{1}{2\pi i} \int \frac{e^{pt} \, dp}{p + S(p)} = \frac{1}{2\pi i} \int e^{pt} F(p) \, dp \tag{55}$$

$$g(t) = \frac{1}{2\pi i} \int \frac{e^{pt} R(p) \, dp}{p + S(p)}. \tag{56}$$

In investigating whether or not equilibrium is approached, we shall be primarily concerned with the limiting values (that omit oscillatory terms):

$$\lim_{p \to 0^+} pF(p) = \lim_{p \to 0^+} p \int_0^\infty e^{-pt} f(t) \, dt = f(\infty) \tag{57}$$

$$f(\infty) = \lim_{p \to 0^+} \frac{p}{p + S(p)} \tag{58}$$

$$g(\infty) = \lim_{p \to 0^+} \frac{pR(p)}{p + S(p)} \tag{59}$$

In order to obtain $S(p)$ and $R(p)$, we must solve Eqs. (50) and (51). To obtain S we solve these equations first setting $n_i = 0$. To obtain R we must solve these equations retaining the n_i but setting $Y_{00} = 0$. Since the equations of motion are linear the results are necessarily expressible in the form of Eq. (52).

VI. Lowest Order Perturbation Theory Results

We can obtain a qualitative understanding of the nature of our results by solving for them in the lowest order of perturbation theory. To obtain $S(p)$ we set $Y_{jk} = 0$ in Eq. (50) and iterate on Eqs. (50) and (51) to obtain our result in the form of

$$S(p) = \sum_j \frac{|\kappa_j|^2 2p}{(\omega_{0j})^2 + p^2} = 2p \int \frac{\rho(\omega)\, d\omega}{(\omega_0 - \omega)^2 + p^2}, \tag{60}$$

where the density function $\rho(\omega)$ is defined by

$$\rho(\omega) \equiv \sum_j |\kappa_j|^2 \delta(\omega - \omega_j). \tag{61}$$

In the limit, as the number of reservoir oscillators approaches infinity, this density function approaches a continuous function. To obtain $R(p)$, we set $Y_{00} = 0$ and start with

$$y_{ij}(t) \approx y_{ij}(0) = n_i \delta_{ij}; \qquad Y_{ij}(p) = (n_i/p)\delta_{ij}. \tag{62}$$

One iteration then leads to

$$R(p) = 2 \sum_j \frac{|\kappa_j|^2 n_j}{(\omega_{0j})^2 + p^2} = 2 \int \frac{\rho(\omega)n(\omega)\, d\omega}{(\omega_0 - \omega)^2 + p^2}, \tag{63}$$

where we have set $n_j = n(\omega_j)$, a continuous function of ω.

A. Case 1. $\rho(\omega_0) \neq 0$

In this case we can take the limit $p \to 0^+$ to obtain the asymptotic results

$$S(0^+) = 2\pi\rho(\omega_0) \equiv \gamma \tag{64}$$

$$\lim_{p \to 0^+} pR(p) = 2\pi n(\omega_0)\rho(\omega_0) \tag{65}$$

$$f(\infty) = 0 \tag{66}$$

$$g(\infty) = n(\omega_0) \equiv \bar{n}. \tag{67}$$

We see from Eq. (66) that if the density of states does not vanish at the frequency ω_0 of our special oscillator equilibrium is approached. We see from Eq. (67) that the final excitation number of our system oscillator is determined by the excitation number of the reservoir oscillators at the frequency of the system oscillator.

If we assume that the behavior of our $S(p)$ and $R(p)$ functions can be extended from small p to all p in the form

$$S(p) \approx \gamma; \qquad R(p) \approx \gamma\bar{n}/p, \tag{68}$$

then we immediately obtain results in agreement with the Markoffian procedure of Eqs. (31–34).

B. CASE 2. $\rho(\omega_0) = 0$

In this case we can also obtain the limiting values

$$\lim_{p \to 0^+} [S(p)/p] = 2 \int \rho(\omega) \, d\omega/(\omega_0 - \omega)^2 \tag{69}$$

$$R(0^+) = 2 \int \rho(\omega)n(\omega) \, d\omega/(\omega_0 - \omega)^2 \tag{70}$$

$$f(\infty) = \left[1 + 2 \int \rho(\omega) \, d\omega/(\omega_0 - \omega)^2 \right]^{-1} > 0 \tag{71}$$

$$g(\infty) = R(0^+)f(\infty) > 0. \tag{72}$$

We see from Eq. (71) that when the density of states $\rho(\omega_0)$ vanishes at our oscillator frequency ω_0 the system never approaches equilibrium. This is basically a consequence of the function $S(p)$ vanishing linearly in the neighborhood of $p = 0$.

In this section, we have shown that, to lowest order perturbation theory, equilibrium is attained if $\rho(\omega_0) > 0$, and is not attained if $\rho(\omega_0) = 0$. We shall show in the next section that an exact calculation replaces these by the corresponding conditions $\rho(\Omega_0) > 0$ and $\rho(\Omega_0) = 0$ where Ω_0 is the exact perturbed frequency of the oscillator. These conditions are closely related: if ω_0 is outside the continuous spectrum, we would expect a turn-on of the coupling between system oscillator and bath to introduce repulsions that would prevent Ω_0 from entering the continuum. If $\rho(\omega_0) > 0$, however, sufficiently strong coupling may push Ω_0 out.

VII. Exact Expressions for the Mean Oscillator Excitation

Perhaps the simplest way to obtain exact expressions for the mean motion of our system oscillator is to transform to the new normal coordinates B_J and then transform back again. These normal coordinates can be assumed to obey

$$B_J(t) = B_J(0) \exp(i\Omega_J t), \tag{73}$$

where $B_J \sim b_j$ and the frequency $\Omega_J \sim \omega_j$. The transformation to the new variables is given as a unitary transformation

$$b_i = \sum_J U_{iJ} B_J. \tag{74}$$

The inverse transformation can therefore be written as

$$B_J = \sum (U^{-1})_{Js} b_s = \sum U^*_{sJ} b_s. \tag{75}$$

The mean excitation of our system oscillator can therefore be given in the form

$$\langle b_0^\dagger(t) b_0(t) \rangle = \sum U^*_{0I} U_{0J} \exp[i(\Omega_I - \Omega_J)t] \langle B_I^\dagger B_J \rangle$$

$$= \sum U^*_{0I} U_{0J} \exp[i(\Omega_I - \Omega_J)t] U_{rI} U^*_{sJ} \langle b_r^\dagger b_s \rangle, \tag{76}$$

into which we can insert the initial condition

$$\langle b_r^\dagger b_s \rangle = n_r \delta_{rs}. \tag{77}$$

Thus we obtain the exact expressions

$$f(t) = \sum_{I,J} |U_{0I}|^2 |U_{0J}|^2 \exp[i(\Omega_I - \Omega_J)t] \tag{78}$$

$$g(t) = \sum_{I,J} U^*_{0I} U_{0J} \exp[i(\Omega_I - \Omega_J)t] \sum_{r \neq 0} U_{rI} U^*_{rJ} n_r. \tag{79}$$

If $n_r = \bar{n}$ is independent of r, we obtain a simple relation between g and f:

$$g(t) = \bar{n}[1 - f(t)]. \tag{80}$$

The Laplace transform of $f(t)$ is given by

$$F(p) = \sum_{I,J} |U_{0I}|^2 |U_{0J}|^2 p/[p^2 + (\Omega_I - \Omega_J)^2]. \tag{81}$$

Our limiting value then takes the form

$$f(\infty) = \lim_{p \to 0} pF(p) = \sum_I |U_{0I}|^4. \tag{82}$$

To get a limiting behavior independent of N as $N \to \infty$ we must have

$$\int \rho(\omega) \, d\omega = \sum_j |\kappa_j|^2 = \text{independent of } N, \tag{83}$$

in other words

$$\kappa_j = O(N^{-1/2}) \tag{84}$$

and

$$U_{0I} = O(N^{-1/2}); \qquad I \neq 0. \tag{85}$$

Thus in the limit as the number of reservoir oscillators goes to infinity we obtain

$$\lim_{N \to \infty} f(\infty) = \lim_{N \to \infty} |U_{00}|^4. \tag{86}$$

To obtain the normal mode transformation, we take all of the linear equations of motion for the destruction operators and assume that all operators have the same time dependence $\exp(-i\Omega t)$. From this we learn that the relative amplitudes must obey

$$b_i = [\kappa_i^*/(\Omega - \omega_i)]a. \tag{87}$$

For mode J, we must replace Ω by Ω_J. We are primarily interested in the mode 0 which is that mode that resembles most closely our system oscillator. With this mode the elements of our unitary transformation must obey

$$U_{i0} = [\kappa_i^*/(\Omega_0 - \omega_i)]U_{00}. \tag{88}$$

The amplitude U_{00} is determined by normalization to take the value

$$U_{00} = \left[1 + \sum_i |\kappa_i|^2/(\Omega_0 - \omega_i)^2\right]^{-1/2}. \tag{89}$$

Making use of Eqs. (61) and (86) we can therefore write our asymptotic value for f in the form

$$f(\infty) = \left[1 + \int \frac{\rho(\omega)\,d\omega}{(\Omega_0 - \omega)^2}\right]^{-2}. \tag{90}$$

As long as the perturbed frequency Ω_0 is outside the range of the spectrum of the reservoir oscillators the integral in Eq. (90) converges and $f(\infty)$ does not equal zero. Note moreover, that in the weak coupling limit the expression (90) reduces to our lowest order result, Eq. (71).

The equation obeyed by the special oscillator variable a leads to the relation

$$\Omega - \omega_0 = \sum_i |\kappa_i|^2/(\Omega - \omega_i) \to \int \rho(\omega)\,d\omega/(\Omega - \omega) \tag{91}$$

that determines all of the normal frequencies of the perturbed system. The root Ω_0 is the root closest to the value ω_0 of the unperturbed isolated system mode. In a similar way we obtain the exact limiting expression

$$g(\infty) = \sum_I |U_{0I}|^2 \sum_{r \neq 0} |U_{rI}|^2 n_r. \tag{92}$$

If we introduce

$$\bar{n}_I = \sum_{r \neq 0} |U_{rI}|^2 n_r \Big/ \sum_{r \neq 0} |U_{rI}|^2 \tag{93}$$

as an appropriate average of reservoir excitations, our limiting value takes the form of

$$g(\infty) = \langle n \rangle - \bar{n}_0 f(\infty), \tag{94}$$

where $\langle n \rangle$ is defined by

$$\langle n \rangle = \sum |U_{0I}|^2 \, \bar{n}_I. \tag{95}$$

Equation (86) assumes that only one mode exists outside the continuous spectrum. If there are several, with frequencies Ω_L, Eq. (90) is replaced by

$$f(\infty) = \sum_L \left[1 + \int \frac{\rho(\omega) \, d\omega}{(\Omega_L - \omega)^2} \right]^{-2} \tag{96}$$

so that, a fortieri, $f(\infty) > 0$, and equilibrium is not reached when one or more isolated (perturbed) modes exist.

We interpret the failure of the system to approach equilibrium as inability of the system to perform the multiphonon transitions that are needed when the system frequency is outside that of the continuum. Equation (86) essentially states that the system energy is given to the perturbed mode which resembles most closely the system mode. A subsequent measurement of the system energy simply measures the extent to which the perturbed mode makes its energy available to the unperturbed system mode. The reduction of $f(\infty)$ from unity is thus a measure of this overlap effect and not evidence for the existence of any transition processes.

Conversely, if all perturbed frequencies Ω_I are inside the continuous spectrum, Eq. (85) is valid for all I, and it follows from Eq. (82) that $f(\infty) \to 0$ as $N \to \infty$. Alternatively, if no isolated Ω_L exists, there are no terms in Eq. (96). Thus if no isolated modes are created, $f(\infty) = 0$ and equilibrium is approached.

An interesting borderline case can occur if $\rho(\omega_0) \neq 0$ but $\rho(\Omega_I) = 0$ for some I. In this case $f(\infty) > 0$ and complete equilibrium is not approached. But if the mode I is very unlike the unperturbed system mode, $f(\infty)$ will be quite small, and a near equilibrium may result.

Note added in Proof. After the submission of this paper, Professor N. G. Van Kampen kindly informed us that in a doctoral thesis by Pieter Ullersma of University of Zurich this problem has also been treated.

REFERENCES

Argyres, P. N. (1963). "Proceedings of the Eindhoven Conference on Magnetic and Electric Resonance" (J. Smidt, ed.) p. 555. North-Holland, Amsterdam.
Classical Noise
    I. Lax, M. (1960). *Rev. Mod. Phys.* **32**, 25.
    II. Lax, M. (1960). *J. Phys. Chem. Solids* **14**, 248.
    III. Lax, M. (1966). *Rev. Mod. Phys.* **38**, 356.
    IV. Lax, M. (1966). *Rev. Mod. Phys.* **38**, 541.
Quantum Noise
    QI. Lax, M. (1958). *Phys. Rev.* **109**, 1921.
    QII. Lax, M. (1963). *Phys. Rev.* **129**, 2342.
    QIII. Lax, M. (1964). *J. Phys. Chem. Solids* **25**, 487.

QIV. Lax, M. (1966). *Phys. Rev.* **145**, 110.

QV. Lax, M. (1965). *Proc. Puerto Rico Conf. Physics Quantum Electronics* (P. L. Kelley, B. Lax, and P. E. Tannenwald, eds.). McGraw-Hill, New York.

QVI. Lax, M. Moment Treatment of Maser Noise (unpublished).

QVII. Lax, M. Rate Equation and Amplitude Fluctuation, to be published in *J. Quantum Electronics*.

QVIII. This paper.

QIX. Lax, M. Quantum Fokker-Planck Solutions for Laser Noise, to be published in *J. Quantum Electronics*.

Louisell, W. H., and Walker, R. L. (1965). *Phys. Rev.* **137**, B204.

The Projected Hartree-Fock Method
An Extension of the Independent-Particle Scheme

PER-OLOV LÖWDIN

QUANTUM THEORY PROJECT
UNIVERSITY OF FLORIDA, GAINESVILLE, FLORIDA
DEPARTMENT OF QUANTUM CHEMISTRY
UPPSALA UNIVERSITY, UPPSALA, SWEDEN

I. Introduction

In the quantum theory of matter, there are two fundamental ideas which are closely associated with discoveries by Professor John C. Slater, namely the Slater determinants and the Hartree-Fock method. Our physical understanding of the structure of atoms, molecules, solids, and atomic nuclei is essentially based on the independent-particle model (1), and these are the fundamental mathematical and conceptual tools for dealing with this model. The self-consistent-field (SCF) scheme was first developed intuitively by Hartree (2) for atoms. In a study of complex atomic spectra, Slater (3) introduced the now famous determinants which carry his name, and in a subsequent paper (4), he showed that Hartree's method could be justified and extended by treating Schrödinger's many-electron wave equation by the variation principle for a determinantal wave function. Together with a paper published about simultaneously and independently by Fock (5), this forms the basis for the so-called Hartree-Fock method. Few discoveries have been of such importance for the application of quantum mechanics to the study of the properties of matter.

Slater's interest in the independent-particle model has continued through the years, and, in a series of papers, he has studied in particular the phenomena of "exchange" and "correlation" (see references). In treating the symmetry properties of various systems, Slater also noted some peculiarities in the Hartree-Fock method that form the starting point of this paper, which is dedicated to him.

II. Symmetry Dilemma in the Hartree-Fock Method

In Hartree's original calculations of the electronic structure of atoms (2), it was always assumed that the electronic orbitals would be symmetry-adapted and of s, p, d, f, etc., character, and that, in the calculations, the self-consistent-field potentials should be replaced by their spherically symmetric part. This scheme was essentially refined when Slater and Fock suggested that the total wave function Ψ should be approximated by a single Slater determinant D built up from one-electron functions or spin-orbitals and that the best result would be obtained by applying the variation principle $\delta \langle D | \mathscr{H} | D \rangle = 0$ subject to the constraint $\langle D | D \rangle = 1$, to the many-electron Hamiltonian $\mathscr{H}$ associated with the system.

It seems to have been generally assumed that, if the system has a certain symmetry property explicitly manifested in $\mathscr{H}$, the solutions to the Hartree-Fock equations associated with the variation principle would automatically be symmetry-adapted. It was proven by Delbrück (6) that, if the total system is spherically symmetrical and one requires that the total determinant has ^1S character, then the associated Hartree-Fock functions are eigenfunctions of the orbital angular momentum and of the spin. In the cases of more general types of symmetry occurring in molecular and solid-state theory, it has been shown by Roothaan (7) and the author (8) that the assumption that the solutions to the Hartree-Fock equations are symmetry-adapted, i.e., form a basis for an irreducible representation, is always self-consistent and corresponds to a specific extreme value of the total energy. The only question is whether this extreme value is associated with the *absolute minimum* of the energy or not?

The question of the character of the extreme values of $\langle D | \mathscr{H} | D \rangle$ has been studied by Thouless (9) and Adams (10). These values may be maxima, minima, or terrace points, and it is somewhat confusing that Adams uses the term "absolute minimum" for every point where the second variation of the total energy $\langle \mathscr{H} \rangle$ is positive definite, whereas one usually reserves this term for the lowest of all possible minima. In an interesting study of the He atom, in this volume, Coulson has emphasized the saddle-point character of $\langle \mathscr{H} \rangle$ with respect to orbitals splitting of the closed-shell $(1s^2)$ to the form $(1s', 1s'')$ introduced by Hylleraas (11). So far, no one has found any simple criterion for the absolute minimum or succeeded in studying its properties. In connection with the international symposia in Boulder (1958) and in Tokyo (1962), several authors expressed the opinion that it seemed extremely *plausible* that the absolute minimum of the total energy $\langle D|\mathcal{H}|D\rangle$ found by solving the Hartree-Fock equations should correspond to a set of orbitals which are necessarily symmetry-adapted, but no proof was given. At the Hylleraas symposium on Sanibel Island (1963), the author *(12)* tried to draw attention to the problem again, particularly to the aspects reviewed in this section.

The problems may be somewhat simplified by studying the Slater determinant D itself, instead of the set of individual spin-orbitals involved. Some confusion may arise from the fact that the exact eigenfunction Ψ and the approximate eigenfunction D may have rather different properties. For instance, if Λ is a *normal constant of motion* satisfying the relations

$$\mathcal{H}\Lambda = \Lambda\mathcal{H}, \qquad \Lambda\Lambda^\dagger = \Lambda^\dagger\Lambda, \tag{1}$$

then every eigenfunction Ψ to $\mathcal{H}$ is automatically an eigenfunction to Λ or (in the case of a degenerate energy level) may be chosen in that way, so that

$$\mathcal{H}\Psi = E\Psi, \qquad \Lambda\Psi = \lambda\Psi. \tag{2}$$

For the exact eigenfunction, the second eigenvalue relation is hence simply a consequence of the first. On the other hand, for the approximate wave function D, one replaces in the Hartree-Fock scheme the first eigenvalue relation by the variation principle $\delta\langle D|\mathcal{H}|D\rangle = 0$, subject to the extra condition $\langle D|D\rangle = 1$. So far, no one has proven in general that, out of this principle, there follows the second equation $\Lambda D = \lambda D$, and this relation should then be considered as a *constraint* which necessarily raises the energy above the absolute minimum. The argument is here given for a single constant of motion Λ but will later be extended also to groups $G = \{g\}$.

The first one to notice that the Hartree-Fock scheme and the symmetry requirements were not automatically compatible was probably Slater *(13)* in his fundamental study of the connection between the VB- and MO-methods, as exemplified by the applications to the hydrogen molecule, in his classical paper about cohesion in monovalent metals in 1930, and this fact has later been more explicitly stated in several of his papers *(14)*. In studying the energy curves as functions of the internuclear separation R, he found that, for sufficiently separated atoms a and b, the single determinant $(a\alpha, b\beta)$ has a lower energy than the corresponding symmetry-adapted Hartree-Fock solution of type $(\sigma_g)^2$ depending on the simple fact that the latter has a wrong asymptotic behavior leading to ionized states with high energy for $R \to \infty$.

Another example of a similar type but referring to the equilibrium distance itself is provided by the benzene molecule having the symmetry D_{6h}, where recent calculations by Pauncz *et al.* *(15)* indicate that there are single determinants associated with the symmetry D_{3h} which have a considerably lower energy than the corresponding determinants of symmetry D_{6h}. Even if the latter are not exact solutions to the Hartree-Fock equations, the approximations seem good enough to indicate that the results have definite significance.

It has further been pointed out by Slater (14) that, in systems with unbalanced spins in which the spin does not explicitly enter the Hamiltonian, the electrons with plus spins will be influenced by another exchange potential than the electrons with minus spin, since exchange interactions occur only between electrons having parallel spins. One could therefore expect that electrons with different spins would have different orbitals due to this *exchange polarization*. A simple example of such a system is the ^2S ground state of the lithium atom, for which the conventional form $(1s\alpha, 1s\beta, 2s\alpha)$ due to this effect is changed over to $(1s'\alpha, 1s''\beta, 2s\alpha)$. The exchange polarization is of essential importance in treating magnetic phenomena (16), but here we will only stress the fact that the solution of the Hartree-Fock equations, i.e., the variation principle, for open shells leads to approximate wave functions which are no longer exact eigenfunctions to the total spin S^2.

It is evident from these examples that the basic symmetry properties of approximate wave functions do not automatically follow from the variation principle and that a great deal of attention should be devoted to this problem. In this situation, it may be worthwhile to distinguish between the various types of self-consistent-field schemes more clearly and to emphasize the definitions. In the *conventional Hartree-Fock scheme*, one apparently starts out from two basic equations:

$$\delta\langle D| \mathscr{H}|D\rangle = 0, \qquad \Lambda D = \lambda D, \tag{3}$$

and the corresponding minimum could then be said to be Λ-adapted. It is easily shown (8) that, if Λ is a fundamental symmetric function of the one-electron operators $\Lambda_1, \Lambda_2, \Lambda_3, \ldots$, then the spin-orbitals entering D which correspond to the energy minimum are automatically eigenfunctions to Λ_1 or can be chosen in that way.

On the other hand, if one drops the constraint $\Lambda D = \lambda D$ and considers only the relation

$$\delta\langle D| \mathscr{H}|D\rangle = 0, \tag{4}$$

one obtains a *nonrestricted Hartree-Fock scheme*, and the solution D corresponding to the absolute minimum has now usually lost its eigenvalue property with respect to Λ, i.e., the corresponding Hartree-Fock functions are no longer "symmetry-adapted." As a consequence of Slater's idea about exchange polarization, many open-shell systems have now been investigated by this approach (17).

It is clear that the Hartree-Fock scheme based on a single Slater determinant is in a *dilemma with respect to symmetry properties and other constants of motion.* If one looks for the absolute minimum of the energy, one loses the symmetry properties, and, if one includes the symmetry properties, the energy is increased considerably—often as much as 1 eV per electron pair or even more.

Some of the most striking examples of this symmetry dilemma may perhaps be found in solid-state theory. In considering a system of free electrons in a uniform positive background in a box, it has almost universally been assumed that the plane waves would give the essential solution of the Hartree-Fock equations. However, by studying, for example, a one-dimensional Fermi gas with δ-function repulsions, Overhauser *(18)* has shown that there exist self-consistent solutions in the form of " giant spin waves" having a lower energy than the plane-wave state. Such results look paradoxical only if one believes that the second relation in Eq. (3) necessarily follows from the first. Some examples involving negative atomic ions have also been given recently *(19)*.

There are several ways out of the symmetry dilemma, but there is probably only one way in which one can keep the contact with the independent-particle model. The determinant D corresponding to the absolute minimum of $\langle D|\mathscr{H}|D \rangle$ subject to the condition $\langle D|D \rangle = 1$ has lost its fundamental symmetry properties. It may be shown, however, that this determinant is now a unique sum of components of various symmetry types, and that at least one of the components has an even lower energy than D. Such a "component analysis" is carried out by means of a set of projection operators O, and, in order to proceed, we will now first study their properties.

III. Component Analysis with Respect to an Arbitrary Constant of Motion

Let Λ be an arbitrary normal constant of motion satisfying the relations (1). Further, let the eigenvalues of Λ be situated in a finite number of points $\lambda_1, \lambda_2, \ldots, \lambda_n$ in the complex plane each of which may be infinitely degenerate. Such an operator satisfies always a reduced Cayley-Hamilton equation of the type

$$F(\Lambda) \equiv \prod_{k=1}^{n} (\Lambda - \lambda_k) = 0. \tag{5}$$

As an example, we may consider the exchange operator P_{12} which satisfies the relation $P_{12}^2 = 1$. It has the eigenvalues ± 1, which are both infinitely degenerate, and the reduced Cayley-Hamilton equations takes the form:

$$(P_{12} + 1)(P_{12} - 1) = 0. \tag{6}$$

Let us now introduce the reduced characteristic polynomial $F(z) \equiv \Pi(z - \lambda_k)$ of degree n in the complex variable z.

The associated function

$$O_k(z) = \frac{F(z)}{(z - \lambda_k)F'(\lambda_k)} = \prod_{l \neq k} \frac{z - \lambda_l}{\lambda_k - \lambda_l}, \tag{7}$$

is a polynomial of degree $(n - 1)$ which has the value 1 for $z = \lambda_k$ and the value 0 for $z = \lambda_l$ $(l \neq k)$; it has hence the character of a Lagrange's interpolation polynomial. It is interesting to study the function

$$G(z) \equiv 1 - \sum_{k=1}^{m} O_k(z), \tag{8}$$

since it is a polynomial of degree $(n - 1)$ having n different zero points: $z = \lambda_1, \lambda_2, \ldots \lambda_n$. The function $G(z)$ is hence identically vanishing for all values of z, and one has the simple algebraic identity $G(z) \equiv 0$, or

$$1 \equiv \sum_{k=1}^{n} O_k(z). \tag{9}$$

Of fundamental importance in the theory is the operator $O_k(\Lambda)$ obtained by replacing the complex variable z in Eq. (7) by the operator Λ:

$$O_k(\Lambda) = \prod_{l \neq k} \frac{\Lambda - \lambda_l}{\lambda_k - \lambda_l} = \prod_{l \neq k} \left\{ 1 + \frac{\Lambda - \lambda_k}{\lambda_k - \lambda_l} \right\}. \tag{10}$$

According to the reduced Cayley-Hamilton equation (5), one had $(\Lambda - \lambda_k)O_k = F(\Lambda)/F'(\lambda_k) = 0$, which gives

$$\Lambda O_k = O_k \Lambda = \lambda_k O_k. \tag{11}$$

This relation shows that O_k is an *eigenoperator* to Λ associated with the eigenvalue λ_k. By using Eqs. (5) and (9), one obtains further

$$O_k^2 = O_k, \qquad O_k O_l = 0, \qquad 1 = \sum_{k=1}^{n} O_k, \tag{12}$$

which means that the set of operators $O_1, O_2, \ldots, O_n$ are idempotent, mutually exclusive, and form a resolution of the identity. For details of the proof, we refer to some previous publications (20).

Let us now consider an arbitrary trial wave function Φ and let us investigate whether it may be written as a sum of eigenfunctions to Λ. Introducing the notation $\Phi_k = O_k \Phi$ and using the resolution of the identity in Eq. (12), one obtains

$$\Phi = 1 \cdot \Phi = (\sum_k O_k)\Phi = \sum_k O_k \Phi = \sum_k \Phi_k, \tag{13}$$

and further

$$\Lambda \Phi_k = \Lambda O_k \Phi = \lambda_k O_k \Phi = \lambda_k \Phi_k, \tag{14}$$

which shows that such a " component analysis " exists. Using the properties

(12) of the projection operators, it is also easily shown that the component analysis is unique.

Using the normality of the operator Λ, i.e., $\Lambda \Lambda^\dagger = \Lambda^\dagger \Lambda$, one can prove that all the operators O_k are self-adjoint:

$$O_k^\dagger = O_k. \tag{15}$$

In combination with Eqs. (1) and (12), this gives

$$O_k^\dagger O_l = \delta_{kl} O_l, \qquad O_k^\dagger \mathcal{H} O_l = 0 \qquad (k \neq l). \tag{16}$$

These relations imply that the functions Φ_k in the component analysis (13) are not only *orthogonal* but also *noninteracting* with respect to $\mathcal{H}$:

$$\langle \Phi_k | \mathcal{H} | \Phi_l \rangle = \langle O_k \Phi | \mathcal{H} | O_l \Phi \rangle$$
$$= \langle \Phi | O_k^\dagger \mathcal{H} O_l | \Phi \rangle = 0, \tag{17}$$

for $l \neq k$. By means of the projection operators $O_1, O_2, \ldots, O_n$, the entire Hilbert space is hence split into n subspaces which are orthogonal and noninteracting.

In studying the trial wave function Φ, it is convenient to introduce the positive weight factors

$$\omega_k = \frac{\langle \Phi_k | \Phi_k \rangle}{\langle \Phi | \Phi \rangle} = \frac{\langle \Phi | O_k | \Phi \rangle}{\langle \Phi | \Phi \rangle}, \tag{18}$$

satisfying

$$0 \leq \omega_k \leq 1, \qquad \sum_k \omega_k = 1, \tag{19}$$

and, for $\omega_k \neq 0$, the expectation value of the energy with respect to the wave function Φ_k:

$$\mathscr{E}_k = \frac{\langle \Phi_k | \mathcal{H} | \Phi_k \rangle}{\langle \Phi_k | \Phi_k \rangle} = \frac{\langle \Phi | \mathcal{H} O_k | \Phi \rangle}{\langle \Phi | O_k | \Phi \rangle}. \tag{20}$$

Using Eqs. (13) and (17), one finds particularly

$$\langle \mathcal{H} \rangle_\Phi = \frac{\langle \Phi | \mathcal{H} | \Phi \rangle}{\langle \Phi | \Phi \rangle} = \frac{\sum_{kl} \langle \Phi_k | \mathcal{H} | \Phi_l \rangle}{\langle \Phi | \Phi \rangle}$$

$$= \sum_k \frac{\langle \Phi_k | \mathcal{H} | \Phi_k \rangle}{\langle \Phi | \Phi \rangle} = \sum_k \omega_k \mathscr{E}_k, \tag{21}$$

i.e., the expectation value $\langle \mathcal{H} \rangle_\Phi$ is an average value of all quantities $\mathscr{E}_1, \mathscr{E}_2, \ldots, \mathscr{E}_n$ with positive weights. Unless all these quantities are the same, there exists at least one quantity $\mathscr{E}_k$ which is lower than $\langle \mathcal{H} \rangle$, and the component analysis is hence a valuable tool for lowering the energy. It may be applied, for instance, in studying the properties of the covalent band (21) where it gives the energy stabilization connected with the exchange operator $\Lambda = P_{12}$. The component analysis has further turned out to be of particular value in studying the properties of angular momenta (22) and their eigenfunctions.

IV. Projection Operators and Component Analysis for Finite Groups

Let us now consider the case when all normal constants of motion form a finite group $G = \{g\}$ of order $|G| = n$. In order to deal with the group, it is convenient to introduce the *invariant mean* over the group:

$$\underset{s}{\mathsf{M}} f(s) = \frac{1}{|G|} \sum_s f(s), \tag{22}$$

which fulfills the relations

$$\underset{s}{\mathsf{M}} f(s) = \underset{s}{\mathsf{M}} f(s^{-1}) = \underset{s}{\mathsf{M}} f(gs) = \cdots \quad \text{etc.} \tag{23}$$

The "group algebra" is the linear space consisting of all elements formed by linear combinations ("addition") of the elements of the group multiplied by complex coefficients. Let us consider two arbitrary elements A and B defined by the relations

$$A = \underset{s}{\mathsf{M}} \alpha(s)s^{-1},$$

$$B = \underset{s}{\mathsf{M}} \beta(s)s^{-1}, \tag{24}$$

Their product is defined by the distributive law and the group multiplication i.e., $\left(\sum_k a_k g_k\right)\left(\sum_l b_l g_l\right) = \sum_{kl} a_k b_l g_k g_l$, and using (23) one obtains:

$$
\begin{aligned}
AB &= \underset{s}{\mathsf{M}} \underset{t}{\mathsf{M}} \alpha(s)\beta(t)s^{-1}t^{-1} \\
&= \underset{s}{\mathsf{M}} \underset{u}{\mathsf{M}} \alpha(s)\beta(us^{-1})u^{-1} \\
&= \underset{u}{\mathsf{M}} [\underset{s}{\mathsf{M}} \alpha(s)\beta(us^{-1})]u^{-1} \\
&= \underset{u}{\mathsf{M}} \gamma(u)u^{-1}.
\end{aligned}
\tag{25}
$$

One says that A and B correspond to the functions α and β over the group, respectively, and that the product AB corresponds to a new function γ which is the *convolution product* of α and β denoted by

$$\gamma = \alpha * \beta \tag{26a}$$

and defined by the relation

$$\gamma(u) = \underset{s}{\mathbf{M}}\, \alpha(s)\beta(us^{-1}), \tag{26b}$$

according to Eq. (25). We note that there is a complete isomorphism between the group algebra and the functions over the group, and that the products in the former correspond to convolution products in the latter, and vice versa.

Let V be a subspace of order f of the group algebra which is stable under all operations of the group, so that gV belongs to V, and let the set $X = (X_1, X_2, \ldots, X_f)$ form a basis for the subspace. According to the definition, one has

$$gX_l = \sum_k X_k \Gamma_{kl}(g), \tag{27}$$

and to each element g there is hence associated a matrix $\Gamma(g) = \{\Gamma_{kl}(g)\}$, so that $gX = X\Gamma(g)$. This gives further

$$ghX = gX\Gamma(h) = X\Gamma(g)\Gamma(h) = X\Gamma(gh) \tag{28}$$

and

$$\Gamma(g)\Gamma(h) = \Gamma(gh). \tag{29}$$

Since the matrices Γ have the same multiplication table as the elements of the group, they are said to form a *representation* of the group. Every stable subspace V defines a representation. The trace of Γ is said to be the character of the representation:

$$\chi(g) = \mathrm{Tr}\,\{\Gamma(g)\} = \sum_k \{\Gamma(g)\}_{kk}. \tag{30}$$

A stable subspace V is said to be *irreducible*, if there exists no proper subspace of V which is also stable under the group operations; the associated representation is then called an irreducible representation. Let us now consider two irreducible subspaces V_α and V_β of order f_α and f_β respectively, with the associated representations Γ_α and Γ_β, and also let A be a linear mapping of V_β on V_α associated with the rectangular matrix $\mathbf{A}$. The operator corresponding to the matrix

$$\mathbf{T} = \underset{s}{\mathbf{M}}\, \Gamma_\alpha(s)\mathbf{A}\Gamma_\beta(s^{-1}) \tag{31}$$

is a linear operator which maps V_β into V_α, and it satisfies the fundamental relation

$$\mathbf{T}\Gamma_\beta(g) = \Gamma_\alpha(g)\mathbf{T}, \tag{32}$$

for all g in the group. According to Schur's famous lemma, one has either $\mathbf{T} = 0$ or $\mathbf{T}^{-1}$ exists; in the latter case, the representations Γ_α and Γ_β are equivalent. It is now convenient to introduce the symbol:

$$\delta_{\alpha\beta} = \begin{cases} 0, & \text{if } \Gamma_\alpha \text{ and } \Gamma_\beta \text{ are nonequivalent,} \\ 1, & \text{if } \Gamma_\alpha \text{ and } \Gamma_\beta \text{ are identical,} \end{cases} \tag{33}$$

which means that one essentially excludes the case when Γ_α and Γ_β are equivalent but not identical. For the case when $V_\alpha \equiv V_\beta$, $\Gamma_\alpha \equiv \Gamma_\beta$, a second application of Schur's lemma gives $\mathbf{T} = \lambda \cdot \mathbf{1}$, where $\mathbf{1}$ is the identity operation in V_α. Hence one obtains:

$$\mathbf{T} = \underset{s}{\mathsf{M}}\,\Gamma_\alpha(s)\mathbf{A}\Gamma_\beta(s^{-1}) = \delta_{\alpha\beta}\cdot\lambda\cdot\mathbf{1}_\alpha. \tag{34}$$

Formation of the trace gives $\lambda = f_\alpha^{-1}\,\mathrm{Tr}\,\{\mathbf{A}\}$ for $\alpha = \beta$, i.e.,

$$\underset{s}{\mathsf{M}}\,\Gamma_\alpha(s)\mathbf{A}\Gamma_\beta(s^{-1}) = f_\alpha^{-1}\,\delta_{\alpha\beta}\,\mathrm{Tr}\{\mathbf{A}\}\cdot\mathbf{1}_\alpha. \tag{35}$$

The substitution $\mathbf{A} = \mathbf{A}'\Gamma(g)$ gives further

$$\underset{s}{\mathsf{M}}\,\Gamma_\alpha(s)\mathbf{A}'\Gamma_\beta(gs^{-1}) = f_\alpha^{-1}\,\delta_{\alpha\beta}\,\mathrm{Tr}\{\mathbf{A}'\cdot\Gamma(g)\}\cdot\mathbf{1}_\alpha. \tag{36}$$

Let us take the (k, l)-element of this relation; since the matrix $\mathbf{A}' = \{A'_{mn}\}$ is completely arbitrary, the coefficients of A'_{mn} of both sides must be identical, which gives

$$\underset{s}{\mathsf{M}}\,\{\Gamma_\alpha(s)\}_{km}\{\Gamma_\beta(gs^{-1})\}_{nl} = f_\alpha^{-1}\,\delta_{\alpha\beta}\delta_{kl}\{\Gamma_\beta(g)\}_{nm}, \tag{37}$$

or in terms of the convolution notation (26):

$$\{\Gamma_\alpha\}_{km} * \{\Gamma_\beta\}_{nl} = f_\alpha^{-1}\delta_{\alpha\beta}\delta_{kl}\{\Gamma_\beta\}_{nm}. \tag{38}$$

Putting $m = k$ and summing over k, one obtains

$$\chi_\alpha * \{\Gamma_\beta\}_{nl} = f_\alpha^{-1}\delta_{\alpha\beta}\{\Gamma_\beta\}_{nl}, \tag{39}$$

and, putting $n = l$ and summing over l, one gets further

$$\chi_\alpha * \chi_\beta = f_\alpha^{-1}\delta_{\alpha\beta}\chi_\beta, \tag{40}$$

which is the fundamental *convolution relation* for the characters of the irreducible representations; it contains the standard orthogonality relations for the characters for $g = e$, where e is the neutral element.

Of essential importance in the quantum-mechanical applications are the elements $\{P_\alpha\}_{km}$ of the group algebra associated with the functions $f_\alpha\{\Gamma_\alpha\}_{km}$ through the relation:

$$\{P_\alpha\}_{km} = f_\alpha\,\underset{s}{\mathsf{M}}\,\{\Gamma_\alpha(s)\}_{km}s^{-1}. \tag{41}$$

Starting from Eqs. (25) and (26) and using the convolution product (38), one obtains the product relation

$$\{P_\alpha\}_{km}\{P_\beta\}_{nl} = \delta_{\alpha\beta}\delta_{kl}\{P_\beta\}_{nm}. \tag{42}$$

It is evident that the quantities $\{P_\alpha\}_{kk}$ form a set of projection operators which are idempotent and mutually exclusive. From the properties of the regular representation, one obtains

$$\sum_\alpha f_\alpha \chi_\alpha(g) = \begin{cases} |G| & \text{for} \quad g = e \\ 0 & \text{for} \quad g \neq e \end{cases} \tag{43}$$

and, since the first relation implies that $\sum_\alpha f_\alpha^2 = |G|$, they are often referred to as the completeness relations. By means of them, one obtains directly

$$\sum_\alpha \sum_k \{P_\alpha\}_{kk} = e, \tag{44}$$

i.e., the projection operators $\{P_\alpha\}_{kk}$ form a "resolution of the identity."

If the elements g of the group G represent symmetry operations which leave the length of the vectors Φ invariant, so that $\|g\Phi\| = \|\Phi\|$, one has

$$\|g\Phi\|^2 = \langle g\Phi|g\Phi\rangle = \langle \Phi|g^\dagger g|\Phi\rangle = \langle \Phi|\Phi\rangle \tag{45}$$

for all Φ, i.e., $g^\dagger g = g g^\dagger = e$. This relation implies that the elements of the symmetry group G are unitary with respect to the metric used in quantum mechanics. If the representation Γ_α is further chosen to be unitary, one obtains

$$\{P_\alpha\}_{km} = \{P_\alpha\}_{mk}^\dagger . \tag{46}$$

We note particularly that the projection operators $\{P_\alpha\}_{kk}$ are self-adjoint.

By using Eq. (42), it is easily shown that the operators $\{P_\alpha\}_{km}$ are linearly independent and, since the total number of operators is $\sum_\alpha f_\alpha^2 = |G|$, they span the entire group algebra of order $|G|$. From the definition (41), it follows that

$$g\{P_\alpha\}_{km} = f_\alpha \, \underset{s}{\mathsf{M}} \, \{\Gamma_\alpha(s)\}_{km} g s^{-1}$$

$$= f_\alpha \, \underset{r}{\mathsf{M}} \, \{\Gamma_\alpha(rg)\}_{km} r^{-1} = \sum_l \{P_\alpha\}_{kl} \{\Gamma_\alpha(g)\}_{lm}, \tag{47}$$

i.e., the operators $\{P_\alpha\}_{km}$ of a row $(m = 1, 2, \ldots, f_\alpha)$ form a stable subspace connected with the irreducible representation Γ_α.

Let us now consider an arbitrary trial wave function Φ and the associated functions $g\Phi$. It is further convenient to introduce the functions

$$\Phi_{km}^\alpha = \{P_\alpha\}_{km} \Phi = f_\alpha \, \underset{s}{\mathsf{M}} \, \{\Gamma_\alpha(s)\}_{km} s^{-1} \Phi, \tag{48}$$

and to arrange these functions in matrices:

$$\Phi^\alpha = \begin{bmatrix} \Phi_{11}^\alpha & \Phi_{12}^\alpha & \Phi_{13}^\alpha & \cdots & \Phi_{1f_\alpha}^\alpha \\ \Phi_{21}^\alpha & \Phi_{22}^\alpha & \Phi_{23}^\alpha & \cdots & \Phi_{2f_\alpha}^\alpha \\ \cdot & \cdot & \cdot & & \cdot \\ \Phi_{f_\alpha 1}^\alpha & \Phi_{f_\alpha 2}^\alpha & \Phi_{f_\alpha 3}^\alpha & \cdots & \Phi_{f_\alpha f_\alpha}^\alpha \end{bmatrix} \tag{49}$$

It should be observed that, according to Eq. (42), functions in the same row may be obtained from each other by means of a *shift-operator*:

$$\Phi_{km}^{\alpha} = \{P_{\alpha}\}_{nm}\, \Phi_{kn}^{\alpha}. \tag{50}$$

This implies that the functions in the same row are either all vanishing or all nonvanishing; according to Eqs. (42) and (46), they have actually the same norm:

$$\langle \Phi_{km}^{\alpha} | \Phi_{km}^{\alpha} \rangle = \langle \Phi_{kk}^{\alpha} | \Phi_{kk}^{\alpha} \rangle. \tag{51}$$

It follows further from Eq. (47) that the functions Φ_{km}^{α} in a row do transform according to the irreducible representation Γ_{α}.

By combining the relations (42) and (46), one obtains the operator formulas

$$\{P_{\alpha}\}_{mk}^{\dagger}\, \{P_{\beta}\}_{nl} = \delta_{\alpha\beta}\delta_{kl}\, \{P_{\beta}\}_{nm}, \tag{52}$$

$$\{P_{\alpha}\}_{mk}^{\dagger}\, \mathscr{H}\, \{P_{\beta}\}_{nl} = \delta_{\alpha\beta}\delta_{kl}\, \mathscr{H}\, \{P_{\beta}\}_{nm}, \tag{53}$$

which are of fundamental importance in the quantum-mechanical applications. As a consequence, one obtains directly the relations

$$\langle \Phi_{mk}^{\alpha} | \Phi_{nl}^{\alpha} \rangle = \delta_{\alpha\beta}\delta_{kl}\, \langle \Phi | \Phi_{nm}^{\beta} \rangle, \tag{54}$$

$$\langle \Phi_{mk}^{\alpha} | \mathscr{H} | \Phi_{nl}^{\beta} \rangle = \delta_{\alpha\beta}\delta_{kl}\, \langle \Phi | \mathscr{H} | \Phi_{nm}^{\beta} \rangle, \tag{55}$$

which show that functions associated with *different irreducible representations* or with *different columns* within the same irreducible representation are not only *orthogonal* but also *noninteracting* with respect to $\mathscr{H}$.

Let us now turn to the question of "component analysis." Using Eq. (44) one obtains

$$\Phi = e\Phi = \left[\sum_{\alpha}\sum_{k} \{P_{\alpha}\}_{kk}\right]\Phi = \sum_{\alpha k} \Phi_{kk}^{\alpha}, \tag{56}$$

i.e., a resolution of Φ in terms of functions Φ_{kk}^{α} of "diagonal" character. To every nonvanishing Φ_{kk}^{α}, one may construct a complete row by means of the shift operators according to Eq. (50), and one obtains a set of orthogonal functions Φ_{km}^{α} ($m = 1, 2, ...f_{\alpha}$) which transforms according to the irreducible representation Γ_{α}. It follows from (55) that these functions have not only the same norm but also the same energy:

$$\langle \Phi_{km}^{\alpha} | \mathscr{H} | \Phi_{km}^{\alpha} \rangle = \langle \Phi | \mathscr{H} | \Phi_{kk}^{\alpha} \rangle = \langle \Phi_{kk}^{\alpha} | \mathscr{H} | \Phi_{kk}^{\alpha} \rangle. \tag{57}$$

The relation (56) gives hence a component analysis of Φ completely analogous to (13), and the expectation value of $\mathscr{H}$ with respect to Φ is thus a weighted mean of the energies associated with the various components in accordance with Eq. (21). Even in group theory, the component analysis is hence an important tool to lower the energy.

The situation may be further improved by considering the various columns in (49). Let us for a moment assume that the trial wave function Φ has no symmetry properties whatsoever and that the functions $g\Phi$ form a linearly independent set of order $|G|$; the same applies then to the functions Φ_{km}^α. The functions in different columns of (49) are orthogonal and noninteracting and we will now construct the secular equation associated with one specific column, say the kth one. According to Eq. (55), one has

$$\langle \Phi_{mk}^\alpha | \mathcal{H} - E | \Phi_{nk}^\alpha \rangle = \langle \Phi | \mathcal{H} - E | \Phi_{nm}^\alpha \rangle, \tag{58}$$

i.e., the matrix elements are independent of k. This implies that every column leads to one and the same "block" in the secular equation, that every block will be repeated f_α times, and that every root E will hence be repeated at least f_α times leading to an energy degeneracy characterized by the order of the irreducible representation Γ_α. It seems as if the characteristic polynomial in z given by the secular determinant

$$|\langle \Phi_{mk}^\alpha | \mathcal{H} - z | \Phi_{nk}^\alpha \rangle| = |f_\alpha \underset{s}{\mathsf{M}} \{\Gamma_\alpha(s)\}_{nm} \langle \Phi | \mathcal{H} - z | s^{-1}\Phi \rangle| \tag{59}$$

would depend explicitly on the matrix elements of Γ_α, but Byers-Brown has shown in an interesting paper in this volume that it depends only on the characters χ_α. If the function Φ is in any way symmetry-adapted, the functions Φ_{mk}^α in a column may be linearly dependent, and it is then necessary to construct an orthonormal set before setting up the secular equation which otherwise becomes identically vanishing for all values of z.

The component analysis in Eq. (56) is used also in studying the properties of the exact wave function Ψ satisfying $\mathcal{H}\Psi = E\Psi$. One has

$$\Psi = \sum_{\alpha k} \Psi_{kk}^\alpha, \tag{60}$$

and, if a specific term Ψ_{kk}^α is nonvanishing, one may construct a full row by means of the shift operators according to (50):

$$\Psi_{km}^\alpha = \{P_\alpha\}_{km} \Psi_{kk}^\alpha = \{P_\alpha\}_{km} \Psi. \tag{61}$$

These functions are all nonvanishing and orthogonal, and they form a basis for the irreducible representation Γ_α. One has further

$$\begin{aligned}
\mathcal{H} \Psi_{km}^\alpha = \mathcal{H}\{P_\alpha\}_{km} \Psi &= \{P_\alpha\}_{km} \mathcal{H} \Psi \\
&= E\{P_\alpha\}_{km} \Psi = E \Psi_{km}^\alpha,
\end{aligned} \tag{62}$$

i.e., the functions Ψ_{km}^α are hence all exact eigenfunctions to the Hamiltonian $\mathcal{H}$ associated with the eigenvalue E, and the order of the degeneracy is at least f_α. This is the fundamental theorem in the applications of group theory to quantum mechanics.

The group algebra ideas in this section go back to Wedderburn, Schur, Frobenius, and Young. For a survey of the applications to quantum theory, the reader is referred to the classical books by Weyl, Wigner, and van der Waerden (*23*).

We have here discussed only finite groups, but many of the ideas based on the concept of the "invariant mean" defined by Eq. (22) may be extended to compact infinite groups. It should perhaps also be observed that the projection operators for the rotation group and the translation group may be obtained from the simple product form (10); see particularly reference (*22*).

V. The Projected Hartree-Fock Scheme

The projection operators O are valuable tools in discussing the constants of motion for both single operators Λ and groups $G = \{g\}$. Using the component analysis based on the resolution of the identity, for these quantities, one can prove that every exact eigenfunction Ψ either automatically fulfills the relations

$$\mathscr{H}\Psi = E\Psi, \qquad O\Psi = \Psi, \tag{63}$$

or may be written as a unique sum of components satisfying these relations. We note that for a single constant of motion Λ, the projection operator O is given by the product form (10), whereas, for a group $G = \{g\}$, it is given by the diagonal operator $\{P_\alpha\}_{kk}$ associated with an irreducible representation Γ_α defined by Eq. (41).

In the Hartree-Fock scheme based on a single normalized Slater determinant, D, the Schrödinger equation is replaced by the variation principle, and the *conventional Hartree-Fock method* is actually based on the two relations

$$\delta\langle D|\mathscr{H}|D\rangle = 0, \qquad OD = D. \tag{64}$$

Even if these relations are analogous to Eq. (63), the second equation is certainly a constraint which is going to raise the energy. In order to improve the wave function, it seems hence desirable to remove the constraint and to look for the absolute minimum of $\langle D|\mathscr{H}|D\rangle$, which leads to the *nonrestricted Hartree-Fock scheme* discussed in a previous section. The Slater determinant D associated with the absolute minimum is usually not an eigenfunction to the constants of motion, but the results obtained in the previous sections show that it may be written in the form

$$D = \sum_k D_k, \qquad D_k = O_k D, \qquad \text{case of } \Lambda \tag{65}$$

or

$$D = \sum_{\alpha k} D_{kk}^\alpha, \qquad D_{kk}^\alpha = \{P_\alpha\}_{kk} D, \qquad \text{case of } G = \{g\} \tag{66}$$

and that this component analysis is unique, that the components are orthogonal and noninteracting, and that at least one of the components has a lower energy than D itself. This implies that, by selecting a proper component OD, one may both restore the symmetry properties and lower the energy. A further lowering of the energy may even be possible by a more detailed study of the specific component OD, if one minimizes the energy with respect to this wave function rather than with respect to D. This line of thinking leads to the *projected Hartree-Fock scheme* suggested in 1954 by the author (24).

In using the variation principle to solve the Schrödinger equation, the Eckart criterion (25) tells us that the accuracy of the trial wave function is improved as the energy is lowered, and this implies that one cannot obtain particularly good results in the conventional Hartree-Fock scheme, even if they may be valuable and important from qualitative points of view. In the nonrestricted Hartree-Fock scheme, one is lowering the energy in a more effective way, but one has instead lost track of the symmetry properties and the normal constants of motion. One natural way out of this dilemma is to approximate the wave functions Ψ by a *proper projection of a single Slater determinant*:

$$\Psi \approx OD, \tag{67}$$

where $O = O_k(\Lambda)$ for a single constant of motion Λ, and $O = \{P_\alpha\}_{kk}$ for a group $G = \{g\}$, and to apply the variation principle to the expression

$$\langle \mathscr{H} \rangle = \frac{\langle OD|\mathscr{H}|OD \rangle}{\langle OD|OD \rangle} = \frac{\langle D|O^\dagger \mathscr{H} O|D \rangle}{\langle D|O^\dagger O|D \rangle} = \frac{\langle D|\mathscr{H} O|D \rangle}{\langle D|O|D \rangle}. \tag{68}$$

The wave function OD is in a sense actually the same as in the conventional Hartree-Fock scheme, only that we have removed the constraint $OD = D$ in Eq. (64). It is evident that the wave function OD associated with the *absolute minimum* of (68) is no longer going to be a single Slater determinant. However, even if we have consequently departed from the main idea of the Hartree-Fock scheme, the wave function OD is still associated with the *independent-particle model* in the sense that it is uniquely defined by a Hartree-product through the component analysis.

In this connection, it is helpful to reconsider how the Hartree-Fock scheme was introduced by Slater (34). The basis for the independent-particle model of an N-particle system was originally the Hartree-product:

$$\Psi_1(x_1)\Psi_2(x_2)\Psi_3(x_3) \cdots \Psi_N(x_N), \tag{69}$$

where $x_k = (\mathbf{r}_k, \zeta_k)$ is the combined space-spin coordinate. If the particles are *fermions*, they have to satisfy the Pauli principle, and the associated anti-symmetry property may be introduced by using the *antisymmetric component* of Eq. (69) selected by the projection operator

$$O_{AS} = (N!)^{-1} \sum_P (-1)^P P, \tag{70}$$

of type (41) for the antisymmetric representation of the symmetry group S_N. This projection changes the Hartree-product (69) into a Slater determinant D, and it should be observed that this projection usually *increases* the energy depending on the fact that fermions (in contrast to bosons) cannot be packed into the bottom of the energy-level scheme more tightly than one fermion per spin-orbital. A little mixture of "bosonic" character into the wave function may hence lower the energy considerably but, for fermions, such a procedure is certainly highly improper, and the projection operator, Eq. (70), is essential in formulating the theory.

The basic idea of the *projected Hartree-Fock scheme* is to extend the projection to cover not only the antisymmetry property but *all symmetry properties* of the wave function associated with the normal constants of motion, and the wave function OD may hence be considered as the proper symmetry projection of a single Hartree product (69) associated with the independent-particle model. It should be observed that this projection is *unique*, that the other members D_{km}^{α} may be obtained from the component D_{kk}^{α} by means of the shift operators:

$$D_{km}^{\alpha} = \{P_{\alpha}\}_{km} D_{kk}^{\alpha} = \{P_{\alpha}\}_{km} D, \tag{71}$$

and that all these functions have the same energy.

One common objection against the projected Hartree-Fock scheme is that the wave function OD is no longer a single Slater determinant but rather a *sum* of such determinants, and that the scheme is hence closer to the method of superposition of configuration than to the independent-particle model. This is true in the same sense as a Slater determinant is the *sum* of $N!$ Hartree products, but it should be observed that the wave functions D and OD are both uniquely defined by a Hartree product (69), i.e., by a set of N spin-orbitals $\Psi_1, \Psi_2, \ldots \Psi_N$, whereas the standard method of superposition of configurations is based on a set of spin-orbitals having an order M which is larger than the number of particles: $M > N$. The fact that the wave function OD is uniquely defined by exactly N spin-orbitals $\Psi_1, \Psi_2, \ldots \Psi_N$ is of essential importance both for the physical interpretations as to the connection with the independent-particle model and for the simplicity of the mathematical calculations in minimizing the energy (68). We note that the wave function OD should be considered as a *conceptual entity* in the same way as D previously was, and that expansions in terms of Hartree products or Slater determinants are not necessarily the best clue for understanding the fundamental properties of OD.

As an example of this principle, we will consider an arbitrary nonsingular transformation of the basic spin-orbitals:

$$\Psi_k' = \sum_l \Psi_l a_{lk}. \tag{72}$$

As pointed out by Slater, one has the theorem

$$\det \{\Psi'_k(x_i)\} = \det \{\Psi_l(x_i)\} \cdot \det \{a_{lk}\},$$

i.e., $D' = D \cdot \det \{a_{lk}\}$, which says that the determinantal wave function is going to be changed only by a constant factor. This theorem is of fundamental importance in the Hartree-Fock scheme, since the basic spin-orbitals without loss of generality may be chosen *orthonormal*, so that $\langle \Psi_k | \Psi_l \rangle = \delta_{kl}$. Since the projection operators O defined in the previous sections are *linear* operators, one obtains directly

$$OD' = (OD) \det \{a_{lk}\}, \tag{73}$$

i.e., even in the projected Hartree-Fock scheme the wave function OD is changed only by a constant factor under the transformation (72). Even in this scheme, the basic spin-orbitals may hence be chosen orthonormal without loss of generality.

It is evident from Eq. (73) that the wave function OD does not depend on the choice of individual spin-orbitals Ψ_k but on the *linear space M_N* spanned by these spin-orbitals which is characterized by the projection operator (*26*):

$$\rho = |\Psi\rangle\langle\Psi|\Psi\rangle^{-1}\langle\Psi|, \tag{74}$$

where $\Psi = \{\Psi_1, \Psi_2, \ldots, \Psi_N\}$. One has the fundamental relations

$$\rho^2 = \rho, \qquad \rho^\dagger = \rho, \qquad \mathrm{Tr}(\rho) = N. \tag{75}$$

If the set Ψ is chosen orthonormal, one has $\langle\Psi|\Psi\rangle = 1$ and further

$$\rho = |\Psi\rangle\langle\Psi| = \sum_{k=1}^{N} |\Psi_k\rangle\langle\Psi_k|. \tag{76}$$

If one looks at the (x_1, x_2)-component of this operator, one obtains

$$\rho(x_1, x_2) = \sum_{k=1}^{n} \Psi_k(x_1)\Psi_k^*(x_2), \tag{77}$$

which shows that the kernel of the projection operator ρ is identical with the Fock-Dirac density matrix (*26*). Since the wave function OD depends uniquely on ρ, the main problem in the projected Hartree-Fock scheme is to vary ρ so that the energy (68) becomes an absolute minimum.

In the same way as the variational problem in the nonrestricted Hartree-Fock scheme leads to a reduced eigenvalue problem in the one-electron space:

$$\mathscr{H}_{\mathrm{eff}}(1)\Psi_k(x_1) = \epsilon_k\Psi_k(x_1), \tag{78}$$

involving an effective Hamiltonian, $\mathscr{H}_{\mathrm{eff}}(1)$, which depends only on ρ, the same is true also in the projected Hartree-Fock scheme. Introducing the

PER-OLOV LÖWDIN

notation $\overline{\mathscr{H}} = \langle \mathscr{H} \rangle$, one obtains by varying the energy expression (68):

$$\delta \langle \mathscr{H} \rangle = \frac{1}{\langle D|O|D \rangle^2} \{ \langle \delta D|(\mathscr{H} - \overline{\mathscr{H}})|OD \rangle + \text{complex conjugate} \} = 0 \quad (79)$$

which gives

$$\langle \delta D|(\mathscr{H} - \overline{\mathscr{H}})O|D \rangle = 0. \quad (80)$$

This implies that the resulting equations will be exactly the same as those obtained in the ordinary nonrestricted Hartree-Fock scheme if one replaces the original Hamiltonian $\mathscr{H}$ by the *composite* Hamiltonian $(\mathscr{H} - \overline{\mathscr{H}})O$, which contains both the projection operator O and the final expectation value $\overline{\mathscr{H}}$ of the energy. The composite Hamiltonian is usually a many-body Hamiltonian but, in a previous paper (27), the author has shown that the ordinary Hartree-Fock theory may be extended to include also such Hamiltonians and that the resulting effective Hamiltonian depends only on the quantity ρ defined by Eq. (77).

These extended Hartree-Fock equations were suggested in 1954, but they have so far not been solved "exactly" for any particular system. In this connection, it may be worthwhile to remember that the ordinary Hartree-Fock equation for the absolute minimum of the nonrestricted scheme suggested much earlier have not been solved "exactly" for even the simplest atomic systems and that much work remains to be done in this field. Instead one has to be satisfied with numerical approximations which have been successively refined as the capacity and speed of the modern electronic computers have been increased. One of the most successful approximations is based on the ASP-MO-LCAO-SCF idea (28), in which the basic spin-orbitals Ψ_k are expanded in terms of a truncated set $\{\phi_\mu\}$ of order M:

$$\Psi_k = \sum_{\mu=1}^{M} \phi_\mu c_{\mu k}. \quad (81)$$

Introducing the charge- and bond-order matrix $\mathbf{R} = \mathbf{c}\mathbf{c}^\dagger$, where

$$R_{\mu\nu} = \sum_{k=1}^{N} c_{\mu k} c_{\nu k}^*, \quad (82)$$

one obtains $\rho = |\Psi\rangle\langle\Psi| = |\phi\rangle\mathbf{c}\mathbf{c}^\dagger\langle\phi| = |\phi\rangle\mathbf{R}\langle\phi|$ and

$$\rho(x_1, x_2) = \sum_{\mu,\nu=1}^{M} \phi_\mu(x_1) R_{\mu\nu} \phi_\nu^*(x_2), \quad (83)$$

which shows that the fundamental invariant ρ may be approximately described by the discrete matrix $\mathbf{R}$ of order $M \times M$. The main problem is now to vary $\mathbf{R}$ so that the energy (68) becomes an absolute minimum, and, in practice, this procedure may be carried out as described in a previous paper (*28*) dealing with the Hartree-Fock method for many-body Hamiltonians.

The projected Hartree-Fock scheme is conceptually simple, but the mathematics involved looks rather complicated because we are not familiar with it. In the discussion, we will indicate that, for electronic systems, the method seems to give good results—with a relative accuracy of better than 5×10^{-4} in the total energy—but we don't want to give the impression that such numerical results can be obtained without a considerable amount of work and computation. The best way to gain a deeper understanding of the features of the projected Hartree-Fock scheme probably is to calculate the first- and second-order reduced density matrixes associated with the wave function OD which depend only on the quantity ρ. The first-order density matrix is actually the clue for obtaining the extended Hartree-Fock equations for the projected scheme (78) in explicit form. The first-order density matrix for spin-projected determinants OD has been found by Harriman (*29*), and further work on this problem is in progress.

In conclusion, it should be observed that we are here dealing with spin-orbitals, i.e., one-electron functions of the form

$$\Psi(x) = \Psi(\mathbf{r}, \zeta) = \Psi_+(\mathbf{r})\alpha(\zeta) + \Psi_-(\mathbf{r})\beta(\zeta). \tag{84}$$

It is not yet known whether such general spin-orbitals are of importance in treating systems where the spin does not enter the Hamiltonian explicitly, but they are of fundamental importance as soon as spin-orbit couplings or spin-spin couplings are introduced in the Hamiltonian. In such a scheme, the fundamental invariant ρ has four space components ρ_{++}, ρ_{+-}, ρ_{-+}, ρ_{--}, rather than two.

VI. The Correlation Problem

A study of the independent-particle model would be incomplete without a discussion of the correlation problem. Since in the independent-particle model, each particle moves in the outer field and in the "average-field" of all the other particles, one neglects the correlation between their motions depending on the fact that they may strongly repel each other due to Coulomb repulsion and hard-core interaction. In this section, we will essentially discuss the correlation problem in electronic systems, but the arguments may be extended to general systems of fermions.

For electrons, the correlation problem is associated with the Coulomb repulsion e^2/r_{12} which creates a "Coulomb hole" around each electron with respect to all other electrons.

For electrons with parallel spins, the exchange interations will create a "Fermi hole" which will take care also of the main part of the Coulomb hole, so the essential part of the correlation problem deals with pair of electrons having antiparallel spins. The problem is complicated by the fact that, depending on the classical formulation of the Pauli principle, one assigns, in the *conventional Hartree-Fock scheme*, two electrons with antiparallel spins, α and β, to each orbital available. This pairing of the electrons is essential also for constructing determinants D of correct symmetry, but, since the two electrons are forced to stay in one and the same orbital, the arrangement gives rise to a considerable correlation error.

In order to get an idea of the order of magnitude of this error, the correlation energy is introduced (*30*) as the difference between the exact energy of the Hamiltonian and the energy of the *conventional* Hartree-Fock scheme:

$$E_{corr} = E_{exact} - E_{HF}. \tag{85}$$

A simple study of the two-electron systems (*30*), the He-like ions and the hydrogen molecule, indicates that the correlation errors amount to about -1.1 eV of which $+1.1$ eV refers to the kinetic energy and -2.2 eV to the potential energy according to the virial theorem. The correlation energy per electron pair is not a constant, and it goes up considerably with increasing atomic number (*31*). As a rule of thumb, the correlation energy is approximately 1% of the total energy.

One may ask how much the correlation error would go down, if one released the "pairing constraint" and let the electrons with different spins go into different orbitals, to avoid each other, "if they so desire." The first example of this type was treated by Hylleraas (*11*) and involved the splitting of the $(1s^2)$-shell for the helium atom into the form $(1s', 1s'')$ with a remarkable energy lowering as a result. A second example was given by Slater (*13*) in his study of the monovalent metals in which he showed that the energy curves for separated atoms could be lowered enough to obtain their correct asymptotic form by permitting electrons with different spin to be on different sublattices. In the *nonrestricted* Hartree-Fock scheme, one can hence remove a large part of the correlation error simply by permitting "different orbitals for different spins" (DODS).

The problem of treating the symmetry properties in this connection is solved in the *projected Hartree-Fock scheme*, which permits also a further lowering of the total energy. The simple applications carried out to atomic and molecular systems, so far, indicate that about 95% of the correlation energy can be removed in this way, and the remaining error in the total energy should then be about 0.05%, which is perhaps sufficient to explain the main qualitative features of the systems under consideration.

A special case of the method of different orbitals for different spins in the projected Hartree-Fock scheme is the *alternant-molecular-orbital* (AMO) method suggested by the author (*32*) in 1953. In this method, electrons having different spins in alternant systems may accumulate on different subsystems, and their separation may be regulated by a single variable parameter ϑ which is determined by the variation principle applied to Eq. (68), or by using one parameter ϑ_k per electron pair. The method has now been extensively applied to conjugated systems (*33*), and the correlation problem for the infinite linear chain has been treated in this way by Pauncz and de Heer (*34*). It is presently being used for a study of the cohesive properties of the alkali metals by Calais (*35*). More applications of the general method of different orbitals for different spins in the projected Hartree-Fock method to atoms and small molecules are in progress or are being planned in the Uppsala and Florida projects.

The success of the independent-particle model in treating atoms, molecules, solids, and particularly nuclei has often been hard to explain, and it was suggested by Brueckner (*36*) that it may depend essentially on another form of the self-consistent-field scheme based on the effective two-body part of the so-called reaction operator. The author (*37*) has shown that this approach may be refined to an *exact self-consistent-field scheme* by considering the full reaction operator. It is my opinion that, at least for electrons, one may remove the essential part of the correlation effects simply by a proper treatment of the symmetry properties, and this leads to a close connection between the shell structure and the constants of motion underlying the independent-particle model. For electrons, only the last 0.05% of the total energy would require studies of the reaction operator through infinite-order perturbation theory (*38*), whereas, for atomic nuclei, the situation may be considerably more complicated.

ACKNOWLEDGMENTS

The author would like to express his sincere gratitude to Professor John C. Slater for the immense hospitality he has enjoyed during many periods of stay at the Solid-State and Molecular Theory Group at M.I.T. and for many valuable suggestions and fruitful discussions about the quantum theory of matter.

This work has been sponsored by the National Science Foundation and the National Aeronautics and Space Administration under research grants GP-1695 and NSF-512, respectively, with the University of Florida and by Aeronautical Research Laboratory, OAR, through the European office, Aerospace Research, U.S. Air Force under contract AF61(052)-701 with Uppsala University which is gratefully acknowledged.

REFERENCES

1. N. Bohr, *Proc. Phys. Soc.* (*London*) **35**, 296 (1923).
2. D. R. Hartree, *Proc. Cambridge Phil. Soc.* **24**, 89 (1928).
3. J. C. Slater, *Phys. Rev.* **34**, 1293 (1929).
4. J. C. Slater, *Phys. Rev.* **35**, 210 (1930).

5. V. Fock, *Z. Physik* **61**, 126 (1930).
6. M. Delbrück, *Proc. Roy. Soc. (London)* **A129**, 686 (1930).
7. C. C. J. Roothaan, *Rev. Mod. Phys.* **32**, 179 (1960).
8. P.-O. Löwdin, *J. Appl. Phys. Suppl.* **33**, 251 (1962).
9. D. J. Thouless, *Nucl. Phys.* **21**, 225 (1960).
10. W. H. Adams, *Phys. Rev.* **127**, 1650 (1962).
11. E. A. Hylleraas, *Z. Physik* **54**, 347 (1929); C. Eckart, *Phys. Rev.* **36**, 878 (1930); H. Shull and P.-O. Löwdin, *J. Chem. Phys.* **25**, 1035 (1956).
12. P. O. Löwdin, *Rev. Mod. Phys.* **35**, 496 (1963).
13. J. C. Slater, *Phys. Rev.* **35**, 509 (1930).
14. J. C. Slater, *Rev. Mod. Phys.* **6**, 209 (1934); *Phys. Rev.* **81**, 385 (1951).
15. R. Pauncz, J. de Heer, and P.-O. Löwdin, *J. Chem. Phys.* **66**, 2247, 2257 (1962).
16. J. C. Slater, *Phys. Rev.* **82**, 538 (1951); *Rev. Mod. Phys.* **25**, 199 (1953).
17. R. K. Nesbet, *Proc. Roy. Soc. (London).* **A230**, 312 (1955); G. W. Pratt, Jr., *Phys. Rev.* **102**, 1303 (1956); J. H. Wood and G. W. Pratt, Jr., *Phys. Rev.* **107**, 995 (1957); R. K. Nesbet and R. E. Watson, *Ann. Phys. (N.Y.)* **9**, 260 (1960); L. M. Sachs, *Phys. Rev.* **117**, 1504 (1960); R. E. Watson and A. J. Freeman, *Phys. Rev.* **210**, 1125, 1134 (1960).
18. A. W. Overhauser, *Phys. Rev. Letters* **4**, 415, 462 (1960); W. Kohn and S. J. Nettel, *Phys. Rev. Letters* **5**, 8 (1960); K. Sawada and N. Fukuda, *Progr. Theoret. Phys. (Kyoto)* **25**, 653 (1961); E. M. Henley and Th. W. Ruijgrok, *Ann. Phys. (N.Y.)* **12**, 409 (1961); E. M. Henley and L. Wilets, *ibid* **14**, 120 (1961); T. Arai, Tech. Rep. 1961, Argonne National Laboratories (unpublished).
19. T. A. Kaplan and W. H. Kleiner, Paper read at the Sanibel Island Quantum Theory Conference 1966; also *Bull. Am. Phys. Soc.* **11**, 234 (1966).
20. P.-O. Löwdin, *Phys. Rev.* **97**, 1509 (1955); *Proc. 10th Solvay Conf., 1954*, p. 71 (Inst. internat. de physique Solvay. 10ᵉ conseil de physique tenu à Bruxelles 1954: Les électrons dans les métaux, Rapports et discussions, Bruxelles 1955); *Rev. Mod. Phys.* **32**, 328 (1960); **34**, 520 (1962).
21. P.-O. Löwdin, *Rev. Mod. Phys.* **34**, 80 (1962).
22. P.-O. Löwdin, *Rev. Mod. Phys.* **36**, 966 (1964).
23. H. Weyl, "Gruppentheorie und Quantenmechanik." Hirzel, Leipzig, 1931 [*English Transl.*: "Theory of Groups and Quantum Mechanics." Princeton Univ. Press, Princeton, New Jersey, 1931]; B. J. van der Waerden, "Die Gruppentheoretische Methode in der Quantenmechanik." Springer, Berlin, 1932; E. P. Wigner, "Gruppentheorie." Vieweg, Brunswick, Germany, 1931 [*English Transl.*: "Group Theory and Its Application to the Quantum Mechanics of Atomic Spectra." Academic Press, New York, 1959].
24. P.-O. Löwdin, Quart. Progr. Rept. *Solid-State Molecular Theory Group M.I.T.*, June 15, 1954; *Phys. Rev.* **97**, 1509 (1955); *Ann. Acad. Reg. Sci. Upsalien.* **2**, 127 (1958); *J. Appl. Phys. Suppl.* **33**, 251 (1962); *Rev. Mod. Phys.* **34**, 520 (1962).
25. C. Eckart, *Phys. Rev.* **36**, 877 (1930); B. A. Lengyel, *J. Math. Anal. Appl.* **5**, 451 (1962).
26. V. Fock, *Z. Physik* **61**, 126 (1930); P. A. M. Dirac, *Proc. Cambridge Phil. Soc.* **26**, 376 (1930); **27**, 240 (1931).
27. P.-O. Löwdin, *Phys. Rev.* **97**, 1474 (1955).
28. C. C. J. Roothaan, *Rev. Mod. Phys.* **23**, 69 (1951).
29. J. Harriman, *J. Chem. Phys.* **40**, 2827 (1964).
30. P.-O. Löwdin, *Advan. Chem. Phys.* **2**, 207 (1959).
31. E. Clementi, *IBM J. Res. Develop.* **9**, (1), (1965).

32. P.-O. Löwdin, *Nikko Symp. Mol. Phys.* (Symposium on molecular physics held at Nikko on the occasion of the Internat. Conf. on Theor. Physics, Sept. 1953 in Tokyo and Kyoto; Maruzen, Tokyo 1954) p., 13; *Phys. Rev.* 97, 1509 (1955); *Proc. 10th Solvay Conf., 1954* p. 71, (Inst. internat. de physique Solvay. 10ᵉ conseil de physique tenu à Bruxelles 1954: Les électrons dans le métaux, Rapports et discussions, Bruxelles 1955); *Rev. Mod. Phys.* 32, 328 (1960).

33. T. Itoh and H. Yoshizumi, *J. Phys. Soc. Japan* 10, 201 (1955); *J. Chem. Phys.* 23, 412 (1955); *Busseiron Kenkyu* 83, 13 (1955); R. Lefebvre, H. H. Dearman, and H. M. McConnell, *J. Chem. Phys.* 32, 176 (1960); P.-O. Löwdin, R. Pauncz, and J. de Heer, *ibid* 36, 2247, 2257, (1962); J. de Heer, *ibid* 37, 2080 (1962); R. Pauncz, *ibid* 37, 2739 (1962); J. de Heer, *Rev. Mod. Phys.* 35, 631 (1963); R. Pauncz *in* "Molecular Orbitals in Chemistry, Physics, and Biology" (P.-O. Löwdin, ed.), p. 433. Academic Press, New York, 1964; *Tetrahedron* 19, Suppl. 2, 43 (1963); *J. Chem. Phys.* 43, S69 (1965); O. Goscinski and J. L. Calais, *Arkiv Fysik* 29, 135 (1955); J. de Heer and R. Pauncz, *J. Chem. Phys.* 39, 2314 (1963).

34. P.-O. Löwdin, R. Pauncz, and J. de Heer, *J. Chem. Phys.* 36, 2257 (1962).

35. J. L. Calais, *Arkiv Fysik* 28, 479, 511, 539 (1965); 29, 255 (1965).

36. K. A. Brueckner, C. A. Levinson, and H. M. Mahmoud, *Phys. Rev.* 95, 217 (1954); K. A. Brueckner, *ibid* 96, 508 (1954); 97, 1353 (1955); 100, 36 (1955); K. A. Brueckner and C. A. Levinson, *ibid* 97, 1344 (1955); H. A. Bethe, *ibid* 103, 1353 (1956); J. Goldstone, *Proc. Roy. Soc. (London)* A239, 267 (1957); H. A. Bethe and J. Goldstone, *ibid* A238, 511 (1957); L. S. Rodberg, *Ann. Phys. (N.Y.)* 2, 199 (1957); to mention only a selection of the rich literature on this subject.

37. P.-O. Löwdin, *J. Math. Phys.* 3, 1171 (1962).

38. For references, see P.-O. Löwdin, *Phys. Rev.* 139, A357 (1965); *J. Chem. Phys.* 43, S175 (1965).

Author Index

Numbers in parentheses are reference numbers and indicate that an author's work is referred to although his name is not cited in the text. Numbers in italic show the page on which the complete reference is listed.

Subject Index

A

Absorption spectra, 170, 312, 315
Acid-base equilibrium, 300
Activation coefficients, 178
Addition theorems, 73
Alkali metals, 17 ff.
Alloys, 485
  disordered, 469
Alternant-molecular-orbital method, 620
Angular overlap model, 312
Annihilation operator, 107
Annihilation rates, 214
Anticommutator, 107
Antisymmetrizer, 83
Antisymmetry property, 615
Aperiodic fields, 469
Argon, 203, 205, 208, 210
Atomic hydrogen, 205
Atomic orbitals, 217, 231
Atomic radii, 314
Augmented plane wave (APW) method, 361, 429

B

Balmer series, 171
Band theory, 361, 381, 429, 445, 465, 469, 497
Benzene, 228
  localized molecular orbitals, 277
Beryllium atom, 308
Bethe-Goldstone equations, 161 ff.
BF, 222
Black-white group, 582
Bloch function, 449
Bloch sums, 68
Bond(s), angles, 60
  distances, 60
  length, 59
  order, 115, 296
  strength, 232
Bonding characteristics, 231
Bonding powers, 232
Born approximation, 453
Born-Oppenheimer approximation, 282

C

C_2, localized molecular orbitals, 274
C_2H_6, localized molecular orbitals, 268
CH molecule, 237
CH_4, localized molecular orbitals, 268
Characteristic equation, 572
Character table, 124
Charge transfer complexes, 345
Chemical orbitals, 231
Chemical reactivity, 296
CO, 222
Cohesive forces, 17 ff.
Collision strength, 175
Collisional excitations, 175
Commutation relations, 112
Component analysis, 605, 614
Composite Hamiltonian, 618
Compound characters, 128
Conductivity, 24
Configurational interaction, 54, 114, 182
Configurational promotion, 234
Constant of motion, 603
Convolution product, 608
Convolution relation for character, 610
Coordinates
  interparticle, 148
  Hylleraas, 148
  Kinoshita, 148
  perimetric, 149
Correlation energy, 49, 619
Coulomb energy, 476
Coulomb hole, 619
Coulomb wave approximation, 180
Creation operator, 106
Cross section
  annihilation, 204
  collisional, 176
  deactivation, 177
  differential, 204, 206
    elastic, 208
  excitation, 177
  minimum, 210
  total, 203
  momentum loss, 206, 208 ff.

636